Evaluation Guide for
Physics: Principles & Problems

Physics: Principles & Problems presents a modern basic approach to physics. The concepts and principles of physics are developed in a logical order to make your students' study of physics both challenging and interesting. Many features have been included to strengthen the presentation of the textual material with the intent of increasing your students' understanding and interest in physics. To examine the features of *Physics: Principles & Problems*, please turn to the following pages:

PHYSICS
Principles & Problems

AUTHORS

James T. Murphy
Formerly Science Department
Chairperson
Reading Memorial High School
Reading, Massachusetts

James Max Hollon
Physics and Chemistry Teacher
North High School
Evansville, Indiana

Paul W. Zitzewitz
Physics Professor
University of Michigan-Dearborn
Dearborn, Michigan

Consultant

Robert C. Smoot
Science Department Chairperson
McDonogh School
McDonogh, Maryland

Content Consultants

Robert F. Neff
Physics Teacher
Suffern High School
Suffern, New York

Douglas A. Johnson
Physics Teacher
James Madison Memorial High School
Madison, Wisconsin

Charles E. Merrill Publishing Company
A Bell & Howell Company
Columbus, Ohio

Toronto • London • Sydney

Preface

The *Teacher's Annotated Edition* of *Physics: Principles & Problems* is an integral part of the Merrill Physics Program. Teachers will find that this annotated edition provides all of the material essential for organizing and teaching a manageable and effective course in physics. The *Teacher's Annotated Edition* consists of two parts—the Annotated Student Text and the Teacher's Guide.

Annotated Student Text

Annotations are overprinted in red on the student text. These annotations include answers to problems, suggested teaching strategies, demonstrations, and additional related information. In a few cases, these annotations refer to material located in the Teacher's Guide. Numerical answers to all problems appear as annotations. Detailed solutions are found in the Teacher's Guide.

Teacher's Guide

The Teacher's Guide is bound at the front of the *Teacher's Annotated Edition*. An explanation of the text organization and design is included to acquaint you with the many features of *Physics: Principles & Problems*. Included is a Planning Guide that provides for maximum flexibility in organizing and presenting the course material to students with a wide range of abilities and interests. The Planning Guide also serves as an aid in integrating the laboratory program and in scheduling your time efficiently during school terms of varying duration. A general discussion of Performance Objectives presents suggestions for using objectives in teaching your course and evaluating student progress.

Physics: Principles & Problems is a total physics program. Additional information concerning the laboratory, testing program, and a complete list of audiovisual aids is also included.

The chapter-by-chapter material contains suggested performance objectives for all chapters. It also includes complete answers to all questions and detailed solutions to all problems.

Project Editor: Robert A. Roth; **Editor:** Peter R. Apostoluk; **Design:** Patrick J. McCarthy; **Project Artist:** David L. Gossell; **Artist:** Dick Smith; **Production Editor:** Janice E. Wagner

ISBN 0-675-07070-8

Published by
Charles E. Merrill Publishing Company
A Bell & Howell Company
Columbus, Ohio 43216

Contents

Chapter-by-Chapter Teaching Suggestions

Includes: Teaching Techniques, Demonstrations, Detailed Solutions to all Questions and Problems.

Philosophy

Physics: Principles & Problems employs the highly-effective problem solving method of teaching physics. The content is geared to produce a genuine understanding of the physical laws fundamental to all sciences. Physics concepts are introduced to students in their most logical sequence. Each chapter covers basic ideas and illustrates how these basics clarify more complex concepts. The sequence within each chapter is arranged in a manner that allows students to work a sufficient number of problems and gain familiarity with each new concept. Students are rarely asked to memorize details; rather, they are led to understand the basis for each major physics concept. This approach eliminates student frustration and promotes higher physics enrollments.

Physics: Principles & Problems, fifth edition, reflects changes in the sequencing and content of previous editions of the text. The importance of measurements in physics has been introduced first in order to emphasize the use of SI units and to reinforce the use of significant digits throughout the text. The second chapter demonstrates the use of algebra, trigonometry, and graphing in physics while providing a review of these topics within the text. The concepts of momentum and energy have been moved closer together to emphasize conservation laws. The discussion of electrostatic fields has been expanded. The quantum nature of light and electromagnetic radiation is developed only after a thorough introduction of electromagnetism. Two new chapters have been added. One chapter discusses sound; the other discusses the nucleus and elementary particle physics using the most current taxonomy of elementary particles.

The text uses problem solving as the primary means of studying physics. Example problems have been revised to provide coherent models for solving physics and other quantitative problems. Variables are clearly identified both in words and symbols. Given and unknown quantities are isolated. Solutions are concisely presented. Special attention has been given to vector notation as well as proper significant digit operations.

Illustrations of the many teaching features of *Physics: Principles & Problems* are found on the next eight pages.

Teacher annotations are overprinted on the student's text in red. These annotations include answers to the Problems as well as teaching suggestions. Detailed solutions to the Problems and all Chapter End Questions and Problems appear in this Teacher's Guide.

The **Goal statement,** found at the beginning of each chapter, identifies the main objective of the chapter for students.

Performance Objectives in this Teacher's Guide are an expansion of the Goal statement.

Sound   Chapter **16**

Chapter 16 introduces the concept of sound. How it is measured, produced, and perceived is discussed.

Sound and music are important parts of the human experience. At a first glance music and physics might seem very far apart. However, there are many interesting relationships between the two. Many important discoveries about what makes sounds harmonious were made in the sixth century B.C. by the Greek mathematician Pythagoras. Johannes Kepler discovered one of the laws of the motion of the planets while imagining the celestial music that might be played by the planets. Scientists study acoustics, the science of sound, in order to understand the production of sound by musical instruments as well as to design electronic systems that can record and produce sounds without distortion. In addition, architects study acoustics so they can construct auditoriums in which music and voice can be heard by every member of the audience.

Goal: You will gain understanding of sound and music as applications of wave motion.

16:1 Sound Waves

You have previously studied waves and oscillating motion. Sound is a longitudinal wave in which the pressure of the air oscillates about an average value, the mean air pressure. The frequency of the wave is the number of oscillations in pressure each second.

Sound waves move through air because the molecules of the air are constantly in motion. The molecules collide, transmitting the pressure oscillations away from the source of the sound. Figure 16-1 shows the relationships between the motion of molecules and the air pressure in a sound wave. Sound is a longitudinal wave because the motion of the air molecules is parallel to the direction of motion of the wave.

A sound wave is an oscillation in the pressure in the medium.

Sound is a longitudinal wave.

271

The description of sound is partly physical and partly subjective; each listener hears a particular sound differently. Some properties of sound can be described physically; others are perceived. What are these properties of sound? How does the construction of these organ pipes determine the nature of the sounds they produce and the sounds we hear?

Each of the 31 chapters is divided into **numbered sections** to facilitate planning lessons and assigned reading. Phrases and sentences to be emphasized are printed in italic type.

The **chapter introduction** includes a photograph and an accompanying paragraph that relates real world scenes to the topics presented in this chapter.

electric energy to kinetic energy. Like generators, motors are not 100 percent efficient. Perhaps 10 percent of the electric energy is changed into thermal energy instead of kinetic energy.

The drop in potential energy of electrons in a motor creates kinetic energy.

The net change in potential of the electrons going completely around the circuit is zero. The potential increase produced by the generator equals the potential loss in the motor. The total amount of charge (number of electrons) in the circuit does not change. If one coulomb flows through the generator in one second, one coulomb will also flow through the motor in one second.

The net change in potential around a circuit is zero. Current is the same everywhere in a circuit.

If the difference in potential between the two wires is 120 V, the generator must do 120 J of work on each coulomb of charge that it transfers from the positive wire to the negative wire. Thus, every coulomb of charge that moves from the negative wire through the motor and then back to the positive wire delivers 120 J of energy to the motor. Note that electric energy serves as a way to transfer the initial potential energy of falling water to the kinetic energy of a turning motor.

23:3 The Ampere and Electric Power

The unit used for quantity of electric charge is the **coulomb**. Thus, the rate of flow of electric charge, or electric current (I), is measured in coulombs per second. A flow of one coulomb per second is one **ampere**, A.

One ampere of current is the flow of one coulomb of charge each

$$1 \text{ C/s} = 1 \text{ A}$$

The ampere is named for the French scientist André (1775-1836). An ammeter is a device that measures

Energy in

Potential difference = 90 V
Each coulomb of charge transfers 90 J of energy to the motor.

Falling water turns a water wheel

Generator

Electron flow.

Readability is enhanced by using a single column text and a wide margin to avoid cluttered appearance.

Student margin notes, printed in blue, highlight important points in the text. Students can use these margin notes for preview, review, and study.

$$P = \frac{W}{t}$$

Power is measured in **watts** (W). A watt is one joule per second. A machine that does work at a rate of one joule per second has a power of one watt. Since a joule is a newton-meter, a watt is a newton-meter per second. A watt is a relatively small unit of power. For example, the power needed to lift a glass of water in a normal way is about one watt. Thus, power is often measured in kilowatts (kW). A kilowatt is 1000 watts.

Justify this estimate. What force, distance, and time is used to obtain the value of 1 W?

A 12-oz glass weighs 3.3 N. It is lifted about 0.30 m in about 1.0 s.

EXAMPLE

Power

An electric motor hoists an elevator (weighing 1.20×10^4 N) 9.00 m in 15.0 s.   **a.** What is the power of the motor in watts?   **b.** in kilowatts?

Given: $F = 1.20 \times 10^4$ N   **Unknown:** Power (P)

$d = 9.00$ m

$t = 15.0$ s   **Basic equation:** $P = \dfrac{W}{t}$

Solution:

a. $P = \dfrac{W}{t}$ **b.** $P = 7.20 \times 10^3 \text{ W} \times \dfrac{(\text{kW})}{(10^3 \text{ W})}$

$= \dfrac{Fd}{t}$ $P = 7.20$ kW

$= \dfrac{(1.20 \times 10^4 \text{ N})(9.00 \text{ m})}{(1.5 \times 10^1 \text{ s})}$

$= 7.20 \times 10^3 \dfrac{\text{N} \cdot \text{m}}{\text{s}}$

$= 7.20 \times 10^3 \dfrac{\text{J}}{\text{s}}$

$P = 7.20 \times 10^3$ W

Problems

13. 2.00×10^3 W, 2.00 kW

13. A box that weighs 1.00×10^3 N is lifted a distance of 20.0 m straight up by a rope and pulley system. The work is done in 10.0 s. What is the power developed in watts and in kilowatts?

14. 44.1 kW

14. A diesel engine lifts a 2.25×10^3-N hammer of a pile driver 20.0 m in 5.00 s. What is the power of the engine in kilowatts?

15. a. 960 J
b. 5.9×10^3 J

15. A rock climber wears a 12.0-kg knapsack while scaling a cliff. After 30.0 minutes, the climber is 8.2 m above the starting point.
 a. How much work in joules is done on the knapsack?
 b. If the climber weighs 6.00×10^2 N, how much total work is done?

Example problems are used extensively throughout the text to help students apply their mathematical skills to physics calculations. These Example problems follow a clear, logical format to be used as problem-solving models for students. The **factor-label method** is used throughout the text. Unit cancellation lines are printed in blue.

All **photographs** and **illustrations** are positioned close to the appropriate text material. Clear, simple diagrams are used to help students visualize difficult concepts. The captions relate the photos and illustrations to the text and provide additional relevant information.

310   Reflection and Refraction

a

b

c

Eyepiece lens

Reversing prisms

Objective lens

Light path

FIGURE 18-11. The passage of light through the reflecting prisms in a pair of binoculars shows total internal reflection (a).

Solving the equation for sin θ_t

$$\sin \theta_t = \frac{(1.00)(\sin 90°)}{(1.33)}$$

$$= 0.750$$

$$\theta_t = 48.6°$$

...t ray of light passing from water to air makes an angle ...le of refraction is 90°.

...ngle that causes the refracted ray to lie right along the ...substance, angle i_c is unique to the substance. It is ...ritical angle of the substance.

...gle, i_c, of any substance may be calculated as follows.

$$n_1 \sin \theta_1 = n_2 \sin \theta_2$$

..., $\theta_1 = i_c$; $n_2 = 1.000$ (vacuum); and $\theta_2 = 90°$

$$\sin i_c = \frac{(1.00)(\sin 90°)}{n_1}$$

$$\sin i_c = \frac{1}{n_1}$$

..., the critical angle can be calculated as follows.

$$\sin i_c = \frac{1}{1.52} = 0.658$$

$$i_c = 41°$$

...ls on the surface of water at an angle greater than the ...y 3) cannot be refracted. All of the light is reflected. ...eflection has occurred.

---

64   Graphical Analysis of Motion

FIGURE 4-5. A velocity-time graph for uniformly accelerated motion.

Velocity versus Time

Time (s)	Velocity (m/s)
0	0
1	+20
2	+40
3	+60
4	+80
5	+100

The velocity-time graph of constant acceleration is a straight line which passes through the origin.

uniform acceleration, the velocity varies directly with time. The equation that describes the velocity of an object (starting from rest) as a function of time is $v = at$. This is a direct variation.

For uniform acceleration, the slope of a velocity-time graph is constant along its entire length. The slope gives the acceleration of the object. Between points A and B.

The slope of the curve of a velocity-time graph is the acceleration.

$$\text{slope} = \frac{\Delta y}{\Delta x} = \frac{v_f - v_i}{t} = \frac{40 \text{ m/s} - 0 \text{ m/s}}{2 \text{ s}} = 20 \text{ m/s}^2$$

The acceleration of an object is the slope of the curve of a velocity-time graph.

In Section 4:3 you found that, for a moving object with constant velocity, the area under the curve of a velocity-time graph gives the displacement (change of position) of the object. This is also true of an object undergoing uniform acceleration. In fact, the area under any velocity-time curve gives the displacement, regardless of the type of motion.

Look at the shaded area under the curve between points A and B. The shaded area is a triangle. The altitude of the triangle is 40 m/s. This value is the velocity attained by the jet plane when it is accelerated from rest at the rate of 20 m/s² for 2 seconds. This velocity can be expressed as the product of its acceleration and the time interval, or $v = at$. Thus, the altitude of the triangle is at. The base of the triangle is the time interval, t, during which the acceleration is taking place. The area of a triangle can be found by multiplying the product of the altitude and the base by one half. Therefore, the area under the curve of the graph is $\frac{1}{2}(at)(t)$, or $\frac{1}{2}at^2$. This quantity is the displacement of an object undergoing uniform acceleration from rest. The area under the curve of a velocity-time graph represents the displacement of the object.

Graphs are used extensively to show the relationships between measured quantities.

Tables are included to summarize and organize text material.

change them from the liquid to the vapor state. This temperature is known as the boiling point. Water boils at 373 K at a pressure of 1 atm (101 kPa). The amount of thermal energy needed to vaporize a unit mass of liquid is called the **heat of vaporization.** For water, the heat of vaporization is 2.26×10^6 J/kg. Each substance has a characteristic heat of vaporization.

The heat of vaporization is the thermal energy increase needed to boil one kilogram of a substance.

TABLE 12-2

■ Heats of Fusion and Vaporization of Common Substances ■			
Material	Heat of Fusion (J/kg)	Material	Heat of Fusion (J/kg)
alcohol	1.09×10^5	lead	2.30×10^4
copper	2.05×10^5	mercury	1.15×10^4
gold	6.30×10^4	silver	1.05×10^5
iron	2.76×10^5	water (ice)	3.34×10^5
	Heat of Vaporization (J/kg)		Heat of Vaporization (J/kg)
alcohol	8.78×10^5	lead	8.64×10^5
copper	4.82×10^6	mercury	3.06×10^5
gold	1.64×10^6	silver	
iron	6.29×10^6	water	

The heat, Q_f, required to melt a solid of mass, m_f, is

$$Q_f = mH_f$$

The value of some heats of fusion, H_f, can be found
Similarly, the heat, Q_v, required to vaporize a mass given by

$$Q_v = mH_v$$

Heats of vaporization, H_v, can also be found in Tab

EXAMPLE

Heat of Fusion

If 5.00×10^3 J is added to ice at 273 K, how muc

Given: heat added (Q_f)
            $= 5.00 \times 10^3$ J

            heat of fusion (H_f)
            $= 3.34 \times 10^5$ J/kg

Unknown: mass (m)

Basic equation: $Q_f = mH_f$

New terms are printed in boldface type. Difficult terms are respelled phonetically for students. Once a term is introduced it is used repeatedly throughout the chapter for reinforcement.

---

174   Work, Power, and Simple Machines

   c. $IMA = \dfrac{d_e}{d_r}$

       $d_e = (IMA)(d_r)$
         $= (8.0)(0.90 \text{ cm})$
       $d_e = 7.2$ cm

Problems

18. a. 1.51
    b. 90.6%

18. A pulley system is used to raise a 225 N carton. To move the carton 1.65 m, a force of 149 N must travel 2.75 m.
    a. What is the mechanical advantage of the pulley system?
    b. What is the efficiency of the pulley system?

19. 1.45 m

19. A force of 2.25×10^3 N is exerted on a lever to raise a 1.20×10^3 N rock 1.32 m. If the efficiency of the lever is 58.7%, how far did the effort force move?

20. 0.183 m

20. A wheel and axle is a machine made so the wheel (larger diameter) and axle will rotate at the same speed. A resistance of 275 N, attached to the wheel, is displaced by an effort of 85.0 N. The machine has an efficiency of 78.5%. If the axle has a diameter of 8.00×10^{-2} m and makes 3 revolutions, what is the displacement of the resistance?

Physics Focus pages provide additional insight into the practicality of physics. The relevance of science and its impact on everyday life is stressed.

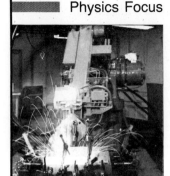

Physics Focus   Robotics

The Robot Institute of America says that a robot is a "programmable, multifunctional manipulator designed to move material, parts, or specialized devices through variable programmed motions for the performance of a variety of tasks." The mid-1970's development of microprocessors has made industrial robots practical.

Robots are used mainly in metal-working industries, such as automaking. They perform many repetitious, boring jobs with consistently high quality. They work 24 hours a day and do not get sick. This greatly increases productivity and reduces cost.

A human must put a robot through its task step-by-step and put each step into the memory of the robot's microprocessor. Then robots use a variety of sensing devices such as television cameras and pressure- and weight-sensing instruments to make comparisons with the stored data. For example, a robot that spray paints car bodies must "recognize" the body type of the car before it paints it.

A new Saturn division of GM will use many robots, as the Japanese auto industry already does. Saturn cars will compete in quality and cost with many Japanese imports.

Chapter-end materials include:

Questions—a section that contains simple recall and application questions.

Detailed answers to all Questions and Problems are given in the Teacher's Guide at the front of this book.

Questions

1. Explain the difference between an object's external and its thermal energy. Give an example.
2. Distinguish between thermal energy and temperature.
3. How does heat differ from thermal energy?
4. What is the temperature of a typical winter day on the
   a. Celsius scale,
   b. Kelvin scale?
5. What is the temperature of an extremely hot summer day on the
   a. Celsius scale,
   b. Kelvin scale?
6. Ten grams of aluminum and ten grams of lead are heated to the same temperature. The pieces of metal are placed on a block of ice. Which metal melts more ice?
7. An automobile is brought to a stop by applying friction brakes to the wheels. The brakes get hot; their thermal energy is increased. The decrease in kinetic energy of the car is equal to the increase in thermal energy of the brakes. According to the first law of thermodynamics, the brakes could cool and return the thermal energy to the car, causing it to resume its

in your physics course could

ter, water or alcohol? Explain.

lvin temperatures.
   d. 302°C
sius temperatures.
   d. 302 K
e the temperature of 50.0 kg of

50.0 g of aluminum at 25°C to

d to raise the temperature of
plied to 50.0 g of zinc. What is

1. a. 324 K
   b. 428 K
   c. 66 K
   d. 575 K
2. a. −222°C
   b. −118°C
   c. 0°C
   d. 29°C
3. 1.6 × 10⁴ J
4. 4.5 × 10³ J
5. 1080°C

Summary

12:1   1. Thermal energy of an object is the sum of kinetic and potential energies of the internal motion of the particles.

12:2   2. The temperature of an object is proportional to the average kinetic energy of the particles.

12:3   3. When two bodies are in thermal equilibrium their temperatures are equal.

12:3   4. Thermometers use some property of a substance, such as thermal expansion, that depends on temperature.

12:4-12:5   5. The Celsius and Kelvin temperature scales are widely used. One kelvin is equal to one degree Celsius.

12:5   6. At absolute zero, 0 K or −273°C, the average kinetic energy of the particles is zero.

12:6   7. Heat is thermal energy transferred by means of a difference in temperature.

12:6   8. Heat naturally flows from a hot to a cold body.

12:6   9. The first law of thermodynamics states that the increase in thermal energy of a body is equal to the sum of the heat and mechanical energy added.

12:6   10. A heat engine continuously converts heat to mechanical energy.

12:6   11. A heat pump or refrigerator uses mechanical energy to remove heat from something at a low temperature and add heat to something at a higher temperature.

12:7   12. Entropy, a measure of disorder, never decreases in natural processes.

12:8   13. The specific heat is the quantity of heat required to raise the temperature of one kilogram of a substance one kelvin.

12:9   14. In an isolated system, the thermal energy of one part may change but the total thermal energy is constant.

12:10   15. The heat of fusion is the quantity of heat required to melt one kilogram of a substance at its melting point.

12:10   16. The heat of vaporization is the quantity of heat required to change one kilogram of a substance from the liquid to vapor state at its boiling point.

12:10   17. The heat transferred during a change of state does not produce a change in temperature.

the **Summary**—a numbered listing of major points presented in the chapter. Section references, printed in blue, key each point to the numbered section where it is discussed.

Chapter 21 Review **365**

Problems—A

1. A positive charge of 1.8×10^{-6} C and a negative charge of -1.0×10^{-5} C are 0.014 m apart. What is the force between the two particles?   1. -83 N

2. Two negative charges of -5.0×10^{-5} C are 0.20 m from each other. What force acts on each particle?   2. 5.6×10^2 N

3. The hydrogen atom contains a proton and an electron separated by 5.0×10^{-11} m. Find the force of attraction between the two particles.   3. -9.2×10^{-8} N

4. Charges of 4.5×10^{-6} C exist on the three spheres shown in Figure 21-10, page 361. Find the magnitude of the total force on the top sphere.   4. 280 N

Problems—B

1. Two pith balls shown in Figure 21-12 have a mass of 1.0 g each and have equal charges. One pith ball is suspended by an insulating thread. The other is brought to 3.0 cm from the suspended ball. The suspended ball is now hanging with the thread forming an angle of $30.0°$ with the vertical. The ball is in equilibrium with F_E, mg, and T adding vectorially to yield zero. Calculate
   a. mg.   b. F_E.   c. the charge on the balls.

FIGURE 21-12. Use with Problem B-1.

2. Benjamin Franklin once wrote that he had "erected [illegible] lightning down into my house, in order to make [illegible] with two bells to give notice when the rod shoul[illegible] chime had two small bells mounted side by side. O[illegible] the iron rod (source of charge), the other was attach[illegible] the two, a small metal ball was suspended on a silk[illegible] back and forth, striking the two bells. Explain wh[illegible] charged, the ball would keep swinging, hitting firs[illegible]

3. Water drips slowly from a narrow dropper insi[illegible] metal ring (Figure 21-13).
   a. Will the drops be charged?
   b. If they are charged, are they positive or neg[illegible] The drops fall into a can that is on an insulatin[illegible]
   c. Will the can be charged?
   d. What will be the sign of the charge on the [illegible]

Readings

Bardeen, John, "To A Solid State." *Science*, Nove[illegible]

Bier, M., "Electrophoresis: Mathematical Modeling[illegible] tion." *Science*, March, 1983.

Eskow, Dennis, "Striking Back at Lightning." *Popu[illegible] 1983.

Appendix A

Relativity

Of all physicists, living or dead, Albert Einstein is best known. Relativity is the theory most closely associated with Einstein's name. Why, then, is relativity left for an appendix at the end of the text? Relativity uses the results of mechanics, optics, and electricity and magnetism. Thus, in order to present relativity as a single unit, it must be placed near the end of the text.

Relativity encompasses two theories, called special relativity and general relativity. Special relativity treats motion at constant velocity, while general relativity includes accelerated motion and motion in a gravitational field. Special relativity can be understood with mathematics no more complicated than algebra, while general relativity requires considerably more complex mathematics. For this reason, we will consider only special relativity.

Working as a clerk in the patent office in Bern, Switzerland, Albert Einstein published three papers in the year 1905. One, on the photoelectric effect, won him the 1921 Nobel prize. The second, on the random motion of particles called Brownian motion, explained this important demonstration of kinetic theory. The third, "On the Electrodynamics of Moving Bodies," presented the special theory of relativity, and won him a central place in physics and recognition not only by scientists but the general public as well. At the time the paper was published, relativity was ignored by some physicists and opposed by others. However, the results of every experimental test have confirmed its predictions. Thus, it has become accepted as one of the foundations of modern physics. It has solved major problems in physics.

A:1 Galilean Relativity

In Chapter 7 it was shown that the shape of a trajectory depends on the observer. Consider a ball tossed straight up in an airplane flying at a constant horizontal velocity of 200 m/s. A passenger in the airplane finds the horizontal velocity of the ball zero. However, a person on the ground viewing the ball through a telescope would see the ball thrown with a 200 m/s horizontal velocity. Each person could define a coordinate system, an x-axis and a y-axis, and use Newton's laws to analyze the motion. Each coordinate system in called a frame of reference. Newton's laws work in these two frames of reference. The only difference in the two frames is the horizontal velocity of the ball. To the passenger, the velocity is zero; to the person on the ground, it is 200 m/s. The frame of reference of the passenger is moving at a velocity of 200 m/s with respect to the frame of reference of the ground. The two frames are said to be equivalent because Newton's laws can be used to analyze motion in either frame. Although the ball is initially at rest in one frame—that is, its horizontal velocity is zero—there is nothing special about that frame.

Suppose an airplane, initially at rest, accelerates forward. A passenger on the plane will notice that a ball lying on the floor begins to move backward. The passenger will find the ball accelerating even though there is no force on it in the direction of the acceleration. Newton's laws will be violated. However, the person on the ground will see the ball remaining stationary. Newton's laws will still work as far as he is concerned. The two frames of reference are not equivalent because one is accelerated.

The fact that Newton's laws, the laws of mechanics, are true in any nonaccelerated frame of reference is called Galilean relativity. Galilean relativity also applies if the ball has a horizontal velocity in both frames. Suppose the airplane is moving again at a constant 220 m/s, but this time the ball is thrown forward. If the passenger measures the velocity of the ball as 10 m/s relative to the plane, the observer on the ground would measure the velocity as 220 m/s + 10 m/s = 230 m/s. That is, the velocity of the ball is the sum of the relative velocity of the frames of reference plus the velocity of the ball in the moving frame.

A:2 Electromagnetism

Einstein was only 16 when he posed a question for himself. What, he thought, would a light wave look like if you were moving alongside it at the speed of light? The electric fields would now be stationary. But stationary electric fields do not induce magnetic fields. Thus, Einstein reasoned, the laws of electromagnetism are not true in this frame of reference. That is, Galilean relativity does not hold for one frame of reference moving with the velocity of light with respect to another.

There was another problem with electromagnetism. Nineteenth-century physicists, believing that mechanics was the most important part of physics, tried to build mechanical models of everything, including electromagnetic waves. Sound is a pressure wave traveling through a medium. What is the medium for a light wave traveling through space? A substance was invented, the ether, in which the electric and magnetic fields oscillated. The ether was at rest, making it the preferred frame of reference, and all bodies moved through it. This gave the ether some

---

Problems A—additional practice problems to check students' understanding of the chapter material.

Problems B—a section containing more challenging problems.

Readings—suggested references for students to take the chapter material and research beyond it.

Appendix A—a supplementary discussion of Einstein's Theory of Relativity;

Appendix C—a set of reference tables.

Appendix C

TABLE C-1
SI Base Units

Measurement	Unit	Symbol
length	meter	m
mass	kilogram	kg
time	second	s
electric current	ampere	A
temperature	kelvin	K
amount of substance	mole	mol
intensity of light	candela	cd

TABLE C-2
SI Prefixes

Prefix		Multiplication Factor	Prefix		Multiplication Factor
exa	E	1 000 000 000 000 000 000 = 10^{18}	deci	d	$0.1 = 10^{-1}$
		10^{15}	centi	c	$0.01 = 10^{-2}$
		0^{12}	milli	m	$0.001 = 10^{-3}$
		0^{9}	micro	μ	$0.000\ 001 = 10^{-6}$
		0^{6}	nano	n	$0.000\ 000\ 001 = 10^{-9}$
		0^{3}	pico	p	$0.000\ 000\ 000\ 001 = 10^{-12}$
		0^{2}	femto	f	$0.000\ 000\ 000\ 000\ 001 = 10^{-15}$
		0^{1}	atto	a	$0.000\ 000\ 000\ 000\ 000\ 001 = 10^{-18}$

TABLE C-3
es Derived from SI Base Units

Symbol	Expressed in Base Units
J	$kg \cdot m^2/s^2$
N	$kg \cdot m/s^2$
Hz	$1/s$
lx	$cd \cdot sr/m^2$ (lm/m^2)
lm	$cd \cdot sr$
V	$kg \cdot m^2/A \cdot s^3$ (W/A)
W	$kg \cdot m^2/s^3$ (J/s)
Pa	$kg/m \cdot s^2$ (N/m^2)
C	$A \cdot s$
Ω	$m^2 \cdot kg/s^3 \cdot A^2$ (V/A)
T	$kg/C \cdot s$ $(1\ N/A \cdot m)$

Appendix B

B:1 Law of Cosines

To use the trigonometry of the right triangle, two of the sides of a triangle must be perpendicular. That is, you must have a right triangle. But sometimes you will need to work with a triangle that is not a right triangle. The law of cosines applies to all triangles. Consider the two triangles shown in Figure B-1. They are not right triangles. When angle C is known, the lengths of the sides obey the following relationship.

$$c^2 = a^2 + b^2 - 2ab \cos C$$

If a, b, and angle C are known, the length of side c is

$$c = \sqrt{a^2 + b^2 - 2ab \cos C}$$

In triangle 1 of Figure B-1, the length of side a is 4.00 cm, side b is 5.00 cm, and angle C is 60.0°. Substituting the values in the equation, side c is obtained. Substituting the appropriate values yields

$$a^2 = (4.0 \text{ cm})^2 = 16.0 \text{ cm}^2$$
$$b^2 = (5.0 \text{ cm})^2 = 25.0 \text{ cm}^2$$
$$2ab \cos \theta = 2(4.00 \text{ cm})(5.00 \text{ cm})(\cos 60.0°)$$
$$= 2(4.00 \text{ cm})(5.00 \text{ cm})(0.500)$$
$$2ab \cos \theta = 20.0 \text{ cm}^2$$

Therefore,

$$c = \sqrt{a^2 + b^2 - 2ab \cos \theta}$$
$$= \sqrt{16.0 \text{ cm}^2 + 25.0 \text{ cm}^2 - 20.0 \text{ cm}^2}$$
$$= \sqrt{21.0 \text{ cm}^2}$$
$$c = 4.58 \text{ cm}$$

If angle C is larger than 90°, its cosine is negative and is numerically equal to the cosine of its supplement. In triangle 2, Figure B-1, angle C is 120.0°. Therefore, its cosine is the negative of the cosine of (180.0° − 120.0°) or 60.0°. The cosine of 60.0° is 0.500. Thus, the cosine of 120.0° is −0.500.

B:2 Law of Sines

Just as the law of cosines applies to all triangles, the law of sines also applies to all triangles. The relationship is

$$\frac{a}{\sin A} = \frac{b}{\sin B} = \frac{c}{\sin C}$$

Using the values for triangle 1 shown in Figure B-1, angle A can be calculated by the law of sines.

$$\frac{a}{\sin A} = \frac{c}{\sin C}$$

$$\sin A = \frac{a}{c} \sin C$$

$$\sin A = \frac{4.00 \text{ cm}}{4.50 \text{ cm}} \sin (60.0°)$$

$$= \frac{(4.00 \text{ cm})(0.867)}{(4.58 \text{ cm})}$$

$$= 0.757$$

$$A = 49.2°$$

FIGURE B-1.

$b = 5.00$ cm $\theta = 60.0°$ $a = 4.00$ cm $\theta = 120.0°$

Appendix B—a supplementary discussion of the law of sines and cosines;

Appendix D

Physics-Related Careers

Careers in physics-related fields are many and varied. Requirements for some jobs in these fields may consist only of on-the-job training. Others may consist of seven or eight years of formal college training plus experience through on-the-job programs.

Below is a list of just a few of the jobs open in physics-related fields. This list includes brief job descriptions and minimum training requirements. These may vary somewhat from place to place or job to job. You will want to check with local companies, schools, and professional groups for details.

Training and Education Key

Job	= On-the-job training
VoTech	= Vocational or technical school
JC	= Junior college (2 yr)

BS	= Bachelor of Science degree
MS	= Master of Science degree
PhD	= Doctor of Philosophy degree (science)

PHYSICIST

Physicists attempt to discover the basic interactions between matter and energy. Some physicists perform research to learn facts. Others (theoretical physicists) analyze data and invent theoretical models. Many theoretical and research physicists are also involved in teaching.

Career	Training	Job Description
Acoustical scientist	BS, MS	does research in the control of sound; develops acoustical systems
Astrophysicist	BS, MS, PhD	studies the structure and motion of the universe and all its bodies
Biophysicist	BS, MS, PhD	applies physics to biology, medical fields, and related areas
Elementary-particle physicist	BS, MS, PhD	studies properties of the electron, the proton, and the many other particles produced in high-energy colli-
Geophysicist	BS, MS, PhD	
Low-temperature physicist	BS, MS	
Nuclear physicist	BS, MS, PhD	
Optical scientist	BS, MS	
Plasma physicist	BS, MS, PhD	
Radiological physicist	BS	
Teacher (High school)	BS	
Teacher (College)	BS, MS, PhD	

ENGINEE

It is often difficult to distinguish between the duties of a physic engaged in pure research or a physicist designing a specialized principles to practical problems. They design equipment, develop and power sources into useful products. Engineers are also frequ

Career	Training
Aerospace engineer	BS
Biomedical engineer	BS
Ceramic engineer	BS

Appendix D—a special feature on physics-related careers. Background information, educational requirements, and additional references are included.

563

Glossary

absolute zero: Temperature at which gas would have zero volume.

absorption spectrum: Spectrum of energy absorbed by the gaseous atoms of an element when white light is passed through the gas.

acceleration: Rate of change of velocity.

acceleration of gravity: Rate of change of velocity due to gravitational attraction of the earth.

accuracy: Closeness of a measurement to the standard value of a quantity.

adhesion: Attraction between unlike particles.

alpha particles: Helium nuclei consisting of two protons and two neutrons.

ammeter: Electric device used to measure current.

ampere: Unit for the rate of flow of charged particles. One ampere equals a flow of one coulomb of charge per second.

amplitude: Maximum displacement from zero of any periodic phenomenon.

aneroid barometer: Device using a partially evacuated box to measure atmospheric pressure.

angle of incidence: Angle between a light ray and a line perpendicular to the surface that the ray is striking.

angle of refraction: Angle between a refracted ray and a line perpendicular to the surface that the ray is leaving.

antenna: Device used to receive or radiate electromagnetic waves.

antinodal line: Line connecting points at which two waves interfere constructively at their maximum amplitudes.

antiparticle: Particle having the same mass and spin as its counterpart but opposite charge and magnetic moment. When a particle and its antiparticle collide, both are annihilated and energy is released.

Archimedes' principle: An object immersed in a fluid is buoyed up by a force equal to the weight of the fluid displaced by the object.

armature: Coil of wire that produces current in a generator and rotation in an electric motor.

atomic number: Number of protons in the nucleus of an atom.

back-EMF: Potential difference created by the motion of the armature in an operating motor.

barometer: Device for measuring the pressure of the atmosphere.

battery or galvanic cell: Two dissimilar conductors and an electrolyte that produces a potential difference.

beat: Oscillation in amplitude of complex wave.

Bernoulli's principle: The pressure exerted by a fluid decreases as its velocity increases.

beta particles: High-speed electrons emitted by a radioactive nucleus.

bimetallic strip: Two dissimilar metals welded together so that thermal expansion causes the strip to bend.

binding energy: Energy equivalent of the mass defect representing the amount of energy required to separate the nucleus into individual nucleons.

black hole: Collapsed astronomical object of sufficient mass to prevent the escape of light.

Boyle's law: Volume of a fixed mass of gas at a constant temperature varies inversely with the pressure.

breeder reactor: A nuclear reactor that converts nonfissionable material to fissionable material with the production of energy.

components of a vector: Two or more vectors (usually perpendicular) that when added together, produce the original vector.

Compton effect: Interaction of X rays and electrons as the X rays traverse matter resulting in a lengthening of the X-ray wavelength.

concurrent forces: Forces acting on the same point.

condensation: Change of a gas to a liquid.

conductor: Material through which charged particles move readily.

control rods: Devices in a nuclear reactor used to regulate the rate of the nuclear reaction.

convection current: Current caused by motion of a body of fluid due to differences in density resulting from thermal expansion.

converging lens: Lens, thick in the middle and thin at the edge, that causes parallel rays to converge.

converging mirror: Concave mirror capable of causing parallel rays to converge.

coulomb: Unit of quantity of electric charge equal to the charge found on 6.25×10^{18} electrons.

candela: Unit of luminous intensity.

capillary action: Rise of a liquid in a narrow tube due to surface tension.

Celsius temperature scale: Scale with 0° equal to the freezing point of air-saturated water and 100° equal to the boiling point of water at standard atmospheric pressure.

center of curvature: Center of the sphere from which a spherical mirror is taken.

centripetal acceleration: Acceleration always at right angles to the velocity of a particle.

centripetal force: Force directed toward the center of a circle, keeps particles moving in uniform circular motion.

Charles' law: The volume of a fixed mass of gas at constant pressure varies directly with the absolute temperature.

chromatic aberration: Failure of a lens to bring all wavelengths of light to focus at the same point.

coherent light: Light in which all waves leaving the source are in phase.

cohesive force: Attraction between like particles.

complimentary colors: Primary and secondary color that when added produce white light.

The Glossary lists all important terms used in the text. Students have a quick reference to the vocabulary of physics.

Text Features

Organization and Sequence

Physics: Principles & Problems is designed for maximum flexibility in teaching. The text is divided into 31 chapters. Each chapter is then further divided into numbered sections that aid students in locating specific topics and assist you in arranging assignments.

The nature and role of measurements in physics is introduced in Chapter 1 to emphasize the quantitative nature of physics. Mathematical relationships are introduced in Chapter 2 to provide a brief review of algebra, trigonometry, and graphing physical quantities. The mathematics review makes the text self-sustaining and eliminates the use of outside resources.

Mechanics is the first concept presented, and it provides the basis for discussing heat and states of matter. Wave phenomena are introduced and also used to describe sound and light. Electricity, magnetism, and electromagnetic waves follow. Atomic and nuclear physics complete the text with a discussion of quantum and elementary particle physics.

Readability

Readability aids in determining the success of a textbook in the classroom. A text that is easily comprehended by the majority of students in a class promotes student interest and involvement in the subject area. This feature, in turn, promotes teachability of the text and helps facilitate classroom management.

To control the reading level, careful attention has been given to vocabulary, sentence construction, paragraph structure, chapter organization, illustrations, and format.

The vocabulary in the text is consistent with the developmental level of the students for whom the text is designed. In addition, important science terms are printed in boldface or italic type when first presented. Some terms are followed by their phonetic spellings. Each term is then clearly defined and reinforced throughout the discussion.

An open format is achieved with wide margins and appropriate spacing between sections, problems, and illustrations. The typeface and size in which the text is set is another feature that enhances readability.

Example problems are used extensively throughout the text to provide clear and logical models for solving physics problems. Each Example problem is clearly identified in words and symbols, and is then isolated in terms of given or unknown variables.

Basic equations relating the quantities are stated. The factor-label method is used to solve problems with unit cancellation lines printed in blue to aid the student. The SI system of measurement is emphasized in the Example problems. Likewise, close adherence to the use of significant digits in each Example problem provides reinforcement for students in performing significant digit operations.

Student Notes

Student notes are placed in the margin to serve as a reading aid and review guide. They provide a ready outline of the concepts discussed within the chapter and also make concise statements about those concepts.

Photographs and Illustrations

This edition of *Physics: Principles & Problems* has expanded the use of material to provide the students with visual links between physics principles and real-world happenings. Each chapter opening consists of a large color photograph and a thought-provoking paragraph designed to stimulate student interest in the upcoming material. In addition, over 300 color illustrations and graphs are included throughout the text. They serve to reinforce and clarify concepts presented in adjacent paragraphs.

Nine Physics Focus essays present current and relevant information not directly covered in the text. Physics careers, research, and technological applications are presented with appropriate photographs to stimulate and motivate the students to research additional information.

Section- and Chapter-End Materials

Problems follow many sections of the text. They are designed for students to check their understanding of the previous material. Answers are provided in blue for all odd-numbered problems within a chapter to aid students in gaining confidence with the new material.

This text is designed for student success in problem solving. Your students' abilities to solve problems indicate how well they understand the basic principles in a chapter.

The Chapter-End material begins with a Summary that concisely reviews the major concepts and principles of the chapter. Each Summary statement is numbered and refers back to the appropriate section of the chapter.

The Summary statements along with the student margin notes provide an adequate review of the text material for testing purposes.

The Questions section contains recall questions to help students review the previous material.

The Problems-A section provides additional practice problems to check students' abilities to apply basic physics concepts. These problems provide an adequate review of the major concepts in each chapter.

The Problems-B section can be used to individualize your course to the ability level of your students. These problems tend to be more challenging than those in the Problems-A sections, and can be used as enrichment. Therefore, you may wish to use them as supplementary material.

Role of Teacher Demonstration

Good teacher demonstrations are important in helping students visualize abstract concepts. Good demonstrations allow for development of observational skills and proper techniques. Safety rules and procedures can be emphasized. Demonstrations can be preceded with a clearly identified problem; several demonstrations are designed for students to generate conclusions through observations. A good demonstration allows students to recognize and verbalize relationships as a result of their own experiences. Demonstrations allow you to present a maximum amount of text information while providing concrete and illustrative experiences. You will find a number of demonstrations included throughout the chapter-by-chapter information in this Teacher's Guide.

Supplementary Materials

Teacher Resource Book

The **Teacher Resource Book** is designed to enhance the *Physics: Principles & Problems* program by assisting the teacher in all areas of physics instruction. It is organized with tabbed dividers that correspond to each text chapter. Use the **Teacher Resource Book** as a time-saving teaching aid in the planning, preparation, instruction, and evaluation of the high school physics course. The material provided includes a Program Planning Guide, Textbook Inventory, Mathematics Inventory, Lab Safety Guide, Basic Skills Masters, Teaching Masters, Mini-Lab/Demonstration Masters, Review Guide Masters, Challenge Masters, Evaluation Masters, and Additional Tables.

Program Planning Guide

The Program Planning Guide lists all resources available in the pupil's text, the Teacher's Guide, the Teacher Resource Book, the Laboratory Physics program, and the Evaluation Program for *Physics: Principles & Problems*.

Basic Skills Masters

The Basic Skills Masters are designed for use as paper and pencil exercises of fundamental reading and mathematical skills. The exercises stress the areas of measurement (SI units), problem solving, scientific reading, instrumentation, error analysis, and data analysis.

Teaching Masters

The Teaching Masters are designed to be used as transparencies and/or student reference sheets. They facilitate class discussion and aid in the reinforcement of basic physics concepts. Teaching Masters are provided for each chapter of the text.

Mini-Lab/Demonstration Masters

The Mini-Lab/Demonstration Masters are designed to aid both teacher and students through brief demonstrations of specific concepts. Each master describes short performances of observable physics principles.

Review Activity Masters

The Review Activity Masters contain pencil and paper exercises that are designed to aid student mastery of problem-solving skills. The exercises include both example problems and practice problems.

Enrichment Masters

The Enrichment Masters are designed to enrich the most motivated students. The exercises emphasize inference and other conceptual skills. Expansion of chapter concepts is often the goal of these exercises.

Evaluation Masters

The Evaluation Masters are designed to reinforce student learning, evaluate student progress, and discover areas of weakness in instruction. The program consists of a four-part test for each chapter. The sections include the following:

Discovering Concepts—a set of completion questions related directly to the fundamental definitions and ideas found in the chapter.

Understanding Concepts—a set of questions requiring students to select the correct answer from several choices.

Using Concepts—requires students to apply concepts and skills learned in solving mathematical problems.

Extending Concepts—requires students to apply learned concepts to an abstract situation.

The major focus on each chapter is to help students improve their knowledge of physics. These tests help you discover any weaknesses in instruction that may become apparent using the Evaluation Masters. The program is also available as Spirit Duplicating Masters.

Additional Tables

The **Teacher Resource Book** contains supplementary tables of physical and mathematical data. These tables serve as a student aid in completing physics assignments by offering a readily available source of information.

Laboratory Program

The **Laboratory Physics** program is an integral part of the high school physics curriculum. It provides students with a variety of laboratory experiences that serve to reinforce physics principles. The quantitative aspects of laboratory procedures are emphasized. Each experiment involves the manipulation of apparatus, observation, data gathering and processing, and interpretation to form conclusions.

A suggested laboratory sequence can be found in the Planning Guide. By effectively correlating the laboratory experiments and textbook, students are able to understand physics concepts.

Distributors of Films and Film Loops

Audiovisual materials for purchase or rental may be obtained from the following distributors. All materials should be ordered months in advance, with alternate choices of dates for their use.

A list of university audiovisual distributors is included for your convenience. All audiovisual materials can be obtained from one of these suggested sources.

Bergwall Productions, Inc.
839 Stewart Ave.
Garden City, NY 11530

Collier-Macmillan School
and Library Services
866 Third Ave.
New York, NY 10022

Ealing Film Loops
BFA Educational Media
2211 Michigan Ave.
Santa Monica, CA 90404

Education Development Center
39 Chapel St.
Newton, MA 02160

Educational Materials Co.
46 Lafayette Ave.
New Rochelle, NY 10801

Encyclopaedia Britannica
Educational Corporation
425 North Michigan Ave.
Chicago, IL 60611

Handel Film Corp.
8730 Sunset Blvd.
West Hollywood, CA 90069

Learning Corporation of America
1350 Avenue of the Americas
New York, NY 10019

Pyramid Films
P.O. Box 1048
Santa Monica, CA 90406

Time-Life Multimedia
100 Eisenhower Drive
Paramus, NJ 07652

University Rental Services

The University of Arizona
Film Library
Tucson, AZ 85719
(602) 621-3282

University of Illinois
Visual Aids Service
1325 South Oak
Champaign, IL 61820
(217) 333-1360

Indiana University
Audio Visual Center
Bloomington, IN 47405
(812) 335-2103

Kent State University
Audio-Visual Services
Kent, OH 44242
(216) 672-3456

Syracuse University
Film Rental Center
1455 E. Colvin
Syracuse, NY 13210
(315) 479-6631

Washington State Univ.
Audio-Visual Center
Pullman, WA 99164
(509) 335-4535

Planning Guide

The Planning Guide for *Physics: Principles & Problems* is designed to help you arrange your physics course within the framework of a single academic year. This table suggests time allotments, levels of emphasis, and the use of laboratory experiments and films to plan a complete physics program. Using this guide you can gear the study pattern of each class to suit the needs and abilities of the students.

The suggested time allotments are those needed for class lecture time. Laboratory work and films will require extra time. You can best determine these needs because laboratory periods can vary from school to school.

Physics: Principles & Problems is designed to provide students with a strong background in physics by stressing the major concepts they will consistently apply throughout the course. In developing a unit plan the following breakdown may be helpful.

Mechanics	Chapters 1-11
Thermodynamics	Chapters 12-14
Wave Theory, Sound, and Optics	Chapters 15-20
Electricity and Magnetism	Chapters 21-27
Modern Physics	Chapters 28-31

It is a major goal of this text that students achieve a thorough understanding of each topic before proceeding to new material. To quote Sir Isaac Newton, "It is better to achieve a little with certainty than a great deal that one is not sure of."

Chapter	Sections	Lecture Time Days	Lecture Time Weeks	Emphasis	Laboratories and Films
1	1:1-1:5	2		High	Measurement of Length (Lab)
	1:6-1:8	2	1	High	Measurement of Mass and Density
	1:9-1:12	1		Moderate	(Lab)
	Review	1			Physicists (Film)
					Powers of Ten (Film)
2	2:1-2:5	2		High	Graphing Experimental Data (Lab)
	2:6-2:7	1	1	Moderate	Change of Scale (Film)
	Review	1			The Relation of Mathematics
					to Physics (Film)
3	3:1-3:4	1		High	Measurement of Time (Lab)
	3:5-3:8	2	1.5	High	Straight Line Kinematics (Film)
	3:9-3:11	2		High	
	Review	1			
4	4:1-4:3	1		Moderate	Graphical Analysis of Motion (Lab)
	4:4-4:7	2	1	Moderate	Graphical Analysis of Motion:
	Review	1			Uniform Acceleration (Lab)
5	5:1-5:3	2		High	Force and Acceleration (Lab)
	5:4-5:5	1	2	High	Mass and Acceleration (Lab)
	5:6	2		High	Friction (Lab)
	5:7-5:10	2		High	Inertia (Film)
	Review	1			Inertial Mass (Lab)

Chapter	Sections	Lecture Time		Emphasis	Laboratories and Films
		Days	Weeks		
6	6:1-6:3	2		High	Addition of Force Vectors (Lab)
	6:4-6:5	1		High	Vectors (Film)
	6:6-6:7	1	2	High	
	6:8-6:10	2		High	
	Review	1			
7	7:1	1		High	Analysis of the Path of a Projectile
	7:2	1		High	(Lab)
	7:3	1	1.5	Moderate	Centripetal Force (Lab)
	7:4	1		Moderate	The Pendulum (Lab)
	7:5	1		Low	Free Fall and Projectile Motion
	Review	1			(Film)
8	8:1-8:2	2		High	Kepler's Law of Equal Areas (Lab)
	8:3-8:7	2	1	Moderate	Forces (Film)
	Review	1			
9	9:1	1		High	Conservation of Momentum:
	9:2-9:3	2		High	Internal Force (Lab)
	9:4	1	1.5	High	Conservation of Momentum:
	9:5	1		Moderate	A Collision in Two
	Review	1			Dimensions (Lab)
10	10:1-10:2	2		High	Pulleys (Lab)
	10:3-10:5	1	1	High	Energy and Work (Film)
	Review	1			
11	11:1-11:2	1		High	Conservation of Energy:
	11:3-11:4	1	1	High	The Inclined Plane (Lab)
	11:4-11:6	1		High	
	Review	1			
12	12:1-12.5	1		Moderate	The Conservation of Thermal Energy
	12:6	1		High	(Lab)
	12:7-12:9	1	1+	High	Specific Heat of a Metal (Lab)
	12:10	1		High	Heat of Fusion of Ice (Lab)
	Review	1			
13	13:1-13:2	1		Moderate	The Diameter of a Molecule (Lab)
	13:3-13:7	2	1	Moderate	Boyle's Law (Lab)
	Review	1			Random Events (Film)
14	14:1-14:4	1		Moderate	Archimedes Principle (Lab)
	14:5-14:9	1	0.5	Moderate	
	Review	1			
15	15:1-15:2	1		Moderate	Wave Properties (Lab)
	15:3-15:6	1	1	High	Pulses in a Ripple Tank (Lab)
	15:7-15:11	2		High	Wavelength, Frequency, and Speed
	Review	1			(Lab)
					Refraction of Waves (Lab)
					Diffraction and Interference of
					Waves (Lab)
					Simple Waves (Film)

Chapter	Sections	Lecture Time		Emphasis	Laboratories and Films
		Days	Weeks		
16	16:1-16:3	1		High	Speed of Sound in Air (Lab)
	16:4-16:6	1	0.5	Moderate	
	Review	1			
17	17:1-17:4	1		High	Luminous Intensity and Efficiency
	17:5-17:8	1	0.5	Moderate	of Light Bulbs (Lab)
	Review	1			Light: Illumination and Its
					Measurement (Film)
					The Speed of Light (Film)
18	18:1-18:4	2		High	Law of Reflection of Light (Lab)
	18:5-18:8	1	1	High	Snell's Law (Lab)
	Review	1			
19	19:1-19:5	1		High	Images Produced by Curved Mirrors
	19:6-19:7	1		High	(Lab)
	19:8-19:9	1	1	High	Convex Lenses (Lab)
	19:10-19:14	1		Moderate	
	Review	1			
20	20:1-20:2	2		High	Measuring the Wavelengths
	20:3-20:5	1	0.5	Moderate	of Light Waves (Lab)
	Review				
21	21:1-21.5	1		Moderate	Static Electricity (Lab)
	21:6-21:8	1	0.5	High	Coulomb's Law (Lab)
	Review	1			Coulomb's Law (Film)
22	22:1-22:3	1		Moderate	Charging and Discharging a
	22:4-22:8	1	0.5	High	Capacitor (Lab)
	Review				
23	23:1-23:2	1		High	Ohm's Law (Lab)
	23:3-23:6	1	1	High	Electrical Equivalent of Heat (Lab)
	23:7-23:9	1		High	
	Review	1			
24	24:1-24:2	1		High	Series Circuits (Lab)
	24:3-24:4	1	1	High	Parallel Circuits (Lab)
	24:5-24:6	1		High	Series-Parallel Circuits (Lab)
	Review	1			
25	25:1-25:3	1		Moderate	Magnetic Field Around Magnets
	25:4-25:6	1		Moderate	(Lab)
	25:7-25:8	1	1	Moderate	Magnetic Fields Around a
	25:9-25:10	1		Moderate	Current-Carrying Wire (Lab)
	Review	1			Current and Field Strength (Lab)
26	26:1-26:2	1		High	Induced Current and Lenz's Law
	26:3-26:4	1	1	High	(Lab)
	26:5-26:8	1		Moderate	The DC Generator-
	Review	1			The DC Motor (Lab)
					Energy Transfer by an Electric
					Motor (Lab)
					Magnetic Fields and Electric
					Currents, 1 and 2 (Film)

Chapter	Sections	Lecture Time		Emphasis	Laboratories and Films
		Days	Weeks		
27	27:1-27:3	1		Moderate	Magnetic Field Strength (Magnetic Induction) (Lab)
	27:4-27:7	1	0.5	Moderate	Charge to Mass Ratio of the Electron (Lab)
	Review	1			Mass of the Electron (Film)
28	28:1-28:3	1		Moderate	A Model for the Quantum Concept (Lab)
	28:4-28:5	1	0.5	Moderate	Matter Waves (Film)
	Review	1			Photons (Film)
29	29:1-29:3	1		High	The Spectra of Elements (Lab)
	29:4-29:8	2	1	High	The Laser Beam (Film)
	Review	1			Light: Wave and Quantum Theory (Film)
30	30:1-30:5	2		High	Half-Life Simulation (Lab)
	30:6-30:12	2	1	Moderate	
	Review	1			
31	31:1-31:3	1		High	Simulation of Nuclear Collisions (Lab)
	31:4-31:7	2	1	High	Fusion (Film)
	Review	1			

Performance Objectives

What is a Good Performance Objective?

Statements of performance objectives can usually be divided into three distinct parts. First is a description of the conditions under which the desired behavior will be observed. Some examples include

"When presented with typical graph forms. . . ."
"When asked to write the equation for. . . ."
"When presented with the materials suggested on page. . . ."
"After having read and discussed. . . ."
"In groups of three students, given a volunteer, an ammeter, and. . . ."

A good performance objective includes a condition that tells causes or circumstances of behaviors that will be performed, and stimulates the student to accomplish the stated objective.

The second part of a well-stated performance objective is a clear description of exactly what behavior is to be observed. A good performance objective would avoid using such terms as "know about," "appreciate," or "sense the relationship between." Rather, a good performance objective will include terms that describe what you could observe students doing if they do "know about" or "appreciate." It is almost impossible to observe students "appreciating," but you can gather some evidence that they are appreciating science if they read science books for entertainment, request additional laboratory time before or after school, ask to perform a class demonstration, or express any other form of interest in physics.

In other words, a good performance objective uses verbs that express some type of observable action. Examples of such action verbs are constructs, distinguishes between, expresses, identifies, lists, manipulates, matches, measures, recalls, states hypotheses, states orally, and observes.

The third part of a well-stated performance objective is a description of some level of performance or criteria that may help you know if the student or class has performed to the degree you have specified.

For example, if you were teaching students to use a balance, would you want all of your class to be able to accurately measure the mass of a solid or liquid? Would you feel satisfied if 90% of your class could perform this skill? 80%? 50%? Obviously, the level of performance would vary for each class, each student, each teacher, and each task.

What do we mean by accurately? Would you be satisfied if students could measure a mass to the nearest centigram? Milligram? More accurately than that? Just how accurately do you wish your students to measure a given mass? Here is another aspect of a performance objective—a statement of how precise, how accurate, or how well the behavior should be performed so you know if the student has really achieved the objective.

Another criterion of measure or performance level that might be included in a performance objective is a statement of how often or how many times students must perform the behavior. For example, if a mass is accurately measured with a balance in one trial, would you conclude that the students have learned to determine the mass of an object. What if you asked them to measure the mass of five objects to the nearest centigram, and only four of them were determined correctly? Would you be satisfied?

Again, this decision will have to be made on the basis of what you know about the student's ability, and the task at hand. For some individuals, you may be satisfied with one accurate reading; for others, you may demand perfection.

By incorporating the three essential parts of a performance objective, you should come up with assertive statements, such as the following:

Conditions—tell you how to plan and organize your class, and what materials you will need.

Working individually, when presented with a laboratory balance, several solids, and a graduated cylinder. . .

Performance—tells you what student behaviors to look for.

Students will measure the masses of solids to the nearest 0.01 g and measure the volumes of solids by liquid displacement. Students will be able to calculate the densities of the solids to the correct number of significant digits.

Criterion Measure—tells you how many students, or to what degree the objective should be achieved.

Of all the students, 95% will achieve 100% of the above objectives.

How Do You Use the Performance Objectives in This Teacher's Guide?

Performance objectives are listed for each chapter of *Physics: Principles & Problems*. Each section relates to the four board goals of science education.

A   Attitudes: To develop students' attitudes of curiosity and involvement with phenomena in their natural environment; to develop an appreciation for the contribution of science to daily living; and to develop the value and logic of solving problems in a scientific manner.

P   Processes: To develop those intellectual processes of inquiry by which scientific poblems and phenomena are explained, predicted, and/or controlled.

K   Knowledge: To develop knowledge of facts, terminology, concepts, generalizations, and principles that help the students confront and interpret their environment.

S   Skills: To develop the student's ability to handle, construct, and manipulate materials and equipment in a productive and safe manner, and to develop the ability to measure, organize, and communicate scientific information.

Next to each performance objective you will find one or more of the following letters: A, P, K, S. They indicate the goal on which the objective is based—Attitudes, Processes, Knowledge, Skills. Keep in mind a balance should be maintained among these four goals, since they are of equal priority.

The statements of performance objectives that are identified as "A"—developing Attitude goals—are behaviors that you might observe as students increase their enjoyment of science activities, and as they demonstrate an interest in the scientific objects and events in their environment.

You will find such statements as the following:

Students will request that the demonstration is repeated.

Students will volunteer to conduct outside research.

Students will request the use of the physics laboratory during free periods.

When given a choice between study hall and working at a physics experiment, students will choose the physics activity.

Students will volunteer to do research and report their findings in class.

As you can see, few of these behaviors are prompted by the teacher. They are voluntary behaviors that indicate an affinity for, an inclination toward, and a preference for science. You will find suggested attitudinal behaviors throughout the list and particularly at the end of each area or chapter when students may have an opportunity to go beyond the information presented in the text.

The statements of performance objectives that are identified as "P"—developing Process goals—are behaviors that you might observe as students use the thinking process of analyzing, experimenting, applying, hypothesizing, theorizing, comparing and contrasting, classifying, observing, etc. You will find such statements as the following:

When presented with various objects, students will place them in groups by comparing and contrasting their similarities and differences.

Given data, the students will calculate the amount of heat needed to raise the temperature of 1000 kg of iron from 20°C to 1000°C.

Given a complex problem, students will apply the proper equations and concepts.

The statements of performance objectives that are identified as "K"—developing Knowledge goals—are behaviors that you might observe as students demonstrate they have gained an understanding and use certain terms, concepts, and generalizations of science. You will find such statements as the following:

When asked, students will define the term "excitation" correctly.

Students will explain the reason temperatures change.

Students will correctly identify the curves on a graph.

Students will describe the effects of a force on a mass.

Generally, a knowledge objective is one that calls upon the student to recall or explain information, concepts, or principles that have been learned in the past or that have been presented in the text and other materials.

The statements of performance objectives that are identified as "S"—developing Skills goals—are behaviors that you might observe as students gain skill in using scientific equipment correctly, and organizing, recording, or reporing information accurately. Some examples of such statements are the following:

Students will use voltmeters and ammeters correctly in a circuit.

Students will record observations in their notebooks.

Students will avoid parallax while reading scales.

In the Teacher's Guide that follows, a specific statement of the goal for each chapter is given. A goal statement is also given at the beginning of each chapter in the student's text. Following the goal statement in the Teacher's Guide, the specific performance objectives for each section of the chapter are listed. There may be several objectives in each section. Each objective is numbered to correspond to that section of the chapter. For example, 22:5 is Chapter 22, Section 5. From these objectives, you should be able to determine and plan for the achievement of the objectives for each section of a chapter.

Remember, these performance objectives are not meant to be all-inclusive. You should supplement them with objectives from other sources and with those you create yourself.

You will also find that the criterion or level of performance for each objective is not included. The intent was to create guidelines and not to state levels of expectancies for you. Only you can decide if 100% or only 50% of your students should be able to accomplish each task. You will need to develop and insert these criterion levels for your students based upon your materials and your own situation.

How Do You Know You Have Achieved Your Objectives?

When you try to find out if students have learned anything, you probably give some form of written test—true-false, completion, matching, or essay type of examination. All of these forms of evaluation are important in determining whether or not students have achieved their objectives. Evaluation materials are available to accompany *Physics: Principles & Problems*.

Bibliography

Bloom, Benjamin S., *All Our Children Learning: A Primer for Parents, Teachers, and Other Educators.* McGraw-Hill Book Co., New York, 1982.

Bloom, Benjamin, Hastings, J. Thomas, and Madaus, George, *Handbook on Formative and Summative Evaluation of Student Learning.* McGraw-Hill Book Co., New York, 1971.

Dreikurs, Rudolf, et al. *Maintaining Sanity in the Classroom: Classroom Management Techniques.* Harper & Row, Inc., New York, 1982.

Lindvall, C. M., ed., *Defining Educational Objectives.* University of Pittsburgh Press, Pittsburgh, 1964.

Mager, Robert, *Preparing Instructional Objectives.* Fearon Publishers, Inc., Palo Alto, CA, 1962.

Popham, W. James, *The Teacher-Empiricist.* Aegeus Publishing Co., Los Angeles, 1965.

Popham, W. James, and Baker, Eva L., *Establishing Instructional Goals.* Prentice-Hall, Inc., Englewood Cliffs, NJ, 1970.

Physics: A Mathematical Science   Chapter 1

Teaching Technique

The purpose of this chapter is to introduce the science of physics, and especially the role of mathematics in physics. To begin the course, give the students a brief overview of what they will learn this year. Make students familiar with their textbook. Review To the Student with them so that they are aware of all the features of the text.

Initiate a discussion of what physics is and what it is not. Distinguish between physics and other sciences, and also mathematics. Introduce the scientific method; emphasize the need for physical laws to be tested experimentally. Differentiate between physics as a science and its applications in technology. Demonstrate how they complement each other.

Encourage the proper use of all units in the International System. Rather than relating SI to English units, work on developing a concept of the magnitude of the units.

Note that throughout the first part of the text, both words and abbreviations are used to express units. Students should learn these abbreviations as only abbreviations will be used later in the text. The tables in Appendix C provide a reference to both units and their abbreviations.

Illustrate significant digits using actual measurements. Students should be taught to estimate the last digit rather than to ignore it. Calculators provide more digits than are significant, especially when performing multiplication and division. If students recognize this and report the correct number, you will have accomplished the major objective of this section.

Films

Physicists (university rental)
Powers of Ten (Pyramid film)

Laboratory Investigation

Measurement of Length
Measurement of Mass and Density

Performance Objectives

Goal: Students will learn that mathematics is the language of physics. They will also learn the basic units of the metric (SI) system, and that uncertainties exist in all physical measurements.

Objectives: Upon completion of the reading, questions, and problems, students will, on oral or written tests:

1:1	K	define physics and list applications.
1:2	A	appreciate the difference in the approach to science of Galileo and the ancient Greeks.
1:2	P	recognize the importance of the scientific method.
1:3	K	list the standard units for mass, length, and time.
1:4	K	interpret metric prefixes.
1:5	K	state the fundamental units and be able to distinguish between fundamental and derived units.
1:6	S/P	demonstrate an ability to use scientific notation.
1:7	K/S/P	be able to add and subtract large and small numbers using scientific notation.
1:8	K/S/P	be able to multiply and divide small and large numbers using scientific notation.
1:9	K/A	be aware that all measured quantities have an uncertainty.
1:10	K	be able to distinguish between accuracy and precision.
1:11	P/K/S	demonstrate an understanding of the use of significant digits as a means of stating the precision of measured quantities.
1:12	K/S	use significant digits correctly when recording measured data.
	S/A	Students will use laboratory materials in the prescribed manner when conducting lab investigations.

Upon completion of the reading and practice problems, students will exhibit an interest in physics by:

	A/S	expanding on an answer to one or more of the questions or problems at the end of the chapter.
	S/P	discussing the way the definition of the length standard as the distance light travels in a certain time interval changes our ideas of the meaning of length.
	A/S	preparing a list of famous physicists and their contributions, discussing the applications of physics in our world, or discussing the difference between physics and its applications.
	A	reading unassigned literature related to the ideas presented in the chapter.

Solutions to Problems

Page 8.

1. **a.** 0.011 m
   b. 7.62×10^{-11} m
   c. 2.1×10^3 m
   d. 1.23×10^5 m
2. 0.31 mg, 1021 μg, 0.6 cg, 11.6 mg

Page 10.

3. **a.** 5.8×10^3 m
   b. 4.5×10^5 m
   c. 3.02×10^8 m
   d. 8.6×10^{10} m
4. **a.** 5.08×10^{-4} kg
   b. 4.5×10^{-7} kg
   c. 3.6×10^{-3} kg
   d. 4×10^{-3} kg
5. **a.** 3×10^8 s
   b. 1.86×10^5 s
   c. 9.3×10^7 s
6. **a.** 7.3×10^{-3} m
   b. 8.7×10^{-4} m
   c. 3.2×10^{-3} m
7. **a.** 5×10^{24} m
   b. 1.66×10^{-19} m
   c. 2.033×10^9 m
   d. 1.030×10^{-7} m

Page 11.

8. **a.** 6.5×10^5 kg
   b. 5×10^6 s
   c. 2.26×10^2 m
   d. 4.5×10^3 s
9. **a.** 2.5×10^{-2} m
   b. 2.5×10^{-4} m
   c. 6×10^{-4} s
   d. 1.9×10^{-13} s
10. **a.** 8×10^7 m
    b. 8×10^8 m
    c. 7.8×10^4 m
    d. 4.3×10^9 m
11. **a.** 8×10^{-7} kg
    b. 7×10^{-3} kg
    c. 3.96×10^{-19} kg
    d. 4.6×10^{-12} kg

Page 12.

12. **a.** 2×10^8 cm
    b. 1.9×10^{12} cm
    c. 3.0×10^9 cm
    d. 1.75×10^4 cm
13. **a.** 2×10^{-8} m^2
    b. -1.5×10^{-11} m^2
    c. 3.0×10^{-9} m^2
    d. 4.6×10^{-19} m^2
14. **a.** 6.4×10^8 kg
    b. 7.2×10^4 kg
    c. 3.4×10^5 kg
    d. 5.6×10^{11} kg
15. **a.** 5.4×10^{-7} cg
    b. 6.2×10^{-3} cg
    c. 3.2×10^{-14} cg
    d. 4.6×10^{-12} cg
16. **a.** 4.6×10^{-7} L
    b. 5.8×10^{-3} L
    c. 2.8×10^{-14} L
    d. 7.8×10^{-16} L
17. **a.** 9×10^8 m
    b. 5.8×10^4 m
    c. 5.6×10^8 m
    d. 1.0×10^6 m
18. **a.** 5.2×10^{-8} g
    b. 2.0×10^7 g
    c. 5.4×10^{-8} g
    d. 1.4×10^{12} g

Page 13.

19. **a.** 8×10^{12} m^2
    b. 6×10^{10} m^2
    c. 3×10^{-11} m^2
    d. 6.3×10^9 m^2
20. **a.** 3×10^4 kg/m^3
    b. 3×10^{12} kg/m^3
    c. 3×10^{-12} m/s
    d. 3×10^{-4} m/s
21. **a.** 2×10^4 kg · m/s
    b. 3×10^{12} kg · m/s^2

Page 16.

22. **a.** 4 **b.** 3 **c.** 2 **d.** 4 **e.** 2 **f.** 3
23. **a.** 2 **b.** 4 **c.** 4 **d.** 3 **e.** 4 **f.** 3

Page 18.

24. 26.3 cm
25. 78.5 m
26. 71.7 kg
27. 362.1 m
28. 2.5 g
29. 17.30 mL
30. 48.2 kg
31. **a.** 3.0×10^2 cm^2 **b.** 15 cm^2 **c.** 13.6 km^2
32. **a.** 2.73 cm/s **b.** 0.253 cm/s **c.** 4.73 m/s
33. $A = (15.72 \text{ m})(4.40 \text{ m}) = 69.168 = 69.2$ m^2

Chapter End Questions

Pages 19-20.

1. Physics is the study of the basic scientific laws that can be applied to all the sciences.
2. Fundamental units are units for mass, length, and time. Derived units are combinations of fundamental units. Units for temperature and elementary charge are also fundamental units.
3. The fundamental units used in mechanics are kilogram, meter, and second.
4. Speed is m/s, km/h, or cm/s.
5. The international system of units allows scientists all over the world to make measurements in the same system. Thus scientists know exactly what is meant by measurements made by other scientists.
6. **a.** centimeter **b.** millimeter **c.** kilometer
7. **a.** Mass is the quantity of matter that a body contains.
   b. The kilogram is the SI mass unit.
8. The final digit is doubtful.
9. The precision of a measuring device is limited by the finest division on its scale.
10. **a.** Zeros are necessary to indicate the magnitude of the value, but there is no way of knowing whether or not the instrument used to measure the values actually measured the zeros. The zeros may serve only to locate the six.
    b. Write the number in scientific notation, including only the significant digits.

Problems A

Page 20.

1. **a.** 3 **b.** 4 **c.** 1 **d.** 5
2. **a.** 3 **b.** 1 **c.** 3
3. **a.** 34.7 m
   b. 25.022 m
   c. 46.00 cm^2
   d. 3.1 kg
4. **a.** 1.7 cm^2
   b. 21 m^2
   c. 188 cm^2
   d. 12.0 cm^3
   e. 36 cm^2
   f. 3.2×10^{15} m^2
   g. 1.5×10^{-6} m
5. 2.4×10^2 m^3

Problems B

Page 20.

1. The difference in area for the pans is

$$\pi\left(\frac{26\ \text{cm}}{2}\right)^2 - \pi\left(\frac{23\ \text{cm}}{2}\right)^2 = 115\ \text{cm}^2$$

$(115\ \text{cm}^2)(0.25\text{¢/cm}) = \$0.29$
Each pizza costs 29 cents more.

2. $D = \dfrac{M}{V}$ $V = \dfrac{4}{3}\pi r^3$

$V = \dfrac{M}{D} = \dfrac{2.0 \times 10^{30}\ \text{kg}}{2.0 \times 10^{11}\ \text{kg km}^3} = 1.0 \times 10^{19}\ \text{cm}^3$

$r = \sqrt[3]{\dfrac{3V}{4\pi}}$

$\quad = \sqrt[3]{\dfrac{(3)(1.0 \times 10^{19}\ \text{cm}^3)}{4\pi}}$

$\quad = 1.3 \times 10^6\ \text{cm}$

$d = 2r$

$\quad = 2.6 \times 10^6\ \text{cm}$

$\quad = 27\ \text{km}$

Page 21.

3.

Side	Surface area	Volume	Surface area / Volume
(m)	(m²)	(m³)	
1.0	6.0	1.0	6
2.0	24	8.0	3
3.0	54	27	2
4.0	96	64	1.5
5.0	150	130	1.2
6.0	220	220	1

The table shows that surface area to volume ratio decreases with size. Since heat is lost through the walls of a building, the large cube-shaped building would cost less to heat than the one floor building with many wings.

4. a. An elephant's body has a small surface area to volume ratio. Wallowing in the water helps to cool it.
   b. The ears have a large surface area to volume ratio which allows rapid cooling.
   c. A large surface area to volume ratio allows rapid energy loss. Constant eating replenishes the lost energy.
   d. Like the hummingbird, the shrew has a large surface area to volume ratio and must eat large quantities of food to replace lost energy.

Mathematical Relationships   Chapter 2

Teaching Techniques

This chapter introduces the mathematical systematics that are used in this course. A brief quiz might be used to determine if students need help in a particular area.

Help students become proficient at the manipulation of algebraic equations. Begin with numerical examples, but emphasize that it is always better to simplify and transpose equations when they are in symbolic form. Elaborate on the use of units in equations and stress unit cancellation methods. Units can often provide a check on the correctness of the equation.

Graphing equations is an important skill because it shows relationships in a dynamic rather than static form. Illustrate this concept by distinguishing between a motion picture and a photograph. Give students practice in plotting data and drawing graphs. Explain that by drawing a line through data points you can predict the value of a dependent variable, provided that a measurement was made at a given value of the independent variable. Point out that all measured quantities seldom fall exactly on the line, but that the line represents a best fit to experimental data.

Emphasize the fact that linear, parabolic, and hyperbolic (inverse) relationships will be used throughout the book. Help students to learn the shapes of these curves.

Review the trigonometry of the right triangle. Give students practice in recognizing the common functions (sine, cosine, and tangent) with triangles in a variety of positions.

Demonstrations

Section 2:4

Hooke's law can be demonstrated easily. Using a helical spring or strip of steel, show that doubling the weight (force) causes a doubled elongation of the helical spring or a doubled bending of the strip. Have students plot the data and fit a straight line through the points.

A syringe can be used to demonstrate Boyle's law. With the end plugged, weights may be placed on the plunger and the volume of air in the syringe read off the scale. Again, have the students plot the data and draw the best hyperbola through the points. Discuss the possibility that friction causes uncertainties in the data and elaborate on how they may be decreased.

Films

Change of Scale (university rental, PSSC film)
The Relation of Mathematics to Physics (EDC film)

Laboratory Investigations

Graphing Experimental Data

Performance Objectives

Goal: Students will review elementary algebra and trigonometry, and learn to use graphical analysis of data.

Objectives: Upon completion of the reading, questions, and problems, students will be able to:

2:1	K/S/P	demonstrate the ability to manipulate algebraic equations.
2:2	K/S/P	use dimensional analysis to test the validity of an equation.
2:3	K/P	distinguish between dependent and independent variables. Interpret the meaning of linear, parabolic, and hyperbolic curves on graphs.
2:4	K	recognize linear and direct relationships.
2:5	K	recognize quadratic (parabolic) relationships.
2:6	K	recognize inverse (hyperbolic) relationships.
2:7	K	demonstrate a capacity to use the trigonometry of right triangles.
	S/A	Students will use laboratory materials in the prescribed manner when conducting lab investigations.

Upon completion of the reading, questions, and practice problems, students will exhibit an interest in physics by:

A/S	expanding on an answer to one or more of the questions or problems at the end of the chapter.
S/P	listing and discussing linear, parabolic, and hyperbolic relationships in fields outside physics.
A	reading unassigned literature related to ideas presented in this chapter.

Solutions to Problems

Page 24.

1. **a.** $8 = 2 \times 4$ **b.** $4 = \dfrac{8}{2}$

2. **a.** $v = \dfrac{d}{t}$ **b.** $v = \dfrac{d}{t}$

    c. $v = \pm \sqrt{2ad}$ **d.** $v = \dfrac{ab}{c}$

3. $t^2 = \dfrac{2d}{a}$ $a = \dfrac{2d}{t^2}$ $2 = \dfrac{at^2}{d}$

4. **a.** $E = fs$ **b.** $E = \dfrac{1}{2}mv^2$ **c.** $E = mc^2$

5. $v = \dfrac{P}{F}$ $F = \dfrac{P}{v}$

6. $d = \dfrac{v^2}{2a}$ $a = \dfrac{v^2}{2d}$

7. **a.** $x = \dfrac{w}{f}$ **b.** $x = \dfrac{f}{g}$

    c. $x = ny$ **d.** $x = \pm \sqrt{2d/a}$

Page 25.

8. **a.** $A = (0.2 \text{ cm})(30 \text{ cm}) = 6 \text{ cm}^2$
    b. $P = 0.25\,\text{m} + 0.25\,\text{m} + 2.00\,\text{m} + 2.00\,\text{m} = 4.50 \text{ m}$
9. **a.** $area = (length)(width)(height) = \text{m} \times \text{m} \times \text{m}$
    $= \text{m}^3$ incorrect
    b. $time = \dfrac{distance}{speed} = \dfrac{\text{m}}{\text{m/s}} = \text{s}$
    correct
    c. $distance = (speed)(time)^2 = (\text{m/s})(\text{s})^2 = \text{ms}$
    incorrect

Page 31.

10. **a.** r **b.** s **c.** $\text{sine } R = \dfrac{r}{t}$

    $\text{tangent } R = \dfrac{r}{s}$ $\text{cosine } R = \dfrac{s}{t}$

11. **a.** 30.0°   **b.** 80.0°   **c.** 45.0°   **d.** 45.0°
    e. 45.0°   **f.** 20.0°   **g.** 64.0°   **h.** 30.0°
12. **a.** The lengths should agree with answer b.
    b. opposite side = 2.05 cm
    adjacent side = 5.64 cm
13. $\tan 35° = 14 \text{ cm /adjacent side}$
    adjacent side = 14 cm /tan 35°
    $= 2.0 \times 10^1 \text{ cm}$
14. $\tan R = \dfrac{21 \text{ m}}{84 \text{ m}} = 0.25$ $R = 14°$

    $\sin R = \dfrac{21 \text{ m}}{\text{hyp}}$ $\text{hyp} = \dfrac{21 \text{ m}}{\sin R} = 87 \text{ m}$

Chapter End Questions

Pages 32-33.

1. Check units for dimensional accuracy.
2. Independent and dependent variables, respectively.

3. **a.** Independent variable values are plotted horizontally
   b. dependent variable values vertically.
4. Slope is the vertical interval, or rise, Δy, divided by the corresponding horizontal interval, or run, Δx, between any two points on a graph.
5. The independent variable is manipulated and the dependent variable is one that is observed.
6. If the rate at which an object falls were to be inversely proportional to the density of the medium, then an object would fall infinitely fast in a vacuum. Aristotle was aware that falling objects had finite speeds, so he decided there could be no such thing as a vacuum.
7. Parabola; straight line.

Problems A

Page 33.

1. **a.** $V = (4.23 \text{ cm})^3 = 75.7 \text{ cm}^3$
   b. $m = (D)(V) = (19.3 \text{ g/cm}^3)(75.7 \text{ cm}^3) = 1460 \text{ g}$

2. **a.** $m = (D)(V) = (10.5 \text{ g/cm}^3)(65.0 \text{ cm}^3) = 683 \text{ g}$
   b. $m = 683 \text{ g} - 616 \text{ g} = 67 \text{ g}$

   $$V = \frac{m}{D} = \frac{67 \text{ g}}{10.5 \text{ g/cm}^3} = 6.4 \text{ cm}^3$$

3. **a.** $v = \dfrac{m}{s}$ correct

   b. $Area = \dfrac{m}{m^3}, = \dfrac{1}{m^2}$, incorrect

   c. $d = \dfrac{m/s}{s} = \dfrac{m}{s^2}$, incorrect

   d. $Time = \dfrac{m}{m/s^2} = s^2$, incorrect

4. **a.**

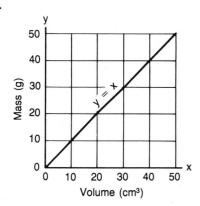

   b. Straight line passing through origin
   c. The mass of water varies directly with its volume

5. **a.** A straight line **b.** The acceleration of the mass varies directly with the applied force.

Page 34.

6. **a.**

   b. hyperbola
   c. Acceleration varies inversely with the mass.
7. **a.** 5.00° **b.** 31.00° **c.** 18.00°
   d. 11.00° **e.** 39.00° **f.** 75.00°
   g. 20.00° **h.** 45.00° **i.** 72.00°
8. $\sin 26° = \dfrac{Y}{11 \text{cm}}$ $Y = 4.8 \text{ cm}$

   $\cos 26° = \dfrac{X}{11 \text{cm}}$ $X = 9.9 \text{ cm}$

9. $\tan 50.0° = \dfrac{8.50 \text{cm}}{adj}$ $adj = \dfrac{8.50 \text{cm}}{\tan 50.0°} = 7.13 \text{ cm}$

   $\sin 50.0° = \dfrac{8.50 \text{cm}}{hyp}$ $hyp = \dfrac{8.50 \text{cm}}{\sin 50.0°} = 11.1 \text{ cm}$

Problems B

Page 34.

1. a. $v = \dfrac{d}{t} = \dfrac{(2\pi)(1.50 \times 10^8 \text{ km})}{(365\frac{1}{4}\text{ day})(24\ \dfrac{\text{h}}{\text{day}})} = \dfrac{9.4248 \times 10^8 \text{ km}}{8.766 \times 10^3 \text{ h}}$

$v = 1.08\ \times 10^5\ \dfrac{\text{km}}{\text{h}}$

b. $v = \dfrac{(1.089 \times 10^5 \text{ km/h})(1000 \text{ m/km})}{(3600 \text{ s/h})}$

$= 3.00 \times 10^4 \text{ m/s}$

Page 35.

2. $\tan 76.0° = \dfrac{d}{30.0 \text{ m}}$

$d = 30.0 \text{ m } \tan 76.0° = 1.20 \times 10^2 \text{ m}$

Motion in a Straight Line   Chapter 3

Teaching Techniques

Both the material and the approach to problem solving included in this chapter are fundamental to all that follows. Encourage students to follow the procedures as described in the solutions of example problems.

Selection of the basic equation to be solved is essential to successful problem solving. Equations should be solved for the unknown before any numerical values are substituted for the symbols. The factor-label method is designed to check the dimensionality of all terms in an equation. Whenever solving example problems, retain units on all terms and show students how dimensional checks can be used to find errors.

Stress that the equations of motion can be easily obtained from the definitions of velocity and acceleration. Avoid the temptation to bring the calculus into discussions.

Table (3-1) in Section 11 should be used to help students learn the rationale behind the choice of an equation in solving a problem. Write it on the board during problem solving sessions. Explain that the construction of a table of given and unknown quantities is fundamental to problem solving.

Demonstrations

To illustrate uniform motion, roll a smooth ball across a laboratory bench. A long ramp along one side of the classroom is of great help in showing accelerated motion. A metronome can be used to generate uniform time intervals, and the distance traveled at the end of each interval can be marked with chalk. The acceleration equations should then be demonstrated by plotting distance versus time, and distance versus (time)².

Galileo's thought experiment that compares the time of two balls falling separately or tied together can be used to support acceleration due to gravity.

Films

Straight Line Kinematics (university rental, PSSC film)

Film Loops

Falling Bodies in a Vacuum (BFA-Ealing film loop)

Laboratory Investigation

Measurement of Time

Performance Objectives

Goal: Students will gain an understanding of the fundamentals of kinematics.

Objectives: Upon completion of the reading, questions, and problems, students will, on oral or written tests:

3:1	P/S/K	describe, qualitatively, the relationship among distance moved, the time it takes, and the speed or velocity of the body.
3:2	K/S	distinguish scalar from vector quantities, giving examples of each.
3:3	P/K/S	demonstrate the ability to add two vectors in one dimension, recognizing that order is unimportant.
3:4	P/K	distinguish distance from displacement, giving examples.
3:5	P/K/S	define and give examples of instantaneous speed, distinguishing speed from velocity.
3:6	P/K/S	demonstrate the ability to calculate average speed and velocity and to use the factor-label method of unit conversion. Be able to solve a basic equation for the unknown.

3:7	K/S	demonstrate the ability to calculate acceleration, both positive and negative, giving examples of zero velocity with nonzero acceleration and vice versa.
3:8	K/S	write the equation for final velocity after acceleration, applying the equation in solution of problems.
3:9	P/K/S	write the two equations for the distance traveled during uniform acceleration and the equation for the final velocity of the object after acceleration over a given distance. Apply the equations in solving problems. Be able to recognize symmetry in motion problems.
3:10	P/K/S	be able to state the value for the acceleration due to gravity and demonstrate the ability to use this value in the acceleration equations.
3:11	P/K/S	show the ability to use Table 3-1 to select the correct equation to use by analyzing the quantities present in the problem. Demonstrate an orderly approach to problem solving.
	S/A	Students will use laboratory materials in the prescribed manner when conducting lab investigations.

Upon completion of the reading and practice problems, students will exhibit an interest in physics by:

A/S	expanding on an answer to one or more of the questions or problems at the end of the chapter.
K/P	discussing the use of symmetry in motion problems.
A/P	discussing the role of Galileo in discovering the laws of motion of uniformly accelerated bodies.
A	reading unassigned literature related to the ideas presented in the chapter.

Solutions to Problems

Page 42.

1. $\bar{v} = \dfrac{d}{t} = 13 \text{ km}/2.0 \text{ h} = 6.5 \text{ km/h}$

$6.5 \text{ km/h} = \dfrac{(6.5 \text{ km})(1000 \text{ m/km})}{(1 \text{ h})(3600 \text{ s/h})} = 1.8 \text{ m/s}$

2. $\bar{v} = \dfrac{d}{t} = 1.00 \times 10^2 \text{ m}/12.20 \text{ s} = 8.20 \text{ m/s}$

$8.20 \text{ m/s} = \dfrac{(8.2 \text{ m})(3600 \text{ s/h})}{(1000 \text{ m/km})(1 \text{ s})} = 29.5 \text{ km/h}$

3. a. $t = \dfrac{d}{v} = \dfrac{324.00 \text{ m}}{720.0 \text{ m/s}} = 0.4500 \text{ s}$

b. $720.0 \text{ m/s} = \dfrac{(720.0 \text{ m})(3600 \text{ s/h})}{(1000 \text{ m/km})(1 \text{ s})} = 2592 \text{ km/h, E}$

4. $\bar{v} = \dfrac{d}{t} = \dfrac{240000 \text{ km}}{6.0 \text{ h}} = 4.0 \times 10^4 \text{ km/h}$

$4.0 \times 10^4 \text{ km/h} = \dfrac{(40000 \text{ km})(1000 \text{ m/km})}{(1 \text{ h})(3600 \text{ s/h})} = 11000 \text{ m/s}$

5. $d = \bar{v}t = \dfrac{(3.00 \times 10^8 \text{ m/s})(8.3 \text{ min})(60 \text{ s/min})}{1000 \text{ m/km}}$

$= 1.5 \times 10^8 \text{ km}$

Page 43.

6. $t = \dfrac{d}{v} = \dfrac{18.5 \text{ m}}{38.5 \text{ m/s}} = 0.481 \text{ s}$

7. $\bar{v} = \dfrac{d}{t} = \dfrac{(60 \text{ km} + 70 \text{ km})}{(40 \text{ min} + 50 \text{ min})} = \dfrac{(130 \text{ km})(60 \text{ min/h})}{(90 \text{ min})}$

$= 90 \text{ km/h}$

$\bar{v} = \dfrac{(60 \text{ km} - 70 \text{ km})}{(40 \text{ min} + 50 \text{ min})} = \dfrac{(-10 \text{ km})(60 \text{ min/h})}{90 \text{ min}}$

$= 7 \text{ km/h, E}$

8. $t = t_{train} - t_{sound}$

$= \dfrac{(360 \text{ m})(3600 \text{ s/h})}{(3.01 \times 10^2 \text{ km/h})(1000 \text{ m/km})} - \dfrac{(360 \text{ m})}{(330 \text{ m/s})}$

$= 4.31 \text{ s} - 1.09 \text{ s} = 3.2 \text{ s}$

Page 45.

9. $F_v = v_i + at$ $v_f - v_i = at$

$= \dfrac{v_f - v_i}{t} = \dfrac{66 \text{ m/s} - 44 \text{ m/s}}{11 \text{ s}} = 2.0 \text{ m/s}^2,$

10. $a = \dfrac{v_f - v_i}{t} = \dfrac{44 \text{ m/s} - 66 \text{ m/s}}{11 \text{ s}}$

$= \dfrac{-22 \text{ m/s}}{11 \text{ s}} = -2.0 \text{ m/s}^2, \text{S}$

11. $a = \dfrac{v_f - v_i}{t} = \dfrac{17 \text{ m/s} - 15 \text{ m/s}}{12 \text{ s}}$

$= \dfrac{2 \text{ m/s}}{12 \text{ s}} = 0.2 \text{ m/s}^2$

12. $a = \dfrac{v_f - v_i}{5} = \dfrac{72 \text{ m/s} - 0 \text{ m/s}}{5.0 \text{ s}} = 14 \text{ m/s}^2$

13. $v_f = F_i + at$

$$a = \frac{v_f - v_i}{t} = \frac{2.6 \times 10^5 \text{ m/s} - 0}{6.5 \times 10^{-7} \text{ s}}$$

$$= 4.0 \times 10^{11} \text{ m/s}^2$$

Page 46.

14. $v_f = v_i + at = 8.0 \text{ m/s} + (1.2 \text{ m/s}^2)(12 \text{ s})$
    $= 8.0 \text{ m/s} + 14.4 \text{ m/s} = 22 \text{ m/s}$

15. $v_f = v_i + at = 95 \text{ m/s} + (0.50 \text{ m/s}^2)(10.0 \text{ s}) =$
    $1.0 \times 10^2 \text{ m/s, E}$

$$100 \text{ m/s} = \frac{(100 \text{ m})(1000 \text{ m/km})}{(1 \text{ s})(3600 \text{ s/h})}$$

$$= 360 \text{ km/h E}$$

16. **a.** $v_f = v_i + at = 45 \text{ m/s} + (-1.5 \text{ m/s}^2)(9.8 \text{ s})$
    $= 3.0 \times 10^1 \text{ m/s}$

Page 47.

17. $d = \bar{v}t = \frac{(v_f + v_i)}{2} t$

$$= \frac{(41 \text{ m/s} + 0)(8.0 \text{ s})}{2} = 1.6 \times 10^2 \text{ m}$$

18. $d = \bar{v}t = \frac{(v_f + v_i)}{2} t$

$$= \frac{(22 \text{ m/s} + 44 \text{ m/s})(11 \text{ s})}{2} = 360 \text{ m}$$

Page 48.

19. $d = \frac{(v_f + v_i)}{2} t$

$$= \frac{(132 \text{ m/s} + 88 \text{ m/s})(15 \text{ s})}{2} = 1700 \text{ m}$$

20. **a.** $v_f = v_i + at$

$$t = \frac{v_f - v_i}{a} = \frac{61 \text{ m/s} - 0 \text{ m/s}}{1.5 \text{ m/s}^2} = 41 \text{ s}$$

b. $v_f^2 = v_i^2 + 2ad$ (combined equations)

$$d = \frac{v_f^2 - v_i^2}{2a} = \frac{(61 \text{ m/s})^2 - (0 \text{ m/s})^2}{(2)(1.5 \text{ m/s}^2)}$$

$$= \frac{3721 \text{ m}^2/\text{s}^2}{3.0 \text{ m/s}^2} = 1200 \text{ m}$$

Page 49.

21. $d = v_i t + \frac{1}{2} at^2$

$$= 0 + \frac{1}{2}(3.0 \text{ m/s}^2)(30.0 \text{ s})^2 = 1400 \text{ m}$$

22. **a.** $v_f = v_i + at$

$$a = \frac{v_f - v_i}{t} = \frac{-88 \text{ m/s} - 0 \text{ m/s}}{11 \text{ s}} = -8.0 \text{ m/s}^2$$

b. $d = \frac{(v_f + v_i)}{2} t = \frac{(0 + 88 \text{ m/s})(11 \text{ s})}{2}$

$$= 480 \text{ m}$$

23. $d = v_i t + \frac{1}{2} at^2$

$$= 0 + \frac{1}{2}(1.0 \text{ m/s}^2)(6.0 \times 10^1 \text{s})^2 = 1800 \text{ m}$$

24. $d = v_i t + \frac{1}{2} at^2$

$$a = \frac{2(d - v_i t)}{t^2} = \frac{2(201 \text{ m} - 0)}{(5.0 \text{ s})^2}$$

$$= \frac{400 \text{ m}}{25 \text{ s}^2} = 16 \text{ m/s}^2, \text{S}$$

25. **a.** $v_f = v_i + at$

$$a = \frac{v_f - v_i}{t} = \frac{(0 - 21 \text{ m/s})}{8.0 \text{ s}} = -2.6 \text{ m/s}^2$$

b. $d = \bar{v}t = \frac{(v_f + v_i)t}{2}$

$$= \frac{(0 + 21 \text{ m/s})(8.0 \text{ s})}{2} = 84 \text{ m}$$

26. $d = v_i t + \frac{1}{2} at^2$

$$a = \frac{2(d - v_i t)}{t^2} = \frac{2(-490 \text{ m} - 0)}{(10.0 \text{ s})^2}$$

$$= \frac{-980 \text{ m}}{1.00 \times 10^2 \text{ s}} = -9.8 \text{ m/s}^2$$

27. $d = v_i t + \frac{1}{2} at^2$

$$= (4.5 \text{ m/s})(12 \text{ s}) + \frac{1}{2}(0.40 \text{ m/s}^2)(12 \text{ s})^2 = 83 \text{ m}$$

Page 50.

28. $v_f^2 = v_i^2 + 2ad$

$$v_f = \sqrt{v_i^2 + 2ad}$$

$$= \sqrt{(2.0 \text{ m/s})^2 + (2)(3.0 \text{ m/s}^2)(530 \text{ m})}$$

$$= 56 \text{ m/s}$$

29. $v_f^2 = v_i^2 + 2ad$

$$v_i = \sqrt{v_f^2 - 2ad}$$

$$= \sqrt{0 - (2)(-8.0 \text{ m/s}^2)(484 \text{ m})}$$

$$= \sqrt{7744 \text{ m}^2/\text{s}^2} = 88 \text{ m/s}$$

30. $v_f^2 = v_i^2 + 2ad$

$$v_i = \sqrt{v_f^2 - 2ad}$$

$$= \sqrt{0 - (2)(-5.0 \text{ m/s}^2)(62.5 \text{ m})}$$

$$= \sqrt{625 \text{ m}^2/\text{s}^2} = 25 \text{ m/s}$$

Page 53.

31. $v_f = v_i + at = 1210 \text{ m/s} + (-150 \text{ m/s}^2)(1.8 \text{ s}) = 940$
    m/s

Chapter End Questions

Pages 54-55.

1. **a.** $a = \dfrac{\Delta v}{t}$ **b.** $v_f = v_i + at$ **c.** $d = \dfrac{v_f + v_i}{2}t$

2. Tables should indicate that, for a body accelerating uniformly from rest, distance traveled and speed attained are numerically the same at the end of two seconds.

Car	Speed (m/s)	Distance (m)
A	12	12
B	11	11
C	16	16
D	24	24

3. Both bodies have traveled the same distance. The body shot straight up rises to the same height from which the other body fell.

4. The earth pulls on the steel ball with more force than on the aluminum ball. However, the steel ball has more mass to be accelerated. Thus, both masses are accelerated equally.

5. Velocity is reduced at a constant rate as the ball travels up into the air. As the ball begins to drop, the velocity again begins to increase until it reaches the height from which it was initially released. At that point the ball will have the same velocity it had upon release. The acceleration is constant.

Problems A

Page 55.

1. $d = vt = \dfrac{(55 \text{ km/h})(0.75 \text{ s})(1000 \text{ m/km})}{(3600 \text{ s/h})} = 11 \text{ m}$

2. **a.** $v_f^2 = v_i^2 + 2ad$

$d = \dfrac{v_f^2 - v_i^2}{2a} = \dfrac{0 - (+55 \text{ m/s})^2}{(2)(-11 \text{ m/s}^2)} = 140 \text{ m}$

b. $d = \dfrac{v_f^2 - v_i^2}{2a} = \dfrac{0 - (110 \text{ m/s})^2}{(2)(-11 \text{ m/s}^2)} = 550 \text{ m}$

3. $d = v_i t + \dfrac{1}{2}at^2$

$t = \sqrt{\dfrac{2d}{a}} = \sqrt{\dfrac{(2)(1.2 \text{ m})(6)}{(9.8 \text{ m/s}^2)}} = 1.2 \text{ s}$

4. $v_f = v_i + at$

$a = \dfrac{v_f - v_i}{t} = \dfrac{96 \text{ m/s} - 32 \text{ m/s}}{8.0 \text{ s}}$

$= \dfrac{64 \text{ m/s}}{8.0 \text{ s}} = 8.0 \text{ m/s}^2$

5. **a.** $v_f = v_i + at$

$t = \dfrac{v_f - v_i}{a} = \dfrac{0 - (+155 \text{ m/s})}{-31.0 \text{ m/s}^2} = 5.00 \text{ s}$

b. $d = v_i t + \dfrac{1}{2}at^2$

$= (+155 \text{ m/s})(5.00 \text{ s}) + \dfrac{1}{2}(-31.0 \text{ m/s}^2)(5.00 \text{ s})^2$

$= 387.5 \text{ m} = 388 \text{ m}$

c. -93 m/s   The rocket is moving backwards.

6. $v_f = v_i + at = 22 \text{ m/s} + (1.6 \text{ m/s}^2)(6.8 \text{ s})$
$= 32.88 \text{ m/s} = 33 \text{ m/s, E}$

7. $v_f = v_i + at$

$= 2.35 \times 10^5 \text{ m/s} + (-1.10 \times 10^{12} \text{ m/s}^2) \times$

$(1.50 \times 10^{-7} \text{ s}) = 7.0 \ \times 10^4 \text{ m/s}$

8. **a.** $v_f = v_i + at$
$= 2.0 \times 10^1 \text{ m/s} + (23.1 \text{ m/s}^2)(20.0 \text{ s})$
$= 482 \text{ m/s}$

b. $N = \dfrac{482 \text{ m/s}}{331 \text{ m/s}} = 1.46 \text{ times}$

Page 56.

9. $d = \dfrac{(v_f + v_i)}{2}t = \dfrac{(88 \text{ m/s} + 66 \text{ m/s})(12 \text{ s})}{2}$

$= 920 \text{ m, S}$

10. $d = \dfrac{(v_f + v_i)}{2}t = \dfrac{(145 \text{ m/s} + 75 \text{ m/s})(15 \text{ s})}{2}$

$= 1650 \text{ m} = 1700 \text{ m}$

11. $v_f^2 = v_i^2 + 2ad$

$a = \dfrac{v_f^2 - v_i^2}{2d} = \dfrac{(600 \text{ m/s})^2 - 0}{(2)(0.9 \text{ m})}$

$= \dfrac{3.6 \times 10^5 \text{ m}^2/\text{s}^2}{1.8 \text{ m}} = 2 \times 10^5 \text{ m/s}^2$

12. $v_i = v_f - at = 0 - (-9.0 \text{ m/s}^2)(8.0 \text{ s}) = 72 \text{ m/s}$

$d = \dfrac{1}{2}(v_i + v_f)t = \dfrac{1}{2}(72 \text{ m/s} + 0 \text{ m/s})(8.0 \text{ s})$

$= 290 \text{ m}$

13. $v_f = \sqrt{v_i^2 + 2ad} = \sqrt{0 + 2(5.0 \text{ m/s}^2)(5.0 \times 10^2 \text{ m})}$
$v_f = 71 \text{ m/s}$

14. **a.** $v_f = v_i + gt = 0 + (-9.8 \text{ m/s}^2)(8.0 \text{ s})$

$= -78 \text{ m/s (down)}$

b. $d = v_i t + \dfrac{1}{2}gt^2 = 0 + \dfrac{1}{2}(-9.8 \text{ m/s}^2)(8.0 \text{ s})^2$

$= -310 \text{ m (down)}$

15. **a.** $v_f^2 = v_i^2 + 2gd$

$d = \dfrac{v_f^2 - v_i^2}{2a} = \dfrac{(-73.5 \text{ m/s})^2 - 0}{(2)(-9.8 \text{ m/s}^2)}$

$= \dfrac{5402 \text{ m}^2/\text{s}^2}{19.6 \text{ m/s}^2} = -276 \text{ m}$

b. $v_f = v_i + gt$

$$t = \frac{v_f - v_i}{g} = \frac{-73.5 \text{ m/s} - 0}{-9.8 \text{ m/s}^2} = 7.5 \text{ s}$$

16. falling object $(v_i = 0)$

$$d = \frac{1}{2}gt^2 + v_i t$$

$$d = \frac{1}{2}(-9.8 \text{ m/s}^2)(7.0 \text{ s})^2 = -240 \text{ m}$$

$$d_{up} = d_{down}$$

rising object $(v_i = 69 \text{ m/s})$

$$d = \frac{1}{2}gt^2 + v_i t = \frac{1}{2}(-9.8 \text{ m/s}^2)(7.0 \text{ s})^2 + (69 \text{ m/s})(7.0 \text{ s})$$

$$= -240 \text{ m} + 480 \text{ m} = 240 \text{ m}$$

The distance is the same but the displacement is opposite.

17. $d = v_i t + \frac{1}{2}gt^2 = 0 + \frac{1}{2}(-9.8 \text{ m/s}^2)(3.0 \text{ s})^2 = -44 \text{ m}$

18. $v_f^2 = v_i^2 + 2gd$

$$v_f = \sqrt{v_i^2 + 2gd} = \sqrt{0 + (2)(-9.8 \text{ m/s}^2)(-12.0 \text{ m})}$$

$$= \sqrt{235.4 \text{ m}^2/\text{s}^2} = 15.3 \text{ m/s}$$

19. a. $d_{car} = v_i t + \frac{1}{2}at^2 = 0 + \frac{1}{2}(6.0)t^2 = 3.0t^2 \text{ m/s}^2$

$$d_{truck} = v_i t + \frac{1}{2}at^2 = (21 \text{ m/s}) t$$

$d_{car} = d_{truck}$, when the truck overtakes the car
$3.0t^2 \text{ m/s}^2 = (21 \text{ m/s}) t$
$t = 7.0 \text{ s}$
$d_{car} = (3.0 \text{ m/s}^2)(7.0 \text{ s})^2 = 150 \text{ m}$

b. $v_f = v_i + at = 0 + (6.0 \text{ m/s}^2)(7.0 \text{ s}) = 42 \text{ m/s}$

Problems B

Page 56.

1. a. $v_f = v_i + gt = (+6.0 \text{ m/s}) + (-9.8 \text{ m/s}^2)(2.0 \text{ s})$
$= -14 \text{ m/s}$

b. The wrench was falling while the helicopter was rising. The displacement of the wrench below where it was released is given by

$$d_w = v_i t + \frac{1}{2}gt^2$$

$$= (+6.0 \text{ m/s})(2.0 \text{ s}) + \frac{1}{2}(-9.8 \text{ m/s}^2)(2.0 \text{ s})^2$$

$$= -7.6 \text{ m}$$

Since the helicopter has risen (2.0 s)(6.0 m/s) or 12 m in this time, the wrench is 12 m + 7.6 m or 20 m below the helicopter.

Page 57.

2. $d = \frac{1}{2}gt^2$ $t = \sqrt{\frac{2d}{g}}$

3. a. $v_i = \frac{(90.0 \text{ km/h})(1000 \text{ m/km})}{(3600 \text{ s/h})} = 25.0 \text{ m/s}$

$v_f = v_i + at$

$t = \frac{v_f - v_i}{a} = \frac{0 - (25.0 \text{ m/s})}{-10.0 \text{ m/s}^2} = 2.50 \text{ s}$

The car will travel
$d = vt = (25.0 \text{ m/s})(0.75 \text{ s}) = 18.75 \text{ m} = 19 \text{ m}$
before the driver applies the brakes.
The total distance the car must travel to stop is

$$d = 19 \text{ m} + v_i t + \frac{1}{2}at^2$$

$$= 19 \text{ m} + (25.0 \text{ m/s})(2.50 \text{ s})$$

$$+ \frac{1}{2}(-10.0 \text{ m/s}^2)(2.50 \text{ s})^2$$

$$= 50 \text{ m, yes it hits the barrier.}$$

b. $d_{total} = d_{constant_v} + d_{decelerating} = 40.0 \text{ m}$
$d_c = vt = (0.75 \text{ s})v$
$d_d = -v^2/2a = -v^2/2(-10.0 \text{ m/s}^2) = v^2/20.0 \text{ m/s}^2$
$40.0 \text{ m} = (0.75 \text{ s})v + v^2/20.0 \text{ m/s}^2$
$v^2 + 15v - 800 = 0$
Using the quadratic equation:
$v = 22 \text{ m/s}$ (The sense of the problem excludes the negative value.)

4. a. $t = \frac{d}{v}$ $t_{total} = t_1 + t_2$ **b.** no

$$\frac{d}{90 \text{ km/h}} = \frac{0.5d}{50 \text{ km/h}} + \frac{0.5d}{v}$$

$$\frac{1}{v} = \frac{1}{45 \text{ km/h}} - \frac{1}{50 \text{ km/h}}$$ $v = 450 \text{ km/h}$

Graphical Analysis   Chapter 4

Teaching Techniques

Graphical analysis of kinematics is important as it illustrates the variation in quantities. This concept is in contrast to the static picture given by numbers plugged into equations. Thus the chapter reinforces and gives new meaning to the results of the previous chapter.

Demonstrations

Use the same equipment as in the previous chapter, but graph the results. Dynamics carts with several weights, interval timers, and timer tapes can also be used. As students make sample tapes, plot the data and develop the graphs associated with the motion of the cart.

Laboratory Investigations

Graphical Analysis of Motion
Graphical Analysis of Motion: Uniform Acclera-tion

Performance Objectives

Goal: Students will gain knowledge and understanding of the uses of graphs and their applications in the analysis of motion.

Objectives: Upon completion of the reading, questions, and problems, students will, on oral or written tests:

4:1	K/S	understand the meaning of points on a position-time graph of constant velocity.
4:2	K/S	be able to determine the slope of a curve on a position-time graph and calculate the velocity.
4:3	K/S	interpret and plot position-time graphs for constant and changing motion, negative values, and varying slopes.
4:4	P/K/S	understand the meaning of the area under the curve in a velocity-time graph and be able to calculate the displacement from such a graph.
4:5	K/S	be able to calculate the area under the curve of a velocity-time graph and interpret it as the displacement.
4:6	P/K/S	understand the relation of the position-time graph to the velocity-time graph; recognize the meaning of the parabolic shape; find the slope at any point and interpret it correctly.
4:7	K/S	understand that uniformly accelerated motion versus time must yield a straight line; recognize the meaning of the area under the curve.
	S/A	Students will use laboratory materials in the prescribed manner when conducting lab investigations.

Upon completion of the reading and practice problems, students will exhibit an interest in physics by:

A/S	expanding on an answer to one or more of the questions or problems at the end of the chapter.
A/S	developing overhead transparencies that demonstrate the relationships discussed in this chapter.
A/S/K	taking data on the motion of a vehicle like a car or bicycle, using the techniques of this chapter to find velocity, acceleration, and distance travelled.
A	reading unassigned literature related to the ideas presented in the chapter.

Solutions to Problems

Page 62.

1. a.

$t(s)$	$d(m)$
0	0
1	50
2	100
3	150
4	200
.....	.....
10	500

b.

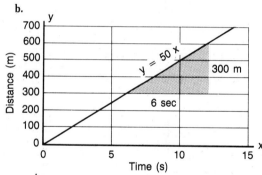

c. $\dfrac{\Delta y}{\Delta x} = 50$ m/s

d.

e. $d = \bar{v}t = (50 \text{ m/s})(3 \text{ s}) = 150 \text{ m}$

2. a. 400 m   **b.** 0 m   **c.** 200 m

3.   a. $\bar{v} = \dfrac{\Delta d}{\Delta t} = \dfrac{400 \text{ m}}{40 \text{ s}} = 10 \text{ m/s}$

c.

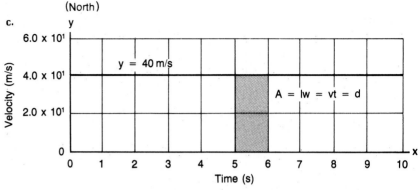

(North)

The area under the line is vt and thus represents total distance traveled during a given time interval.

Page 63.

b. $\bar{v} = \dfrac{\Delta d}{\Delta t} = \dfrac{0 \text{ m}}{30 \text{ s}} = 0 \text{ m/s}$

c. $\bar{v} = \dfrac{\Delta d}{\Delta t} = \dfrac{-200 \text{ m}}{20 \text{ s}} = -10 \text{ m/s}$

d. $\bar{v} = \dfrac{\Delta d}{\Delta t} = \dfrac{-200 \text{ m}}{10 \text{ s}} = -20 \text{ m/s}$

d. $A = l\,w = vt = (40 \text{ m/s})(1\text{s}) = 40 \text{ m}$

7.   a.

4.

t(s)	v(m/s)
0	0
10	10
20	10
30	10
40	10
50	0
60	0
70	0
80	−10
90	−10
100	−20

5.

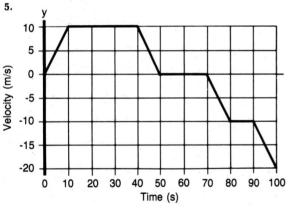

b. 5.0×10^1 m south of location A.

c. 3.0×10^2 m

Chapter End Questions

Pages 68-69.

1. Slope of a position-time graph indicates velocity.

2. The area beneath a velocity-time graph represents distance.

3. The slope of a velocity-time graph indicates acceleration.

4. When the velocity-time graph is line parallel to the t-axis, the acceleration is zero.

5. Area beneath an acceleration-time graph represents velocity.

6. The velocity rises quickly at first, then the rate slows. At times the velocity remains constant for a second, as gears are shifted. At other times the rise in velocity slows greatly.

7. Acceleration is greatest at $t = 0$ and immediately after each pause. It is zero at the pauses, and has the smallest nonzero values at the highest velocity.

6.   a.

b. $\dfrac{\Delta y}{\Delta x} = 40 \text{ m/s}$

Problems A

Page 69.

1. a.

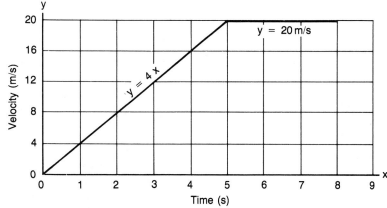

b. $d = \bar{v}t = (4 \text{ m/s})(2 \text{ s}) = 8 \text{ m}$
c. $d = \bar{v}t = (8 \text{ m/s})(4 \text{ s}) = 32 \text{ m}$
d. $d = (10 \text{ m/s})(5 \text{ s}) + (20 \text{ m/s})(3 \text{ s})$
$= 50 \text{ m} + 60 \text{ m} = 110 \text{ m}$

e. $a = \dfrac{\Delta v}{\Delta t} = \dfrac{16 \text{ m/s} - 0 \text{ m/s}}{4 \text{ s} - 0 \text{ s}} = 4 \text{ m/s}^2$ acceleration

f. $a = \dfrac{\Delta v}{\Delta t} = \dfrac{20 \text{ m/s} - 20 \text{ m/s}}{7 \text{ s} - 5 \text{ s}} = 0$ constant velocity

2. a.

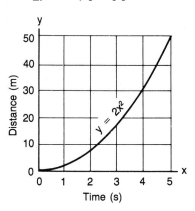

b. parabola
c. $y = 2x^2 = (2)(2.2 \text{ s})^2 = 9.7 \text{ m}$

d. $d = \dfrac{(v_f + v_i)}{2} t$

$v_f = \dfrac{2d}{t} - v_i = \dfrac{(2)(18 \text{ m})}{(3.0 \text{ s})} - 0 = \dfrac{36 \text{ m}}{3.0 \text{ s}} = 12 \text{ m/s}$

The slope represents the speed at the end of 3.0 s.

Page 70.

3. a. $a = \dfrac{\Delta v}{\Delta t} = \dfrac{30 \text{ m/s}}{5 \text{ s}} = 6 \text{ m/s}^2, \text{N}$

b. $a = \dfrac{\Delta v}{\Delta t} = \dfrac{0}{5 \text{ s}} = 0$

c. $a = \dfrac{\Delta v}{\Delta t} = \dfrac{-10 \text{ m/s}}{5 \text{ s}} = -2 \text{ m/s}^2$

d. $a = \dfrac{\Delta v}{\Delta t} = \dfrac{0 \text{ m/s} - 20 \text{ m/s}}{5 \text{ s}} = -4 \text{ m/s}^2$

4. a. $d = \dfrac{(v_f + v_i)}{2} t = \dfrac{(30 \text{ m/s} + 0)(5 \text{ s})}{2} = 8 \times 10^1$

b. $d = \bar{v}t = (30 \text{ m/s})(5 \text{ s}) = 2 \times 10^1$

c. $d = \dfrac{(v_f + v_i)}{2} t = \dfrac{(20 \text{ m/s} + 30 \text{ m/s})(5 \text{ s})}{2} = 1 \times 10^1$

d. From $t = 15$ s to $t = 20$ s,
$d = \bar{v}t = (20 \text{ m/s})(5 \text{ s}) = 100 \text{ m}$
and from $t = 20$ s to $t = 25$ s,

$d = \dfrac{(v_f + v_i)}{2} t = \dfrac{(0 \text{ m/s} + 20 \text{ m/s})(5 \text{ s})}{2} = 50 \text{ m}$

Between $t = 0$ and $t = 25$ s
$d = 80 \text{ m} + 200 \text{ m} + 100 \text{ m} + 100 \text{ m} + 50 \text{ m}$
$= 530 \text{ m}$

5. A—B = acceleration, B—C = constant speed, C—D = deceleration, D—E = rest, E—F = acceleration in opposite direction, F—G = constant speed, G—H = deceleration

6. a.

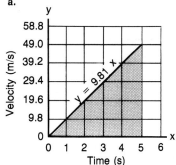

b. The area represents the displacement through which the object fell (122.5 m).

7. a.

$t(s)$	$d(m)$
1	4.9
2	19.6
3	44.1
4	78.4
5	123

b.

c. They should be about 20 m/s and 39 m/s, but accurate values using data taken from the graph will be difficult to obtain.

$v_f = v_i + gt = 0 + (9.8 \text{ m/s}^2)(2 \text{ s}) = 20 \text{ m/s}$
$v_f = v_i + gt = 0 + (9.8 \text{ m/s}^2)(4 \text{ s}) = 39 \text{ m/s}$

Page 71.

8. a. A straight line through the origin.

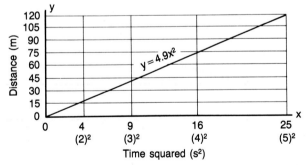

b. The slope will be 4.9 m/s² which is the proportionality constant between d and t^2 or $g/2$.

c. Yes, since $d \propto t^2$.

9. a. constant velocity   **b.** velocity

10. a. constant velocity   **b.** displacement

11. a. uniform acceleration
   b. acceleration   **c.** displacement

12. velocity

13. a. parabola   **b.** instantaneous velocity
   c. The slopes would be larger at higher points indicating larger velocities.

Problems B

Page 72.

1.

A.

B.

C.

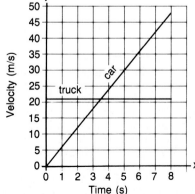

2. a.

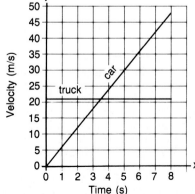

b. yes

3. a. $d_{Express} = v_i t + \frac{1}{2}at^2$

$(36.0 \text{ m/s})(12.0 \text{ s}) + \frac{1}{2}(-3.00 \text{ m/s}^2)(12.0 \text{ s})^2$

$= 432 \text{ m} - 216 \text{ m} = 216 \text{ m}$

$d_{Local} = 100 \text{ m} + v_i t + \frac{1}{2}at^2$

$= 100 \text{ m} + (11.0 \text{ m/s})(12.0 \text{ s}) + 0$
$= 100 \text{ m} + 132 \text{ m} = 232 \text{ m}$

on this basis no collision will occur.

b.

t	d(Local)	d(Express)
(s)	(m)	(m)
1	111	35
2	122	66
3	133	95
4	144	120
5	155	143
6	166	162
7	177	179
8	188	192
9	199	203
10	210	210
11	221	215
12	232	216

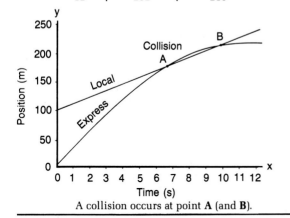

A collision occurs at point **A** (and **B**).

Page 73.

4. a.

Acceleration is greatest between 0 and 3 seconds; least between 12 and 30 seconds.

b.

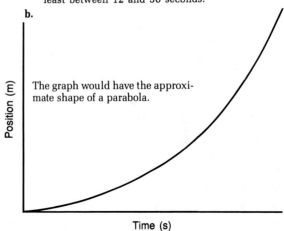

The graph would have the approximate shape of a parabola.

Forces   Chapter 5

Teaching Techniques

Students should be given an insight to the development of physics by searching for the unification of seemingly different forces. Presently, Grand Unification Theories search for unification of nuclear forces with electromagnetic. Experimental tests that are often in the news lead us to ask—does the proton decay? . . . do magnetic monopoles exist? Even more ambitious is completion of Einstein's dream, the unification of gravity. These so-called super symmetric theories are too speculative to make the news.

The simplicity of Newton's laws makes them difficult for students to appreciate. Students must understand that Newton's laws govern all motion. Emphasize that the result of a net force is the acceleration of a body, and if no net force exists, the body will remain in equilibrium. Equilibrium includes moving with constant velocity. Motion in the heavens also obeys Newton's laws. Discuss forces on the moon, Earth, other planets, stars, etc. Ask why bodies keep moving, and perhaps use Newton's cryptic reply—why not?

Stress the necessity for students to identify the origin of forces on bodies. Objects such as floors, ropes, hands, etc., all exert force. However, *ma* is not a force, but acceleration is the result of a net force. If students recognize that all motion is governed by Newton's laws, the extension to motion in two dimensions will be simplified.

Differentiate between mass and weight. Explain that mass doesn't vary, but that weight is simply another name for the gravitational force acting on an object. Show that weight can be used to measure mass. The frequent confusion in press stories about the weight of objects in Earth orbit should be discussed. Have students prepare a chart of the weight of common objects in newtons to make them more comfortable with this unit.

The origin of frictional forces may be made clearer by using the analogy of two apparently smooth surfaces in contact with each other. A close-up view of the contact zone shows one rough surface meshing into another. Discuss the difference between static friction and sliding friction, even though static friction is not treated quantitatively. Use examples of a car spinning its wheels or locking its brakes to demonstrate a method of reducing friction.

The concept of free-fall might be discussed in terms of weightlessness in satellite orbit. As the force of gravity extends to satellite orbits, objects in orbit have weight. However, both the people and the satellites are in free-fall—accelerating toward Earth at the same rate. Thus, the floor of the satellite does not have to exert a force on the astronaut and the astronaut feels weightless. Similar effects occur in any object accelerating at a rate equal to gravity, such as elevators or airplanes.

Demonstrations

An air track or air table is of great assistance in illustrating Newton's first and second laws. However, a steel ball rolling across a smooth table has low enough friction to be useful as well. Point out that the object tends to keep moving. Ask students why the object will eventually stop. When they mention friction, ask them if this is in accordance with Newton's second law. Place a book on the table and point out that it is just as unreasonable to expect the book to start moving of its own accord as it is to expect the moving ball to stop moving of its own accord.

Many other toys and classic demonstrations illustrate the inertia of matter and the need for forces to create acceleration.

Films

Inertia (university rental, PSSC film)
Inertial Mass (university rental, PSSC film)

Laboratory Investigations

Force and Acceleration
Mass and Acceleration
Friction

Performance Objectives

Goal: Students will gain knowledge and understanding of Newtonian dynamics and the distinction between mass and weight.

Objectives: Upon completion of the reading, questions, and problems, students will, on oral or written tests:

5:1	K	name the four basic types of forces, recognize that many seemingly different forces are actually electromagnetic in origin, and know the relative strengths of the forces.
5:2	P/K/S	state the first law of motion; understand the concept of inertia; display an understanding of the universality of the first law.
5:3	P/K/S	state the second law of motion; understand the fact that the first law is a special case of the second; display an understanding of the universality of the second law.
5:4	S/K	understand the definition of the newton; use the second law in solving problems.
5:5	S/K	distinguish between weight and mass; understand the agent that gives rise to weight; use the second law to relate mass and weight.
5:6	P/K	differentiate between the two concepts of mass.
5:7	S/K	demonstrate an understanding of the nature of frictional forces; be able to use the coefficient of friction in solving problems.
5:8	S/K	demonstrate an understanding of the meaning of net force and an ability to find the acceleration that results.
5:9	P/S/K	understand the definition of free-fall and the origin of air resistance; recognize the reason terminal velocities exist.
5:10	P/S/K	state the third law; understand that forces act in pairs on different bodies.
	S/A	Students will use laboratory materials in the prescribed manner

when conducting lab investigations.

Upon completion of the reading and practice problems, students will exhibit an interest in physics by:

A/S   expanding on an answer to one or more of the questions or problems at the end of the chapter.

A/S   studying the roles of Galileo and Newton in the development of the science of mechanics.

A/S   preparing a report on the history of ideas of the relationship of motion of planets and stars to motion on the earth.

A/S   writing a report on the present status of the physicists' search for unification of forces.

A   reading unassigned literature related to the ideas presented in the chapter.

Solutions to Problems

Page 80.

1. $a = \dfrac{F}{m} = \dfrac{25 \text{ N}}{12 \text{ kg}} = 2.1 \text{ m/s}^2 \text{ E}$

2. $a = \dfrac{F}{m} = \dfrac{16 \text{ N}}{2 \text{ kg}} = 8 \text{ m/s}^2$

3. $m = \dfrac{F}{a} = \dfrac{140 \text{ N}}{19 \text{ m/s}^2} = 7.4 \text{ kg}$

4. $F = ma = (1.5 \text{ kg})(16 \text{ m/s}^2) = 24 \text{ N}$

5. $F = ma$

    $a = \dfrac{F}{m} = \dfrac{-20.0 \text{ N}}{3.75 \text{ kg}} = -5.33 \text{ m/s}^2$

6. $F = ma$

    $m = \dfrac{F}{a} = \dfrac{965 \text{ N}}{54.5 \text{ m/s}^2} = 17.7 \text{ kg}$

7. $a = \dfrac{F}{m} = \dfrac{(25 \text{ N})}{4.0 \text{ kg}} = 6.3 \text{ m/s}^2$

8. $F = ma$

    $m = \dfrac{F}{a} = \dfrac{6.00 \times 10^3 \text{ N}}{8.00 \text{ m/s}^2} = 7.50 \times 10^2 \text{ kg}$

9. $d = v_i t + \dfrac{1}{2}at^2$

    $a = \dfrac{2(d - v_i t)}{t^2} = \dfrac{2(120 - 0)}{(3.0 \text{ s})^2}$

    $= \dfrac{240}{9.0 \text{ s}^2} = 27 \text{ m/s}^2$

    $F = ma = (710 \text{ kg})(27 \text{ m/s}^2)$
    $= 1.9 \times 10^4 \text{ N}$

10. $v_f^2 = v_i^2 + 2ad$

    $a = \dfrac{v_f^2 - v_i^2}{2d} = \dfrac{(770 \text{ m/s})^2 - 0}{(2)(1.5 \text{ m})}$

    $= 2.0 \times 10^5 \text{ m/s}^2$

    $F = ma = (55 \text{ kg})(2.0 \times 10^5 \text{ m/s}^2)$
    $= 1.1 \times 10^7 \text{ N}$

Page 82.

11. a. $W = mg = (14 \text{ kg})(9.8 \text{ m/s}^2) = 140 \text{ N}$
     b. $W = mg = (0.43 \text{ kg})(9.8 \text{ m/s}^2) = 4.2 \text{ N}$
     c. $W = mg = (0.7 \text{ kg})(9.8 \text{ m/s}^2) = 7 \text{ N}$

12. a. $m = \dfrac{W}{g} = \dfrac{98 \text{ N}}{9.8 \text{ m/s}^2} = 1.0 \times 10^1 \text{ kg}$

     b. $m = \dfrac{W}{g} = \dfrac{80 \text{ N}}{9.8 \text{ m/s}^2} = 8 \text{ kg}$

     c. $m = \dfrac{W}{g} = \dfrac{0.98 \text{ N}}{9.8 \text{ m/s}^2} = 0.10 \text{ kg}$

Page 83.

13. $W = mg = 20 \text{ N}$

14. $W = mg = (800 \text{ kg})(9.8 \text{ m/s}^2) = 8 \times 10^3 \text{ N}$

15. $W = mg = (1000 \text{ kg})(9.8 \text{ m/s}^2) = 10000 \text{ N} = 1 \times 10^4 \text{ N}$

16. $m = \dfrac{W}{g} = \dfrac{14700 \text{ N}}{9.80 \text{ m/s}^2} = 1.50 \times 10^3 \text{ kg}$

17. $F = mg$

    $g = \dfrac{F}{m} = \dfrac{78.4 \text{ N}}{7.5 \text{ kg}} = 1.0 \times 10^1 \text{ m/s}^2, \text{ down}$

18. $F = ma = (1200 \text{ kg})(1.6 \text{ m/s}^2) = 1.9 \times 10^3 \text{ N}$

Page 86.

19. $F_f = \mu F_N$

    $\mu = \dfrac{F_f}{F_N} = \dfrac{18 \text{ N}}{52 \text{ N}} = 0.35$

20. $F_f = \mu F_N = (0.012)(702 \text{ N}) = 8.4 \text{ N}$

Page 87.

21. $m = \dfrac{W}{g} = \dfrac{49 \text{ N}}{9.8 \text{ m/s}^2} = 5.0 \text{ kg}$

    $a = \dfrac{F}{m} = \dfrac{(69 \text{ N} - 49 \text{ N})}{5.0 \text{ kg}} = 4.0 \text{ m/s}^2$

22. a. $W = mg = (20.0 \text{ kg})(9.81 \text{ m/s}^2) = 196 \text{ N}$
     b. $F = W + ma$
         $= 196 \text{ N} + (20.0 \text{ kg})(10 \text{ m/s}^2) = 400 \text{ N}$

Page 88.

23. a. $m = \dfrac{W}{g} = \dfrac{9800 \text{ N}}{9.8 \text{ m/s}^2} = 1.0 \times 10^3 \text{ kg}$

     b. $F = ma + W$
         $= (1.0 \times 10^3 \text{ kg})(4.0 \text{ m/s}^2) + 9800 \text{ N} = 13\,800 \text{ N}$

24. $F_f = \mu F_N = (0.94)(22.7 \text{ kg})(9.8 \text{ m/s}^2) = 210 \text{ N}$

25. $F_f = \mu F_N = \mu mg$
$= (0.19)(4.0 \times 10^2 \text{ kg})(9.8 \text{ m/s}^2) = 7.5 \times 10^2 \text{ N}$
$F = ma$
$a = \dfrac{F}{m} = \dfrac{2250 \text{ N} - 7.5 \times 10^2 \text{ N}}{4.0 \times 10^2 \text{ kg}} = 3.8 \text{ m/s}^2$

26. a. $m = \dfrac{W}{g} = \dfrac{14.7 \text{ N}}{9.81 \text{ m/s}^2} = 1.50 \text{ kg}$

b. $a = \dfrac{F}{m} = \dfrac{(10.2 \text{ N} - 14.7 \text{ N})}{1.5 \text{ kg}}$
$= \dfrac{-4.5 \text{ N}}{1.5 \text{ kg}} = -3.0 \text{ m/s}^2 \text{ downward}$

27. a. $F = mg = (0.75 \text{ kg})(9.8 \text{ m/s}^2) = 7.4 \text{ N}$
b. $F = 91 \text{ N} - 7.4 \text{ N} = 84 \text{ N upward}$

c. $a = \dfrac{F}{m} = \dfrac{84 \text{ N}}{0.75 \text{ kg}} = 110 \text{ m/s}^2 \text{ upward}$

28. a. $m = \dfrac{W}{g} = \dfrac{7840 \text{ N}}{9.81 \text{ m/s}^2} = 799 \text{ kg}$

b. $a = \dfrac{F}{m} = \dfrac{(10440 \text{ N} - 7840 \text{ N})}{799 \text{ kg}} = 3.25 \text{ m/s}^2 \text{ upward}$

c. $v_f = v_i + at = 0 + (3.25 \text{ m/s}^2)(8.0 \text{ s})$
$= 26 \text{ m/s upward}$

29. a. $W = mg = (5.0 \text{ kg})(9.8 \text{ m/s}^2) = 49 \text{ N}$

b. $a = \dfrac{F}{m} = \dfrac{+98 \text{ N} - 49 \text{ N}}{5.0 \text{ kg}} = \dfrac{+49 \text{ N}}{5.0 \text{ kg}}$
$= -9.8 \text{ m/s}^2 \text{ (upward)}$

c. $v_f = v_i + at = 0 + (9.8 \text{ m/s}^2)(10 \text{ s})$
$= 98 \text{ m/s} = 100 \text{ m/s (upward)}$

d. $F = 49 \text{ N downward (its weight)}$
e. $v_f = v_i + at$
$t = \dfrac{v_f - v_i}{a} = \dfrac{0 - (+100 \text{ m/s})}{-9.8 \text{ m/s}^2} = 10 \text{ s}$

Chapter End Questions

Pages 91-92.

1. An unbalanced force, friction, acts on the ball. The ball could remain in motion if friction were removed or a force equal to the frictional force but opposite in direction were applied to it.

2. 3 kg

3. An object at rest tends to remain at rest. An object in motion tends to remain in motion.

4. In city driving a car is constantly being accelerated and brought to rest. Each time the car is accelerated more gasoline is used. On an interstate highway the car is accelerated to speed and then the motor must only offset friction.

5. Mass is the amount of matter in an object; weight is the gravitational pull of Earth on that object.

6. a. 490 N

b. $m = \dfrac{W}{g} = \dfrac{490 \text{ N}}{9.8 \text{ m/s}^2} = 5.0 \times 10^1 \text{ kg}$
$F = ma = 5.0 \times 10^1 \text{ kg} \times 2.2 \text{ m/s}^2 = 110 \text{ N}$
$490 \text{ N} + 110 \text{ N} = 6.0 \times 10^3 \text{ N}$
c. 490 N
d. Decrease
e. Decrease
f. 490 N
g. 0

7. At a great distance, Earth's gravitational field has a negligible effect on the spacecraft. Thus, the spacecraft does not need to continue firing its rockets to maintain its motion.

8. The momentum of the rocket-gas system must be conserved. Thus, when the gases move away from the rocket, the rocket also moves.

Problems A

Page 92.

1. $F_f = \mu F_N = (0.0765)(12 \text{ kg})(9.8 \text{ m/s}^2) = 9.0 \text{ N}$
$F = 10.0 \text{ N} - 9.0 \text{ N} = 1.0 \text{ N}$
$F = ma$
$a = \dfrac{F}{m} = \dfrac{1.0 \text{ N}}{12 \text{ kg}} = 8.3 \times 10^{-2} \text{ m/s}^2$

2. $a = \dfrac{F}{m} = \dfrac{8950 \text{ N} - (752 \text{ kg})(9.81 \text{ m/s}^2)}{752 \text{ kg}} = 2.09 \text{ m/s}^2$

3. a. $a = \dfrac{F}{m} = \dfrac{(5 \text{ kg})(9.8 \text{ m/s}^2)}{5 \text{ kg} + 5 \text{ kg}} = 5 \text{ m/s}^2$

b. $F = mg = (5 \text{ kg})(9.8 \text{ m/s}^2) = 50 \text{ N}$

Page 93.

4. $F_{net} = 50 \text{ N} - F_f = 50 \text{ N} - \mu F_N$
$= 50 \text{ N} - (0.31)(5 \text{ kg})(9.8 \text{ m/s}^2) = 35 \text{ N}$
$F = ma$
$a = \dfrac{F}{m} = \dfrac{35 \text{ N}}{10 \text{ kg}} = 4 \text{ m/s}^2$

Problems B

Page 93.

1. $m = (20)(75 \text{ kg}) + 500 \text{ kg} = 2000 \text{ kg}$
$W = mg = (2000 \text{ kg})(9.8 \text{ m/s}^2) = 19600 \text{ N}$
$F_{tensile} = W + F_{accelerating}$
$29600 \text{ N} = 19600 \text{ N} + F$
$F = 10000 \text{ N}$
$a = \dfrac{F}{m} = \dfrac{10000 \text{ N}}{2000 \text{ kg}} = 4.8 \text{ m/s}^2$

2. a. upward
b. $F_{net} = F_3 - F_2$
$= (3.0 \text{ kg})(9.8 \text{ m/s}^2) - (2.0 \text{ kg})(9.8 \text{ m/s}^2)$
$= 9.8 \text{ N}$
$F = ma$
$a = \dfrac{F}{m} = \dfrac{9.8 \text{ N}}{2.0 \text{ kg} + 3.0 \text{ kg}} = 2.0 \text{ m/s}^2$

Vectors   **Chapter 6**

Teaching Techniques

Be certain that students understand the difference between scalar and vector quantities. Introduce the graphical method of vector addition utilizing the head-to-tail method. The parallelogram method may produce the correct answer, but it does not teach the concepts of adding vector quantities.

While graphical techniques may not produce results as precise as arithmetic methods, they do lead to a greater feeling for magnitudes and improve ability to check the answer against intuition.

There are many practical examples of vector addition, and several should be discussed in class. Some of these include the motion of a boat in water, an airplane in wind, and a sled in snow. Statics, the equilibrium condition of point objects, also has many common examples. The need for vector, rather than scalar, addition of forces is best displayed by means of a demonstration.

Demonstrations

Section 6:3

Make a 20 N weight from two 1 kg masses and one 50 g mass tied in a 30-cm square piece of cloth. Tie the cloth with a piece of string and mark clearly as 20 N. Hang two spring scales calibrated in newtons a distance apart above the chalkboard. Connect the scales with a piece of string and suspend the 20 N weight with a paper clip at the center of the string. Point out that the algebraic sum of the two forces shown on the scales is greater than 20 N. Ask the class to relate the source of the extra force. The result will usually be silence. Students will usually add forces like scalars, and thus will not be able to account for the extra force.

After letting your students think for a while, explain the system. Mark the directions of the three forces by running a piece of chalk along the strings. Record the magnitude of the three forces; removing the scales, strings, and weight, draw the appropriate vectors. Work through the vector addition to show that the sum of the two scale forces is 20 N straight up, which balances the weight down. Repeat with the 20 N weight suspended closer to one scale.

Section 6:7

Load a dynamics cart with several bricks. Use a demonstration scale to pull the cart along the bench. Start by holding the scale parallel with the bench and then raise the scale so that it acts on the cart at increasingly large angles.

Place a textbook on the bench. Have a student push on the book, first parallel to the bench, and then at increasingly large angles. At some angle the book will simply not move, no matter how hard it is pushed.

Section 6:9

Place a dynamics cart of known weight on an inclined plane. Suspend the cart from a scale that is parallel to the plane. Record the scale force as you raise the angle of the plane. To introduce a more difficult concept, use a block and give it a small push so that sliding friction slows it down. Raise the plane until the component of its weight along the plane balances the frictional force and the block slides at constant velocity. There are three forces on this equilibrium body—weight, friction, and the normal force. Solve and find the coefficient of sliding friction.

Film

Vectors (university rental, PSSC film)

Laboratory Investigations

Addition of Force Vectors

Performance Objective

Goal: Students will become familiar with the principles of vector algebra and capable of solving problems that involve objects in equilibrium.

Objectives: Upon completion of the reading, questions, and problems, students will, on oral or written tests:

6:1	S/K/P	show an ability to add vectors by the graphical method, recognizing the commutative law of vector addition.
6:2	K/S	recognize the independence of vector quantities; accurately interpret vectors separately and in combinations; be able to add velocities.
6:3	K/S/P	understand the addition of forces and be able to solve problems by graphical techniques.
6:4	K/S/P	recognizing the applications of elementary geometry and trigonometry to vector algebra and be able to solve problems using these methods.
6:5	K/S/P	understand the addition of more than two vectors; know that the order of addition is not impor-

tant; be able to solve problems graphically.

6:6   K/S   state the requirements for equilibrium.

6:7   K   state the meaning of equilibrant; differentiating between resultant and equilibrant.

6:8   P/S/K   specify the proper method of resolving vectors into perpendicular components; be able to choose axes and resolve vectors graphically.

6:9   K/S   be able to specify axes, resolve vectors, and solve inclined plane problems.

6:10   S/K   explain the resolution of non-perpendicular components.

S/A   Students will use laboratory materials in the prescribed manner when conducting lab investigations.

Upon completion of the reading and practice problems, students will exhibit an interest in physics by:

A/S   expanding on an answer to one or more of the questions or problems at the end of the chapter.

A   reading unassigned literature related to the ideas presented in the chapter.

Solutions to Problems

Page 97.

1. a. 11 km + 11 km = 22 km

b. $c = \sqrt{a^2 + b^2} = \sqrt{(11 \text{ km})^2 + (11 \text{ km})^2}$
$= 16 \text{ km}$

$\tan \theta = \dfrac{b}{a} = \dfrac{11}{11} = 1$

$\theta = 45°$

11 km east

11 km north   45°

Resultant = 17 km

2. $c = \sqrt{a^2 + b^2} = \sqrt{(50 \text{ m/s})^2 + (100 \text{ m/s})^2}$
$= 112 \text{ m/s}$

$\tan \theta = \dfrac{b}{a} = \dfrac{50}{100}$ $\theta = 27°$

$360° - 27° = 333°$

50 m/s west

Resultant = 112 m/s   R   a   100 m/s north   θ

3. a. $c = \sqrt{a^2 + b^2} = \sqrt{(9 \text{ m/s})^2 + (16 \text{ m/s})^2}$
$= 18 \text{ m/s}$

$\tan \theta = \dfrac{a}{b} = \dfrac{9}{16}$

$\theta = 29°$
$90° + 29° = 119°$

b. $t = \dfrac{d}{v} = \dfrac{136 \text{ m}}{16 \text{ m/s}} = 8.5 \text{ s}$

c. $d = \bar{v}t = (9.0 \text{ m/s})(8.5 \text{ s}) = 77 \text{ m}$

16 m/s east

θ   b
Resultant = 18.4 m/s   R   a   9 m/s south

4. $c = \sqrt{a^2 + b^2} = \sqrt{(45 \text{ km/h})^2 + (120 \text{ km/h})^2}$
$= 130 \text{ km/h}$

$\tan \theta = \dfrac{b}{a} = \dfrac{40.0}{120} = .38$ $\theta = 21°$

$270° + 21° = 291°$
$v = 130 \text{ km/h at } 291°$

40 km/h north   b   R   130 km/h

120 km/h west   a   θ   288°

5. $c^2 = a^2 + b^2 - 2ab \cos c$

$c = \sqrt{(26)^2 + (62)^2 - (2)(26)(62)(\cos 120°)} = 78 \text{ km}$

$\dfrac{b}{\sin B} = \dfrac{c}{\sin C}$

$$\sin B = \frac{(62 \text{ km})(\sin 120°)}{78 \text{ km}} = 0.688$$

$$B = 44°$$

displacement = 78 km at 44°

6. $c = \sqrt{a^2 + b^2} = \sqrt{(66 \text{ N})^2 + (88 \text{ N})^2}$
$= 1.1 \times 10^2 \text{ N}$

$$\tan \theta = \frac{b}{a} = \frac{88}{66} = 1.33$$

$$\theta = 53°$$

Page 98.

7. a. 124 N

Resultant = 124 N

b. 120 N

Resultant = 120 N

c. 110 N

Resultant = 110 N

d. 88 N

Resultant = 88 N

e. 0 N

Resultant = 0 N

8. As the angle between two concurrent forces increases, their resultant force decreases.

9. $c^2 = a^2 + b^2$

$$c = \sqrt{(15 \text{ m/s}^2)^2 + (6.5 \text{ m/s}^2)^2}$$
$$= 16 \text{ m/s}^2$$

$$\tan \theta = \frac{6.5}{15} = 0.433$$

$$\theta = 23°$$

The angle with the horizontal is 67°.

10. 65 N − 32 N = 33 N, east

11. $R = \sqrt{(225)^2 + (55)^2} = 230 \text{ km/h}$

$$\tan \theta = \frac{55}{225} = 0.24$$

$$\theta = 14°$$
$v = 230 \text{ km/h}, 14°$ east of north

12. The solution:

$$b = \sqrt{a^2 + c^2 - 2ac \cos B}$$

$$= \sqrt{480^2 + 600^2 - (2)(480)(600) \cos 50°}$$
$$= 470 \text{ N}$$

$$\sin c = \frac{(600 \text{ N})(\sin 50°)}{470}$$

$c = 78°$ $\theta = 78° - 40° = 38°$

The situation:

The solution:

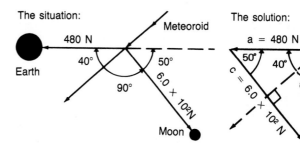

Page 100.

13. $c = \sqrt{(55 \text{ N})^2 + (110 \text{ N})^2} = 120 \text{ N}$

$\tan \theta = \dfrac{55}{110} = 0.5$

$\theta = 27°$

14. **a.** $c = \sqrt{(8.5)^2 + (3.8)^2} = 9.3 \text{ m/s}$

$\tan \theta = \dfrac{3.8}{8.5} = 0.447$

$\theta = 24°$ downstream

b. $t = \dfrac{d}{v} = \dfrac{110 \text{ m}}{8.5 \text{ m/s}} = 13 \text{ s}$

15. **a.** $c = \sqrt{(2.2)^2 + (3.8)^2} = 4.4 \text{ m/s}$

$\tan \theta = \dfrac{2.2}{3.8} = 0.579$

$\theta = 30°$ downstream

b. $t = \dfrac{d}{v} = \dfrac{41 \text{ m}}{3.8 \text{ m/s}} = 11 \text{ s}$

c. $d = \bar{v}t = (2.2 \text{ m/s})(11 \text{ s}) = 24 \text{ m}$

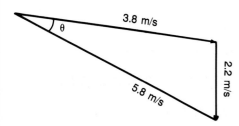

16. $c = \sqrt{a^2 + b^2} = \sqrt{(152)^2 + (42)^2} = 160 \text{ m/s}$

$\tan \theta = \dfrac{42}{152} = 0.276$

$\theta = 15.4°$

$125° + 15° = 140°$

17. **a.** 30 N

b. $c = \sqrt{(15)^2 + (15)^2 - [2 \times 15 \times 15 \, (-0.866)]}$

$= \sqrt{840} = 29 \text{ N}$

c. $c = \sqrt{(15)^2 + (15)^2} = \sqrt{450} = 21 \text{ N}$

d.

e. 0 N

18. **a.**

$v = \sqrt{(3.8)^2 + (1.6)^2} = 4.1 \text{ m/s}$

b. $t = \dfrac{d}{v} = \dfrac{240 \text{ m}}{3.8 \text{ m/s}} = 63 \text{ s}$

c. $d = \overline{v}t = (1.6 \text{ m/s})(63 \text{ s}) = 1.0 \times 10^2 \text{ m}$

19. a. $40 \text{ N} + 70 \text{ N} = 110 \text{ N}$

b.

$c = \sqrt{(70)^2 + (40)^2 - (2)(70)(40)(\cos 150°)}$
$= 110 \text{ N}$

c.

$c = \sqrt{(70)^2 + (40)^2 - (2)(70)(40)(\cos 120°)}$
$= 96 \text{ N}$

d.

$c = \sqrt{(70)^2 + (40)^2} = 81 \text{ N}$

e. $70 \text{ N} - 40 \text{ N} = 3.0 \times 10^1 \text{ N}$

Page 102.

20. 55 N, due east

21. a. $R = \sqrt{(80)^2 + (60)^2} = 100 \text{ N} = 1.0 \times 10^2 \text{ N}$

$\tan \theta = \dfrac{60}{80} = 0.75$

$\theta = 37°$

b. $1.0 \times 10^2 \text{ N at } 180° + 37° = 217°$

22. a. $c^2 = a^2 + b^2 - 2ab \cos C$

$c = \sqrt{(62)^2 + (62)^2 - [2 \times 62 \times 62 \, (-0.866)]}$
$= 120 \text{ N}$

$\dfrac{c}{\sin C} = \dfrac{b}{\sin B}$

$\sin B = \dfrac{b \sin C}{c} = \dfrac{62 \times 0.5}{120} = 0.258$

$B = 15°$

$R = 120 \text{ N}, 45.0°$

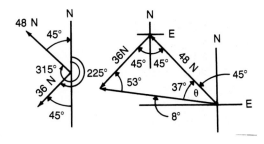

b. 120 N, 225°

23. This is a 3, 4, 5 right triangle, therefore the resultant is $6.0 \times 10^1 \text{ N}$

$\sin \theta = \dfrac{36}{60.0} = 0.60$

$\theta = 37°$

$315° - 37° = 278°$

Page 103.

24. $c = \sqrt{a^2 + b^2 - 2ab \cos C}$

$= \sqrt{(33)^2 + (44)^2 - (2)(33)(44)(\cos 150°)}$

$= \sqrt{5540} = 74 \text{ N}$

$\dfrac{b}{\sin B} = \dfrac{c}{\sin C}$

$$\sin B = \frac{(44)(\sin 150°)}{(74)} = 0.297$$

$$B = 17.3°$$
$$180° + 17° = 197°$$

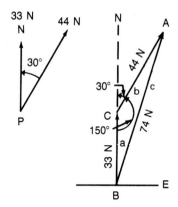

Page 105.

25. $\cos 60° = \dfrac{F_h}{80 \text{ N}}$

$F_h = (80 \text{ N}) \cos 60° = 40 \text{ N}$

26. **a.** $v_n = (500 \text{ km/h})(\sin 31°) = 260 \text{ km/h}$
   b. $v_w = (500 \text{ km/h})(\sin 59°) = 430 \text{ km/h}$

27. **a.** $F_h = F \cos \theta = (72 \text{ N})(0.5) = 36 \text{ N}$
   b. $F_h = F \cos \theta = (72 \text{ N})(0.766) = 55 \text{ N}$
   c. $F_h = F \cos \theta = (72 \text{ N})(0.866) = 62 \text{ N}$

Page 106.

28. $\sin 40.0° = \dfrac{W}{F_{chain}}$

$F_{chain} = \dfrac{W}{\sin 40°} = \dfrac{4.5 \text{ N}}{0.6427} = 7.0 \text{ N}$

29. $F = (350 \text{ N})(\cos 55°) = (350 \text{ N})(0.574) = 200 \text{ N}$
$= 2.0 \times 10^2 \text{ N}$

Page 107.

30. **a.** $F_\parallel = W (\sin \theta) = (5.0 \times 10^2 \text{ N})(\sin 66°)$
$= 460 \text{ N}$
$F_\perp = W (\cos \theta) = (5.0 \times 10^2 \text{ N})(\cos 66°)$
$= 200 \text{ N}$

   b. $F_\parallel = W (\sin \theta) = (5.0 \times 10^2 \text{ N})(\sin 30°)$
$= 250 \text{ N}$
$F_\perp = W (\cos \theta) = (5.0 \times 10^2 \text{ N})(\cos 30°)$
$= 430 \text{ N}$
$F_\parallel$ is less and $F_\perp$ is greater than the example in part a.

   c. As the angle of the incline increases, $F_\parallel$ increases and $F_\perp$ decreases.

31. **a.** $F_\parallel = W (\sin \theta) = (12000 \text{ N})(\sin 36°)$
$= 7100 \text{ N}$

   b. $F_\perp = W (\cos \theta) = (12000 \text{ N})(\cos 36°)$
$= 9700 \text{ N}$

32. $F_{applied} = F_f + F_\parallel$

$F_\parallel = W \sin \theta = (325 \text{ N})(\sin 20.0°) = 111 \text{ N}$

$F_f = F_{app} - F_\parallel = 211 \text{ N} - 111 \text{ N} = 1.00 \times 10^2 \text{ N}$

Chapter End Questions

Page 109.

1. When two or more forces act concurrently on an object and their vector sum is zero, the object is in equilibrium.

2. Vectors are added head to tail.

3. The resultant is drawn from the tail of the first vector to the head of the last vector. The head of the resultant vector coincides with the head of the last vector to be added.

4. Concurrent forces are two or more forces acting on the same point at the same time.

5. If the angle increases, the resultant decreases.

6. By lowering the handle of the mower, the horizontal component is increased.

7. The vector sum of forces forming a closed triangle is zero. It implies that the object is in equilibrium with no net force acting on it.

8. Find the resultant of the two forces. The equilibrant will be the negative of that.

9. By pulling the lawnroller, the vertical component is directed upward. This helps lift the roller over the lawn. Pushing the roller causes the vertical component to act down, pushing the roller into the ground.

Problems A

Page 109.

1. $F = (102 \text{ N})(\cos 30°) + (102 \text{ N}) + (102 \text{ N})(\sin 60°)$
$= 88.3 \text{ N} + 102 \text{ N} + 88.3 \text{ N} = 279 \text{ N}$

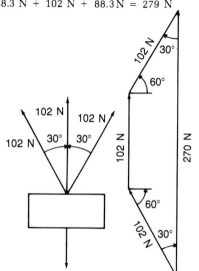

Page 110.

2. $d_N = d \cos \theta = (3.00 \times 10^2 \text{ km})(\cos 50.0°)$
    $= 190 \text{ km} = 1.93 \times 10^2 \text{ km}$
  $d_E = d \sin \theta = (3.00 \times 10^2 \text{ km})(\sin 50.0°)$
    $= 230 \text{ km} = 2.30 \times 10^2 \text{ km}$

3. **a.** $v = \sqrt{(35 \text{ m/s})^2 + (55 \text{ m/s})^2} = 65 \text{ m/s}$

  b. $\tan \theta = \dfrac{35}{55} = 0.636$

    $\theta = 32°$
    The angle with the vertical is $90° - 32° = 58°$

4. **a.** $F_h = F \cos \theta = (95 \text{ N})(0.50) = 48 \text{ N}$
      $F_v = F \sin \theta = (95 \text{ N})(0.866) = 82 \text{ N}$
  b. $F_h = F \cos \theta = (95 \text{ N})(0.866) = 82 \text{ N}$
      $F_v = F \sin \theta = (95 \text{ N})(0.50) = 48 \text{ N}$

5. $F_h = F_v = F \sin 45° = (92 \text{ N})(0.707) = 65 \text{ N}$

6. **a.** $v_c = (6.0 \text{ m/s})(\tan 27°) = 3.1 \text{ m/s}$

  b. $v_b = \dfrac{(6.0 \text{ m/s})}{(\cos 27°)} = 6.7 \text{ m/s}$

7.

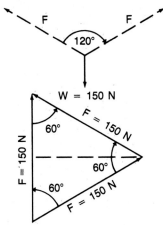

Forms an equilateral triangle—all sides are equal. Therefore, the two forces are 150 N each.

8. $\dfrac{a}{\sin A} = \dfrac{c}{\sin C}$

  $a = \dfrac{(\sin 45°)(150 \text{ N})}{(\sin 90°)} = \dfrac{(0.707)(150 \text{ N})}{(1.0)}$

  $a = 106 \text{ N}$
  $b = 106 \text{ N}$

9. **a.**

  b.

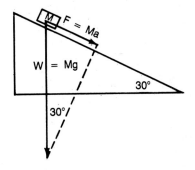

  c. Added head to tail, each arrangement of the vectors should give the same resultant. This is about 144 N at 74°.

Problems B

Page 111.

1. **a.** $F = W(\sin 30.0°) = 0.5 \text{ W}$
      $ma = 0.5 \text{ mg}$
      $a = 0.5 \text{ g} = 4.9 \text{ m/s}^2$

  b. $v_f^2 = v_i^2 + 2ad$
      $d = \dfrac{v_f^2 - v_i^2}{2a} = \dfrac{(24 \text{ m/s})^2 - 0}{(2)(9.8 \text{ m/s}^2)}$

      $d = \dfrac{576 \text{ m}^2/\text{s}^2}{(2)\, 4.9 \text{ m/s}^2} = 29 \text{ m}$

  c. $v_h = v \cos 30° = (24 \text{ m/s})(0.866) = 21 \text{ m/s}$
      $t = \dfrac{d}{v_h} = \dfrac{21 \text{ m}}{21 \text{ m/s}} = 1 \text{ s}$

2. $F_{\parallel} = W \sin \theta$
    The force of the 3.0 kg mass is
    $F_3 = mg \sin \theta$
    $= (3.0 \text{ kg})(9.8 \text{ m/s}^2)(\sin 25°) = 12.4 \text{ N}$
    The force of the 2.0 kg mass is
    $F_2 = mg \sin \theta$
    $= (2.00 \text{ kg})(9.8 \text{ m/s}^2)(\sin 45°) = 13.9 \text{ N}$

Since F_2 is greater than F_3, a net force, F will accelerate the two masses.
$$F = F_2 - F_3$$
$$= 13.9 \text{ N} - 12.4 \text{ N} = 1.5 \text{ N}$$
$$F = ma$$
$$a = \frac{F}{m} = \frac{1.5 \text{ N}}{5.0 \text{ kg}} = 0.300 \text{ m/s}^2 \text{ down}$$

Motion in Two Dimensions   Chapter 7

Teaching Techniques

This chapter extends the concepts of linear motion to curvilinear motion. It is not likely that introductory physics students will recognize that the motion of projectiles is the result of an object having linear motion in two directions at the same time. The concept of the independence of these velocities gives students considerable difficulty. Although they will repeat statements of the concept, they may not grasp its implications. The three suggested film loops (Galilean Relativity) are of great help and should be shown if possible. Demonstrations, laboratory exercises, and solutions of problems will also help in teaching this concept.

Circular motion is a concept that frequently causes confusion for nonscientists. Centripetal motion must be analyzed from a nonaccelerated point of view. Only then can Newton's second law be applied. Stress the necessity of finding the physical source of the force that causes the acceleration toward the center of a circle. Students will be less likely to call mv^2/r a force rather than the right-hand side of the equation $F = ma$.

Simple harmonic motion is interesting and appears in various forms later in the book. Discuss the concept of resonance from a qualitative viewpoint.

Demonstrations

Section 7:1

One of the simplest and most effective means of demonstrating the independence of velocities involves the use of a flexible ruler and two marbles or steel balls. Both balls, when flipped with the ruler, will leave the edge of the table at the same time. If students listen carefully, they will hear only one "click" as both balls strike the floor simultaneously.

A more elaborate method of demonstrating the independence of velocities is to arrange the "monkey and hunter" demonstration. The title of the demonstration originates from a classic physics problem.

This demonstration can be arranged across the supports of the demonstration bench but is more effective if a greater distance is used. A small piece of chalk can be used as a projectile while a piece of glass tubing serves as a blowgun.

An electromagnet is connected to a switch and a dry cell; the connecting wires make contact by being loosely crossed in front of the blowgun. As the projectile emerges from the gun it will break the contact when it hits the wires, and the target (a tin-can lid) will start to fall. The projectile and target will start to fall at the same time. If the gun is aimed straight at the target (by sighting through the gun) the only way the projectile can hit the target is for it to fall at the same rate as the target while it is traveling toward the target horizontally. The fact that the projectile strikes the target shows that its vertical fall is not affected by its horizontal motion. On occasion, the wires will deflect the projectile, but generally the demonstration works satisfactorily.

Films

Free Fall and Projectile Motion (university rental, PSSC film)

Laboratory Investigations

Analysis of the Path of a Projectile
Centripetal Force
The Pendulum

Performance Objectives

Goal: Students will gain knowledge and understanding of the fundamentals of two-dimensional motion. They will recognize the concepts on which projectile motion, uniform circular motion, and simple harmonic motion are based. They will learn to solve problems based on these three types of two-dimensional motion.

Objectives: Upon completion of the reading, questions, and problems, students will, on oral or written tests:

7:1   S/K/P   display an understanding of the independence of the vertical and horizontal velocities of a projectile. Begin to understand the notion of Galilean relativity and reference frames. Apply this knowledge in solving problems of projectiles launched horizontally.

7:2   S/K/P   demonstrate an understanding of the motion of projectiles fired at an angle by solving problems illustrating such motion.

7:3   S/K   differentiate between centripetal acceleration and centripetal force. Learn Newton's second law as applied to circular motion. Solve problems using these concepts.

7:4   K/S   recognize that the motion of artificial satellites is circular motion about the earth. Solve problems which relate the orbital velocity to distance from center of earth.

7:5   P/S/K   distinguish simple harmonic motion from other forms of vibratory motion. Apply Newton's laws to the motion of a pendulum and mass on a spring. Recognize resonance as a phenomenon often seen in daily life.

S/A   Students will use laboratory materials in the prescribed manner when conducting lab investigations.

Upon completion of the reading and practice problems, students will exhibit an interest in physics by:

A/S   expanding on an answer to one or more of the questions or problems at the end of the chapter.

A/S   testing the equations for projectile motion against the motion of objects launched into the air such as footballs, baseballs, golf balls.

A/S   listing various forms of resonant motion they have experienced and identifying the object in simple harmonic motion as well as the periodically varying force.

A   reading unassigned literature related to the ideas presented in the chapter.

Solutions to Problems

Page 116.

1. **a.** $d_v = v_i t + \dfrac{1}{2} g^2$, vertical initial velocity is zero

$$t = \sqrt{\dfrac{2d_v}{g}} = \sqrt{\dfrac{(2)(\text{-}78.4\ \text{m})}{9.81\ \text{m/s}^2}} = \sqrt{16.0\ \text{s}^2} = 4.00\ \text{s}$$

b. $d_h = \bar{v}t = (10.0\ \text{m/s})(4.00\ \text{s}) = 40.0\ \text{m}$

2. $d_v = v_i t + \dfrac{1}{2} g^2$, with the vertical inital velocity equal to zero,

$$t = \sqrt{\dfrac{2\,d_v}{g}} = \sqrt{\dfrac{(2)(-49.0\ \text{m})}{-9.81\ \text{m/s}^2}}\sqrt{10.0\ \text{s}^2} = 3.16\ \text{s}$$

$d_h = \bar{v}t = (20.0\ \text{m/s})(3.16\ \text{s}) = 63.2\ \text{m}$

3. $d_v = \dfrac{1}{2}gt^2$

$$t = \sqrt{\dfrac{2d_v}{g}} = \sqrt{\dfrac{(2)(-0.950\ \text{m})}{-9.81\ \text{m/s}^2}} = 0.440\ \text{s}$$

$d_h = v_h t = (0.800\ \text{m/s})(0.440\ \text{s}) = 0.352\ \text{m}$

Page 117.

4. $d_h = \bar{v}t$

$$t = \dfrac{d_n}{\bar{v}} = \dfrac{47\ \text{m}}{15.0\ \text{m/s}} = 3.1\ \text{s}$$

$d_h = v_i t + \dfrac{1}{2}gt^2 = 0 + \dfrac{1}{2}\,(-9.8\ \text{m/s}^2)(3.1\ \text{s})^2 = -47\ \text{m}$

height $= 47\ \text{m}$

5. $d_h = v_h t$

$$t = \dfrac{d_h}{v_h} = \dfrac{15.0\ \text{m}}{12.7\ \text{m/s}} = 1.18\ \text{s}$$

$d_v = \dfrac{1}{2}gt^2 = \dfrac{1}{2}\,(9.81\ \text{m/s}^2)(1.18\ \text{s})^2 = 6.83\ \text{m}$

6. $d_v = v_i t + \dfrac{1}{2}at^2$

Since initial vertical velocity is zero,

$$t = \sqrt{\dfrac{2d_v}{g}} = \sqrt{\dfrac{(2)(-1.0\ \text{m})}{-9.8\ \text{m/s}^2}} = \sqrt{0.20} = 0.45\ \text{s}$$

$d_h = \bar{v}t = (89\ \text{m/s})(0.45\ \text{s}) = 4.0 \times 10^1\ \text{m}$
$60\ \text{m} - 40\ \text{m} = 2.0 \times 10^1\ \text{m}$ short of target

Page 118.

7. **a.** $v_f = v_i + at$

$$t_{up} = \dfrac{v_f - v_i}{g} = \dfrac{0 - (\,49\ \text{m/s})}{-\,9.8\ \text{m/s}^2} = 5.0\ \text{s}$$

$t_{up} = t_{down}$

$t_{total} = t_{up} + t_{down} = 5.0 \text{ s} + 5.0 \text{ s} = 10.0 \text{ s}$

b. $d_h = \bar{v}t = (61 \text{ m/s})(1.0 \times 10^1 \text{ s}) = 610 \text{ m}$

c. $v^2 = v_h{}^2 + v_v{}^2$

$v = \sqrt{(61 \text{ m/s})^2 + (49 \text{ m/s})^2} = 78 \text{ m/s}$

$\tan \theta = \dfrac{49 \text{ m/s}}{61 \text{ m/s}} = 0.80$

$\theta = 39° \text{ above horizontal}$

8. a. $v_v = v \sin 60.0° = (196 \text{ m/s})(0.866)$
$= 1.70 \times 10^2 \text{ m/s}$
$v_h = v \cos 60.0° = (196 \text{ m/s})(0.500) = 98.0 \text{ m/s}$

b. $v_f = v_i + at$

$t_{up} = \dfrac{(v_f - v_i)}{g}$

$= \dfrac{[0 - (1.7 \times 10^2 \text{ m/s})]}{- 9.80 \text{ m/s}^2} = 17.3 \text{ s}$

$t_{up} = t_{down}$
$t_{total} = t_{up} + t_{down} = 17.3 \text{ s} + 17.3 \text{ s} = 34.6 \text{ s}$

c. $d_h = \bar{v}t = (98.0 \text{ m/s})(34.6 \text{ s}) = 3390 \text{ m}$

d. $d_v = \dfrac{1}{2}gt^2 = \dfrac{1}{2}(9.81 \text{m/s}^2)(17.3 \text{ s})^2 = 1470 \text{ m}$

9. a. $v_v = v \sin 53° = (200 \text{ m/s})(0.80) = 160 \text{ m/s}$
$v_f = v_i + at$

$t_{up} = \dfrac{v_f - v_i}{g} = \dfrac{0 - (160 \text{ m/s})}{- 9.8 \text{ m/s}^2} = 16.3 \text{ s}$

$t_{up} = t_{down}$
$t_{total} = 16.3 \text{ s} + 16.3 \text{ s} = 33 \text{ s}$

b. $d_h = \bar{v}_h t = (v \cos 53°)(33 \text{ s})$
$= (200 \text{ m/s})(0.60)(33 \text{ s}) = 3960 \text{ m} = 4.0 \times 10^3 \text{ m}$

10. a. $v_f = v_i + at$

$t_{up} = \dfrac{v_f - v_i}{g} = \dfrac{0 - (98 \text{ m/s}^2)}{- 9.8 \text{ m/s}^2} = 1.0 \times 10^1 \text{ s}$

$t_{up} = t_{down}$
$t_{total} = t_{up} + t_{down} = 1.0 \times 10^1 \text{ s} + 1.0 \times 10^1 \text{ s}$
$= 2.0 \times 10^1 \text{ s}$

b. It hits the archer since it has the same horizontal velocity as the truck.

c. $d_h = \bar{v}t = (22 \text{ m/s})(2.0 \times 10^1 \text{ s}) = 4.4 \times 10^2 \text{ m}$

Page 119.

11. $v_f = v_i + at$

$t_{up} = \dfrac{v_f - v_i}{g} =$

$= \dfrac{0 - (52 \sin 45°)}{- 9.8 \text{ m/s}^2} = 3.75 \text{ s}$

$t_{up} = t_{down}$
$t_{total} = t_{up} + t_{down} = 3.75 \text{ s} + 3.75 \text{ s} = 7.5 \text{ s}$
$d_h = \bar{v}_h t = (52 \cos 45°)(7.5 \text{ s})$
$= (37 \text{ m/s})(7.5 \text{ s}) = 280 \text{ m}$

Page 122.

12. $a = \dfrac{v^2}{r} = \dfrac{(20.0 \text{ m/s})^2}{20.0 \text{ m}} = 20.0 \text{ m/s}^2$

13. a. $a = \dfrac{v^2}{r} = \dfrac{(7.9 \text{ m/s})^2}{1.0 \text{ m}} = 62 \text{ m/s}^2$

b. $F_c = ma = (2.0 \text{ kg})(62 \text{ m/s}^2) = 120 \text{ N}$

14. a. $v = \dfrac{2\pi r}{t} = \dfrac{(2)(\pi)(50.0 \text{ m})}{10.0 \text{ s}} = 31.4 \text{ m/s}$

$F_c = \dfrac{mv^2}{r} = \dfrac{(600 \text{ kg})(31.4 \text{ m/s})^2}{50 \text{ m}} = 1.18 \times 10^4 \text{ N}$

b. $a = \dfrac{v^2}{r} = \dfrac{(31.4 \text{ m/s})^2}{50.0 \text{ m}} = 19.7 \text{ m/s}^2$

15. a. $F_c = \dfrac{mv^2}{r} = \dfrac{(0.20 \text{ kg})(5.0 \text{ m/s})^2}{0.80 \text{ m}} = 6.3 \text{ N}$

b. $F_c = \dfrac{mv^2}{r} = \dfrac{(0.20 \text{ kg})(10.0 \text{ m/s})^2}{0.80 \text{ m}} = 25 \text{ N}$

c. ratio $= 25{:}6.3 = 4{:}1$ since the velocity is squared.

16. a. $a = v^2/r = 4\pi^2 r/t^2$
$= 4\pi^2(1.0 \text{ m})/(0.25 \text{ s})^2 = 630 \text{ m/s}^2$

b. $F_c = ma = (1.00 \text{ kg})(630 \text{ m/s}^2) = 630 \text{ N}$

Page 123.

17. a. $W = mg$
$= (1.00 \times 10^2 \text{ kg})(9.81 \text{ m/s}^2) = 9.81 \times 10^2 \text{ N}$

b. $v = \dfrac{(1600 \text{ km/h})(1000 \text{ m/km})}{(3600 \text{ s/h})} = 4.4 \times 10^2 \text{ m/s}$

$F_c = \dfrac{mv^2}{r}$

$= \dfrac{(1.00 \times 10^2 \text{ kg})(4.4 \times 10^2 \text{ m/s})^2}{(6.4 \times 10^6 \text{ m})} = 3.0 \text{ N}$

Page 124.

18. $v = \sqrt{gr} = \sqrt{(9.8 \text{ m/s}^2)(6.5 \times 10^6 \text{ m})}$
$= \sqrt{6.4 \times 10^7 \text{ m}^2/\text{s}^2} = 8.0 \times 10^3 \text{ m/s}$

Page 125.

19. a. $v = \sqrt{gr} = \sqrt{(1.6 \text{ m/s}^2)(1.79 \times 10^6 \text{ m})}$
$= \sqrt{2.9 \times 10^6 \text{ m}^2/\text{s}^2} = 1.7 \times 10^3 \text{ m/s}$
$= 1.7 \text{ km/s}$

b. $v = \dfrac{2\pi r}{t}$

$t = \dfrac{2\pi r}{v} = \dfrac{(2)(\pi)(1.79 \times 10^6 \text{ m})}{1.7 \times 10^3 \text{ m/s}}$

$= 6.6 \times 10^3 \text{ s} = \dfrac{6.6 \times 10^3 \text{ s}}{60 \text{ s/min}} = 1.1 \times 10^2 \text{ min}$

20. $v = \sqrt{gr} = \sqrt{(5.80 \times 10^3 \text{ m/s}^2)(7.11 \times 10^7 \text{ m})}$
$\qquad = 6.42 \times 10^5 \text{ m/s} = 642 \text{ km/s}$

Chapter End Questions

Pages 129-130.

1. Yes. (In fact the monkey would be safe if it did not let go of the branch.) The vertical acceleration of the dart will be the same as that of the monkey. Therefore, the dart will be at the same vertical height when it reaches the monkey.

2. The flare will be directly under the plane provided it does not change course. The flare will retain its horizontal velocity as it falls. Its horizontal velocity is the same as the plane's horizontal velocity.

3. Circular motion results when the direction of the force is constantly perpendicular to the instantaneous velocity of the mass.

4. The period of a vibrating object is the time required for one vibration. The amplitude is the distance from rest position to the point of greatest displacement.

5. The acceleration of a body undergoing simple harmonic motion is always proportional to the displacement of the body.

6. **a.** A,E = greatest vertical velocity
   b. All points. Horizontal velocity is constant and independent of vertical velocity.
   c. C = least vertical velocity
   d. The curve is a parabola.

Problems A

Page 130.

1. $t = \sqrt{\dfrac{2d}{g}} = \sqrt{\dfrac{(2)(78.4 \text{ m})}{(9.8 \text{ m/s}^2)}} = 4.0 \text{ s}$

   $d = \bar{v}t = (8.0 \text{ m/s})(4.0 \text{ s}) = 32 \text{ m}$

2. $d_v = v_it + \dfrac{1}{2}at^2$

   Since initial vertical velocity is zero,

   $t = \sqrt{\dfrac{2d_v}{g}} = \sqrt{\dfrac{(2)(176.4 \text{ m})}{(9.8 \text{ m/s}^2)}} = 6.0 \text{ s}$

   $d_h = \bar{v}_ht = (22 \text{ m/s})(6.0 \text{ s}) = 130 \text{ m}$

3. **a.** $d_v = v_it + \dfrac{1}{2}at^2$, since initial vertical velocity is zero,

   $t = \sqrt{\dfrac{2d_v}{g}} = \sqrt{\dfrac{(2)(490 \text{ m})}{(9.8 \text{ m/s}^2)}} = 1.0 \times 10^1 \text{ s}$

   b. $d_h = \bar{v}_ht = (2.00 \times 10^2 \text{ m/s})(1.0 \times 10^1 \text{ s})$
   $\qquad = 2.0 \times 10^3 \text{ m}$

4. **a.** $d_v = v_it + \dfrac{1}{2}at^2$, since the initial velocity is zero,

$t = \sqrt{\dfrac{2d}{g}} = \sqrt{\dfrac{(2)(1.225 \text{ m})}{(9.8 \text{ m/s}^2)}} = 0.50 \text{ s}$

b. $\bar{v}_h = \dfrac{d_h}{t} = \dfrac{0.40 \text{ m}}{0.50 \text{ s}} = 0.80 \text{ m/s}$

5. $d_v = v_it + \dfrac{1}{2}at^2$, since the initial velocity is zero,

$t = \sqrt{\dfrac{2d}{g}} = \sqrt{\dfrac{(2)(61 \text{ m})}{(9.8 \text{ m/s}^2)}} = \sqrt{12.4 \text{ s}^2} = 3.5 \text{ s}$

$\bar{v}_h = \dfrac{d_h}{t} = \dfrac{23 \text{ m}}{3.5 \text{ s}} = 6.6 \text{ m/s}$

6. $v_v = v \sin 37° = (1.00 \times 10^3 \text{ m/s})(0.602)$
$\qquad\quad = 6.02 \times 10^2 \text{ m/s}$
$v_h = v \cos 37° = (1.00 \times 10^3 \text{ m/s})(0.799)$
$\qquad\quad = 7.99 \times 10^2 \text{ m/s}$

$v_f = v_i + at$

$t_{up} = \dfrac{v_f - v_i}{a} = \dfrac{0 - (6.02 \times 10^2 \text{ m/s})}{- 9.81 \text{ m/s}^2} = 61.4 \text{ s}$

$t_{up} = t_{down}$
$t_{total} = t_{up} + t_{down} = 61.4 \text{ s} + 61.4 \text{ s} = 123 \text{ s}$
$d_h = \bar{v}_ht = (7.99 \times 10^2 \text{ m/s})(123 \text{ s}) = 98.2 \text{ km}$

7. First find the time the ball was in the air.
$v_v = v \sin 53.0° = (30.0 \text{ m/s})(0.799) = 24.0 \text{ m/s}$

$t_{up} = \dfrac{v_f - v_i}{g} = \dfrac{0 - (-24 \text{ m/s})}{- 9.81 \text{ m/s}^2} = 2.44 \text{ s}$

$t_{up} = t_{down}$
$t_{total} = t_{up} + t_{down} = 2.44 \text{ s} + 2.44 \text{ s} = 4.89 \text{ s}$
$v_h = v(\cos 53.0°) = (30.0 \text{ m/s})(0.602) = 18.1 \text{ m/s}$
The distance the ball travels horizontally is
$d_h = v_ht = (18.1 \text{ m/s})(4.89 \text{ s}) = 88.5 \text{ m}$
The distance the outfielder travels is
$d_o = vt = (4.0 \text{ m/s})(4.89 \text{ s}) = 19.6 \text{ m}$
The distance between the batter and outfielder is 88.5 m
$+ 19.6 \text{ m} = 108.1 \text{ m}$

Page 131.

8. **a.** $a = 4\pi^2rf^2 = (4\pi^2)(1.3 \text{ m})(1.0 \text{ 1/s})^2$
$\qquad = 51 \text{ m/s}^2$
   b. $F_c = ma = (7.00 \text{ kg})(51 \text{ m/s}^2) = 360 \text{ N}$

Problems B

Page 131.

1. $F_c = \dfrac{mv^2}{r}$

$v = \sqrt{\dfrac{Fr}{m}} = \sqrt{\dfrac{(7.50 \times 10^{-13} \text{ N})(1.20 \text{ m})}{(1.67 \times 10^{-27} \text{ kg})}}$

$\quad = \sqrt{5.39 \times 10^{14} \text{ m}^2/\text{s}^2} = 2.32 \times 10^7 \text{ m/s}$

2. $v = \sqrt{rg}$

$r = \dfrac{v^2}{g} = \dfrac{(120 \text{ m/s})^2}{9.8 \text{ m/s}^2} = \dfrac{14600}{9.8} = 1500 \text{ m}$

Universal Gravitation   Chapter 8

Teaching Techniques

This chapter shows how Newton used the work of Kepler and Brahe in combination with his own work (the equation of centripetal acceleration) to identify the law governing the gravitational force and its universality.

Any physical law is more meaningful to students if its origins are understood. Derivation of the law of universal gravitation is simple enough for beginners to follow, and if the chapter is covered in sequence, a clear understanding of the relation of Kepler's work to Newton's work as well as the law of gravitation should result.

Lead students to an understanding of what quantities can be determined from the application of the law of gravitation to the motion of planets. Only if the universal constant G is known can the mass of the central body be found. Because the force is proportional to the mass of the planet, the planetary mass cannot be determined this way. Motion of satellites about the planet must be analyzed to learn the mass of the planet.

Note that at this level of knowledge, calculations of gravitational force can only be done between spherical bodies. Use the inverse square law to calculate the weight of a satellite and an astronaut in orbit. Then ask students why astronauts are weightless. The answer is that they and the satellite are in free-fall, accelerating toward the earth.

A field is a difficult concept to understand, but attempts made here will help when electric and magnetic fields are introduced. The rubber sheet analogy can help. Stress that the gravitational field does not explain why gravity exists.

Films

Forces (university rental, PSSC film)

Film Loops

Acceleration Due to Gravity (BFA-Ealing film loop)
Kepler's Laws (BFA-Ealing film loop)

Laboratory Investigations

Kepler's Law of Equal Areas

Performance Objectives

Goal: Students will gain knowledge and understanding of the law of universal gravitation, the methods used to derive and verify this law, and its applications to planetary motion.

Objectives: Upon completion of the reading, questions, and problems, students will, on oral or written tests:

8:1	K/A	demonstrate an appreciation for the persistence required to gain scientific knowledge. List Kepler's laws or planetary motion.
8:2	A/P/K	display an understanding of how Newton combined basic knowledge to arrive at a completely new law. (Students should not be requested to learn the derivation.) Understand the quantities on which the force depends.
8:3	A/P	clearly indicate an understanding of Newton's test of his law.
8:4	S/K	state the method used by Cavendish to verify Newton's law of gravity and to determine G. Understand the importance of knowing G. Solve problems using the law of gravitation.
8:5	K/P/S	be able to illustrate how the law of gravitation demands that the acceleration of gravity be dependent on the mass of the earth and the distance from its center.
8:6	K/A	describe gravitational fields. Recognize that the field concept does not explain the origin of the force.
8:7	A/P/K	display an understanding of Einstein's concept of gravity.
	S/A	Students will use laboratory materials in the prescribed manner when conducting lab investigations.

Upon completion of the reading and practice problems, students will exhibit an interest in physics by:

	A/S	expanding on an answer to one or more of the questions or problems at the end of the chapter.
	A/S	study in more detail the work of Brahe and Kepler or the path Newton took in discovering the law.
	A	reading unassigned literature related to the ideas presented in the chapter.

Solutions to Problems

Page 139.

1. $F = G\dfrac{m_1 m_2}{r^2}$

$= \dfrac{(6.67 \times 10^{-11} \text{ N} \cdot \text{m}^2/\text{kg}^2)(8.0 \text{ kg})(6.0 \text{ kg})}{(2.0 \text{ m})^2}$

$= 8.0 \times 10^{-10} \text{ N}$

2. a. $F = G\dfrac{m_1 m_2}{r^2}$

$= \dfrac{(6.67 \times 10^{-11} \text{ N} \cdot \text{m}^2/\text{kg}^2)(8.0 \text{ kg})(8.0 \text{ kg})}{(5.0 \text{ m})^2}$

$= 1.7 \times 10^{-10} \text{ N}$

b. $F = G\dfrac{m_1 m_2}{r^2}$

$= \dfrac{(6.67 \times 10^{-11} \text{ N} \cdot \text{m}^2/\text{kg}^2)(8.0 \text{ kg})(8.0 \text{ kg})}{(5.0 \times 10^1 \text{ m})^2}$

$= 1.7 \times 10^{-12} \text{ N}$

Page 140.

3. $m_1 = \dfrac{W}{g} = \dfrac{9.8 \times 10^2 \text{ N}}{9.8 \text{ m/s}^2} = 1.0 \times 10^2 \text{ kg}$

$m_2 = \dfrac{W}{g} = \dfrac{1.96 \times 10^2 \text{ N}}{9.8 \text{ m/s}^2} = 2.0 \times 10^1 \text{ kg}$

$F = G\dfrac{m_1 m_2}{r^2}$

$= \dfrac{(6.67 \times 10^{-11} \text{ N} \cdot \text{m}^2/\text{kg}^2)(1.0 \times 10^2 \text{ kg})(2.0 \times 10^1 \text{ kg})}{(4.0 \text{ m})^2}$

$= 8.3 \times 10^{-9} \text{ N}$

4. a. $F = G\dfrac{m_1 m_2}{r^2}$

$m = \sqrt{\dfrac{Fr^2}{G}} = \sqrt{\dfrac{(2.0 \times 10^{-7} \text{ N})(30 \text{ m})^2}{(6.67 \times 10^{-11} \text{ N} \cdot \text{m}^2/\text{kg}^2)}}$

$= \sqrt{21.698 \times 10^6 \text{ kg}^2} = 1.6 \times 10^3 \text{ kg}$

b. $F = ma$

$a = \dfrac{F}{m} = \dfrac{2.0 \times 10^{-7} \text{ N}}{1.6 \times 10^3 \text{ kg}} = 1.3 \times 10^{-10} \text{ m/s}^2$

5. $F = G\dfrac{m_1 m_2}{r^2}$

$m_m = \dfrac{Fr^2}{Gm_e} = \dfrac{(1.9 \times 10^{20} \text{ N})(3.9 \times 10^8 \text{ m})^2}{(6.67 \times 10^{-11} \text{ N} \cdot \text{m}^2/\text{kg}^2)(6.0 \times 10^{24} \text{ kg})}$

$= 7.2 \times 10^{22} \text{ kg}$

6. $F = ma$

$a = \dfrac{F}{m} = \dfrac{1.9 \times 10^{20} \text{ N}}{7.2 \times 10^{22} \text{ kg}}$

$= 2.6 \times 10^{-3} \text{ m/s}^2$

7. $F = G\dfrac{m_1 m_2}{r^2}$

$= \dfrac{(6.67 \times 10^{-11} \text{ N} \cdot \text{m}^2/\text{kg}^2)(9.1 \times 10^{-31} \text{ kg})(1.7 \times 10^{-27} \text{ kg})}{(1.0 \times 10^{-10} \text{ m})^2}$

$= 1.0 \times 10^{-47} \text{ N}$

Chapter End Questions

Pages 144-145.

1. The planet would move faster along its orbit when it is closer to the sun. Thus, angles of shorter radius would have longer arcs during equal time intervals, and the area swept out by the imaginary line would remain the same. It might be good here to point out that this is no more than what we would expect in keeping with the law of conservation of energy. If the planet moves in closer to the sun, it loses potential energy with respect to the sun. It must, therefore, increase its kinetic energy which accounts for its increased speed along its orbit.

2. a. 1800 N   **c.** 450 N   **e.** 200 N
   b. 800 N   **d.** 288 N

Measure all distances from the center of Earth. Hence 6400 km from Earth's surface is two Earth radii and the weight reduces to ¼. At 12800 km from Earth's surface, the weight would reduce to 1/9 and so on.

3. See text Section 8:5.

4. $6.67 \times 10^{-11} \text{ N}$

5. The force is the same on each.

6. See text Section 8:4.

7. A force of 5 g means that the astronaut's weight is five times heavier than on Earth.

8. Einstein's view is that gravity is an effect of the curvature of space due to the presence of mass, while Newton's view of gravity is a force acting directly between objects. Thus, according to Einstein, the attraction between the earth and the moon is due to the curvature of space caused by their combined masses.

Problems A

Page 145.

1. $F = G\dfrac{m_1 m_2}{r^2}$

$= \dfrac{(6.67 \times 10^{-11} \text{ N} \cdot \text{m}^2/\text{kg}^2)(6.8 \text{ kg})(6.8 \text{ kg})}{(0.218 \text{ m})^2}$

$= 6.5 \times 10^{-8} \text{ N}$

2. $F = G\dfrac{m_1 m_2}{r^2}$ $m_2 = 2m_1$

$F = \dfrac{G(m_1)(2m_1)}{r^2}$ $m_1{}^2 = \dfrac{Fr^2}{2G}$

$m_1 = \sqrt{\dfrac{(2.75 \times 10^{-12} \text{ N})(2.6 \text{ m})^2}{(2)(6.67 \times 10^{-11} \text{ N} \cdot \text{m}^2/\text{kg}^2)}} = 0.37 \text{ kg}$

$m_2 = (2)(0.37 \text{ kg}) = 0.75 \text{ kg}$

3. $F = G\dfrac{m_1 m_2}{r^2}$

$= \dfrac{(6.67 \times 10^{-11}\ \text{N} \cdot \text{m}^2/\text{kg}^2)(3.3 \times 10^5)(6.0 \times 10^{24}\ \text{kg})(3.0 \times 10^2)(6.0 \times 10^{24}\ \text{kg})}{(7.8 \times 10^{11}\ \text{m})^2}$

$= 3.9 \times 10^{23}\ \text{N}$

Problems B
Page 145.

1. $\dfrac{r^3}{T^2} = 3.35 \times 10^{18}\ \text{m}^3/\text{s}^2$

$T = \sqrt{\dfrac{r^3}{3.35 \times 10^{18}\ \text{m}^3/\text{s}^2}}$

$= \sqrt{\dfrac{(8)^3\ (1.5 \times 10^{11}\ \text{m})^3}{(3.35 \times 10^{18}\ \text{m}^3/\text{s}^2)}}$

$= 7.2 \times 10^8\ \text{s} = \dfrac{(7.2 \times 10^8\ \text{s})}{(3.15 \times 10^7\ \text{s/yr})} = 23\ \text{yrs}$

2. a. $F = G\dfrac{m_1 m_2}{r^2}$

$m_e = \dfrac{Fr^2}{Gm}$

$= \dfrac{(9.8\ \text{N})(6.4 \times 10^6\ \text{m})^2}{(6.67 \times 10^{-11}\ \text{N} \cdot \text{m}^2/\text{kg}^2)(1.0\ \text{kg})} = 6.0 \times 10^{24}\ \text{kg}$

b. $V = \dfrac{4}{3}\pi r^3$

$= \dfrac{(4\pi)(6.4 \times 10^6\ \text{m})^3}{3} = 1.1 \times 10^{21}\ \text{m}^3$

$D = \dfrac{M}{V} = \dfrac{6.0 \times 10^{24}\ \text{kg}}{1.1 \times 10^{21}\ \text{m}^3} = 5.5 \times 10^3\ \text{kg/m}^3$

Momentum and Its Conservation   Chapter 9

Teaching Techniques

Momentum and energy conservation are concepts that are equivalent to Newton's laws, but are more powerful and, at the same time, more abstract. Forces can be felt and acceleration can be measured; momentum and energy must be calculated.

Have students suggest uses of the word momentum in daily life (especially sports). Compare these uses with the definition in physics. Emphasize the connection of momentum with Newton's second and third laws. Note the importance of defining a system and also stress the universal nature of momentum conservation as well as its limitations.

You will find air hockey tables very useful here. Perhaps a student has one put away in a closet. Ask him or her to donate it to the school and write a letter to the parents acknowledging the donation.

Demonstrations

Section 9:3

Use either an air track or dynamics cart to demonstrate collisions. A toy air hockey game can also be used as an air table. Load one dynamics cart with three bricks, but a second cart with only one (or use light and heavy carts). Keep the lighter cart stationary and roll the heavier cart at it. Have students observe that the ligher cart gains velocity, and thus momentum, as the heavier one loses it.

Section 9:4

Load carts equally and use the spring mechanism to produce an internal force between the two. Have students observe that they move away from one another with equal velocities. Thus they have equal and opposite momenta. The total momentum of the system before and after the collision is the same. Suggest that if they took a movie of this and ran it backwards they would see a collision after which the two carts stuck together.

Chapter 9

Section 9:5

An air table, even a toy one, shows collisions in two dimensions very nicely. If not available, use a collision ball apparatus. Raise one ball to a height and allow it to fall and strike the stationary ball. Have students note how momentum is exchanged.

Laboratory Investigations

Conservation of Momentum: Internal Force
Conservation of Momentum: A Collision in Two Dimensions

Performance Objectives

Goal: Students will learn the law of conservation of momentum, its universality, and examples of its use.

Objectives: Upon completion of the reading, questions, and problems, students will, on oral or written tests:

9:1	K/S/P	define momentum and impulse; recognize the connection between Newton's second law and the impulse-momentum equation; be able to calculate changes in momentum.
9:2	K/A	recognize the connection between the third law of motion and momentum changes.
9:3	K/A/P	define an isolated system; state the law of conservation of momentum; recognize its implications, especially in collision problems.
9:4	K/A	distinguish between external and internal forces and use this distinction in solving problems.
9:5	K/P	explain the extension of the law of conservation of momentum to two and three dimensions; apply vectors to the solution of momentum conservation problems.
	S/A	Students will use laboratory materials in the prescribed manner when conducting lab investigations.

Upon completion of the reading and practice problems, students will exhibit an interest in physics by:

A/S	expanding on an answer to one or more of the questions or problems at the end of the chapter.
A/S	giving examples of the correct and incorrect uses of momentum in everyday life.
A	reading unassigned literature related to the ideas presented in the chapter.

Solutions to Problems

Page 150.

1. a. $m\Delta v = Ft = (6.00 \text{ N})(10.0 \text{ s}) = 60.0 \text{ N} \cdot \text{s}$

b. $\Delta v = \dfrac{Ft}{m} = \dfrac{60.0 \text{ N} \cdot \text{s}}{3.00 \text{ kg}} = 20.0 \text{ m/s}$

2. $m\Delta v = Ft$

$F = \dfrac{m\Delta v}{t} = \dfrac{(1.10 \times 10^3 \text{ kg})(22.0 \text{ m/s} - 0 \text{ m/s})}{20.0 \text{ s}}$

$= 1.21 \times 10^3 \text{ N}$

3. $Ft = m\Delta v$

$t = \dfrac{m\Delta v}{F} = \dfrac{(1.00 \times 10^3 \text{ kg})(2.00 \times 10^2 \text{ m/s} - 0.0 \text{ m/s})}{2.00 \times 10^3 \text{ N}}$

$= 1.00 \times 10^2 \text{ s}$

4. a. $m\Delta v = (2.50 \times 10^2 \text{ kg})(28.0 \text{ m/s} - 6.0 \text{ m/s})$

$= 5.50 \times 10^3 \text{ N} \cdot \text{s}$

b. $Ft = m\Delta v$

$F = \dfrac{m\Delta v}{t} = \dfrac{5.50 \times 10^3 \text{ N} \cdot \text{s}}{60.0 \text{ s}} = 91.7 \text{ N}$

5. a. $mg = W$

$m = \dfrac{W}{g} = \dfrac{15680 \text{ N}}{9.81 \text{ m/s}^2} = 1.60 \times 10^3 \text{ kg}$

b. $mv = (1.60 \times 10^3 \text{ kg})(20.0 \text{ m/s}) = 3.20 \times 10^4 \text{ N} \cdot \text{s}$

c. $m\Delta v = 3.20 \times 10^4 \text{ N} \cdot \text{s} - 0 = 3.20 \times 10^4 \text{ N} \cdot \text{s}$

d. $Ft = m\Delta v$

$t = \dfrac{m\Delta v}{F} = \dfrac{3.20 \times 10^4 \text{ N} \cdot \text{s}}{6.40 \times 10^2 \text{ N}} = 50.0 \text{ s}$

6. a. $m\Delta v = (6.00 \times 10^2 \text{ kg})(44.0 \text{ m/s} - 10.0 \text{ m/s})$

$= 2.04 \times 10^4 \text{ N} \cdot \text{s}$

b. $Ft = m\Delta v$

$F = \dfrac{m\Delta v}{t} = \dfrac{2.00 \times 10^4 \text{ N} \cdot \text{s}}{68.0 \text{ s}} = 3.00 \times 10^2 \text{ N}$

7. $m\Delta v = Ft$

$v_f = \dfrac{Ft}{m} + v_i$

$v_f = \dfrac{(1.5 \times 10^5 \text{ N})(15.0 \text{ s})}{(2.0 \times 10^4 \text{ kg})} + 0 = 1.1 \times 10^2 \text{ m/s}$

Page 155.

8. $m_1v_1 + m_2v_2 = m_1v_1' + m_2v_2',\ v_1' = v_2' = v'$

$v' = \dfrac{m_1v_1 + m_2v_2}{m_1 + m_2}$

$= \dfrac{(7.00 \times 10^2 \text{ kg})(20.0 \text{ m/s}) + (1.40 \times 10^3 \text{ kg})(0)}{(7.00 \times 10^2 \text{ kg} + 1.40 \times 10^3 \text{ kg})}$

$= 6.67 \text{ m/s in its original direction}$

9. $m_1v_1 + m_2v_2 = m_1v_1' + m_2v_2',\ v_1' = v_2' = v'$

$v_1 = \dfrac{(m_1 + m_2)\ v' - m_2v_2}{m_1}$

$= \dfrac{(5.00 \times 10^{-2} \text{ kg} + 5.0 \text{ kg})(10.0 \text{ m/s}) - (5.0 \text{ kg})(0)}{(5.00 \times 10^{-2} \text{ kg})}$

$= 1.0 \times 10^3 \text{ m/s}$

10. $p_1 + p_2 = p_1' + p_2'$

$m_1v_1 + m_2v_2 = m_1v_1' + m_2v_2'$

$m_2v_2 = m_1v_1' + m_2v_2' - m_1v_1$

$v_2 = \dfrac{m_1v_1' + m_2v_2' - m_1v_1}{m_2}$

$$= \frac{(0.50 \text{ kg})(6.0 \text{ m/s}) + (1.00 \text{ kg})(-12.0 \text{ m/s}) - (0.50 \text{ kg})(-14 \text{ m/s})}{1.00 \text{ kg}}$$

$$= -2.0 \text{ m/s}$$

11. $m_1v_1 + m_2v_2 = m_1v_1' + m_2v_2'$

$$v_1' = \frac{m_1v_1 + m_2v_2 - m_2v_2'}{m_1}$$

$$= \frac{(0.200 \text{ kg})(0.30 \text{ m/s}) + (0.100 \text{ kg})(0.10 \text{ m/s}) - (0.100 \text{ kg})(0.26 \text{ m/s})}{(0.200 \text{ kg})}$$

$$= \frac{(0.06 \text{ kg} \cdot \text{m/s}) + (0.01 \text{ kg} \cdot \text{m/s}) - (0.026 \text{ kg} \cdot \text{m/s})}{(0.200 \text{ kg})}$$

$$= \frac{0.044 \text{ kg} \cdot \text{m/s}}{(0.200 \text{ kg})} = 0.22 \text{ m/s in its original direction}$$

Page 157.

12. $m_1v_1 + m_2v_2 = m_1v_1' + m_2v_2'$

$$v_2' = \frac{m_1v_1 + m_2v_2 - m_1v_1'}{2.00 \times 10^3 \text{ kg}}$$

$$= -16.0 \text{ m/s}$$
$$= 16.0 \text{ m/s in the opposite direction.}$$

13. $m_1v_1 + m_2v_2 = m_1v_1' + m_2v_2'$

Since initial velocities are zero,

$$v_2' = \frac{-m_1v_1'}{m_2}$$

$$= \frac{-(5.00 \times 10^{-2} \text{ kg})(6.00 \times 10^2 \text{ m/s})}{(4.0 \text{ kg})}$$

$$= -7.5 \text{ m/s}$$
$$= 7.5 \text{ m/s upward}$$

14. $m_1v_1 + m_2v_2 = m_1v_1' + m_2v_2'$

Since initial velocities are zero,

$$v_2' = \frac{-m_1v_1'}{m_2}$$

$$= \frac{-(80.0 \text{ kg})(4.0 \text{ m/s})}{(110 \text{ kg})}$$

$$= \frac{-320 \text{ kg} \cdot \text{m/s}}{110 \text{ kg}}$$

$$= -2.9 \text{ m/s}$$
$$= 2.9 \text{ m/s in the opposite direction.}$$

15. $m_1v_1 + m_2v_2 = m_1v_1' + m_2v_2'$

Since initial velocities are zero,

$$v_2' = \frac{-m_1v_1'}{m_2}$$

$$= \frac{-(1.5 \text{ kg})(27 \text{ cm/s})}{(4.5 \text{ kg})}$$

$$= \frac{-41 \text{ kg} \cdot \text{cm/s}}{4.5 \text{ kg}}$$

$$= -9.1 \text{ cm/s}$$
$$= 9.1 \text{ cm/s to the right}$$

Page 158.

16. $p_1 + p_2 = p_1' + p_2'$

$$m_1v_1 + m_2v_2 = m_1v_1' + m_2v_2'$$
$$m_2v_2' = m_1v_1 + m_2v_2 - m_1v_1'$$

$$v_2' = \frac{m_1v_1 + m_2v_2 - m_1v_1'}{m_2}$$

$$= \frac{(0.05 \text{ kg})(2.00 \text{ m/s}) + (4.65 \text{ kg})(2.00 \text{ m/s}) - (0.05 \text{ kg})(647 \text{ m/s})}{(4.65 \text{ kg})}$$

$$= -5.0 \text{ m/s}$$
$$= 5.0 \text{ m/s, backwards}$$

Page 160.

17. **a.** Vector constructed parallel with b so that a + b = c
the original momentum of Ball A.

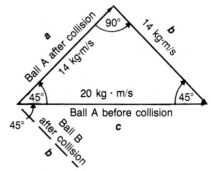

$$a = c \cos 45° = 20 \text{ kg} \cdot \text{m/s} \times 0.707$$
$$= 14 \text{ kg} \cdot \text{m/s}$$
$$b = c \sin 45° = 20 \text{ kg} \cdot \text{m/s} \times 0.707$$
$$= 14 \text{ kg} \cdot \text{m/s}$$

b. For A:

$$mv = 14 \text{ kg} \cdot \text{m/s} = 5 \text{ kg} \times v$$

$$v = \frac{14 \text{ kg} \cdot \text{m/s}}{5 \text{ kg}} = 2.8 \text{ m/s, 45° to the left of its original direction}$$

For B:
$$v = 2.8 \text{ m/s, 45° to the right of ball A's original direction}$$

18. a. $a = c \cos 50.0° = (18 \text{ kg} \cdot \text{m/s})(0.643)$
$= 12 \text{ kg} \cdot \text{m/s}$
$b = c \sin 50.0° = (18 \text{ kg} \cdot \text{m/s})(0.766)$
$= 14 \text{ kg} \cdot \text{m/s}$

b. For A:
$mv_A = 12 \text{ kg} \cdot \text{m/s}$

$v_A = \dfrac{(12 \text{ kg} \cdot \text{m/s})}{(6.0 \text{ kg})} = 2.0 \text{ m/s}$

For B:
$mv_B = 14 \text{ kg} \cdot \text{m/s}$

$v_B = \dfrac{(16 \text{ kg} \cdot \text{m/s})}{(6.0 \text{ kg})} = 2.3 \text{ m/s}$

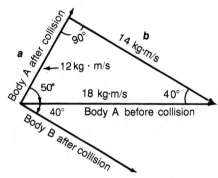

19. $a = c \sin 30° = (1.7 \text{ kg} \cdot \text{m/s})(0.50)$
$= 0.85 \text{ kg} \cdot \text{m/s}$ to the left
$b = c \cos 30° = (1.7 \text{ kg} \cdot \text{m/s})(0.866)$
$= 1.5 \text{ kg} \cdot \text{m/s}$ to the right

For the first ball:
$mv = 1.5 \text{ kg} \cdot \text{m/s}$

$v = \dfrac{(1.5 \text{ kg} \cdot \text{m/s})}{(0.17 \text{ kg})} = 8.8 \text{ m/s } 30°$ to the right of the second ball's original direction

For the second ball:
$mv = 0.85 \text{ kg} \cdot \text{m/s}$

$v = \dfrac{(0.85 \text{ kg} \cdot \text{m/s})}{(0.17 \text{ kg})} = 5.0 \text{ m/s } 60°$ to the left of its original direction

Chapter End Questions

Page 161.

1. The momentum of the rocket-gas system must be conserved. Thus, when the gases move away from the rocket, the rocket also moves.
2. Understanding this problem depends on the careful definition of internal and external forces. The brakes stop the wheels; the force is then between the wheels and the road, an external force.
3. If the pistol is fired in the opposite direction, it will provide the impulse needed to move the astronaut toward the capsule.
4. Ball B must have the same velocity that Ball A had before the collision.
5. A bullet moving at a very high velocity can have the same momentum as a truck moving at a very low velocity (or when both are at rest).
6. The reaction force is the gravitational force of the body acting on Earth.
7. None-no external force is present.

Problems A

Page 162.

1. $Ft = (30.0 \text{ N})(0.80 \text{ s}) = 24 \text{ N} \cdot \text{s}$

2. $m\Delta v = Ft$

$v = \dfrac{(24 \text{ N} \cdot \text{s})}{(0.20 \text{ kg})} = 120 \text{ m/s}$

3. a. $m\Delta v = \dfrac{(1.50 \times 10^3 \text{ kg})(72 \text{ km/h})(1000 \text{ m/km})}{(3600 \text{ s/h})}$
$= 3.0 \times 10^4 \text{ N} \cdot \text{s}$

b. $Ft = m\Delta v$

$F = \dfrac{m\Delta v}{t} = \dfrac{(3.0 \times 10^4 \text{ N} \cdot \text{s})}{(30 \text{ s})} = 1000 \text{ N}$

4. a. $m\Delta v = Ft = (8.0 \text{ N})(5.0 \text{ s}) = 4.0 \times 10^1 \text{ N} \cdot \text{s}$

b. $m\Delta v = Ft$

$\Delta v = \dfrac{Ft}{m} = \dfrac{(4.0 \times 10^1 \text{ N} \cdot \text{s})}{(2.0 \text{ kg})} = 2.0 \times 10^1 \text{ m/s}$, in the direction of the force.

5. a. $mv = (1.6 \times 10^3 \text{ kg})(2.0 \text{ m/s}) = 3.2 \times 10^3 \text{ kg} \cdot \text{m/s}$

b. $Ft = m\Delta v$

$t = \dfrac{m\Delta v}{F} = \dfrac{(3.2 \times 10^3 \text{ kg} \cdot \text{m/s})}{(8.00 \times 10^2 \text{ N})} = 4.0 \text{ s}$

6. $m_1v_1 + m_2v_2 = m_1v_1' + m_2v_2'$

$$v_2' = \frac{m_1v_1 + m_2v_2 - m_1v_1'}{m_2}$$

$$= \frac{(1.00 \times 10^2 \text{ g})(20.0 \text{ cm/s}) + (40.0 \text{ g})(10.0 \text{ cm/s}) - (1.00 \times 10^2 \text{ g})(15.0 \text{ cm/s})}{4.00 \text{ g}}$$

$$= \frac{2000 \text{ g} \cdot \text{cm/s} + 400 \text{ g} \cdot \text{cm/s} - 1500 \text{ g} \cdot \text{cm/s}}{40.0 \text{ g}}$$

$$= \frac{900 \text{ g} \cdot \text{cm/s}}{40.0 \text{ g}}$$

$$= 23 \text{ cm/s in its original direction}$$

Problems B

Page 162.

1. $\tan 30° = \frac{\Delta mv}{m_o v_o}$

$\Delta mv = m_o v_o \tan 30.0°$
$= 0.577 (7600 \text{ kg} \times 120 \text{ m/s})$
$= 5.3 \times 10^5 \text{ N} \cdot \text{s}$

$m = \frac{5.3 \times 10^5 \text{ N} \cdot \text{s}}{v} = \frac{5.3 \times 10^5 \text{ N} \cdot \text{s}}{3.2 \times 10^3 \text{ m/s}}$

$= 170 \text{ kg}$

2. a. $F_\parallel = F_w \sin \theta = (24.5 \text{ N})(\sin 30.0°) = 12.25 \text{ N}$
$F = ma$

$a = \frac{Fg}{W} = \frac{(F_\parallel)(9.81 \text{ m/s}^2)}{F_w} = \frac{(12.25 \text{ N})(9.81 \text{ m/s}^2)}{24.5 \text{ N}}$

$= 4.90 \text{ m/s}^2$

$v_f^2 = v_i^2 + 2 ad$
$v_f = \sqrt{v_i^2 + 2ad}$
$= 0 + (2)(4.9 \text{ m/s}^2)(1.00 \text{ m}) = 3.13 \text{ m/s}$

$p_1 + p_2 = p_1' + p_2'$
$m_1v_1 + m_2v_2 = m_1v_1' + m_2v_2'$
$(m_1 + m_2)v' = m_1v_1 + m_2v_2$

$v' = \frac{m_1v_1 + m_2v_2}{(m_1 + m_2)}$

$$= \frac{\left(\frac{24.5 \text{ N}}{9.81 \text{ m/s}^2}\right)(3.13 \text{ m/s}) + \left(\frac{36.8 \text{ N}}{9.81 \text{ m/s}^2}\right)(0.0 \text{ m/s})}{\frac{24.5 + 36.8 \text{ N}}{9.81 \text{ m/s}^2}}$$

$= 1.25 \text{ m/s}$

b. $F\Delta t = m\Delta v$

$$\Delta t = \frac{m\Delta v}{F}$$

$$\Delta t = \frac{\frac{24.5 \text{ N} + 36.8 \text{ N}}{9.81 \text{ m/s}^2}(1.25 \text{ m/s})}{(5.0 \text{ N})} = 1.6 \text{ s}$$

c. $d = v_{av}t = \frac{v_f + v_i}{2}t$

$$= \frac{(0.0 \text{ m/s} + 1.25 \text{ m/s})(1.6 \text{ s})}{2} = 1.0 \text{ m}$$

Page 163.

3. a. $\Delta p_1 = m_1v_1' - m_1v_1$
$= (5.0 \text{ g})(8.0 \text{ m/s} - 20.0 \text{ m/s})$
$= -6.0 \times 10^1 \text{ g} \cdot \text{m/s}$

b. $p_1 + p_2 = p_1' + p_2'$
$m_1v_1 + m_2v_2 = m_1v_1' + m_2v_2'$

$$v_2' = \frac{m_1v_1 + m_2v_2 - m_1v_1'}{m_2}$$

$$= \frac{(5.0 \text{ g})(20.0 \text{ m/s}) + (10.0 \text{ g})(10.0 \text{ m/s}) - (5.0 \text{ g})(8.0 \text{ m/s})}{(10.0 \text{ g})}$$

$= 16 \text{ m/s}$

$\Delta p_2 = m_2v_2' - m_2v_2$
$= (10.0 \text{ g})(16 \text{ m/s} - 10.0 \text{ m/s})$
$= 6.0 \times 10^1 \text{ g} \cdot \text{m/s}$

Work, Power, and Simple Machines   Chapter 10

Teaching Techniques

This brief chapter familiarizes students with the calculation of work and power, thus paving the way for the consideration of energy in Chapter 11. The fundamentals of simple machines are also discussed.

Students may encounter several difficulties in this chapter with the concept of work. By definition, work is done only when a force moves a body through a distance. Only the component of the force in the direction of the motion actually contributes to the work done. Discuss the difference between carrying a box down a corridor and pushing the same box along the floor. In the first case the upward force exerted to lift the box is perpendicular to the motion, and therefore no work is done. Similarly, the force of gravity does no work. In the second case the force exerted is opposed by friction, acts in the direction of motion, and therefore does work. Many examples of this nature are better explained in terms of energy changes, and therefore should not be discussed until Chapter 11.

Demonstrations

Section 10:2

Use a demonstration spring scale calibrated in newtons to lift a kilogram mass. Show the mass weighs 9.8 N and calculate that the work done lifting the mass a distance of 1 m is 9.8 N·m or 9.8 J. Discuss the work done on the mass by Earth's gravity.

Sections 10:4 and 10:5

A variety of simple machines can be demonstrated, mechanical advantages found, and their efficiency calculated.

Film

Energy and Work (university rental, PSSC film)

Laboratory Investigations

Pulleys

Performance Objectives

Goal: Students will learn the concepts of work and power so they can apply them to the study of energy.

Objectives: Upon completion of the reading, questions, and problems, students will, on oral or written tests:

10:1	K/P/S	display an ability to calculate work from force and distance.
10:2	K/P	recognize the component of a force that does the work.
10:3	K/P/S	differentiate between work and power and correctly calculate power used.
10:4	K/P	demonstrate knowledge of the types of simple machines and the concept of efficiency of a machine.
10:5	K/S	understand the concept of mechanical advantage and use it correctly in solving problems.
	S/A	Students will use laboratory materials in the prescribed manner

when conducting lab investigations.

Upon completion of the reading and practice problems, students will exhibit an interest in physics by:

A/S	expanding on an answer to one or more of the questions or problems at the end of the chapter.
A/S	classifying common tools as one or more types of simple machines and finding the mechanical advantage of each.
A	reading unassigned literature related to the ideas presented in the chapter.

Solutions to Problems

Page 167.

1. $W = Fd = (8.00 \times 10^2 \text{ N})(40.0 \text{ m}) = 3.20 \times 10^4 \text{ J}$
2. $F = mg = (60.0 \text{ kg})(9.81 \text{ m/s}^2) = 589 \text{ N}$
   $W = Fd = (589 \text{ N})(10.0 \text{ m}) = 5890 \text{ J}$
3. $W = Fd = (34 \text{ N})(15 \text{ m}) = 510 \text{ J}$
4. $W = Fd = mgd = (49 \text{ kg})(9.8 \text{ m/s}^2)(10.0 \text{ m})$
   $= 4.8 \times 10^3 \text{ J}$
5. **a.** *Number of blocks* $= (2 \text{ blocks/min})(10.0 \text{ min})$
   $= 20 \text{ blocks}$
   $W = Fd = (20)(1.50 \times 10^2 \text{ N})(8.00 \text{ m})$
   $= 2.40 \times 10^4 \text{ J}$
   b. *Number of blocks* $= (2 \text{ blocks/min})(60.0 \text{ min})$
   $= 120 \text{ blocks}$
   $W = Fd = (120)(1.50 \times 10^2 \text{ N})(8.00 \text{ m})$
   $= 1.44 \times 10^5 \text{ J}$
6. **a.** $W = Fd = mgd$
   $= (1.00 \times 10^2 \text{ kg})(9.81 \text{ m/s}^2)(5.00 \text{ m}) = 4.90 \times 10^3 \text{ J}$
   b. The pile is lifted 6 times per minute.
   $W = (4.90 \times 10^3 \text{ J})(6) = 2.94 \times 10^4 \text{ J}$

Page 168.

7. $W = Fd \cos \theta = (6.00 \times 10^2 \text{ N})(\cos 46°)(15.0 \text{ m})$
   $= 6.3 \times 10^3 \text{ J}$

Page 169.

8. $W = Fd \cos \theta = (40.0 \text{ N})(\cos 45°)(50.0 \text{ m})$
   $= 1.4 \times 10^3 \text{ J}$
9. $W = Fd \cos \theta$
   $\cos \theta = \dfrac{W}{Fd} = \dfrac{1.20 \times 10^4 \text{ J}}{(1.20 \times 10^2 \text{ N})(2.00 \times 10^2 \text{ m})} = 0.500$
   $\theta = 60.0°$
10. **a.** $F_h = F \cos \theta = (2.50 \times 10^3 \text{ N})(\cos 30.0°)$
    $= 2.17 \times 10^3 \text{ N}$
    b. $W = Fd = (2.17 \times 10^3 \text{ N})(2.00 \times 10^2 \text{ m})$
    $= 4.34 \times 10^5 \text{ J})$

11. a. $F_h = F \cos \theta$

$$F = \frac{F_h}{\cos \theta} = \frac{4.00 \times 10^2 \text{ N}}{\cos 56.0°} = 7.15 \times 10^2 \text{ N}$$

b. $W = Fd = (4.00 \times 10^2 \text{ N})(25.0 \text{ m}) = 1.00 \times 10^4 \text{ J}$

12. $W = Fd = (0.95 \text{ N})(2.0 \text{ m}) = 1.9 \text{ J}$

Page 170.

13. $P = \dfrac{W}{t} = \dfrac{Fd}{t}$

$$= \frac{(1.00 \times 10^3 \text{ N})(20.0 \text{ m})}{(10.0 \text{ s})} = 2.00 \times 10^3 \text{ W} = 2.00 \text{ kW}$$

14. a. $P = \dfrac{W}{t} = \dfrac{Fd}{t}$

$$= \frac{(2.25 \times 10^3 \text{ N} (20.0 \text{ m})}{(5.00 \text{ s})} = 9.00 \times 10^3 \text{ W}$$

$$= 9.00 \text{ kW}$$

15. a. $W = Fd$

$$= (12.0 \text{ kg})(9.80 \text{ m/s}^2)(8.2 \text{ m}) = 960 \text{ J}$$

b. $W = Fd$

$$= (6.00 \times 10^2 \text{ N} + 118 \text{ N})(8.2 \text{ m}) = 5.9 \times 10^3 \text{ J}$$

Page 171.

c. $P = \dfrac{W}{t} = \dfrac{5.9 \times 10^3 \text{ J}}{(30.0 \text{ min})(60 \text{ s/min})}$

$$= 3.3 \text{ W} = 3.3 \times 10^{-3} \text{ kW}$$

16. $P = \dfrac{W}{t} = \dfrac{Fd}{t}$

$$F = \frac{Pt}{d} = \frac{(65 \times 10^3 \text{ W})(40.0 \text{ s})}{18.0 \text{ m}} = 1.4 \times 10^5 \text{ N}$$

17. a. $P = \dfrac{W}{t} = \dfrac{Fd}{t} = \dfrac{(150 \text{ N})(60.0 \text{ m})}{20.0 \times 10^1 \text{ s}} = 450 \text{ W}$

b. If the speed doubles the time will become one-half as large, so the power will double.
$P = (450 \text{ W})(2) = 9.0 \times 10^2 \text{ W}$

Page 174.

18. a. $MA = \dfrac{F_r}{F_e} = \dfrac{225 \text{ N}}{149 \text{ N}} = 1.51$

b. $eff = \dfrac{F_r d_r}{F_e d_e} \times 100\% = \dfrac{(225 \text{ N})(1.65 \text{ m})}{(149 \text{ N})(2.75 \text{ m})} = 90.6\%$

19. $eff = \dfrac{F_r \, d_r}{F_e \, d_e} \times 100\%$

$$d_e = \frac{F_r \, d_r}{F_e \, (eff)} \times 100\%$$

$$= \frac{(1.20 \times 10^3 \text{ N}) (1.32 \text{ m})}{(2.25 \times 10^3 \text{ N}) (0.587)} = 1.20 \text{ m}$$

20. $eff = \dfrac{F_r}{F_e} \times \dfrac{d_r}{d_e} \times 100\%$

$$d_r = \frac{eff}{100\%} \times \frac{F_e}{F_r} d_e$$

$$= \frac{(0.785)l(275 \text{ N})(3)(2\pi)(4.00 \times 10^{-2} \text{ m})}{85.0 \text{ N}} = 1.91 \text{ m}$$

Chapter End Questions

Page 175.

1. Work is the product of force and the distance an object is moved in the direction of the force. Power is the time rate at which work is done.

2. Both people are doing the same amount of work, as they are both climbing the same flight of stairs.

3. The person who climbs the stairs in 25 seconds expends the most power, as less time is needed to cover the distance.

4. No work is needed to keep an object moving on a frictionless surface because no force is needed to keep an object moving at constant velocity.

5. Pedals of a bike transfer work from the rider to the machine through a distance.

6. Lengthen the hammer and the handle to make the task easier.

7. Increase the ratio of d_e/d_r to increase the ideal mechanical advantage of a machine.

Problems A

Page 175.

1. $W = Fd = mgh$
$= (150 \text{ kg})(9.8 \text{ m/s}^2)(8.0 \text{ m}) = 1.2 \times 10^4 \text{ J}$

2. **a.** $D = \dfrac{m \text{ dirt}}{V}$

$m \text{ dirt} = DV = (2.00 \times 10^3 \text{ kg/m}^3)(1.15 \text{ m}^3)$
$= 2.30 \times 10^3 \text{ kg}$

$F = mg = (2.30 \times 10^3 \text{ kg})(9.81 \text{ m/s}^2)$
$= 2.26 \times 10^4 \text{ N}$

$W = Fd = (2.26 \times 10^4 \text{ N} + 2.25 \times 10^3 \text{ N})(7.5 \text{ m})$
$= 1.9 \times 10^5 \text{ N} \cdot \text{m}$

b. $1.9 \times 10^5 \text{ J}$

3. $P = \dfrac{W}{t}$

$W = Pt = (420 \text{ W})(5.0 \text{ min})(60 \text{ s/min})$
$= 1.3 \times 10^5 \text{ J}$

Page 176.

4. $P = \dfrac{W}{t} = \dfrac{11250 \text{ J}}{25 \text{ s}} = 450 \text{ W}$

5. $P = \dfrac{W}{t} = \dfrac{mgh}{t}$

$\qquad = \dfrac{(35\ \text{L})(1.00\ \text{kg/L})(9.81\ \text{m/s}^2)(110\ \text{m})}{60\ \text{s}}$

$\qquad = 630\ \text{W}$

6. a. $F_h = F \cos \theta$

$\qquad F = \dfrac{F_h}{\cos \theta} = \dfrac{(8.0 \times 10^2\ \text{N})}{\cos 63°} = 1800\ \text{N}$

b. $W = Fd = (8.0 \times 10^2\ \text{N})(22\ \text{m})$
$\qquad = 1.76 \times 10^4\ \text{J} = 1.8 \times 10^4\ \text{J}$

c. $P = \dfrac{W}{t} = \dfrac{1.8 \times 10^4\ \text{J}}{8.0\ \text{s}} = 2.25 \times 10^3\ \text{W} = 2.3 \times 10^3\ \text{W}$

7. $P = \dfrac{W}{t} = \dfrac{Fd}{t} = Fv$

$\qquad = (6.0 \times 10^3\ \text{N})(15\ \text{m/s}) = 9.0 \times 10^4\ \text{W}$
$\qquad = 9.0 \times 10^1\ \text{kW}$

8. a. $v_f^2 = v_i^2 + 2\ ad$

$\qquad d = \dfrac{v_f^2 - v_i^2}{2a} = \dfrac{(35\ \text{m/s})^2 - (25\ \text{m/s})^2}{(2)(1.25\ \text{m/s}^2)} = 240\ \text{m}$

$W = Fd\quad F = ma$
$W = (ma)d$
$\qquad = (1.0 \times 10^3\ \text{kg})(1.25\ \text{m/s})(240\ \text{m})$
$\qquad = 3.0 \times 10^5\ \text{J}$

b. $v_f = v_i + at$

$\qquad t = \dfrac{v_f - v_i}{a} = \dfrac{35\ \text{m/s} - 25\ \text{m/s}}{1.25\ \text{m/s}^2} = 8.0\ \text{s}$

$\qquad P = \dfrac{W}{t} = \dfrac{3.1 \times 10^5\ \text{J}}{8.0\ \text{s}} = 3.9 \times 10^4\ \text{W} = 39\ \text{kW}$

9. $P = \dfrac{W}{t} = \dfrac{Fd \cos \theta}{t}$

$\qquad d = \dfrac{Pt}{F \cos \theta} = \dfrac{(64.6\ \text{W})(90.0\ \text{s})}{(115\ \text{N})(\cos 22.5)} = 54.7\ \text{m}$

10. $eff = \dfrac{F_r}{F_e} \times \dfrac{d_r}{d_e} \times 100\%$

$\qquad d_e = \dfrac{F_r}{F_e} \times d_r \times \dfrac{100\%}{eff} = \dfrac{(475\ \text{N})(6.23 \times 10^{-1}\ \text{m})}{(178\ \text{N})(0.850)} = 1.96\ \text{m}$

11. $eff = \dfrac{W_o}{W_i} \times 100\%$

$\qquad W_i = W_o \times \dfrac{100\%}{eff} = \dfrac{mgh}{0.725}$

$\qquad = \dfrac{(2.00 \times 10^2\ \text{kg})(9.81\ \text{m/s}^2)(5.65\ \text{m})}{0.725} = 1.53 \times 10^4\ \text{J}$

12. a. $MA = \dfrac{F_r}{F_e} = \dfrac{1340\ \text{N}}{225\ \text{N}} = 5.96$

b. $\dfrac{d_e}{d_r} = \dfrac{7.35\ \text{m}}{0.975\ \text{m}} = 7.54$

c. $eff = \dfrac{F_r d_r}{F_e d_e} \times 100\% = \dfrac{(1340\ \text{N})(0.975\ \text{m})}{(225\ \text{N})(7.35\ \text{m})} \times 100\% = 79.0\%$

13. a. $F_p = F_w \sin \theta = (425\ \text{N})\left(\dfrac{1.28\ \text{m}}{6.40\ \text{m}}\right) = 85.0\ \text{N}$

$\qquad F_f = F - F_p = 95.0\ \text{N} - 85.0\ \text{N} = 10.0\ \text{N}$
$\qquad W = F_f d = (10.0\ \text{N})(6.40\ \text{m}) = 64.0\ \text{J}$

b. $eff = \dfrac{W_o}{W_i} \times 100\% = \dfrac{F_r d_r}{F_e d_e} \times 100\%$

$\qquad = \dfrac{(85.0\ \text{N})(6.40\ \text{m})}{(95.0\ \text{N})(6.40\ \text{m})} \times 100\% = 89.5\%$

Problems B
Page 177.

1. a. $m = \dfrac{\Delta y}{\Delta x} = \dfrac{5.0\ \text{N} - 0.0\ \text{N}}{0.20\ \text{m} - 0.00\ \text{m}}$

$\qquad = \dfrac{5.0\ \text{N}}{0.20\ \text{m}} = 25\ \text{N/m}$

b. $A = \frac{1}{2}lh = (\frac{1}{2})(5.0\ \text{N})(0.20\ \text{m})$
$\qquad = 0.50\ \text{J}$

c. $W = \frac{1}{2}kd^2 = (\frac{1}{2})(25\ \text{N/m})(0.20\ \text{m})^2$
$\qquad = 0.50\ \text{J}$

2. a. $W_{in} = W_{out} = W'_{in} = W'_{out}$
$\qquad W_{in} = W'_{out}$
$\qquad F_e d_e = F_r' d_r'$
$\qquad$ For the complex machine

$\qquad IMA_c = \dfrac{d_e}{d_r'}$

$\qquad \dfrac{d_e}{d_r} = IMA;\ \dfrac{d'_e}{d'_r} = IMA'$

$\qquad d_r = d'_e$

$\qquad \dfrac{d_e}{IMA} = d_r = d'_e = (IMA')(d'_r)$

$\qquad d_e = (IMA)(IMA')(d_r')$

$\qquad \dfrac{d_e}{d_r'} = IMA_c = (IMA)(IMA')$

$\qquad\qquad = (3.0)(2.0) = 6.0$

b. $\dfrac{F_r'}{F_e} = MA_c = \dfrac{(IMA) \times (eff)}{100\%}$

$\qquad \dfrac{F_r'}{F_e} = \dfrac{(6.0)(60.0\%)}{100\%} = 3.6$

$\qquad F_e = \dfrac{F_r'}{3.6} = \dfrac{540\ \text{N}}{3.6} = 150\ \text{N}$

c. $\dfrac{d_e}{d_r'} = IMA_c$

$\qquad d_r' = \dfrac{d_e}{IMA_c} = \dfrac{12.0\ \text{cm}}{6.0} = 2.0\ \text{cm}$

Energy and Its Conservation   Chapter 11

Teaching Techniques

Conservation of energy is an extremely important concept. Take time to discuss energy, as it is an abstract idea that may not be easy for all students to grasp. The calculations developed in this chapter are based on the equations of uniformly accelerated motion, and should be familiar to students. The problems present students with their first quantitative experience with energy.

Only mechanical energy is used in this chapter. Conversion to other forms (thermal, electrical, etc.) will be developed later. Students should concentrate on mechanical energy for now. As they become familiar with these concepts they will be better prepared to deal with more abstract relationships introduced later.

When discussing collisions remind students of the law of conservation of momentum. In elastic collisions energy is not lost, but transformed from mechanical energy to other forms.

Demonstrations

Several demonstrations can illustrate conservation laws.

Section 11:4

A spring-powered toy can demonstrate that work (Fd) is done on a spring, stored in the form of potential energy, and then converted to kinetic energy.

Galileo's pendulum. Hang a pendulum from a support bar. Mount a meter stick horizontally behind the pendulum. Demonstrate that a pendulum starting its swing from a given height on one side of its rest position will swing to the same height on the other side. Measure this with the meter stick. Discuss transformation of energy from kinetic to potential and back.

Now, while the pendulum is swinging, place a pencil in its path at the center of the swing. Show students that the bob rises to the same height as that from which it started its swing.

Section 11:6

An air track or dynamics carts can easily demonstrate elastic collisions. Use two carts of equal mass, one at rest. After collision the cart that was still will move, the other will be at rest. A line of steel balls supported by string or wire can be purchased at many stores. If one mass is pulled back and allowed to strike the row of balls, a single ball leaves the other end. Two balls pulled back results in two leaving the other end.

Film Loops

Energy Conversion (BFA film loop)
Reversibility of Time (BFA film loop)

Laboratory Investigations

Conservation of Energy

Performance Objectives

Goal: Students will gain understanding of energy and its conservation. They will recognize that work done produces a change in energy.

Objectives: Upon completion of the reading, questions, and problems, students will, on oral or written tests:

11:1	K/P	define energy; give the relation between work and energy; define the two forms of energy, kinetic and potential.
11:2	K/P	recognize the arbitrary, but useful, nature of a base level.
11:3	K/P/S	understand that, for a body starting and ending at rest, work is the change in potential energy. Demonstrate this understanding by solving problems.
11:4	K/P/S	define and calculate kinetic energy and recognize that the change in kinetic energy is the work done on the object.
11:5	K/P/A	state the law of conservation of energy; demonstrate understanding by solving problems involving energy changes.
11:6	K/P	understand the difference between elastic and inelastic collisions. Recognize that mechanical energy is conserved only in elastic collisions, but momentum is conserved in both.
	S/A	Students will use laboratory materials in the prescribed manner when conducting lab investigations.

Upon completion of the reading and practice problems, students will exhibit an interest in physics by:

	A/S	expanding on an answer to one or more of the questions or problems at the end of the chapter.
	A/S	applying the results of elastic and inelastic collisions to prob-

lems such as automobile collisions.

A   reading unassigned literature
related to the ideas presented in
the chapter.

Solutions to Problems

Page 183.

1. $PE = Fd = mgd$
   $= (200.0 \text{ kg})(9.81 \text{ m/s}^2)(10.0 \text{ m}) = 1.96 \times 10^4 \text{ J}$

2. **a.** $PE = Fd = mgd$
   $= (60.0 \text{ kg})(9.81 \text{ m/s}^2)(4.0 \times 10^2 \text{ m})$
   $= 2.4 \times 10^5 \text{ J}$

   b. Falling one-half the distance down it will lose
   one-half its energy.

   $\dfrac{2.4 \times 10^5 \text{ J}}{2} = 1.2 \times 10^5 \text{ J}$

3. **a.** $W = Fd = (630 \text{ N})(5.0 \text{ m}) = 3200 \text{ J}$
   b. The work done is the increase in gravitational
   potential energy.
   c. It was stored in the person by eating food.

Page 184.

4. **a.** $KE = \dfrac{1}{2}mv^2 = \left(\dfrac{1}{2}\right)(45 \text{ kg})(10.0 \text{ m/s})^2 = 2.3 \times 10^3 \text{ J}$

   b. $KE = \dfrac{1}{2}mv^2 = \left(\dfrac{1}{2}\right)(45 \text{ kg})(5.0 \text{ m/s})^2 = 5.6 \times 10^2 \text{ J}$

   c. $\dfrac{\cancel{1/2}\,\cancel{m}v_1{}^2}{\cancel{1/2}\,\cancel{m}v_2{}^2} = \dfrac{(10.0)^2}{(5.0)^2} = \dfrac{4}{1}$

5. $v = \dfrac{d}{t} = \dfrac{(1.80 \text{ km})(1000 \text{ m/km})}{(10.0 \text{ min})(60 \text{ s/min})} = 3.0 \text{ m/s}$

   $KE = \dfrac{1}{2}mv^2 = \left(\dfrac{1}{2}\right)(45 \text{ kg})(3.00 \text{ m/s})^2$
   $= 2.0 \times 10^2 \text{ J}$

6. $W = \Delta KE = \left(\dfrac{1}{2}\right)(15.0 \text{ kg})(7.50 \text{ m/s})^2 - \left(\dfrac{1}{2}\right)(15.0 \text{ kg})(3.20 \text{ m/s})^2$

   $= 345 \text{ J}$
   $W = Fd \qquad d = \dfrac{W}{F} = \dfrac{345 \text{ J}}{10.0 \text{ N}} = 34.5 \text{ m}$

Page 185.

7. **a.** $W = mg$

   $m = \dfrac{W}{g} = \dfrac{1.6 \text{ N}}{9.8 \text{ m/s}^2} = 0.16 \text{ kg}$

   $E = \dfrac{1}{2}mv^2 = \left(\dfrac{1}{2}\right)(0.16 \text{ kg})(40.0 \text{ m/s})^2 = 130 \text{ J}$

   b. $\Delta KE = KE_f - KE_i$

   $KE_i = \left(\dfrac{1}{2}\right)(0.16 \text{ kg})(30.0 \text{ m/s})^2 = 72 \text{ J}$

   $\Delta KE = 130 \text{ J} - 72 \text{ J} = 58 \text{ J}$

Page 187.

8. **a.** $KE = \Delta PE = mgd$
   $= (8.0 \text{ kg})(9.8 \text{ m/s}^2)(12.0 \text{ m}) = 940 \text{ J}$

   b. $KE = \dfrac{1}{2}mv^2$

   $v = \sqrt{\dfrac{2KE}{m}} = \sqrt{\dfrac{(2)(940 \text{ J})}{(8.0 \text{ kg})}} = 15 \text{ m/s}$

9. **a.** $KE = \dfrac{1}{2}mv^2 = \left(\dfrac{1}{2}\right)(15.0 \text{ kg})(12.5 \text{ m/s})^2 = 1170 \text{ J}$

   b. $\Delta PE = mgh = (15.0 \text{ kg})(9.80 \text{ m/s}^2)(20.4 \text{ m})$
   $3.00 \times 10^3 \text{ J}$

Page 188.

   c. $\Delta KE = \Delta PE = 3.00 \times 10^3 \text{ J}$
   d. $KE = 1170 \text{ J} + 3.00 \times 10^3 \text{ J} = 4170 \text{ J}$
   e. $KE = \dfrac{1}{2}mv^2$

   $v = \sqrt{\dfrac{2KE}{m}} = \sqrt{\dfrac{(2)(4170 \text{ J})}{15.0 \text{ kg}}} = 23.6 \text{ m/s}$

10. **a.** $KE = \Delta PE = mgd$
    $= (16.0 \text{ kg})(9.80 \text{ m/s}^2)(40.0 \text{ m}) = 6270 \text{ J}$

    b. $KE = \dfrac{1}{2}mv^2$

    $v = \sqrt{\dfrac{2KE}{m}} = \sqrt{\dfrac{(2)(6270 \text{ J})}{(16.0 \text{ kg})}} = 28.0 \text{ m/s}$

11. **a.** $PE = Fd = (98.0 \text{ N})(64.0 \text{ m}) = 6270 \text{ J}$
    b. $W = mg$

    $m = \dfrac{W}{g} = \dfrac{98.0 \text{ N}}{9.81 \text{ m/s}^2} = 1.00 \times 10^1 \text{ kg}$

    $KE = \dfrac{1}{2}mv^2$

    $v = \sqrt{\dfrac{2KE}{m}} = \sqrt{\dfrac{(2)(6270 \text{ J})}{1.00 \times 10^1 \text{ kg}}} = 35.4 \text{ m/s}$

12. $PE = mgd$

    $d = \dfrac{PE}{mg} = \dfrac{(784.0 \text{ J})}{(8.0 \text{ kg})(9.8 \text{ m/s}^2)} = 1.0 \times 10^1 \text{ m}$

13. $PE = mgd$

    $d = \dfrac{PE}{mg} = \dfrac{1960 \text{ J}}{(10.0 \text{ kg})(9.81 \text{ m/s}^2)} = 20.0 \text{ m}$

14. $KE = \dfrac{1}{2}mv^2$

    $v = \sqrt{\dfrac{2KE}{m}} = \sqrt{\dfrac{(2)(560 \text{ J})}{(5.0 \text{ kg})}} = 15 \text{ m/s}$

15. **a.** $d_v = d \sin \theta = (17.2 \text{ m})(2 \sin 30.0°) = 8.65 \text{ m}$
    $KE = \Delta PE$

    $\dfrac{1}{2}mv^2 = mgd$

    $v^2 = \dfrac{2\,mgd}{m}$

$v = \sqrt{2\ gd} = \sqrt{(2)(9.81\ \text{m/s}^2)(8.00\ \text{m})} = 12.5\ \text{m/s}$

b. $KE = \frac{1}{2}mv^2 = \left(\frac{1}{2}\right)(10.0\ \text{kg})(12.5\ \text{m/s}^2) = 781\ \text{J}$

Page 189.

16. a. $KE = \frac{1}{2}mv^2 = \left(\frac{1}{2}\right)(5.0\ \text{kg})(15\ \text{m/s}^2)^2 = 560\ \text{J}$

b. $PE = mgh = \Delta KE$

$d = \frac{\Delta KE}{mg} = \frac{(560\ \text{J})}{(5.0\ \text{kg})(9.8\ \text{m/s}^2)} = 11\ \text{m}$

Chapter End Questions

Pages 191-192.

1. Forces transfer energy between points and between objects.

2. A wound-up watch spring has potential energy. Work was done to wind the spring. When running, the watch uses the potential energy of the spring converted to kinetic energy. When the watch has been run down, its energy has been converted to heat and sound.

3. The Earth-sun system possesses both kinetic and potential energy. As a matter of fact, the two are constantly interchanging. This is why Earth moves faster along its orbit when closer to the sun, in accordance with Kepler's law.

4. If Earth moves farther away from the sun, as it does in the summer, it loses kinetic energy and gains potential energy. (See the above answer.)

5. **a.** If the ball had bounced 8 m, collision would be perfectly elastic.
   b. If the ball had not bounced at all, collision would be perfectly inelastic.
   c. Some of the ball's kinetic energy is converted to heat and sound as it collides with Earth.

6. "Flubber" would violate the law of conservation of energy. Such a substance cannot exist as far as we know at the present time.

Problems A

Page 192.

1. **a.** $W = Fd = (98\ \text{N})(50\ \text{m}) = 5000\ \text{J}$
   b. $\Delta PE = W = 5000\ \text{J}$
   c. $KE = \Delta PE = 5000\ \text{J}$

2. $KE = \frac{1}{2}mv^2 = \left(\frac{1}{2}\right)(1600\ \text{kg})(12.5\ \text{m/s})^2 = 1.3 \times 10^5\ \text{J}$

3. $v = \frac{(108\ \text{km/h})(1000\ \text{m/km})}{(3600\ \text{s/h})} = 30.0\ \text{m/s}$

$KE = \frac{1}{2}mv^2 = \left(\frac{1}{2}\right)(1500\ \text{kg})(30.0\ \text{m/s})^2 = 6.8 \times 10^5\ \text{J}$

4. a. $W = KE$

$Fd = \frac{1}{2}mv^2$

$v^2 = \frac{2Fd}{m}$

$v = \sqrt{\frac{2Fd}{m}} = \sqrt{\frac{(2)(200\ \text{N})(1.3\ \text{m})}{(0.30\ \text{kg})}} = 42\ \text{m/s}$

b. $PE = \Delta KE$

$mgd = \frac{1}{2}mv^2$

$d = \frac{v^2}{2g} = \frac{(42\ \text{m/s})^2}{(2)(9.8\ \text{m/s}^2)} = 9.0 \times 10^1$

5. a. $v = \frac{(72\ \text{km/h})(1000\ \text{m/km})}{(3600\ \text{s/h})} = 2.0 \times 10^1\ \text{m/s}$

$a = \frac{\Delta v}{\Delta t} = \frac{2.0 \times 10^1\ \text{m/s}}{20.0\ \text{s}} = 1.0\ \text{m/s}^2$

$v_f^2 = v_i^2 + 2\ ad$

Since $v_i = 0$

$d = \frac{v_f^2}{2a} = \frac{(2.0 \times 10^1\ \text{m/s})^2}{(2)(1.0\ \text{m/s}^2)} = 2.0 \times 10^2\ \text{m}$

b. $F = ma = (1200\ \text{kg})(1.0\ \text{m/s}^2) = 1200\ \text{N}$
$F_{engine} = 1200\ \text{N} + F_{friction} = 1200\ \text{N} + 450\ \text{N}$
$\qquad = 1600\ \text{N}$

c. $W = Fd = (1600\ \text{N})(2.0 \times 10^2\ \text{m}) = 3.2 \times 10^5\ \text{J}$

6. $W = Fd = (410\ \text{N})(2.0\ \text{m}) = 820\ \text{J}$
$W = \Delta KE$
$mgd = \Delta KE$
$d = \frac{\Delta KE}{mg} = \frac{820\ \text{J}}{32\ \text{N}} = 26\ \text{m}$

7. a. $PE = mgh = (20\ \text{kg})(9.8\ \text{m/s}^2)(100\ \text{m}) = 20\ 000\ \text{J}$
   b. $KE = \Delta PE = 20\ 000\ \text{J}$

c. $KE = \frac{1}{2}mv^2$

$v = \sqrt{\frac{2KE}{m}} = \sqrt{\frac{(2)(20\ 000\ \text{J})}{(20\ \text{kg})}} = 40\ \text{m/s}$

8. a. $KE = \frac{1}{2}mv^2 = \left(\frac{1}{2}\right)(4.0\ \text{kg})(62\ \text{m/s})^2$

$\qquad = 7200\ \text{J} = 7.7 \times 10^3\ \text{J}$

b. $W = Fd$

$F = \frac{W}{d} = \frac{7.7 \times 10^3\ \text{J}}{22\ \text{m}} = 350\ \text{N}$

Page 193.

9. a. $mv = (5.0 \times 10^5 \text{ kg})(8.0 \text{ m/s}) = 4.0 \times 10^6 \text{ kg} \cdot \text{m/s}$
  b. Since momentum is conserved it must be
    4.0×10^6 kg · m/s.
  c. Before the collision:

$$KE_1 = \frac{1}{2}mv^2 = \left(\frac{1}{2}\right)(5.0 \times 10^5 \text{ kg})(8.0 \text{ m/s})^2 = 1.6 \times 10^7 \text{ J}$$

$KE_2 = 0$ since it is at rest
After the collision:

$$KE = \frac{1}{2}mv^2 = \left(\frac{1}{2}\right)(5.0 \times 10^5 \text{ kg} + 5.0 \times 10^5 \text{ kg})(4.0 \text{ m/s})^2$$
$$= 8.0 \times 10^6 \text{ J}$$

  d. While momentum was conserved during the collision, KE was not. The amount not conserved was turned into heat and sound.

Problems B

Page 193.

1. a. $\Delta PE = Fd = (420 \text{ N})(1.00 \text{ m} - 0.40 \text{ m}) = 250 \text{ J}$

$$KE = \Delta PE = \frac{1}{2}mv^2$$

$$v = \sqrt{\frac{2KE}{m}} = \sqrt{\frac{(2)(250 \text{ J})}{420 \text{ N}/9.8 \text{ m/s}^2}} = 3.4 \text{ m/s}$$

  b. $W = \Delta KE = 250 \text{ J} - \left(\frac{1}{2}\right)\left(\frac{420 \text{ N}}{9.8 \text{ m/s}^2}\right)(2.0 \text{ m/s})^2$

$$= 250 \text{ J} - 86 \text{ J} = 164 \text{ J} = 160 \text{ J}$$

2. $W = \Delta KE$
  $PE = mgh = (10.0 \times 10^{-3} \text{ kg})(9.80 \text{ m/s}^2)(1.0 \text{ m})$
    $= 9.8 \times 10^{-2} \text{ J}$

$$\Delta KE = 9.8 \times 10^{-2} \text{ J} = \frac{1}{2}mv^2$$

$$\Delta v = \sqrt{\frac{2KE}{m}} = \sqrt{\frac{(2)(9.8 \times 10^{-2} \text{ J})}{1.0 \times 10^{-2} \text{ kg}}} = 4.4 \text{ m/s}$$

$v_f - v_i = \Delta v$
$v_i = v_f - \Delta v = 5.5 \text{ m/s} - 4.4 \text{ m/s} = 1.1 \text{ m/s}$

Thermal Energy   Chapter 12

Teaching Techniques

This chapter introduces the concepts of thermal physics using a microscopic point of view. It expands the concept of conservation of energy, and prepares students for the study of kinetic theory and gas laws presented in Chapters 13 and 14.

The first law of thermodynamics is treated as an extension of conservation of energy, with heat defined as the transfer of energy by means of a difference in temperatures. This definition of heat is carefully used throughout the chapter. Note this fact, because the common use of the noun "heat" is not consistent with this definition.

Demonstrations

Section 12:3

Demonstrate the measurement of temperature with a Galilean air thermometer. Despite its sensitivity to temperature variations, it is rarely used due to its sensitivity to atmospheric pressure variations. Warm the flask with one hand and point out the air bubbles rising in the water as evidence of the expansion of air inside the flask. After air has been forced out of the flask, allow it to cool. Ask students to observe water rising in the tube. The water level can now be shown to be a sensitive measure of temperature by once again putting your hand on the flask.

Section 12:8

To demonstrate differences in specific heat, warm a block of iron and an equal mass of water simultaneously over hot plates. After the water becomes only slightly warm, allow several drops of water to fall on the iron block. The sizzling noise will indicate that the iron is at a much higher temperature. Compare and discuss the specific heats of water and iron. Discuss the use of water as a coolant.

Section 12:9

To show the pedictability of final temperatures, pour equal amounts of cold and hot water of known temperatures into an empty Styrofoam® cup. Quickly stir the mixture and take its final temperature. Show that it is almost exactly midway between the two initial temperatures. Encourage students to discuss why the temperature might not be exactly at the midway point.

Section 12:10

The magnitude of the heat of fusion of ice can be shown using a two-pan balance. Place beakers containing equal masses of warm water on each pan. Take a third beaker containing a mixture of ice and water. Pour only the cold water into one of the beakers on the balance. Then put an equal mass (shown by the balanced scale) of ice into the other beaker. Compare the final temperatures and discuss the heat of fusion of ice.

Film

Basic Theory of Heat, Part I and II (university rental)

Film Loop

Heat of Fusion (BFA-Ealing film loop)

Laboratory Investigations

The Conservation of Thermal Energy
Specific Heat of a Metal
Heat of Fusion of Ice

Performance Objectives

Goal: Students should become familiar with the concepts of thermal energy, temperature, heat, and heats of fusion and vaporization.

Objectives: Upon completion of the reading, questions, and problems, students will, on oral or written tests:

12:1	K/P	understand the nature of thermal energy in the kinetic theory.
12:2	K/P	define temperature and distinguish it from thermal energy.
12:3	K/P	understand the process of obtaining equilibrium and its application to the measurement of temperature.
12:4	K	decribe the Celsius scale.
12:5	K/P/S	describe the Kelvin scale; demonstrate the ability to convert between Celsius and Kelvin.
12:6	K/P/S	state the first law of thermodynamics; distinguish heat from work and both from thermal

		energy; define a heat engine, refrigerator, and heat pump.
12:7	K/P	state the second law of thermodynamics; define entropy.
12:8	K/P/S	define and display an understanding of specific heat; be able to calculate heat transfer.
12:9	K/P	display an understanding of the application of conservation of energy to energy transfers; be able to calculate temperature changes due to energy transfer.
12:10	K/P/S	define heats of fusion and vaporization; understand the microscopic basic of changes of state; calculate heat transfers needed to effect changes of state.
	S/A	Students will use laboratory materials in the prescribed manner when conducting lab investigations.

Upon completion of the reading and practice problems, students will exhibit an interest in physics by:

A/S	expanding on an answer to one or more of the questions or problems at the end of the chapter.
A/S	reporting on the contributions of Rumford and Joule to the development of the kinetic theory.
A	reading unassigned literature related to the ideas presented in the chapter.

Solutions to Problems

Page 199.

1. $K = °C + 273 = 43 + 273 = 316$ K
2. $°C = K - 273 = 43 - 273 = -230°C$
3. $K = °C + 273 = 273 + 273 = 546$ K
4. $°C = K - 273 = 273 - 273 = 0°C$
5. $°C = K - 273 = 27 - 273 = -246°C$
6.   **a.** $°C = K - 273 = 110 - 273 = -163°C$
    b. $°C = K - 273 = 22 - 273 = -251°C$
    c. $°C = K - 273 = 373 - 273 = 100°C$
    d. $°C = K - 273 = 323 - 273 = 50°C$
    e. $°C = K - 273 = 402 - 273 = 129°C$

Page 205.

7. $\Delta Q = mC\Delta T$
$= (2.50 \times 10^2 \text{ g})(4.18 \text{ J/g} \cdot \text{K})(85.0°C - 10.0°C) = 7.84 \times 10^4 \text{ J}$

8. $\Delta Q = mC\Delta T$
$= (60.0 \text{ g})(0.385 \text{ J/g} \cdot \text{K})(80.0°C - 20.0°C) = 1390 \text{ J}$

9. $\Delta Q = mC\Delta T$
$= (38 \text{ kg})(130 \text{ J/kg} \cdot \text{K})(180°C - (-26°C)) = 1.0 \times 10^6$

10. a. $\Delta Q = mC\Delta T$

$\Delta T = \dfrac{\Delta Q}{mC} = \dfrac{836.0 \text{ kJ}}{(20.0 \text{ kg})(4.18 \text{ J/g} \cdot \text{C°})} = 10.0°C$

b. $\Delta Q = mC\Delta T$

$\Delta T = \dfrac{\Delta Q}{mC} = \dfrac{836.0 \text{ kJ}}{(0.80 \text{ g/L})(20.0 \text{ L})(2.48 \text{ J/g} \cdot \text{C°})} = 21 \text{ C}$

c. Water is the better coolant. It transfers heat better.

11. $\Delta Q = mC\Delta T$
$= (4.00 \times 10 \text{ g})(0.664 \text{ J/g} \cdot \text{K})(80.0°C - 20.0°C) = 1.59 \times 10^4 \text{ J}$

12. $\Delta Q = mC\Delta T = (5.0 \text{ kg})(2060 \text{ J/kg} \cdot \text{K})(-4.0°C - (-17°C))$
$= 1.3 \times 10^5 \text{ J}$

13. $\Delta Q = m_w C_w \Delta T + m_i C_i \Delta T$
$m_w = \dfrac{\Delta Q - m_i C_i \Delta T}{C_w \Delta T}$

$= \dfrac{4.4 \times 10^6 \text{ J} - (2.50 \times 10^2 \text{ kg})(450 \text{ J/kg} \cdot \text{K})(25°C)}{(4180 \text{ J/kg} \cdot \text{K})(25°C)} = 15 \text{ kg}$

14. a. $\Delta Q = mC\Delta T$
$= (2.50 \times 10^2 \text{ g})(4.18 \text{ J/g} \cdot \text{K})(7.8°C) = 8200 \text{ J}$

b. $\Delta Q = mC\Delta T$

$C_{lead} = \dfrac{\Delta Q}{m\Delta T} = \dfrac{8200 \text{ J}}{(8.00 \times 10^2 \text{ g})(80.0°C)}$

$= 0.13 \text{ J/g} \cdot \text{K} = 130 \text{ J/kg} \cdot \text{K}$

Page 207.

15.
$$Q_{lost} = Q_{gained}$$
$$m_1 C_1 \Delta T = m_2 C_2 \Delta T$$
$$m_1 \Delta T = m_2 \Delta T$$
$$(2.00 \times 10^2 \text{ g})(80.0°C - T_f) = (2.00 \times 10^2 \text{ g})(T_f - 10.0°C)$$
$$T_f = \dfrac{18000 \text{ g} \cdot \text{C°}}{4.00 \times 10^2 \text{ g}}$$
$$= 45.0°C$$

16.
$$Q_{lost} = Q_{gained}$$
$$m_1 C_1 \Delta T = m_2 C_2 \Delta T$$
$$m_1 \Delta T = m_2 \Delta T$$
$$(6.0 \times 10^2 \text{ g})(90.0°C - T_f) = (4.00 \times 10^2 \text{ g})(T_f - 22°C)$$
$$5.4 \times 10^4 \text{ g} \cdot \text{C°} - (6.0 \times 10^2 \text{ g}) T_f = (4.00 \times 10^2 \text{ g}) T_f - 8.8 \times 10^3 \text{ g} \cdot \text{C°}$$
$$T_f = \dfrac{6.28 \times 10^4 \text{ g} \cdot \text{C°}}{1.00 \times 10^3 \text{ g}}$$
$$= 63°C$$

Page 208.

$$Q_{lost} = Q_{gained}$$
$$m_1C_1\Delta T = m_2C_2\Delta T$$

17. $(4.00 \times 10^2 \text{ g})(4.18 \text{ J/g} \cdot \text{C}°)(85.0°C - T_f) = (4.00 \times 10^2 \text{ g})(2.45 \text{ J/g} \cdot \text{C}°)(T_f - 16.0°C)$

$$T_f = \frac{(142000 \text{ J} + 15600 \text{ J})}{(1670 \text{ J/C}° + 980 \text{ J/C}°)} = 59.6°C$$

18.

$$Q_{lost} = Q_{gained}$$
$$m_1C_1\Delta T = m_2C_2\Delta T$$
$(1.00 \times 10^2 \text{ g})(0.376 \text{ J/g} \cdot \text{C}°)(90.0°C - T_f) = (2.00 \times 10^2 \text{ g})(4.18 \text{ J/g} \cdot \text{C}°)(T_f - 20.0°C)$

$$T_f = \frac{20080 \text{ J}}{873.6 \text{ J/C}°}$$
$$= 23.0°C$$

19.

$$Q_{lost} = Q_{gained}$$
$$m_{Al}C_{Al}\Delta T = m_wC_w\Delta T$$
$$C_{Al} = \frac{m_wC_w\Delta T}{m_{Al}\Delta T}$$
$$= \frac{(1.00 \times 10^2 \text{ g})(4.18 \text{ J/g} \cdot \text{C}°)(15°C)}{(1.0 \times 10^2 \text{ g})(75°C)}$$
$$= 0.836 \text{ J/g} \cdot \text{C}° = 0.84 \text{ J/g} \cdot \text{C}° = 840 \text{ J/kg} \cdot \text{K}$$

20.

$$Q_{lost} = Q_{gained}$$
$$m_1C_1\Delta T = m_2C_2\Delta T$$
$(10.0 \text{ kg})(388 \text{ J/kg} \cdot \text{C}°)(71°C - T_f) = (20.0 \text{ kg})(4180 \text{ J/kg} \cdot \text{C}°)(T_f - 10.0°C)$
$275480 \text{ J} + (3880 \text{ J/C}°)T_f = (83600 \text{ J/C}°)T_f - 836000 \text{ J}$

$$T_f = \frac{1120000 \text{ J}}{87500 \text{ J/C}°} = 12.8°C$$

Page 211.

21. $Q = (50.0 \text{ g})(334 \text{ J/g}) = 16700 \text{ J}$

22. $Q = (50.0 \text{ g})(2260 \text{ J/g}) = 1.13 \times 10^5 \text{ J}$

23. To warm ice to 0.0°C
$Q = mC\Delta T = (1.00 \times 10^2 \text{ g})(2.06 \text{ J/g} \cdot \text{C}°)(20.0°C) = $ 4120 J
To melt the ice: $Q = (100.0 \text{ g})(334 \text{ J/g}) = $ 33400 J
                                              37520 J
$Q_{total} = 38000 \text{ J}$

24. To heat the water to 100°C: $Q = mC\Delta = (2.00 \times 10^2 \text{ g})(4.18 \text{ J/g} \cdot \text{K})(40.0°C) = $ 33400 J
To change the water to steam: $Q = (2.00 \times 10^2 \text{ g})(2260 \text{ J/g})$ = 452000 J
To warm the steam from 100°C to 140.0°C: $Q = mC\Delta T = (2.00 \times 10^2 \text{ g})(2.02 \text{ J/g} \cdot \text{K})(40.0°C) = $ 16200 J
$Q_{total} = 5.02 \times 10^5 \text{ J}$

25. $Q = mC\Delta T = (3.00 \times 10^2 \text{ g})(2.06 \text{ J/g} \cdot \text{C}°)(30.0°C) = 1.85 \times 10^4 \text{ J}$ to warm the ice to 0°C
$Q = (3.00 \times 10^2 \text{ g})(334 \text{ J/g})$ $= 1.00 \times 10^5 \text{ J}$ to melt the ice
$Q = mC\Delta T = (3.00 \times 10^2 \text{ g})(4.18 \text{ J/g} \cdot \text{C}°)(100°C) = 1.25 \times 10^5 \text{ J}$ two warm the water from 0°C to 100°C
$Q = (3.00 \times 10^2 \text{ g})(2260 \text{ J/g})$ $= 6.78 \times 10^5 \text{ J}$ to change the water to steam
$Q = (3.00 \times 10^2 \text{ g})(2.02 \text{ J/g} \cdot \text{C}°)(30.0°C)$ $= 1.82 \times 10^4 \text{ J}$ to warm the steam from 100°C to 131°C
Q_{total} $9.40 \times 10^5 \text{ J}$

26. $Q = (60.0 \text{ g})(2260 \text{ J/g})$ $= 1.36 \times 10^5 \text{ J}$ to change steam to water
$Q = mC\Delta T = (60.0 \text{ g})(4.18 \text{ J/g} \cdot \text{C}°)(80.0°C) = 2.01 \times 10^4 \text{ J}$ to cool water from 100.0°C to 20.0°C
$Q_{total} = 1.56 \times 10^5 \text{ J}$

27. $Q_1 = mC\Delta T = (1.0 \times 10^3 \text{ g})(0.14 \text{ J/g} \cdot \text{C}°)(347°C)$
$= 4.9 \times 10^4 \text{ J}$ to warm the mercury from 10°C to 357°C
$Q_2 = (1.0 \times 10^3 \text{ g})(306 \text{ J/g}) = 3.1 \times 10^5 \text{ J}$ to vaporize the mercury
$Q_{total} = Q_1 + Q_2 = 3.6 \times 10^5 \text{ J}$

28. $Q = (2.00 \times 10^4 \text{ g})(334 \text{ J/g}) = 6.68 \times 10^6 \text{ J}$

Chapter End Questions

Page 213.

1. The external energy of an object, such as a baseball in flight, is the sum of all energy outside of the object. The external energy of the baseball is due to its motion and position above Earth. Thermal energy is the total kinetic and potential energy of all particles that compose the object.

2. Thermal energy is transferred from one object to another in the form of heat; temperature is the measure of the average kinetic energy of the molecules of the object.

3. Heat is the measure of the internal kinetic energy transferred from objects of higher thermal energy to objects of lower thermal energy.

4. **a.** $-2°C$ **b.** 271 K

5. **a.** 34°C   **b.** 307 K

6. The aluminum (specific heat 0.903 J/g · C°) can donate the most heat per gram to the ice in cooling through the same temperature variation. Ths specific heat of lead is only 0.130 J/g · C°.

7. Since the motions of the molecules of the brake are completely random, this will not happen. Statistically, the event is too unlikely to happen. The second law of thermodynamics prohibits such an event on this basis.

8. Entropy is the measure of disorder in a system; a lack of energy in a system can be described in terms of high entropy.

9. The alcoholic beverage would cool a little faster since its specific heat would be a bit less than the specific heat of water.

Problems A

Page 213.

1. **a.** $K = °C + 273 = 51° + 273 = 324$ K
   b. $K = 155° + 273 = 428$ K
   c. $K = -207° + 273 = 66$ K
   d. $K = 302° + 273 = 575$ K

2. **a.** $K = °C + 273$ K
   $°C = K - 273 = 51 - 273 = -222°C$
   b. $°C = K - 273 = 155 - 273 = -118°C$
   c. $°C = K - 273 = 273 - 273 = 0°C$
   d. $°C = K - 273 = 302 - 273 = 29°C$

3. $Q = mC\Delta T$
   $= (50.0 \text{ g})(4.18 \text{ J/g} \cdot \text{C°})(78.5°C) = 1.6 \times 10^4$ J

4. $Q = mC\Delta T$
   $= (50.0 \text{ g})(0.903 \text{ J/g} \cdot \text{C°})(100°C) = 4.52 \times 10^3$ J

5. $$Q_W = Q_{Zn}$$
   $$m_W C_W \Delta T_W = m_{Zn} C_{Zn} \Delta T_{Zn}$$
   $$\Delta T_{Zn} = \frac{C_W}{C_{Zn}} \Delta T_W$$
   $$= \frac{4.18}{0.388}(1.00 \times 10^2 °C) = 1080°C$$

Page 214.

6. $Q = mC\Delta T = (165 \text{ g})(0.385 \text{ J/g} \cdot \text{C°})(18°C) = 1100$ J

7. $$Q_{lost} = Q_{gained}$$
   $$m_1 C_1 \Delta T_1 = m_2 C_2 \Delta T_2$$
   $$\Delta T_1 = \Delta T_2$$
   $$92°C - T_f = T_f - 32°C$$
   $$T_f = \frac{124°C}{2} = 62°C$$

8. $$Q_{lost} = Q_{gained}$$
   $$m_1 C_1 \Delta T = m_2 C_2 \Delta T$$
   $$(2.00 \times 10^2 \text{ g})(0.376 \text{ J/g} \cdot \text{C°})(100.0°C - T_f) = (260 \text{ g})(4.18 \text{ J/g} \cdot \text{C°})(T_f - 20.0°C)$$
   $$7520 \text{ J} - (75.2 \text{ J/C°})T_f = (1086.8 \text{ J/C°})T_f - 21736 \text{ J}$$
   $$T_f = \frac{29256 \text{ J}}{1162 \text{ J/C°}} = 25°C$$

9. $$Q_{lost} = Q_{gained}$$
   $$m_1 C_1 \Delta T = m_2 C_2 \Delta T$$
   $$(1.00 \times 10^2 \text{ g})(C_T)(100.0°C - 21.6°C) = (2.00 \times 10^2 \text{ g})(4.18 \text{ J/g} \cdot \text{C°})(21.6°C - 20.0°C)$$
   $$C_T = \frac{1340 \text{ J}}{7840 \text{ g} \cdot \text{C°}} = 0.17 \text{ J/g} \cdot \text{C°} = 170 \text{ J/kg} \cdot \text{K}$$

10. $Q_1 = mC\Delta T = (10.0 \text{ g})(2.06 \text{ J/g} \cdot \text{C°})(20.0°C)$
    $= 412$ J to warm the ice to 0°C
    $Q_2 = (10.0 \text{ g})(334 \text{ J/g}) = 3340$ J to melt the ice
    $Q_3 = mC\Delta T = (10.0 \text{ g})(4.18 \text{ J/g} \cdot \text{C°})(100.0°C)$
    $= 4180$ J to warm the water to 100°C
    $Q_4 = (10.0 \text{ g})(2260 \text{ J/g}) = 22600$ J to vaporize the water
    $Q_5 = mC\Delta T = (10.0 \text{ g})(2.02 \text{ J/g} \cdot \text{C°})(20.0°C)$
    $= 404$ J to warm the steam to 120°C
    $Q_{total} = Q_1 + Q_2 + Q_3 + Q_4 + Q_5 = 3.09 \times 10^4$ J

11. $H = \dfrac{9870 \text{ J}}{40.0 \text{ g}} = 247$ J/g

12.

$$Q_{lost} = Q_{gained}$$
$$m_1 L_1 + m_w C_w \Delta T_w = m_w C_w \Delta T_w$$
$$(50.0 \text{ g})(334 \text{ J/g} \cdot \text{C}°) + (50.0 \text{ g})(4.18 \text{ J/g} \cdot \text{C}°)(T_f - 0°\text{C}) = (4.00 \times 10^2 \text{ g})(4.18 \text{ J/g} \cdot \text{C}°)(50.0°\text{C} - T_f)$$
$$16700 \text{ J} + (209 \text{ J/C}°)T_f = 83600 \text{ J} - (1672 \text{ J/C}°)T_f$$
$$T_f = \frac{66900 \text{ J}}{1881 \text{ J/C}°} = 35.6°\text{C}$$

13. $Q = mC\Delta T$

$$C = \frac{Q}{m\Delta T} = \frac{5016 \text{ J}}{(5.00 \times 10^2 \text{ g})(10.0°\text{C})} = 1.00 \text{ J/g} \cdot \text{C}°$$

Problems B

Page 214.

1.
$$Q_{lost} = Q_{gained}$$
$$Q_{heater} = m_c C_c \Delta T_c + m_w C_w \Delta T_w$$
$$= (3.00 \times 10^2 \text{ g})(0.664 \text{ J/g} \cdot \text{C}°)(85°\text{C}) + (250 \text{ g})(4.18 \text{ J/g} \cdot \text{C}°)(85°\text{C})$$
$$= 16932 \text{ J} + 88825 \text{ J} = 1.06 \times 10^5 \text{ J}$$

$$P = \frac{E}{t} = \frac{Q_{heater}}{t}$$

$$t = \frac{Q_{heater}}{P} = \frac{1.06 \times 10^5 \text{ J}}{3.00 \times 10^2 \text{ w}} = 350 \text{ s}$$

2. a. $Q = \dfrac{1.0 \times 10^{11} \text{ kJ/day}}{(24 \text{ h/day})(3600 \text{ s/h})} = 1.2 \times 10^6 \text{ kJ/s}$

$$Q = mC\Delta T$$

$$\Delta T = \frac{Q}{mC} = \frac{1.2 \times 10^6 \text{ kJ/s}}{(9.0 \times 10^4 \text{ kg/s})(4.18 \text{ kJ/kg} \cdot \text{C}°)} = 3.2°\text{C}$$

b. $4 \times 3.2°\text{C} = 13°\text{C}$, this temperature increase may cause serious damage to the ecology of the river.

Page 215.

3. $P = \dfrac{E}{t}$

$$E = Pt = (30.0 \text{ W})(3600 \text{ s})$$
$$= 108000 \text{ J}$$

$$Q = mH, \ m = \frac{Q}{H} = \frac{108000 \text{ J}}{2260 \text{ J/g}}$$
$$= 47.8 \text{ g}$$

4.
$$Q_{coal} = Q_{air}$$
$$(0.5)(m_c)\frac{Q}{m} = m_A C_A \Delta T_A$$
$$m_c = \frac{m_A C_A \Delta T_A}{(0.5)\dfrac{Q}{m}}$$
$$= \frac{(1.70 \times 10^4 \text{ kg})(1.1 \text{ kJ/kg} \cdot \text{C}°)(34°\text{C})}{(0.5)(3.35 \times 10^4 \text{ kJ/kg})}$$
$$= 38 \text{ kg}$$

Gas Laws   Chapter 13

Teaching Techniques

The gas laws are a natural result of the kinetic molecular theory and were an important verification of that theory. As the course moves through the gas laws, make the students aware of the agreement between theory and experiment.

Demonstrations

Section 13:3

Either a syringe or a J-shaped tube can be used to demonstrate Boyle's law. A small amount of mercury is poured into the bottom of the J-shaped tube to trap a volume of air. Mercury is then added to the tube until the height of the column in the open end exceeds the height of the mercury column in the closed end by a length equal to the barometer reading. Pressure on the gas is then twice the atmospheric pressure when the gas was trapped, and the volume of air should be one half as large. Be very careful not to spill any mercury. Its vapor is poisonous. Wash hands thoroughly after working with mercury.

Variations in gas volume with pressure changes can be demonstrated more qualitatively by placing a partially inflated balloon in a bell jar. Slowly evacuate the jar with a pump. The increase in balloon volume is dramatic.

Section 13:4

If absolute zero is not determined in the lab, it should be done as a demonstration. Use a capillary tube, sealed at one end, about 50 cm long. A small amount of mercury (0.5 cm) is put in the open end to act as a plug, forming an air column 20 cm to 30 cm in length. The mercury can be put into the tube before or after sealing. To add mercury before sealing, dip one end in mercury and place a finger over the other end of the tube. Then slide the mercury down to the desired level. Hold a finger over one end of the tube while sealing the other. To add mercury to a sealed tube, heat the tube gently (not to the softening point), and quickly place the open end into mercury. As the air in the tube cools, mercury will be trapped in the tube. Be very careful not to spill any mercury. Its vapor is poisonous. Wash hands thoroughly after working with mercury.

An alternate method of determining the relationship between volume and temperature at constant pressure is to use a small sphere equipped with a pressure gauge, which can be obtained commercially.

The glass tube is held vertically, plug-side up. The length of the air column is proportional to the volume because the bore is uniform. Record the length and room temperature. Place the tube in ice water, recording the air column length and temperature. Repeat the procedure with boiling water. Mark the column length while the tube is in the ice or boiling water as the length will change rapidly once the tube is removed. Students then plot temperatures horizontally and lengths vertically. Label the horizontal axis for a temperature range between $-300°C$ and $+1000°C$. The vertical axis should be labeled from 0 cm to 50 cm. Each student then plots the three points and extrapolates the straight line of the graph to the horizontal axis. This predicts the temperature at which the gas volume would be zero. Discuss uncertainties associated with the extrapolation. Encourage students to discuss possible reasons for differences between their value and Charles' value for absolute zero.

Films

Random Events (university rental, PSSC film)

Laboratory Investigations

The Diameter of a Molecule
Boyle's Law

Performance Objectives

Goal: Students will become familiar with the gas laws, their basis on kinetic theory and applications.

Objectives: Upon completion of the reading, questions, and problems, students will, on oral or written tests:

13:1	K/P	list the assumptions of the kinetic theory and the definition of an ideal gas.
13:2	K/P	understand the microscopic cause of gas pressure; demon-

strate an understanding of the measurement of pressure and the definition of the pascal and other pressure units.

13:3	K/P/S	state Boyle's law; understand the microscopic basis of it; demonstrate an ability to use the law in solving problems.
13:4	K/P/S	state Charles' law; understand the relationship of this law to absolute zero; be able to solve problems using Charles' law.
13:5	K/S/P	state the combined gas law and solve problems using it.
13:6	K/P	understand the formulation of the ideal gas law.
13:7	K/P/S	understand the limitations of the ideal gas law and the distinction between real and ideal gases.
	S/A	Students will use laboratory materials in the prescribed manner when conducting lab investigations.

Upon completion of the reading and practice problems, students will exhibit an interest in physics by:

A/S	expanding on an answer to one or more of the questions or problems at the end of the chapter.
A/S	using physics handbooks, investigate the deviations of gases from the ideal gas law.
A	reading unassigned literature related to the ideas presented in the chapter.

Solutions to Problems

Page 221.

1. $P_1V_1 = P_2V_2$

$V_2 = \dfrac{P_1V_1}{P_2} = \dfrac{(236 \text{ kPa})(60.3 \text{ m}^3)}{(354 \text{ kPa})} = 40.2 \text{ m}^3$

2. $P_1V_1 = P_2V_2$

$P_2 = \dfrac{P_1V_2}{V_2} = \dfrac{(200 \text{ kPa})(5.00 \text{ m}^3)}{(12.5 \text{ m}^3)} = 80.0 \text{ kPa}$

3. $P_1V_1 = P_2V_2$

$V_2 = \dfrac{P_1V_1}{P_2} = \dfrac{(1.0 \text{ atm})(16 \text{ m}^3)}{(0.75 \text{ atm})} = 21 \text{ m}^3$

4. $P_1V_1 = P_2V_2$

$V_2 = \dfrac{P_1V_1}{P_2} = \dfrac{(1.0 \text{ atm})(2.0 \text{ L})}{(3.0 \text{ atm})} = 0.67 \text{ L}$

5. $P_1V_1 = P_2V_2$

$$P_2 = \frac{P_1V_1}{V_2} = \frac{(101 \text{ kPa})(2.0 \text{ m}^3)}{(6.0 \text{ m}^3)} = 34 \text{ kPa}$$

6. $P = \dfrac{52 \text{ m}}{10.4 \text{ m/atm}} = 5.0 \text{ atm}$

$P_1V_1 = P_2V_2$

$$V_2 = \frac{P_1V_1}{P_2} = \frac{(6.0 \text{ atm})(2.0 \text{ cm}^3)}{(1.0 \text{ atm})} = 12 \text{ cm}^3$$

Page 223.

7. $\dfrac{V_1}{V_2} = \dfrac{T_1}{T_2}$

$$V_2 = \frac{V_1T_2}{T_1} = \frac{(30.0 \text{ m}^3)(566 \text{ K})}{(293 \text{ K})} = 58.0 \text{ m}^3$$

8. $\dfrac{V_1}{V_2} = \dfrac{T_1}{T_2}$

$$V_2 = \frac{V_1T_2}{T_1} = \frac{(3.0 \times 10^1 \text{ L})(126.5 \text{ K})}{(293 \text{ K})} = 13 \text{ L}$$

9. $\dfrac{V_1}{V_2} = \dfrac{T_1}{T_2}$

$$T_2 = \frac{T_1V_2}{V_1} = \frac{(333 \text{ K})(0.042 \text{ m}^3)}{(0.021 \text{ m}^3)} = 670 \text{ K}$$

10. $\dfrac{V_1}{V_2} = \dfrac{T_1}{T_2}$

$$V_2 = \frac{V_1T_2}{T_1} = \frac{(4.0 \text{ m}^3)(413 \text{ K})}{(313 \text{ K})} = 5.3 \text{ m}^3$$

Page 224.

11. $\dfrac{P_1V_1}{T_1} = \dfrac{P_2V_2}{T_2}$

Since $V_1 = V_2$

$$P_2 = \frac{P_1T_2}{T_1} = \frac{(205 \text{ kPa})(182 \text{ K})}{(91 \text{ K})} = 410 \text{ kPa}$$

Page 225.

12. $\dfrac{P_1V_1}{T_1} = \dfrac{P_2V_2}{T_2}$

$$V_2 = \frac{P_1V_1T_2}{P_2T_1} = \frac{(150 \text{ kPa})(2.0 \times 10^1 \text{ L})(546 \text{ K})}{(350 \text{ kPa})(273 \text{ K})} = 170 \text{ L}$$

13. $\dfrac{P_1V_1}{T_1} = \dfrac{P_2V_2}{T_2}$

$$V_2 = \frac{P_1V_1T_2}{T_1P_2} = \frac{(15 \text{ atm})(50 \text{ L})(400 \text{ K})}{(200 \text{ K})(7.5 \text{ atm})} = 200 \text{ L}$$

Chapter End Questions

Page 227.

1. See Section 13:1

2. One atmosphere (1 atm) of pressure $= 1.013 \times 10^5 \text{ N/m}^2$ $= 1013 \text{ mb} = 760 \text{ Torr} = 101.3 \text{ kPa}$.

3. The liquid is pushed up the straw because the air pressure outside the straw is greater than inside. To reach equilibrium, the greater pressure forces the liquid up the straw.

4. The volume of a gas varies directly with the temperature.

5. The volume of a gas varies inversely with the pressure.

6. 2.28 m

7. At constant pressure, all gasses expand the same amount for a given temperature change. By graphing changes in volume versus temperature and extrapolating backwards, Charles arrived at a temperature for volume equal to zero. This value indicated the possible location of absolute zero.

8. An ideal gas is an imaginary gas made up of particles with mass but no volume and with no attraction for each other. The differences between real gas and ideal gas are discussed in Section 13:7.

Problems A

Page 228.

1. $P_1V_1 = P_2V_2$

$$V_2 = \frac{P_1V_1}{P_2} = \frac{1.2 \text{ atm }(50.0 \text{ cm}^3)}{0.30 \text{ atm}} = 2.0 \times 10^2 \text{ cm}^3$$

2. $\dfrac{P_1V_1}{T_1} = \dfrac{P_2V_2}{T_2}$ $T_2 = \dfrac{P_2V_2T_1}{P_1V_1}$

$$= \frac{(2.02 \times 10^5 \text{ N/m}^2)(30.0 \text{ m}^3)(-50°C + 273°C)}{(50.0 \text{ m}^3)(1.01 \times 10^5 \text{ N/m}^2)}$$

$$= -5.40° \text{ C}$$

3. $\dfrac{V_1}{V_2} = \dfrac{T_1}{T_2}$

$$T_2 = \frac{V_2T_1}{V_1} = \frac{4.00 \text{ m}^3 \times 303 \text{ K}}{2.00 \text{ m}^3} = 606 \text{ K}$$

4. $\dfrac{V_1}{V_2} = \dfrac{T_1}{T_2}$

$$V_2 = \frac{V_1T_2}{T_1} = \frac{1.00 \text{ m}^3 \times 91 \text{ K}}{273 \text{ K}} = 0.33 \text{ m}^3$$

5. $\dfrac{V_1}{V_2} = \dfrac{T_1}{T_2}$

$$V_2 = \frac{V_1T_2}{T_1} = \frac{1.00 \text{ m}^3 \times 637 \text{ K}}{273 \text{ K}} = 2.33 \text{ m}^3$$

6. $\dfrac{P_1V_1}{T_1} = \dfrac{P_2V_2}{T_2}$

$$T_2 = \frac{(2 \times 10^3 \text{ kPa})(10.0 \text{ m}^3)(40 \text{ K})}{(4.0 \times 10^2 \text{ kPa})(10.0 \text{ m}^3)}$$

$$= 200 \text{ K}$$

7. $\dfrac{P_1V_1}{T_1} = \dfrac{P_2V_2}{T_2}$

$V_2 = \dfrac{P_1T_2V_1}{P_2T_1} = \dfrac{(1.0 \text{ atm})(223 \text{ K})(2.0 \times 10^2 \text{ m}^3)}{(0.67 \text{ atm})(293 \text{ K})}$

$= 2.3 \times 10^2 \text{ m}^3$

8. The pressure at the bottom of the tank of mercury is 9.0 atm due to the weight of the mercury plus 1.0 atm due to normal atmospheric pressure. Thus, the original pressure on the bubble is 10.0 atm. At the surface the pressure is 1.0 atm. The volume of the air bubble will increase by 10.0.

$P_1V_1 = P_2V_2$

$V_2 = \dfrac{P_1V_1}{P_2} = \dfrac{10 \text{ atm} \times 0.05 \text{ cm}^3}{1.0 \text{ atm}}$

$= 0.5 \text{ cm}^3$

Problems B

Page 228.

1. $0.76 \text{ m} \times 13.6 = 10.3 \text{ m}$
2. $P_1V_1 = P_2V_2$

$V_2 = \dfrac{P_1V_1}{P_2} = \dfrac{2.0 \text{ atm} \times 6.0 \text{ L}}{1.0 \text{ atm}} = 12 \text{ L}$

3. $P \cdot V: (\text{N/m}^2)(\text{m}^3) = \text{N} \cdot \text{m}$
   $W = Fd: (\text{N})(\text{m}) = \text{N} \cdot \text{m}$

Page 229.

4. $PV = nkT$

$n = \dfrac{PV}{kT} = \dfrac{(120.0 \text{ kPa})(20.0 \text{ L})}{(1.38 \times 10^{-23} \text{ L} \cdot \text{kPa/mol} \cdot \text{K})(296 \text{ K})}$

$= 5.88 \times 10^{23} \text{ molecules}$

States of Matter   Chapter 14

Teaching Techniques

This chapter is a qualitative introduction to the properties of fluids and solids. Connections to the kinetic theory are stressed. Problems that deal with applications of fluids at rest (hydrostatics) and thermal expansion of solids provide interesting examples of the technological applications of physics. Qualitative properties are best understood if students can see demonstrations of these properties.

Demonstrations

Section 14:1

A Cartesian diver shows properties of fluids very nicely. Toys can be used or a diver can be constructed. Take a small test tube, partially filled with water, and cover the open end with part of a balloon, securely fastened with a rubber band. Wait for the tube to float in water, glass end up. Place the tube in a clear plastic squeeze bottle that is completely filled with water. Cap the squeeze bottle securely, squeeze it, and the test tube should sink. You may have to experiment with the amount of water in the tube needed to produce the dramatic effect. Explain how this demonstrates that fluids transmit pressure equally, and that liquids are much less compressible than gases.

Section 14:2

Bernoulli's principle can also be demonstrated by supporting a Ping-Pong® ball in a stream of air blown from a hair dryer. For an alternate method, use an empty sewing thread spool and insert a pin through an index card. Place the pin into one hole of the spool and blow into the other hole. While blowing, turn the spool over. The card will be supported by the reduced pressure between the spool and card.

Section 14:4

The action of soap in reducing cohesive forces and the resulting decrease in surface tension is easily shown.

Section 14:7

The difference in elasticity between metals and nonmetallic solids should be shown. Also show the elastic limit, the point at which the bent metal no longer returns to its original shape.

Section 14:9

You can demonstrate the creation of a plasma if you have a vacuum pump, a glass tube with electrodes that can be evacuated, and a high voltage spark coil. Connect the spark coil to the electrodes. Turn on the voltage and slowly evacuate the tube. The display of light as the pressure drops is impressive. At high pressures ionized atoms are quickly neutralized. At intermediate pressures the plasma stretches across the tube. At low pressures the plasma disappears because of lack of atoms to ionize.

Laboratory Investigations

Archimedes' Principle

Performance Objectives

Goal: To apply kinetic theory to achieve an understanding of the properties of liquids and solids.

Objectives: Upon completion of the reading, questions, and problems, students will, on oral or written tests:

14:1	K/P/S	understand the origin of Pascal's and Archimedes' principles and their respective applications to hydraulic machines and determination of buoyant force.
14:2	K/P	explain Bernoulli's principle and its applications in producing lift; understand the difference between streamlined and turbulent flow.
14:3	K/P	display a knowledge of the difference between liquids and gases and the origin of cohesive forces.
14:4	P/K	describe how cohesive and adhesive forces cause surface tension and capillary action, respectively.
14:5	P/K	understand the origin of evaporation and condensation from the viewpoint of the kinetic energy.
14:6	P/K	recognize the difference between solids and liquids on a microscopic level; understand the origin of the unique properties of water and ice.
14:7	K	learn the definition of elasticity of a solid.
14:8	K/S/P	display an understanding of the origin of thermal expansion; be able to solve problems in linear thermal expansion; state some examples of applications and difficulties caused by thermal expansion.
14:9	K	define a plasma and give examples of plasmas in nature.

S/A	Students will use laboratory materials in the prescribed manner when conducting lab investigations.

Upon completion of the reading and practice problems, students will exhibit an interest in physics by:

A/S	expanding on an answer to one or more of the questions or problems at the end of the chapter.
A/S	cataloging various solids according to their elasticity, malleability, and ductibility; finding patterns in these properties based on the nature of the materials.
A	reading unassigned literature related to the ideas presented in the chapter.

Solutions to Problems

Page 235.

1. Since $A \propto d^2$, doubling the diameter will increase the force by 2^2 or 4.
$F = 4(40 \text{ N}) = 160 \text{ N}$

2. $\dfrac{F_1}{A_1} = \dfrac{F_2}{A_2}$

$F_1 = \dfrac{F_2 A_1}{A_2} = \dfrac{(1600 \text{ N})(72 \text{ cm}^2)}{(1440 \text{ cm}^2)} = 8.0 \times 10^1 \text{ N}$

3. $W_{net} = 0 = mg - F_{buoyant}$
$F_{buoyant} = mg$
$V\rho_{water}g = mg = W$

$V = \dfrac{W}{\rho_{water}g}$

$= \dfrac{600 \text{ N}}{(1.00 \times 10^3 \text{ kg/m}^3)(9.80 \text{ m/s}^2)}$

$V = 6 \times 10^{-2} \text{ m}^3$

4. $W = mg - F_{buoyant}$
$W_{net} = W - V\rho_{water}g$
$= 1250 \text{ N} - (8.3 \times 10^{-2} \text{ m}^3)(1.00 \times 10^3 \text{ kg/m}^3)(9.80 \text{ m/s}^2)$
$= 1250 \text{ N} - 810 \text{ N} = 440 \text{ N}$

Page 245.

5. $\Delta L = \alpha L_0 \Delta T = (25 \times 10^{-6}/\text{C}°)(1.65 \text{ m})(440°\text{C})$
$= 1.8 \times 10^{-2} \text{ m}$
$L_0 t \ \Delta L = 1.65 \text{ m} + (1.8 \times 10^{-2} \text{ m}) = 1.65 \text{ m} + 0.018 \text{ m}$
$= 1.67 \text{ m}$

6. $\Delta L = \alpha L_0 \Delta T$
$= (16.6 \times 10^{-6}/\text{C}°)(0.80 \text{ cm})(828°\text{C})$
$= 1.1 \times 10^{-2} \text{ cm}$
$\Delta L + L_0 = 1.1 \times 10^{-2} \text{ cm} + 0.80 \text{ cm} = 0.81 \text{ cm}$
$\text{Area} = \pi r^2 = \pi(0.41 \text{ cm})^2 = 0.52 \text{ cm}^2$

7. $\Delta L = \alpha\, L_o \Delta T$
       $= (10.5 \times 10^{-6}/C°)(11.5\ \text{m})(-1199\ °C)$
       $= 0.14\ \text{m}$
$\Delta L + L_o = 0.14\ \text{m} + 11.5\ \text{m} = 11.6\ \text{m}$

Chapter End Questions

Page 248.

1. The blade is supported by surface tension.
2. The cohesive forces between naphtha molecules are very weak. Thus, naphtha molecules are easily vaporized because the attractive forces between them do not tend to prevent molecules from leaving the liquid.
3. The cohesive forces between naphtha molecules are not strong and do not contribute to helping one another to stay in place. Thus, it is more difficult for the naphtha molecules to form the solid crystalline structure. Lower temperatures are required.
4. A plasma consists entirely of ions or has a high percentage of ions (more than 99%).
5. Carbon tetrachloride; higher density liquid exerts a greater buoyant force according to $V\rho g$.
6. The coefficient of volume expansion for paraffin is very high, therefore much shrinkage occurs as it cools.

7. Deformation occurs due to stretching and heating.
8. The coefficient of volume expansion for Pyrex® is less than that of glass. Less expansion occurs during temperature changes.

Problems A

Page 248.

1. a. $\dfrac{F_1}{A_1} = \dfrac{F_2}{A_2}$

    $F_1 = \dfrac{F_2 A_1}{A_2} = \dfrac{(2.7 \times 10^3\ \text{N})(7.0 \times 10^{-2}\ \text{m}^2)}{(2.1 \times 10^{-1}\ \text{m}^2)}$

    $= 9.0 \times 10^2\ \text{N}$

    b. $V_1 = V_2$

    $h = \dfrac{A_2 h_2}{A_1} = \dfrac{(2.1 \times 10^{-1}\ \text{m}^2)(0.20\ \text{m})}{(7.0 \times 10^{-2}\ \text{m}^2)}$

    $= 0.60\ \text{cm}$

2. In both cases the scale reading will read the sum of weight of the aquarium and the object. The buoyant force on the rock and the fish is equal to the weight of water displaced, which will be read on the scale.
   a. $195\ \text{N} + 8\ \text{N} = 203\ \text{N}$
       $195\ \text{N} + 2\ \text{N} = 197\ \text{N}$

Page 249.

3. $W_{net} = W - V\rho g$
    $= 54\ \text{N} - (2.3 \times 10^{-3}\ \text{m}^3)(1.00 \times 10^3\ \text{kg/m}^3)(9.8\ \text{m/s}^2)$
    $= 54\ \text{N} - 23\ \text{N} = 31\ \text{N}$

4. The buoyant force will be twice as great as in Problem 3.
    $W_{net} = 54\ \text{N} - 2(23\ \text{N}) = 8\ \text{N}$

5. $W_{net} = W - V\rho g$
    $= 2.8 \times 10^{-1}\ \text{N} - (13\ \text{cm}^3)(10^{-6}\ \text{m}^3/\text{cm}^3)(1.00 \times 10^3\ \text{kg/m}^3)(9.8\ \text{m/s}^2)$
    $= 2.8 \times 10^{-1}\ \text{N} - 1.3 \times 10^{-1}\ \text{N}$
    $= 1.5 \times 10^{-1}\ \text{N}$

    $a = \dfrac{F}{m} = \dfrac{1.5 \times 10^{-1}\ \text{N}}{(2.8 \times 10^{-1}\ \text{N}/9.80\ \text{m/s}^2)} = 5.3\ \text{m/s}^2$

6. $W_{net} = W - F_{buoyant} = V\rho_{He}g - V\rho_{air}g$
    $= (1.00\ \text{m}^3)(0.177\ \text{kg/m}^3)(9.8\ \text{m/s}^2) - (1.00\ \text{m}^3)(1.20\ \text{kg/m}^3)(9.8\ \text{m/s}^2)$
    $= -10.0\ \text{N}$ (net buoyant force is 10.0 N upwards)
    $W_{max} = 10.0\ \text{N}$

7. $\Delta L = L_i \alpha \Delta T$
    $= (2.00\ \text{m})(1.66 \times 10^{-5}°\text{C}^{-1})(978°\text{C} - 23°\text{C})$
    $= 3.17 \times 10^{-2}\ \text{m}$

Problems B

1. $\Delta V = V_1(3\alpha)\Delta T$
    $\Delta V = (1.78\ \text{cm}^3)(3)(2.5 \times 10^{-5}°\text{C}^{-1})(580°\text{C} - 10°\text{C})$
    $= 7.6 \times 10^{-2}\ \text{cm}^3$

2. $\Delta V = V_i(3\alpha)\,\Delta T$
    $V_f - V_i = V_i(3\alpha)\,\Delta T$

    $V_i = \dfrac{V_f}{1 + (3\alpha)\Delta T}$

    $= \dfrac{2.56\ \text{cm}^3}{1 + 3(1.66 \times 10^{-5}°\text{C}^{-1})(972°\text{C})}$

    $= 2.44\ \text{cm}^3$

Wave and Energy Transfer   Chapter 15

Teaching Techniques

A knowledge of the nature of waves is basic to the study of both sound and optics. Emphasize that energy can be transmitted in only two ways—either by transfer of particles or by waves. Stress that all waves have the same general properties and follow the same laws. Thus although there are many kinds of waves, there is only one set of rules of wave behavior that need be learned.

This chapter treats waves that can be easily seen: waves in springs and water waves. The laws of reflection, refraction, diffraction, and interference are developed for these waves and the effects are easily observed. Sound and electromagnetic waves cannot themselves be seen. However, experiments show that these phenomena exhibit the same effects as visible waves. Thus, we infer that sound and light are waves. Inference is widely used in science, and one objective of this chapter is to give examples of this method.

The most important principles of wave behavior that should be made clear to the students are:

1. The velocity of a wave is a function of the medium but independent of amplitude, frequency, or wavelength. All waves of the same kind (transverse, longitudinal, or surface) travel through a given medium at the same speed.
2. Two waves can pass through one another undisturbed by the event. This is the principle of superposition that accounts for constructive and destructive interference.
3. When a wave enters a new medium its frequency remains the same. The wavelength changes, but the new wave is generated by the old wave, and thus must have the same frequency.
4. A wave reaching a boundary between media is always partially transmitted and partially reflected.
5. A wave reflected from a more rigid medium returns inverted; one reflected from a less rigid medium returns erect. It is easier to teach this fact this way than to teach that the phase change is π.

Demonstrations

Wave demonstrations are absolutely necessary to teach wave behavior. A long coil of wire (a Slinky® toy) which can be stretched across the room can be used to demonstrate both longitudinal and transverse waves. Shaking the coil from side to side produces a transverse wave. Holding the spring taut and releasing a group of bunched-up coils produces longitudinal waves. Show that wave velocity is independent of how hard or frequently you shake the coil. A long helical spring, 2-3 cm in diameter and 6 m long, will serve as well, and, together with the Slinky®, illustrates effects of change in media. The coil spring is easier to use to demonstrate the formation of standing waves.

A ripple tank is excellent in showing refraction, diffraction, and interference effects. A shallow dish on an overhead projector also works well.

A mechanical wave machine, available commercially, is fairly expensive, but very useful in demonstrating wave behavior.

Films

Simple Waves (university rental, PSSC film)
Tacoma Narrows Bridge Collapse (BFA film loop)

Laboratory Investigations

Wave Properties
Pulses in a Ripple Tank
Wavelength, Frequency, and Speed
Refraction of Waves
Diffraction and Interference of Waves

Performance Objectives

Goal: Students will learn the fundamentals of wave behavior to develop a foundation for the study of sound and optics.

Objectives: Upon completion of the reading, questions, and problems, students will, on oral or written tests:

15:1	K/P	be aware that all waves exhibit the same behavior; distinguish between mechanical and electromagnetic waves, longitudinal and transverse waves; distinguish between a pulse and a wave.
15:2	K/P/S	define wavelength and frequency; state the equation defining the relationship between speed, wavelength, and frequency; solve problems using the equation.
15:3	K	describe the relationship between the amplitude of a wave and the energy it transfers.
15:4	K	understand that the speed of a wave depends on the medium,

15:5   K/P/S   but is independent of the characteristics of the wave.
list the characteristics of the behavior of waves at the boundaries between media; solve problems involving that behavior.

15:6   K   recognize that the wavelength and not the frequency changes at the boundary between media.

15:7   K   state the principle of superposition; define constructive and destructive interference.

15:8   K/P   define node and antinode; describe the formation of standing waves.

15:9   K   state the law of reflection.
15:10   K   describe the phenomenon of refraction in terms of the behavior of a transmitted wave.

15:11   K   define diffraction; explain the formation of nodal lines.

S/A   Students will use laboratory materials in the prescribed manner when conducting lab investigations.

Upon completion of the reading and practice problems, students will exhibit an interest in physics by:

A/S   expanding on an answer to one or more of the questions or problems at the end of the chapter.

A/S   constructing a demonstration device using toys or toy parts that show wave behavior.

A   reading unassigned literature related to the ideas presented in the chapter.

Solutions to Problems

Page 255.

1. $v = f\lambda = (250 \text{ Hz})(1.30 \text{ m}) = 330 \text{ m/s}$
2. $v = f\lambda = (3.0 \times 10^7 \text{ Hz})(10.0 \text{ m}) = 3.0 \times 10^8 \text{ m/s}$

Page 256.

3. **a.** $v = f\lambda = (4.8 \text{ Hz})(6.0 \text{ cm}) = 29 \text{ cm/s}$

   b. $T = \dfrac{1}{f} = 1/4.8 \text{ Hz} = 0.21 \text{ s}$

4. **a.** $T = \dfrac{1}{f} = \dfrac{1}{2.45 \times 10^9 \text{ Hz}} = 4.08 \times 10^{-10} \text{ s}$

   b. $v = f\lambda$

   $\lambda = \dfrac{v}{f} = \dfrac{3.0 \times 10^8 \text{ m/s}}{2.45 \times 10^9 \text{ Hz}} = 1.2 \times 15^1 \text{ m} = 0.12 \text{ m}$

5. **a.** $d = vt$

   $v = \dfrac{d}{t} = \dfrac{1360 \text{ m}}{4.0 \text{ s}} = 340 \text{ m/s}$

   b. $v = f\lambda$

   $\lambda = \dfrac{v}{f} = \dfrac{340 \text{ m/s}}{5.00 \times 10^2 \text{ Hz}} = 0.68 \text{ m}$

   c. $T = \dfrac{1}{f} = \dfrac{1}{5.00 \times 10^2 \text{ Hz}} = 2.00 \times 10^{-3} \text{ s}$

6. **a.** $v = f\lambda$

   $\lambda = \dfrac{v}{f} = \dfrac{340 \text{ m/s}}{750 \text{ Hz}} = 0.45 \text{ m}$

   b. $t = \dfrac{1}{f} = \dfrac{1}{7.50 \text{ Hz}} = 1.3 \times 10^{-3} \text{ s}$

7. **a.** $\lambda = (580 \text{ nm})(1 \times 10^{-9} \text{ m/nm}) = 5.8 \times 10^{-7} \text{ m}$

   b. $v = f\lambda$

   $f = \dfrac{v}{\lambda} = \dfrac{3.0 \times 10^8 \text{ m/s}}{5.8 \times 10^{-7} \text{ m}} = 5.2 \times 10^{14} \text{ Hz}$

Page 259.

8. It is attached to the wall since the pulse returned inverted.

9. Decreased.

Page 260.

10. **a.** At A the pulse will be partially transmitted and partially reflected. The transmitted pulse will be erect.

    b. The reflected pulse will be erect.

    c. At B the pulse will be almost totally reflected.

    d. inverted

11. **a.** At A the pulse will be partially transmitted and partially reflected. The reflected pulse will be inverted.

    b. At B the pulse will be almost totally reflected. The reflected pulse will be inverted.

12. Boundary A is the boundary of a more rigid medium since the reflected pulse is inverted. Boundary B is the boundary of a less rigid medium since the reflected pulse is erect. Boundary C is the boundary of a less rigid medium since the reflected pulse is erect with respect to the oncoming pulse. Boundary D is the boundary of a more rigid medium since the reflected pulse is inverted in respect to the oncoming pulse.

Chapter End Questions

Page 268.

1. Energy is transferred by particle transfer and by waves. There are many examples that can be given of each, a

baseball and a bullet for particle transfer; sound waves and light waves.

2. The principal distinction is that electromagnetic waves seemingly require no medium, whereas mechanical waves do.

3. A transverse wave causes the particles of the medium to vibrate in a direction that is perpendicular to the direction in which the wave is moving. A longitudinal wave causes the particles of the medium to vibrate in a direction parallel with the direction of the wave. Surface waves have characteristics of both.

4. Once the pulse has passed, the point is exactly as it was prior to the advent of the pulse.

5. A pulse is a single disturbance in a medium, whereas a wave consists of several disturbances.

6. Wavelength is the linear distance from any given point on one wave to the corresponding point on the next wave. Frequency is the number of waves that pass a given point per unit time. The period is the time required for a wave to pass any given point or the time required to generate the wave.

7. $v = f\lambda$

8. Amplitude represents the energy content of a wave.

9. Speed of the waves cannot be changed; frequency can be changed by changing the frequency at which the waves are generated.

10. Amount of reflection is determined by the difference between the properties of the new medium and the properties of the old medium.

11. inverted

12. erect

13. The frequency remains the same, the wavelength and speed change.

14. reflection, refraction, and diffraction

15. Angle of incidence equals angle of reflection.

16. Diffraction is the bending of a wave around the edges of an obstacle placed in its path.

17. (1) Each wave of different wavelength produces its own diffraction pattern.
(2) Each wavelength will produce a central line of reinforcement in the same place. (There are other correct answers.)

Problems A

Page 269.

1. $v = f\lambda = \dfrac{1}{2.05 \text{ s}} (10.0 \text{ m}) = 5.0 \text{ m/s}$

2. a. $v = f\lambda = (1.00 \times 10^6 \text{ Hz})(1.50 \times 10^{-3} \text{ m})$
$= 1.50 \times 10^3 \text{ m/s}$

   b. $T = \dfrac{1}{f} = \dfrac{1}{1.00 \times 10^6 \text{ Hz}} = 1.00 \times 10^{-6} \text{ s}$

   c. $T = 1.00 \times 10^{-6}$ s. The period and frequency remain unchanged.

3. a. $v = f\lambda = (2.0 \text{ Hz})(0.45 \text{ m}) = 0.90 \text{ m/s}$

   b. $v = f\lambda$

   $\lambda = \dfrac{v}{f} = \dfrac{0.90 \text{ m/s}}{6.0 \text{ Hz}} = 0.15 \text{ m}$

   c. $\lambda = \dfrac{v}{f} = \dfrac{0.90 \text{ m/s}}{0.5 \text{ Hz}} = 1.8 \text{ m}$

Problems B

Page 269.

1. a. $v = f\lambda$

   $\lambda = \dfrac{v}{f} = \dfrac{3.0 \times 10^8 \text{ m/s}}{5.5 \times 10^5 \text{ Hz}} = 550 \text{ m}$

   $\lambda = \dfrac{v}{f} = \dfrac{3.0 \times 10^8 \text{ m/s}}{1.6 \times 10^6 \text{ Hz}} = 190 \text{ m}$

   b. $\lambda = \dfrac{v}{f} = \dfrac{3.0 \times 10^8 \text{ m/s}}{8.8 \times 10^7 \text{ Hz}} = 3.4 \text{ m}$

   $\lambda = \dfrac{v}{f} = \dfrac{3.0 \times 10^8 \text{ m/s}}{1.08 \times 10^8 \text{ Hz}} = 2.8 \text{ m}$

2. $t = \dfrac{1.80 \text{ s}}{2}$

   $= 0.900 \text{ s}$, the time for the wave to travel one way

   $d = vt = (1498 \text{ m/s})(0.900 \text{ s}) = 1350 \text{ m}$

Sound   Chapter 16

Teaching Techniques

Music is a human experience of interest to most students. In this chapter wave behavior is applied to sound with an emphasis on music. Even though music has its own vocabulary, stress that the properties of sound waves are those of waves in general.

Musical instruments are a rich source of examples of wave behavior. Have students play them in class to illustrate pitch, intensity, beat notes, and tone quality.

Demonstrations

A microphone connected to an oscilloscope allows the sound wave to be seen. Have students play a tone from an instrument into the microphone. Pitch and loudness are both seen and heard. The difference in tonal quality of different instruments can be seen, as can beat notes. The tonal quality of the human voice as different vowel sounds are intoned is an interesting effect.

Toy instruments provide another source of demonstrations which are inexpensive as well. Two toy slide whistles can demonstrate beat notes as well as dissonant and consonant sounds. Plastic water and drain pipes can be used to show resonant behavior of both open and closed pipes.

Laboratory Investigations

Speed of Sound in Air

Performance Objectives

Goal: Students will extend their knowledge of wave behavior as applied to sound and music.

Objectives: Upon completion of the reading, questions, and problems, students will, on oral or written tests:

16:1	K/S/P	show knowledge of the nature of sound waves; list the wave behaviors of sound shared with other waves; solve problems relating the frequency, wavelength, and velocity of sound waves; define the Doppler effect.
16:2	K	list the properties of sound waves using the terms pitch and intensity or loudness; describe the meaning of the octave interval; use the decibel to define ratios of sound intensity.
16:3	K/P	describe the origin of sound in general and in various musical instruments in particular.
16:4	K/S/P	display an understanding of resonance, especially as applied to an air column; describe or sketch a standing wave; solve problems involving standing waves in resonating air columns.
16:5	K	list the parts of the ear and the function of each in detecting sound.
16:6	K/S/P	define timbre as sound quality; recognize the source of beat notes and solve problems involving beats; define overtones and their origins.
	S/A	Students will use laboratory materials in the prescribed manner when conducting lab investigations.

Upon completion of the reading and practice problems, students will exhibit an interest in physics by:

A/S	expanding on an answer to one or more of the questions or problems at the end of the chapter.
A/S	reading and reporting on an article describing the acoustics of a musical instrument of interest to the student.
A	reading unassigned literature related to the ideas presented in the chapter.

Solutions to Problems

Page 273.

1. $v = f\lambda$

$$\lambda = \frac{v}{f} = \frac{1435 \text{ m/s}}{261.6 \text{ Hz}} = 5.485 \text{ m}$$

2. $v = f\lambda$

$$f = \frac{v}{\lambda} = \frac{343 \text{ m/s}}{0.667 \text{ m}} = 514 \text{ Hz}$$

3. $v = f\lambda = (440 \text{ Hz})(11.66 \text{ m}) = 5100 \text{ m/s}$

Page 278.

4. $v = f\lambda \qquad \lambda = v/f$

$$l = \frac{\lambda}{2} = \frac{v}{2f} = \frac{347 \text{ m/s}}{(2)440 \text{ Hz}} = 0.39 \text{ m}$$

Resonances are spaced by one-half wavelength.

5. $\lambda = 2l = (2)(1.1 \text{ m}) = 2.2 \text{ m}$
   $v = f\lambda = (440 \text{ Hz})(2.2 \text{ m}) = 970 \text{ m/s}$

6. $\lambda = 2l = (2)(0.392 \text{ m}) = 0.784 \text{ m}$
   $v = f\lambda$

$$f = \frac{v}{\lambda} = \frac{347 \text{ m/s}}{0.784 \text{ m}} = 443 \text{ Hz}$$

7. $\lambda = 2l = (2)(2.65 \text{ m}) = 5.30 \text{ m}$
   $v = f\lambda$

$$f = \frac{v}{\lambda} = \frac{343 \text{ m/s}}{5.30 \text{ m}} = 64.7 \text{ Hz}$$

8. $\lambda = 2l = (2)(0.65 \text{ m}) = 1.3 \text{ m}$
   $v = f\lambda$

$$f = \frac{v}{\lambda} = \frac{343 \text{ m/s}}{1.3 \text{ m}} = 260 \text{ Hz}$$

Chapter End Questions

Pages 283-284.

1. No; sound is not transmitted across a vacuum.

2. Sound travels faster in solids such as steel rails.
3. Sound waves cause the ribbons to vibrate in the direction of the source; sound is a longitudinal wave.
4. **a.** increases **b.** decreases **c.** remains the same **d.** remains the same
5. increases-toward; decreases-away
6. 100 times more intense
7. increased by a factor of 2
8. $L = \dfrac{v}{4f}$. If v increases and L is unchanged, f must increase.
9. sound quality or timbre.

Problems A

Page 284.

1. 4.00 s is the time for the sound to travel across and back so the time is 2.00 s for the sound to reach the canyon walls.
   $$d = vt = (343 \text{ m/s})(2.00 \text{ s}) = 686 \text{ m}$$
2. The total distance the sound must travel is 6.00 m
   $$d = vt$$
   $$t = d/v = \frac{6.00 \text{ m}}{343 \text{ m/s}} = 0.0175 \text{ s}$$
3. $v = f\lambda = (4.40 \times 10^2 \text{ Hz})(3.30 \text{ m}) = 1450 \text{ m/s}$
4. **a.** 10 times as intense
   b. 20 dB is 100 times as intense
5. **a.** $v = f\lambda$
   $$\lambda = \frac{v}{f} = \frac{343 \text{ m/s}}{16.4 \text{ Hz}} = 20.9 \text{ m}$$
   $$\lambda = 2l$$
   $$l = \frac{\lambda}{2} = \frac{20.9 \text{ m}}{2} = 10.5 \text{ m}$$

b. The frequency for an open pipe is twice as high as a closed one, so
$$f = \frac{1}{2}(16.4 \text{ Hz}) = 8.20 \text{ Hz}$$

Page 285.

6. 445 Hz − 3 Hz = 442 Hz 445 Hz + 3 Hz = 448 Hz
7. $2f = 740$ Hz $3f = 1110$ Hz $4f = 1480$ Hz
8. $3f = 1110$ Hz $5f = 1850$ Hz $7f = 2590$ Hz

Problems B

Page 285.

1. **a.** $\lambda = 4l = (4)(2.40 \text{ m}) = 9.60 \text{ m}$
   $v = f\lambda$
   $$f = \frac{v}{\lambda} = \frac{343 \text{ m/s}}{9.60 \text{ m}} = 35.7 \text{ Hz}$$
   b. $f = 35.7 \text{ Hz} - 1.40 \text{ Hz} = 34.3 \text{ Hz}$
   $v = f\lambda$
   $$\lambda = \frac{v}{f} = \frac{343 \text{ m/s}}{34.3 \text{ Hz}} = 10.0 \text{ m}$$
   $$\lambda = 4l$$
   $$l = \frac{\lambda}{4} = \frac{10.0 \text{ m}}{4} = 2.50 \text{ m}$$
   The difference in lengths is 2.50 m − 2.40 m = 0.10 m.

2. **a.** $f' = \dfrac{f(v - v_d)}{(v - v_s)} = \dfrac{(305 \text{ Hz})(343 \text{ m/s} - 0)}{(343 \text{ m/s} - 31 \text{ m/s})}$
   $$= 340 \text{ Hz}$$
   b. $f' = \dfrac{f(v - v_d)}{(v - v_s)} = \dfrac{(305 \text{ Hz})(343 \text{ m/s} - (-21 \text{ m/s}))}{(343 \text{ m/s} - 31 \text{ m/s})}$
   $$= 360 \text{ Hz}$$

The Nature of Light   Chapter 17

Teaching Techniques

This chapter is a general introduction to optics. After introducing terminology, discuss some of the methods that are used to measure the speed of light. You might point out that because the speed of light is now a defined quantity, these are really measurements of the meter.

The inverse-square law governing illumination is discussed and illumination problems are presented.

Demonstrations

Section 17:1

A photographic exposure meter can be used to measure the inverse-square law.

Section 17:6

Show the spectrum of sunlight or of an incandescent source using a prism. Collimate the white light through a narrow slit or hole.

Section 17:8

Polarization effects can be shown by laying one Polaroid® sheet on an overhead projector and holding the second sheet a centimeter above it. Rotate the second sheet to find the polarization produced by the first sheet. Rotate the Polaroid® so the minimum amount of light is transmitted. Place crinkled cellophane between the Polaroid® sheets to observe the rotation of polarization by different thicknesses of cellophane. Or use a sandwich bag which you stretch while it is between the two Polaroid® sheets.

Films

The Speed of Light (Encyclopeadia Britannica film)
Light: Illumination and Its Measurement (university rentals, Indiana University film)

Laboratory Investigations

Luminous Intensity and Efficiency of Light Bulbs

Performance Objectives

Goal: Students will learn the fundamentals of the wave nature of light.

Objectives: Upon completion of the reading, questions, and problems, students will, on oral or written tests:

17:1	K/P	define a ray and give examples of evidence that light travels in straight lines.
17:2	K/S/P	describe Roemer's and Michelson's methods of measuring the speed of light; state the speed of light (to 1 or 3 significant digits); solve problems involving Michelson's method.
17:3	K	define transparent, translucent, and opaque.
17:4	K/S/P	define the concepts and units of luminous intensity, luminous flux, and illuminance; solve illumination problems.
17:5	K	recognize that light is an electromagnetic wave and know its wavelength and frequency range.
17:6	K/P	display an understanding of the mixture of light colors and color absorption.
17:7	K	explain the polarization of light.
17:8	K	explain the cause of interference in thin films.
	S/A	Students will use laboratory materials in the prescribed manner when conducting lab investigations.

Upon completion of the reading and practice problems, students will exhibit an interest in physics by:

	A/S	expanding on an answer to one or more of the questions or problems at the end of the chapter.
	A/S	reading and reporting on Edwin Land's retinex theory of color.
	A	reading unassigned literature related to the ideas presented in the chapter.

Solutions to Problems

Page 289.

1. $T = \dfrac{1}{625}s = 1.60 \times 10^{-3}$ s

Page 290.

2. **a.** $T = \dfrac{1}{8}(1.60 \times 10^{-3}\text{ s}) = 2.00 \times 10^{-4}$ s

    b. $d = 2 \times 30\text{ km} = 60$ km

3. **a.** $v = \dfrac{d}{t} = \dfrac{60\text{ km}}{2.00 \times 10^{-4}\text{ s}} = 3 \times 10^5$ km/s

    b. $v = 3 \times 10^5$ km/s $= 3 \times 10^8$ m/s

4. Yes, twice the proper rate of revolution would move two sides of the octagonal mirror through the same distance previously traveled by one side. Thus, a face of the mirror would always be in the proper position to reflect the light.

5. By starting the mirror rotating from rest and increasing its rate of revolution to the first rate that gives the brightest reflected spot.

Page 292.

6. $E = \dfrac{I}{d^2} = \dfrac{32\text{ cd}}{(4.0\text{ m})^2\left(\dfrac{1\text{ cd}}{\text{lm}}\right)} = 2.0\ \dfrac{\text{lm}}{\text{m}^2} = 2.0$ lx

7. Since 90 cm $= 3 \times 30$ cm the illumination at 90 cm will be $\dfrac{1}{3^2} = \dfrac{1}{9}$ of the illumination at 30 cm.

8. $E = \dfrac{I}{d^2}$

    $I = Ed^2$
    $\quad = (10\text{ lx})(3.0\text{ m})^2\ (1\text{ cd/ lm}) = 90$ cd

9. $E = \dfrac{I}{d^2}$

    $I = Ed^2$
    $\quad = (18\text{ lx})(4.0\text{ m})^2\ (1\text{ cd/ lm}) = 450$ cd

10. $E = \dfrac{I}{d^2}$

    $I = Ed^2$
    $\quad = (160\text{ lx})(2.0\text{ m})^2\ (1\text{ cd/ lm }) = 640$ cd

Page 293.

11. $E = \dfrac{I}{d^2}$ $E_1 = E_2$ $\dfrac{I_1}{d_1^2} = \dfrac{I_2}{d_2^2}$

    $d_2^2 = \dfrac{I_2\,(d_1)^2}{I_1} = \dfrac{(190\text{ cd})\,(2.5\text{ m})^2}{125\text{ cd}}$

    $d_2 = 3.1$ m

Chapter End Questions

Page 298.

1. A transparent material is a material through which light can pass without suffering distortion. A translucent material allows light to pass but distorts the light to the point where images are not discernable. An opaque material does not allow light to pass through.

2. A luminous body emits light. An illuminated body is one on which light is falling and being reflected.

3. candelas

4. lux

5. The illumination of a surface is directly proportional to the intensity of the source and inversely proportional to the square of the distance of the surface from the source.

6. White light is a combination of all the colors, or at least the primary colors.

7. Grass appears green because it reflects primarily green light.

8. Black is not a color but is the absence of all color. An object appears to be black because little if any light is being reflected from it.

Problems A

Page 299.

1. $t = \dfrac{1}{f} = \dfrac{1}{5.00 \times 10^2 \text{ Hz}}$

   $= 2.00 \times 10^{-3}$ s for one revolution

   $t = \dfrac{1}{20}(2.00 \times 10^{-3} \text{ s}) = 1.00 \times 10^{-4}$ s

   $v = \dfrac{d}{t} = \dfrac{(3.00 \times 10^4 \text{ m})}{(1.00 \times 10^{-4} \text{ s})} = 3.00 \times 10^8$ m/s

2. $E = \dfrac{I}{d^2} = \dfrac{(64 \text{ cd})}{(3.0 \text{ m})^2 (1 \text{ cd/lm})} = 7.1$ lx

3. The illumination at screen B will be $\dfrac{1}{4}$ of that at screen A since it is twice as far from the source.

4. $E = \dfrac{I}{d^2}$

   $I = Ed^2$
   $= (2.0 \times 10^1 \text{ lx})(4.0 \text{ m})^2 (1 \text{ cd/lm})$
   $= 320$ cd

5. $E = \dfrac{I}{d^2}$

   $E_1 = E_2$

   $\dfrac{I_1}{d_1{}^2} = \dfrac{I_2}{d_2{}^2}$

   $I_2 = \dfrac{(I_1)(d_2{}^2)}{d_1{}^2}$

$I_2 = \dfrac{(101 \text{ cd})(3.0 \text{ m})^2}{(5.0 \text{ m})^2}$

$= 36$ cd

Problems B

Page 299.

1. **a.** $E = \dfrac{I}{d^2}$

   $= \dfrac{4.0 \times 10^2 \text{ lm}}{(5.0 \text{ m})^2} = 16$ lx

   $= \dfrac{4.0 \times 10^2 \text{ lm}}{(10.0 \text{ m})^2} = 4.0$ lx

   $= \dfrac{4.0 \times 10^2 \text{ lm}}{(15.0 \text{ m})^2} = 1.8$ lx

   $= \dfrac{4.0 \times 10^2 \text{ lm}}{(20.0 \text{ m})^2} = 1.0$ lx

   $= \dfrac{4.0 \times 10^2 \text{ lm}}{(25.0 \text{ m})^2} = 0.64$ lx

   b.

d(m)	E(lx)
5.0	16
10.0	4.0
15.0	1.8
20.0	1.0
25.0	0.64

   c.

   d. Hyperbola. Illumination varies inversely with square of the distance from the light source.

2. **a.** $t_{av} = \dfrac{1.188 \text{ s} + 1.356 \text{ s}}{2} = 1.272$ s

   $d = vt = (3.0 \times 10^8 \text{ m/s})(1.272 \text{ s})$
   $= 3.8 \times 10^8$ m

   b. $d_{sun} = vt = (3.0 \times 10^8 \text{ m/s})(8.312 \text{ min})(60 \text{ s/min})$
   $= 1.5 \times 10^{11}$ m

   $\dfrac{d_{e\text{-}s}}{d_{e\text{-}m}} = \dfrac{1.5 \times 10^{11} \text{ m}}{3.8 \times 10^8 \text{ m}} = 390$

Reflection and Refraction   Chapter 18

Teaching Techniques

A ray-optics treatment of the laws of reflection and refraction is presented. Elementary geometry and trigonometry are used to predict the behavior of light striking various boundaries. The trigonometry table in Appendix C should allow students who are weak in the subject to succeed. Dispersion of light in a prism and water droplet follow from the basic study of refraction.

Unusual applications of refraction, such as a mirage and fiber optics, are important not for their own sake but to illustrate how the understanding of basic physical laws can be applied to peculiar effects.

Demonstrations

Section 18:3

Refraction of light can be demonstrated using a tank with plane surfaces (a small aquarium) filled with water into which chalk dust or lycopodium powder has been sprinkled. Darken the room and aim a beam of light from a projector or laser at the water surface. A small mirror placed on the tank bottom shows both refraction and reflection.

Section 18:4

Snell's law is best demonstrated with an optical disk and strong source, ray box, or laser with beam splitter. Use a standard mirror and lens, but just show bending in the lens. Wait for the next chapter to analyze.

Section 18:6

To show total internal reflection use the tank as described above. Add enough dust to make the beams well defined. Support the container well above a table and introduce the beam of light through the side at ever increasing angles. Eventually the beam will be totally reflected from the inner surface of the water. A small piece of paper held above the water surface will show the lack of refracted beam. Total internal reflection in a 90°-45°-45° prism should be shown with a narrow light beam. Short lengths of plastic optical fiber and a laser show the basics of fiber optics very nicely.

Section 18:8

If sunlight enters your room during classes, mount a prism in a holder in a location where it will cast a spectrum on the wall. This spectral demonstration of dispersion will lead to the discussion of spectra later in the course.

Laboratory Investigations

Law of Reflection of Light
Snell's Law

Performance Objectives

Goal: Students will learn about the phenomena of reflection and refraction.

Objectives: Upon completion of the reading, questions, and problems, students will, on oral or written tests:

18:1	K	state the law of reflection.
18:2	K	distinguish between diffuse and regular reflection.
18:3	K/P	define refraction; predict whether the ray will bend toward or away from the normal when light moves from one medium into another.
18:4	K/P/S	state Snell's law; apply the law to the solution of problems.
18:5	K/P/S	relate the index of refraction to the speed of light in the medium; solve problems relating these two quantities.
18:6	K/P	explain total internal reflection and the critical angle.
18:7	K/P	explain effects caused by the refraction of light in a medium with varying refractive index.
18:8	K	explain the dispersion of light in terms of index of refraction.
	S/A	Students will use laboratory materials in the prescribed manner when conducting lab investigations.

Upon completion of the reading and practice problems, students will exhibit an interest in physics by:

A/S	expanding on an answer to one or more of the questions or problems at the end of the chapter.
A/S	reading and reporting on the use of optical fibers to transmit telephone and data communications.
A	reading unassigned literature related to the ideas presented in the chapter.

Solutions to Problems

Page 306.

1. $n = \dfrac{\sin i}{\sin r}$

    $\sin r = \dfrac{\sin i}{n} = \dfrac{\sin 45.0°}{1.52} = 0.465$

    $r = 27.7°$

2. $n = \dfrac{\sin i}{\sin r}$

    $\sin r = \dfrac{\sin i}{n} = \dfrac{\sin 30.0°}{1.33} = 0.376$

    $r = 22.1°$

3. $n = \dfrac{\sin i}{\sin r}$

    $\sin r = \dfrac{\sin i}{n} = \dfrac{\sin 45.0°}{1.54} = 0.484$

    $r = 27.3°$

4. a. $n = \dfrac{\sin i}{\sin r}$

    $\sin r = \dfrac{\sin i}{n} = \dfrac{\sin 45.0°}{2.42} = 0.292$

    $r = 17.0°$

    b. diamond

5. a. $n = \dfrac{\sin i}{\sin r} = \dfrac{\sin 30.0°}{\sin 22.0°} = \dfrac{0.500}{0.375} = 1.33$

    b. water

6. a. should measure 19.2°
    b. 30.0°
    c. away from

Page 308.

7. $n = \dfrac{c}{v}$ $v = \dfrac{c}{n}$

    a. $f = \dfrac{3.00 \times 10^8 \text{ m/s}}{1.36} = 2.20 \times 10^8 \text{ m/s}$

    b. $v = \dfrac{3.00 \times 10^8 \text{ m/s}}{1.54} = 1.95 \times 10^8 \text{ m/s}$

    c. $v = \dfrac{3.00 \times 10^8 \text{ m/s}}{1.61} = 1.86 \times 10^8 \text{ m/s}$

8. $n = \dfrac{c}{v} = \dfrac{3.00 \times 10^8 \text{ m/s}}{2.00 \times 10^8 \text{ m/s}} = 1.50$

9. $n = \dfrac{c}{v} = \dfrac{3.00 \times 10^8 \text{ m/s}}{1.9689 \times 10^8 \text{ m/s}} = 1.52$

Chapter End Questions

Page 314.

1. When light is reflected from a smooth surface, the rays are reflected in the same order in which they are incident upon the surface. The result is an image of the origin of the rays. When light is reflected from a rough surface, it is reflected in many different directions. The rays are diffused or scattered. No image of the source results.

2. There are two possible answers to this question. The angle is 90°. However, the student might mention angles greater than the critical angle. Total internal reflection would mean no refracted rays.

3. Angle of incidence is larger than the angle of refraction.

4. Angle of incidence is smaller than angle of refraction.

5. Whenever a ray of light passes from one medium into another at some angle, the ray is refracted in such a way that the ratio of the sine of the angle of incidence to the sine of the angle of refraction is a constant for all angles of incidence.

6. $n = \dfrac{\sin i}{\sin r}$ $n = \dfrac{c}{v}$ $n_1 \sin \theta_1 = n_2 \sin \theta_2$

7. The term "critical angle" refers to the incident angle that causes the refracted ray to lie right along the boundary of the substance when a ray is passing from a dense to less dense medium. It may also be termed the incident angle, which, if exceeded, will cause total internal reflection.

8. Mirages are caused by a phenomenon of light refraction that is detailed in Section 18:7.

9. Red light; it is refracted the least by glass.

10. The spectrum of sunlight is called a continuous spectrum.

Problems A

Page 314.

1. a. 53°
    b. 53° + 53° = 106°
2. (90.0° − 36.0°) + (90.0° − 36.0°) = 108°

Page 315.

3. $n = \dfrac{\sin i}{\sin r}$

    $\sin r = \dfrac{\sin i}{n} = \dfrac{\sin 60.0°}{1.5} = 0.58$

    $r = 35°$

4. $n = \dfrac{\sin i}{\sin r}$

    $\sin r = \dfrac{\sin i}{n} = \dfrac{\sin 36.0°}{1.33} = 0.442$

    $r = 26.2°$

5. $n = \dfrac{\sin i}{\sin r}$

    $\sin r = \dfrac{\sin i}{n} = \dfrac{\sin 60.0°}{2.42} = 0.358$

    $r = 21.0°$

6.
$$n = \frac{\sin i}{\sin r} \text{ and } n = \frac{c}{v}$$

substituting, $\sin r = \dfrac{(\sin i)(v)}{c} = \dfrac{(\sin 22°)(1.90 \times 10^8 \text{ m/s})}{(3.00 \times 10^8 \text{ m/s})} = 0.24$

$$r = 14°$$

Problems B

Page 315.

1. a.
$$n = \frac{\sin i}{\sin r}$$

$$\sin r = \frac{\sin i}{n} = \frac{\sin 45°}{1.5} = 0.47$$

$$r = 28°$$

b.
$$A = 90° - 28° = 62°$$
$$B = 180° - (62° + 60°) = 58°$$
$$C = 90° - 58° = 32°$$

c.
$$n = \frac{\sin D}{\sin C}$$

$$\sin D = n \sin C = (1.5)(\sin 32°) = 0.795$$
$$D = 53°$$

2. a.
$$\tan i = \frac{1.5}{2.0} = 0.75$$

$$i = 37°$$
$$n_1 \sin i = n_2 \sin r$$

$$\sin r = \frac{n_1 \sin i}{n_2} = \frac{(1.33)(\sin 37°)}{(1.0)} = 0.80$$

$$r = 53°$$

b. It appears shallower than it really is.

Mirrors and Lenses   Chapter 19

Teaching Techniques

Ray optics techniques developed in the last chapter are used to analyze mirrors and lenses. Emphasize the use of ray diagrams to solve problems. Spend time on all the ray diagrams.

Point out that a concave mirror is a converging mirror while a convex mirror is a diverging mirror. For lenses a convex lens converges light while a concave lens is a diverging lens.

Demonstrations

For each of the topics in this chapter use either a candle or a tubular, unfrosted, 25-W lamp with a straight filament, to form a good, distinctive image. The relationships between object and image distances can be easily demonstrated, even without an optical bench. Just hold the light source in one hand and the lens or mirror in the other. First cast a large image on the wall and point out that the object is close to the focal point. Then hold the object far from the mirror and lens and show the small image. Show that plane and convex mirrors and diverging lenses cannot cast real images.

Section 19:1

Place a plane sheet of glass in front of a beaker filled with water. Light a candle and place it in front of the glass sheet so its image appears to be in the water. This demonstration emphasizes that the image in a plane mirror is as far behind the mirror as the object is in front of the mirror.

Chapter 19

Section 19:2

Purchase or make an image box. Obtain a 20 cm × 25 cm black metal box and two surface mounted bulb sockets from an electronic supply house. Mount one socket at the center of the top of the box and the other directly below it inside the box. You can bolt the two sockets together. Wire a lamp cord with a plug to the socket inside the box. Be sure to cover any bare metal with tape or silicone rubber. Screw a 40-W bulb into that socket. Leave one side off the box. Place a large spherical, concave mirror (40-cm diameter Welch No., 3525-A) about 56 cm from the box. Adjust the position of the mirror until a real image appears in the empty socket. Darken the room and as your students arrive for class ask them to unscrew the bulb.

Sections 19:3 and 19:13

Use an optical disk, ray box, or laser to produce rays of light and clearly demonstrate the functions of different types of mirrors and lenses. Show spherical aberration and, with a white light, chromatic aberration.

Laboratory Investigations

Images Produced by Curved Mirrors
Convex Lenses

Performance Objectives

Goal: Students will learn how mirrors and lenses produce images and how these elements are used in optical instruments.

Objectives: Upon completion of the reading, questions, and problems, students will, on oral or written tests:

19:1	K	describe the image produced by a plane mirror.
19:2	K/P	define focal point and explain the rules of ray tracing as applied to concave mirrors.
19:3	K	define spherical aberration and describe the use of parabolic mirrors.
19:4	K	distinguish between real and virtual images.
19:5	K/P/S	explain the formation of real images by concave mirrors; use ray diagrams to locate the image; calculate the location using the mirror equation.
19:6	K/S	explain and demonstrate using ray diagrams the formation of virtual, enlarged images by concave mirrors.
19:7	K/P/S	explain and demonstrate using ray diagrams the formation of virtual images by convex mirrors. Calculate the location of these images.
19:8	K	differentiate between concave and convex lenses.
19:9	K/P/S	describe the formation of an image by a convex lens; use a ray diagram to locate the image; calculate the location using the lens equation.
19:10	K/P/S	describe the formation of a virtual image by a convex lens; diagram and calculate the location of these images.
19:11	K/S	describe the formation of virtual images by concave lenses.
19:12	S	understand the derivation of the lens equation. Reproduction is not necessary.
19:13	K	define chromatic aberration and understand how it is eliminated.
19:14	K/P	explain the operation of the optical instruments described.
	S/A	Students will use laboratory materials in the prescribed manner when conducting lab investigations.

Upon completion of the reading and practice problems, students will exhibit an interest in physics by:

A/S	expanding on an answer to one or more of the questions or problems at the end of the chapter.
A/S	studying the optics of a camera carefully. Find the focal length of the lens and the image distance. Calculate the relative sizes of image and object.
A	reading unassigned literature related to the ideas presented in the chapter.

Solutions to Problems

Page 323.

1. a.

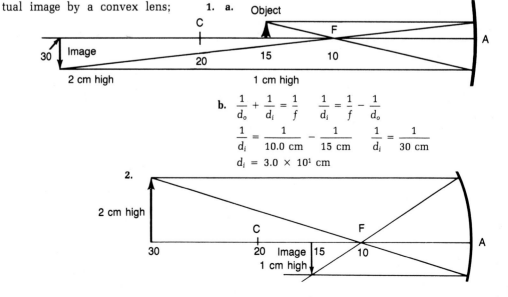

b. $\dfrac{1}{d_o} + \dfrac{1}{d_i} = \dfrac{1}{f} \qquad \dfrac{1}{d_i} = \dfrac{1}{f} - \dfrac{1}{d_o}$

$\dfrac{1}{d_i} = \dfrac{1}{10.0 \text{ cm}} - \dfrac{1}{15 \text{ cm}} \qquad \dfrac{1}{d_i} = \dfrac{1}{30 \text{ cm}}$

$d_i = 3.0 \times 10^1 \text{ cm}$

2.

3. a.

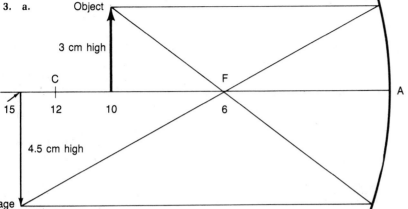

b. $\dfrac{1}{d_o} + \dfrac{1}{d_i} = \dfrac{1}{f}$ $\dfrac{1}{d_i} = \dfrac{1}{f} - \dfrac{1}{d_o}$

$\dfrac{1}{d_i} = \dfrac{1}{6.0 \text{ cm}} - \dfrac{1}{10.0 \text{ cm}} = \dfrac{1}{15 \text{ cm}}$

c. $\dfrac{h_i}{h_o} = \dfrac{d_i}{d_o}$ $h_i = \dfrac{h_o d_i}{d_o}$

$= \dfrac{(3.0 \text{ cm})(15 \text{ cm})}{(10.0 \text{ cm})} = 4.5 \text{ cm}$

Page 324.

4. a.

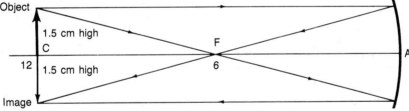

b. $\dfrac{1}{d_o} + \dfrac{1}{d_i} = \dfrac{1}{f}$ $\dfrac{1}{d_i} = \dfrac{1}{f} - \dfrac{1}{d_o}$

$\dfrac{1}{d_i} = \dfrac{1}{6.0 \text{ cm}} - \dfrac{1}{12 \text{ cm}} = \dfrac{1}{12 \text{ cm}}$ $d_i = 12 \text{ cm}$

c. $\dfrac{h_i}{h_o} = \dfrac{d_i}{d_o}$

$h_i = \dfrac{(h_o)(d_i)}{(d_o)} = \dfrac{(1.5 \text{ cm})(12 \text{ cm})}{(12 \text{ cm})}$

$= 1.5 \text{ cm}$

5. a.

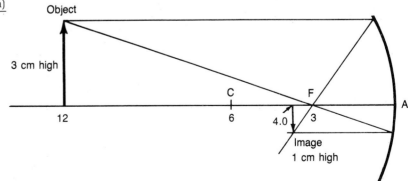

b. $\dfrac{1}{d_o} + \dfrac{1}{d_i} = \dfrac{1}{f}$

$\dfrac{1}{d_i} = \dfrac{1}{f} - \dfrac{1}{d_o} = \dfrac{1}{3.0 \text{ cm}} - \dfrac{1}{12 \text{ cm}} = \dfrac{1}{4.0 \text{ cm}}$

$d_i = 4.0 \text{ cm}$

c. $\dfrac{h_i}{h_o} = \dfrac{d_i}{d_o}$

$h_i = \dfrac{(h_o)(d_i)}{(d_o)} = \dfrac{(3.0 \text{ cm})(4.0 \text{ cm})}{(12 \text{ cm})} = 1.0 \text{ cm}$

6. $\dfrac{1}{d_o} + \dfrac{1}{d_i} = \dfrac{1}{f}$

$\dfrac{1}{d_o} = \dfrac{1}{f} - \dfrac{1}{d_i} = \dfrac{1}{10.0 \text{ cm}} - \dfrac{1}{30.0 \text{ cm}} = \dfrac{1}{15.0 \text{ cm}}$

$d_o = 15.0 \text{ cm}$

7. $\dfrac{1}{d_o} + \dfrac{1}{d_i} = \dfrac{1}{f}$

$\dfrac{1}{d_o} = \dfrac{1}{f} - \dfrac{1}{d_i} = \dfrac{1}{20.0 \text{ cm}} - \dfrac{1}{30.0 \text{ cm}} = \dfrac{1}{60.0 \text{ cm}}$

$d_o = 60.0 \text{ cm}$

Page 325.

8. $\dfrac{1}{d_o} + \dfrac{1}{d_i} = \dfrac{1}{f}$

$\dfrac{1}{f} - \dfrac{1}{d_i} = \dfrac{1}{d_o} = \dfrac{1}{6.0 \text{ cm}} - \dfrac{1}{4.0 \text{ cm}}$

$\dfrac{1}{d_i} = \dfrac{-1}{12 \text{ cm}} \qquad d_i = -12 \text{ cm}$

9. $\dfrac{1}{d_o} + \dfrac{1}{d_i} = \dfrac{1}{f}$

$\dfrac{1}{d_i} = \dfrac{1}{f} - \dfrac{1}{d_o}$

$d_i = \dfrac{d_o f}{d_o - f} = \dfrac{(6.0 \text{ cm})(10.0 \text{ cm})}{(6.0 \text{ cm}) - (10.0 \text{ cm})} = -15 \text{ cm}$

10. a. $\dfrac{1}{d_o} + \dfrac{1}{d_i} = \dfrac{1}{f}$

$d_i = \dfrac{d_o f}{d_o - f} = \dfrac{(10.0 \text{ cm})(16 \text{ cm})}{(10.0 \text{ cm} - 16 \text{ cm})} = -27 \text{ cm}$

b. $\dfrac{h_i}{h_o} = \dfrac{d_i}{d_o}$

$h_i = \dfrac{h_o d_i}{d_o} = \dfrac{(4.0 \text{ cm})(27 \text{ cm})}{(10.0 \text{ cm})} = 11 \text{ cm}$

Page 328.

11. $\dfrac{1}{d_o} + \dfrac{1}{d_i} = \dfrac{1}{f}$

$d_i = \dfrac{d_o f}{d_o - f} = \dfrac{(20.0 \text{ cm})(-15 \text{ cm})}{[20.0 \text{ cm} - (-15 \text{ cm})]} = -8.6 \text{ cm}$

12. a. $\dfrac{1}{d_o} + \dfrac{1}{d_i} = \dfrac{1}{f}$

$d_i = \dfrac{d_o f}{d_o - f} = \dfrac{(60.0 \text{ cm})(-12 \text{ cm})}{[60.0 \text{ cm} - (-12 \text{ cm})]}$

$\qquad = -1.0 \times 10^1 \text{ cm}$

b. $\dfrac{h_i}{h_o} = \dfrac{d_i}{d_o}$

$h_i = \dfrac{d_i h_o}{d_o} = \dfrac{(-10 \text{ cm})(6.0 \text{ cm})}{(60.0 \text{ cm})} = -1.0 \text{ cm}$

13. $\dfrac{1}{d_o} + \dfrac{1}{d_i} = \dfrac{1}{f}$

$d_i = \dfrac{d_o f}{d_o - f} = \dfrac{(6.0 \times 10^2 \text{ cm})(-40.0 \text{ cm})}{[6.0 \times 10^2 \text{ cm} - (-40.0 \text{ cm})]} = -38 \text{ cm}$

14. $\dfrac{1}{d_o} + \dfrac{1}{d_i} = \dfrac{1}{f}$

$\dfrac{1}{d_i} = \dfrac{1}{f} - \dfrac{1}{d_o}$

$d_i = \dfrac{d_o f}{d_o - f} = \dfrac{(1.00 \times 10^3 \text{ cm})(-20.0 \text{ cm})}{(1.00 \times 10^3 \text{ cm}) - (20.0 \text{ cm})} = 20.4 \text{ cm}$

Page 331.

15.

16. a.

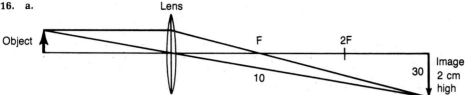

b. $\dfrac{1}{d_o} + \dfrac{1}{d_i} = \dfrac{1}{f}$

$d_i = \dfrac{d_o f}{d_o - f} = \dfrac{(15 \text{ cm})(10.0 \text{ cm})}{(15 \text{ cm} - 10.0 \text{ cm})} = 3.0 \times 10^1 \text{ cm}$

$\dfrac{h_i}{h_o} = \dfrac{d_i}{d_o}$

$h_i = \dfrac{d_i h_o}{d_o} = \dfrac{(3.0 \times 10^1 \text{ cm})(1.0 \text{ cm})}{(15 \text{ cm})} = 2.0 \text{ cm}$

17. $\dfrac{1}{d_o} + \dfrac{1}{d_i} = \dfrac{1}{f}$

$d_i = \dfrac{d_o f}{d_o - f} = \dfrac{(10.0 \text{ cm})(6.0 \text{ cm})}{(10.0 \text{ cm} - 6.0 \text{ cm})} = 15 \text{ cm}$

$\dfrac{h_i}{h_o} = \dfrac{d_i}{d_o}$

$h_i = \dfrac{d_i h_o}{d_o} = \dfrac{(15 \text{ cm})(3.0 \text{ cm})}{(10.0 \text{ cm})} = 4.5 \text{ cm}$

18. a.

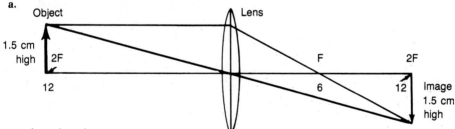

b. $\dfrac{1}{d_o} + \dfrac{1}{d_i} = \dfrac{1}{f}$

$d_i = \dfrac{d_o f}{d_o - f} = \dfrac{(12 \text{ cm})(6.0 \text{ cm})}{(12 \text{ cm} - 6.0 \text{ cm})} = 12 \text{ cm}$

$\dfrac{h_i}{h_o} = \dfrac{d_i}{d_o}$

$h_i = \dfrac{h_o d_i}{d_o} = \dfrac{(1.5 \text{ cm})(12 \text{ cm})}{(12 \text{ cm})} = 1.5 \text{ cm}$

19. a. $\dfrac{1}{d_o} + \dfrac{1}{d_i} = \dfrac{1}{f}$

$d_i = \dfrac{d_o f}{d_o - f} = \dfrac{(12 \text{ cm})(3.0 \text{ cm})}{(12 \text{ cm} - 3.0 \text{ cm})} = 4.0 \text{ cm}$

b. $\dfrac{h_i}{h_o} = \dfrac{d_i}{d_o}$

$h_i = \dfrac{d_i h_o}{d_o} = \dfrac{(4.0 \text{ cm})(3.0 \text{ cm})}{(12 \text{ cm})} = 1.0 \text{ cm}$

20. $\dfrac{1}{d_o} + \dfrac{1}{d_i} = \dfrac{1}{f}$

$d_o = \dfrac{d_i f}{d_i - f} = \dfrac{(12 \text{ cm})(4.0 \text{ cm})}{(12 \text{ cm} - 4.0 \text{ cm})} = 6.0 \text{ cm}$

21. $\dfrac{1}{d_o} + \dfrac{1}{d_i} = \dfrac{1}{f}$

$d_o = \dfrac{d_i f}{d_i - f} = \dfrac{(10.0 \text{ cm})(8.0 \text{ cm})}{(10.0 \text{ cm} - 8.0 \text{ cm})} = 4.0 \times 10^1 \text{ cm}$

Page 333.

22. $\dfrac{1}{d_o} + \dfrac{1}{d_i} = \dfrac{1}{f}$

$d_i = \dfrac{d_o f}{d_o - f} = \dfrac{(6.0 \text{ cm})(20.0 \text{ cm})}{(6.0 \text{ cm} - 20.0 \text{ cm})} = -8.6 \text{ cm}$

23. a. $\dfrac{1}{d_o} + \dfrac{1}{d_i} = \dfrac{1}{f}$

$d_i = \dfrac{d_o f}{d_o - f} = \dfrac{(4.0 \text{ cm})(12 \text{ cm})}{(4.0 \text{ cm} - 12 \text{ cm})} = -6.0 \text{ cm}$

b. $\dfrac{h_i}{h_o} = \dfrac{d_i}{d_o}$

$h_i = \dfrac{d_i h_o}{d_o} = \dfrac{(6.0 \text{ cm})(2.0 \text{ cm})}{(4.0 \text{ cm})} = 3.0 \text{ cm}$

24. $\dfrac{1}{d_o} + \dfrac{1}{d_i} = \dfrac{1}{f}$

$f = \dfrac{d_o d_i}{d_o + d_i} = \dfrac{(8.0 \text{ cm})(-16 \text{ cm})}{[8.0 \text{ cm} + (-16 \text{ cm})]} = 16 \text{ cm}$

Chapter End Questions

Pages 337-338.

1. Image is erect, virtual, as far in back of the mirror as the object is in front of the mirror and the same size as the object. It is best to note that the image is not truly reversed in the full sense of the word but only appears to be reversed. Actually the correct optical term is that the image is perverted, which refers to the same effect as is achieved when a rubber mask is turned inside-out.

2. The image will be between C and F, will be inverted, real, and smaller than the object.

3. The image will be at C, inverted, real, and the same size as the object.

4. The image will be beyond C, inverted, real, and larger than the object.

5. A virtual image cannot be cast upon a screen while a real image can. The rays that form a virtual image only appear to originate at the location of the image and actually originate elsewhere. The rays that form a real image do originate at the position of the image.

6. Image is between F and the mirror.

7. The image in a convex mirror is always virtual, erect, smaller than the object, and located closer to the mirror than the object.

8. All virtual images are erect and are the result of divergent rays.

9. The index of refraction of the material from which the lens is made determines focus.

10. The image will be between F and $2F$, inverted, real, and smaller than the object.

11. Rays parallel to the axis which strike the edges of a concave spherical mirror are not reflected through the focal point. This effect is called spherical abberation.

12. Light passing through a lens is slightly dispersed causing objects viewed through the lens to appear ringed with color. This effect is called chromatic abberation.

13. The film is run through the projector upside-down, so to speak.

14. Convex mirrors are used as rear-view mirrors on school buses. A convex mirror allows for a wide range of view allowing the driver to see a much larger area about the bus than is afforded by ordinary mirrors.

Problems A

Page 338.

1. a.

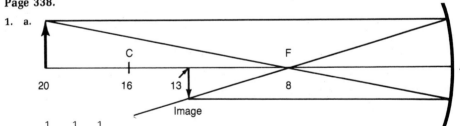

b. $\dfrac{1}{d_o} + \dfrac{1}{d_i} = \dfrac{1}{f}$

$d_i = \dfrac{d_o f}{d_o - f} = \dfrac{(20.0 \text{ cm})(8.0 \text{ cm})}{(20.0 \text{ cm} - 8.0 \text{ cm})} = 13 \text{ cm}$

2. a.

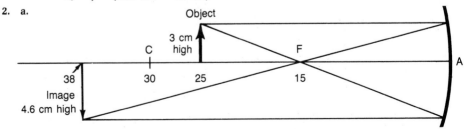

b. $\dfrac{1}{d_o} + \dfrac{1}{d_i} = \dfrac{1}{f}$

$d_i = \dfrac{d_o f}{d_o - f} = \dfrac{(25\ \text{cm})(15\ \text{cm})}{(25\ \text{cm} - 15\ \text{cm})} = 38\ \text{cm}$

$\dfrac{h_i}{h_o} = \dfrac{d_i}{d_o}$

$h_i = \dfrac{d_i h_o}{d_o} = \dfrac{(38\ \text{cm})(3.0\ \text{cm})}{(25\ \text{cm})} = 4.6\ \text{cm}$

3. a. $\dfrac{1}{d_o} + \dfrac{1}{d_i} = \dfrac{1}{f}$

$d_i = \dfrac{d_o f}{d_o - f} = \dfrac{(30.0\ \text{cm})(15\ \text{cm})}{(30.0\ \text{cm} - 15\ \text{cm})} = 3.0 \times 10^1\ \text{cm}$

b. $\dfrac{h_i}{h_o} = \dfrac{d_i}{d_o}$

$h_i = \dfrac{d_i h_o}{d_o} = \dfrac{(3.0 \times 10^1\ \text{cm})(1.8\ \text{cm})}{(30.0\ \text{cm})} = 1.8\ \text{cm}$

4. a. $\dfrac{1}{d_o} + \dfrac{1}{d_i} = \dfrac{1}{f}$

$d_i = \dfrac{d_o f}{d_o - f} = \dfrac{(8.0\ \text{cm})(12\ \text{cm})}{(8.0\ \text{cm} - 12.0\ \text{cm})} = -24\ \text{cm}$

b. $\dfrac{h_i}{h_o} = \dfrac{d_i}{d_o}$

$h_i = \dfrac{d_i h_o}{d_o} = \dfrac{(-24\ \text{cm})(3.0\ \text{cm})}{(8.0\ \text{cm})} = -9.0\ \text{cm}$

5. $\dfrac{1}{d_o} + \dfrac{1}{d_i} = \dfrac{1}{f}$

$d_i = \dfrac{d_o f}{d_o - f} = \dfrac{(3.0\ \text{m})(-0.16\ \text{m})}{[3.0\ \text{m} - (-0.16\ \text{m})]} = -0.15\ \text{m} = -15\ \text{cm}$

Page 339.

6. $\dfrac{1}{d_o} + \dfrac{1}{d_i} = \dfrac{1}{f}$

$d_i = \dfrac{d_o f}{d_o - f} = \dfrac{(8.0\ \text{cm})(30.0\ \text{cm})}{(8.0\ \text{cm} - 30.0\ \text{cm})} = -11\ \text{cm}$

7. $\dfrac{1}{d_o} + \dfrac{1}{d_i} = \dfrac{1}{f}$

$d_i = \dfrac{d_o f}{d_o - f} = \dfrac{(10.0\ \text{m})(-0.060\ \text{m})}{[10.0\ \text{m} - (-0.060\ \text{m})]} = -0.060\ \text{m} = -6.0\ \text{cm}$

8. a. $\dfrac{1}{d_o} + \dfrac{1}{d_i} = \dfrac{1}{f}$

$d_i = \dfrac{d_o f}{d_o - f} = \dfrac{(40.0\ \text{cm})(25.0\ \text{cm})}{(40.0\ \text{cm} - 25.0\ \text{cm})} = 66.7\ \text{cm}$

b. $\dfrac{h_i}{h_o} = \dfrac{d_i}{d_o}$

$h_i = \dfrac{d_i h_o}{d_o} = \dfrac{(66.7\ \text{cm})(h_o)}{(40.0\ \text{cm})} = 1.67\ h_o$

Problems B

Page 339.

1. a. $\dfrac{1}{d_o} + \dfrac{1}{d_i} = \dfrac{1}{f}$

$d_i = \dfrac{d_o f}{d_o - f} = \dfrac{(12\ \text{mm})(10.0\ \text{mm})}{(12\ \text{mm} - 10.0\ \text{mm})}$

$= 6.0\ \text{cm}$

b. $\dfrac{h_i}{h_o} = \dfrac{d_i}{d_o}$

$h_i = \dfrac{d_i h_o}{d_o} = \dfrac{(6.0\ \text{cm})(h_o)}{(1.2\ \text{cm})} = 5.0\ h_o$

c. $\dfrac{1}{d_o} + \dfrac{1}{d_i} = \dfrac{1}{f}$

$d_i = \dfrac{d_o f}{d_o - f} = \dfrac{(10.0\ \text{mm})(20.0\ \text{mm})}{(10.0\ \text{mm} - 20.0\ \text{mm})}$

$= -20.0\ \text{mm}$

d. $\dfrac{h_i}{h_o} = \dfrac{d_i}{d_o}$

$h_i = \dfrac{d_i h_o}{d_o} = \dfrac{(20.0\ \text{mm})(5.0\ h_o)}{(10.0\ \text{mm})} = 10\ h_o$

2. $\dfrac{1}{d_o} + \dfrac{1}{d_i} = \dfrac{1}{f}$

$d_i = \dfrac{d_o f}{d_o - f} = \dfrac{(16\ \text{mm})(20\ \text{mm})}{(16\ \text{mm} - 20\ \text{mm})} = -8\ \text{cm}$

$\dfrac{h_i}{h_o} = \dfrac{d_i}{d_o}$

$h_i = \dfrac{d_i h_o}{d_o} = \dfrac{(8\ \text{cm})(h_o)}{(1.6\ \text{cm})} = 5\ h_o$

3. a. $\dfrac{1}{d_o} + \dfrac{1}{d_i} = \dfrac{1}{f}$

$d_i = \dfrac{d_o f}{d_o - f} = \dfrac{(3.0 \times 10^3\ \text{mm})(50.0\ \text{mm})}{(3.0 \times 10^3\ \text{mm} - 50.0\ \text{mm})}$

$= 5.0 \times 10^1\ \text{mm}$

$= 5.0\ \text{cm}$

b. $\dfrac{1}{d_o} + \dfrac{1}{d_i} = \dfrac{1}{f}$

$d_i = \dfrac{d_o f}{d_o - f} = \dfrac{(125\ \text{m})(1.00\ \text{m})}{(125\ \text{m} - 1.00\ \text{m})} = 1.00\ \text{m}$

$= 1.00 \times 10^3\ \text{mm}$

4. $\dfrac{h_i}{h_o} = \dfrac{d_i}{d_o}$

$h_i = \dfrac{d_i h_o}{d_o} = \dfrac{(5.0\ \text{cm})(0.50\ \text{m})}{(3.0\ \text{m})} = 8.3\ \text{mm}$

Diffraction and Interference of Light   Chapter 20

Teaching Techniques

Diffraction and interference are the most important properties of waves. An understanding of how these effects occur is important not only to a study of light, but also of modern physics as presented in later chapters. This chapter presents a quantitative treatment of diffraction and interference that introduces students to the methods used in finding the wavelength of light or other forms of electromagnetic radiation.

Demonstrations

Section 20:1

Double slits can be made by painting microscope slides with a graphite-alcohol solution. Break a double-edged razor in half and place the two sections back-to-back. Use this razor to scratch a double slit on the painted sides of the slides. Obtain a neon spectral tube to observe line spectra. Have students look at this or other light sources through the slits.

Section 20:4

An inexpensive qualitative spectrometer can be made from a toothpaste tube box and a piece of plastic replica diffraction grating. Cut a 1-mm wide slot in one end of the box and a 1-cm square hole in the other end. Cover the square hole with a piece of the grating, aligning the slits parallel to the slot in the box. Have students view a variety of light sources through the grating end of the "Crestometer."

A quantitative spectrometer can be made by placing a 10 cm square piece of cardboard, with a 1- to 2-mm wide slot, in the center of a meter stick. Mount a diffraction grating 50 cm from this slot. Look through the grating and slot at a spectral source. Images of the spectral lines will appear along the meter stick. In this way, the angles of the interference patterns can be calculated quickly from the locations of the images on the meter stick.

Laboratory Investigations

Measuring the Wavelengths of Light Waves

Performance Objectives

Goal: Students will learn the nature of the diffraction and interference of light, and the use of these phenomena to measure the wavelength of light.

Objectives: Upon completion of the reading, questions, and problems, students will, on oral or written tests:

20:1   K/P   display an understanding of

how two slits produce a pattern of light and dark bands from the constructive and destructive interference of light waves.

20:2   K/P/S   understand the geometry of interference from two slits; use the derived equation to calculate the wavelength of light waves.

20:3   K/P/S   explain how single slit diffraction patterns occur based on geometry; use the derived equation to relate the width of the pattern to slit width and light wavelength.

20:4   K/P/S   explain the advantages of a diffraction grating over two slits; understand the operation of a spectrometer.

20:5   K   explain how diffraction effects cause a small lens to have limited resolution.

S/A   Students will use laboratory materials in the prescribed manner when conducting lab investigations.

Upon completion of the reading and practice problems, students will exhibit an interest in physics by:

A/S   expanding on an answer to one or more of the questions or problems at the end of the chapter.

A/S   observe various streetlights through diffraction gratings and photograph or sketch the results.

A   reading unassigned literature related to the ideas presented in the chapter.

Solutions to Problems

Page 345.

1. $\lambda = \dfrac{xd}{L} = \dfrac{(1.32 \times 10^{-1} \text{ m})(1.90 \times 10^{-6} \text{ m})}{(6.00 \times 10^{-1} \text{ m})}$

    $= 4.18 \times 10^{-7}$ m

2. $x = \dfrac{L\lambda}{d} = \dfrac{(58.0 \text{ cm})(6.0 \times 10^{-7} \text{ m})}{(1.90 \times 10^{-6} \text{ m})} = 18$ cm

3. **a.** $\lambda = \dfrac{xd}{L} = \dfrac{(0.284 \text{ m})(1.90 \times 10^{-4} \text{ cm})}{(1.00 \text{ m})}$

    $= 5.40 \times 10^{-7}$ m

    b. $\lambda = 5.40 \times 10^{-7}$ m $= 540 \times 10^{-9}$ m $= 540$ nm

4. $\lambda = \dfrac{xd}{L} = \dfrac{(1.84 \times 10^{-3}\,\text{m})(2.00 \times 10^{-4}\,\text{m})}{(8.00 \times 10^{-1}\,\text{m})} = 4.60 \times 10^{-7}\,\text{m}$

$v = f\lambda$

$f = \dfrac{v}{\lambda}$

$= \dfrac{3.00 \times 10^8\,\text{m/s}}{4.60 \times 10^{-7}\,\text{m}} = 6.52 \times 10^{14}\,\text{Hz}$

Page 347.

5. $\lambda = \dfrac{yw}{L} = \dfrac{(5.50 \times 10^{-3}\,\text{m})(1.00 \times 10^{-4}\,\text{m})}{(1.00\,\text{m})} = 5.50 \times 10^{-7}\,\text{m}$

6. $\lambda = \dfrac{yw}{L}$

$y = \dfrac{\lambda L}{w} = \dfrac{(4.0 \times 10^{-7}\,\text{m})(80.0\,\text{cm})}{(1.5 \times 10^{-4}\,\text{m})} = 0.21\,\text{cm}$

7. $\lambda = \dfrac{yw}{L} = \dfrac{(0.120\,\text{cm})(0.0295\,\text{cm})}{(60.0\,\text{cm})} = 5.90 \times 10^{-5}\,\text{cm}$

8. $\lambda = \dfrac{yw}{L}$

$w = \dfrac{\lambda L}{y} = \dfrac{(4.80 \times 10^{-7}\,\text{m})(1.20\,\text{m})}{(5.00 \times 10^{-3}\,\text{m})} = 1.15 \times 10^{-4}\,\text{m}$

Chapter End Questions

Page 350.

1. Each wavelength that falls on the slits produces a line of reinforcement along the central bright line. Therefore, the wavelengths are recombined and are not distinguishable.

2. Students' diagrams should resemble Figure 20-1a on page 342.

3. Given the wavelength, the values of x and L can be measured. The equation given in the text is then solved for d.

4. Since $\lambda = \dfrac{xd}{L}$, $x = \dfrac{\lambda L}{d}$. It would appear from this that the value of x can be increased by increasing L or decreasing d. However, gratings used for the measurement of wavelengths of light are not easy to change and reach a maximum effectiveness. To increase the separation of the lines, x, it is usually more convenient to increase L.

5. Single slit diffraction patterns have wider central bright bands. The bands representing the different wavelengths that fall on the slit are much less prominent than the bands obtained by using two slits.

6. The central bright bands extend over 180° around the slit. No dark bands will be evident.

7. The lenses act in the same way as do single slits and cause diffraction patterns. The diffraction patterns produced by each of the point sources overlap, rendering the images of the two sources indistinguishable.

Problems A

Page 351.

1. $\lambda = \dfrac{xd}{L} = \dfrac{(19.0\,\text{cm})(1.90 \times 10^{-4}\,\text{cm})}{(80.0\,\text{cm})}$

$= 4.51 \times 10^{-5}\,\text{cm}$

2. $\lambda = \dfrac{xd}{L}$

$d = \dfrac{\lambda L}{x} = \dfrac{(4.00 \times 10^{-5}\,\text{cm})(2.00\,\text{m})}{(4.00\,\text{cm})}$

$= 2.00 \times 10^{-5}\,\text{m}$

3. $d = \dfrac{1}{2.50 \times 10^3\,\text{lines/cm}} = 4.00 \times 10^{-4}\,\text{cm/line}$

4. $\lambda = \dfrac{xd}{L} = \dfrac{(0.165\,\text{m})(4.00 \times 10^{-4}\,\text{cm})}{(1.00\,\text{m})}$

$= 6.60 \times 10^{-5}\,\text{cm}$

5. $v = f\lambda$

$\lambda = \dfrac{v}{f} = \dfrac{3.0 \times 10^8\,\text{m/s}}{6.0 \times 10^{14}\,\text{Hz}} = 5.0 \times 10^{-7}\,\text{m}$

$= 5.0 \times 10^{-5}\,\text{cm}$

$\lambda = \dfrac{xd}{L}$

$x = \dfrac{\lambda L}{d} = \dfrac{(5.0 \times 10^{-5}\,\text{cm})(50.0\,\text{cm})}{(2.00 \times 10^{-4}\,\text{cm})} = 13\,\text{cm}$

6. $\lambda = \dfrac{yw}{L} = \dfrac{(5.90 \times 10^{-3}\,\text{m})(1.00 \times 10^{-4}\,\text{m})}{(1.00\,\text{m})}$

$= 5.90 \times 10^{-7}\,\text{m}$

Problems B

Page 351.

1. $\lambda = \dfrac{yw}{L}$ and $\lambda = \dfrac{v}{f}$

so $y = \dfrac{L\,v}{w\,f} = \dfrac{(330\,\text{m/s})(12\,\text{m})}{(550\,\text{Hz})(1.2\,\text{m})} = 6.0\,\text{m}$

The people are located 6.0 m to either side of the center of the wall opposite the window.

2. a. $\lambda = \dfrac{v}{f} = \dfrac{(3.0 \times 10^8\,\text{m/s})}{(600 \times 10^3\,\text{Hz})} = 500\,\text{m}$

b. The path difference is $19\,500 - 17\,500 = 2000\,\text{m}$. The reception should be good since it is a multiple of the wavelength, so constructive interference will take place.

Static Electricity   # Chapter 21

Teaching Techniques

A knowledge of static electricity is fundamental to any study of electrical phenomena. Although many students will have encountered the qualitative aspects of this material before, the interpretation and quantitative material will be new, therefore review this chapter carefully. Emphasize that static charges are at rest or not moving. Demonstrations are extremely useful here due to the abstract nature of the discussions.

Demonstrations

Section 21:2

You should have rubber (or vinyl) rods and fur, glass rods and silk cloth, pith balls (or pieces of Styrofoam packing material) suspended by threads, and one or more electroscopes (even homemade ones). Use these materials to perform demonstrations suggested in the text. The type of charge gained by a rubbed object depends on the nature of both items being rubbed together. To demonstrate, rub a rubber rod with Saran® wrap, and describe the charge produced on the rod as positive. Then inflate some balloons and suspend them by silk threads. Rub the balloons with fur to show repulsion. Describe the charge on the balloon as negative. The latter demonstration shows how much stronger electrical forces are than gravitational.

An electrophorus can be charged once and used for hours, even in damp weather. A Van de Graff generator is highly desirable, although expensive. Use a small metal sphere attached to a plastic rod to take charge from the globe. CAUTION—never allow students to play with this device. Even though it cannot supply enough current to cause shock, it can hurt a person with a heart ailment.

Section 21:5

Two spheres mounted on insulating rods are almost essential here to demonstrate induced separation of charge, and charging by induction.

Section 21:8

Place a strong charge on an object and walk around the room showing that the charged object attracts anything that is loose. Have students note that when the loose object touches the charged one it is repelled. This shows the difference between the attractive force on a neutral object and the repulsion when both items are charged in the same way. Even a stream of water can be attracted to a charged object.

Chapter 21

Film

Coulomb's Law (university rental, PSSC film)

Laboratory Investigations

Static Electricity
Coulomb's Law

Performance Objectives

Goal: To understand the nature of static charge, means of charging objects, and the forces between them.

Objectives: Upon completion of the reading, questions, and problems, students will, on oral or written tests:

21:1	K	outline the structure of the atom; know the charges on electron and proton; understand how charging occurs.
21:2	K/P	know that charging is separation, not creation of charge
21:3	K/P	state the differences between conductors, insulators, and semiconductors.
21:4	K/P	be able to summarize the observed forces between charged bodies; know how an electroscope detects the presence of charge and how an item is charged by conduction.
21:5	K/P	explain the separation of charge and charging by induction.
21:6	K/P	state Coulomb's law and how the force depends on charges and their separation.
21:7	K/S/P	state the unit of charge; understand the vector nature of the force; solve problems using Coulomb's law.
21:8	K/P	understand the cause of the attractive force on neutral objects and applications of this force.
	S/A	Students will use laboratory materials in the prescribed manner when conducting lab investigations.

Upon completion of the reading and practice problems, students will exhibit an interest in physics by:

A/S	expanding on an answer to one or more of the questions or

problems at the end of the chapter.

A/S   investigate an industrial process which uses electrostatics.

A   reading unassigned literature related to the ideas presented in the chapter.

Solutions to Problems

Page 361.

1. $F = \dfrac{Kqq'}{d^2} = \dfrac{(9.0 \times 10^9 \text{ N} \cdot \text{m}^2/\text{C}^2)(6.0 \times 10^{-6} \text{ C})(6.0 \times 10^{-6} \text{ C})}{(0.50 \text{ m})^2} = 1.3 \text{ N}$

Page 362.

2. $F = \dfrac{Kqq'}{d^2} = \dfrac{(9.0 \times 10^9 \text{ N} \cdot \text{m}^2/\text{C}^2)(-2.0 \times 10^{-4} \text{ C})(8.0 \times 10^{-4} \text{ C})}{(0.30 \text{ m})^2} = -1.6 \times 10^4 \text{ N}$

3. $F = \dfrac{Kqq'}{d^2} = \dfrac{(9.0 \times 10^9 \text{ N} \cdot \text{m}^2/\text{C}^2)(-1.6 \times 10^{-19} \text{ C})(-1.6 \times 10^{-19} \text{ C})}{(1.5 \times 10^{-10} \text{ m})^2} = 1.0 \times 10^{-8} \text{ N}$

4. $F = \dfrac{Kqq'}{d^2}$

$q' = \dfrac{Fd^2}{Kq} = \dfrac{(65 \text{ N})(0.05 \text{ m})^2}{(9.0 \times 10^9 \text{ N} \cdot \text{m}^2/\text{C}^2)(-6.0 \times 10^{-6} \text{ C})} = 3.0 \times 10^{-6} \text{ C}$

Chapter End Questions

Page 364.

1. Electron $(-)$, proton $(+)$, neutron (0).

2. Touch the charged rod to one end of an object. Touch the other end to an electroscope. If it is charged, it is a conductor.

3. Insulators: plastic, glass, silk, cloth, dry air
Conductors: metal, salt water, graphite, human body
Semiconductors: Ge, Si, Se

4. **a.** Leaves are positive and spread farther.
b. Leaves are more negative and spread less.

5. He made them the same size and charged them while they were still in contact.

6. The force between two charged objects is proportional to the charge on each object, and inversely proportional to the square of separation. Force is attractive if charges are of opposite sign, repulsive if the sign is the same.

Problems A

Page 365.

1. $F = \dfrac{Kqq'}{d^2} = \dfrac{(9.0 \times 10^9 \text{ N} \cdot \text{m}^2/\text{C}^2)(1.8 \times 10^{-6} \text{ C})(-1.0 \times 10^{-6} \text{ C})}{(0.014 \text{ m})^2} = -8.3 \times 10^1 \text{ N} = -83 \text{ N}$

2. $F = \dfrac{Kqq'}{d^2} = \dfrac{(9.0 \times 10^9 \text{ N} \cdot \text{m}^2/\text{C}^2)(-5.0 \times 10^{-5} \text{ C})(-5.0 \times 10^{-5} \text{ C})}{(0.20 \text{ m})^2} = 5.6 \times 10^2 \text{ N}$

3. $F = \dfrac{Kqq'}{d^2} = \dfrac{(9.0 \times 10^9 \text{ N} \cdot \text{m}^2/\text{C}^2)(1.6 \times 10^{-19} \text{ C})(-1.6 \times 10^{-19} \text{ C})}{(5.0 \times 10^{-11} \text{ m})^2} = -9.2 \times 10^{-8} \text{ N}$

4. The force between A and B is

$F = \dfrac{Kq_A q_B}{r^2} = \dfrac{(9.0 \times 10^9 \text{ N} \cdot \text{m}^2/\text{C}^2)(4.5 \times 10^{-6} \text{ C})(4.5 \times 10^{-6} \text{ C})}{(0.03 \text{ m})^2} = 2.0 \times 10^2 \text{ N}$

The magnitude of the force between A and C is the same.
These need to be added as vectors—

$F = \sqrt{(2.0 \times 10^2 \text{ N})^2 + (2.0 \times 10^2 \text{ N})^2} = 280 \text{ N}$

Problems B

Page 365.

1. **a.** $mg = (1.0 \times 10^{-3} \text{ kg})(9.8 \text{ m/s}^2) = 9.8 \times 10^{-3} \text{ N}$

   b. $\tan 30.0° = \dfrac{Fe}{mg}$

   $Fe = mg \tan 30.0° = (1.0 \times 10^{-3} \text{ kg})(9.8 \text{ m/s}^2)(\tan 30.0°)$
   $= 5.7 \times 10^{-3} \text{ N}$

   c. $F = \dfrac{Kqq'}{r^2}$

   $F = \dfrac{Kq^2}{r^2}$

   $q = \sqrt{\dfrac{Fr^2}{K}} = \sqrt{\dfrac{(5.7 \times 10^{-3} \text{ N})(3.0 \times 10^{-2} \text{ m})^2}{(9.0 \times 10^9 \text{ N} \cdot \text{m}^2/\text{C}^2)}} = 2.4 \times 10^{-8} \text{ C}$

2. The metal ball starts neutral. It is attracted toward the charged bell. When it hits, it becomes charged. The ball is now repelled. It is now attracted to the uncharged bell. It hits this bell discharging the ball. The entire process repeats.

3. **a.** yes
   b. positive by induction
   c. yes
   d. positive by conduction

The Electric Field   Chapter 22

Teaching Techniques

The abstract concept of the electric field is presented using a gravitational field as an analogy. The use of N/C as the unit of field reminds the student that the field is defined as force per unit charge.

Electric potential is compared to gravitational potential. Point out the analogy of hills and valleys for regions of high and low electric potential and have students think of the force on a marble as an analogy to the force on a charged body. If use of the unit volt gives students trouble, remind them that it is simply a joule per coulomb. Potential is work per unit charge.

The Millikan oil drop experiment is a good example of the use of uniform fields produced by parallel plates. Note that the average charge of the electron had been known from electrochemistry, but Millikan showed that each electron has the same charge.

Charge sharing is a useful application of energy minimization and describes the grounding process.

Demonstrations

A Van de Graaff generator can be used for many demonstrations in this field.

Section 22:5

An oil drop apparatus or computer simulation should be demonstrated here.

Section 22:7

Place an empty coffee can on an insulating platform and charge it. Sample the charge with a transfer disk on the inside and outside of the can. Use an electroscope to show that the charge is all on the outside. Bring sharp and round grounded objects near an electrophorus or van de Graaff to show the reduction of electric fields by rounding.

Section 22:8

Charge a Leyden jar. Use a rubber rod to lift out the inner conductor, and then touch the inner can with the outer can to put both at the same potential. Using the rod, reassemble the jar. Test to show it is once again charged. This test shows the storage of electric energy in the molecules of the plastic insulator. Take apart a commercial capacitator to show its metal and plastic foils.

Laboratory Investigations

Charging and Discharging a Capacitor

Performance Objectives

Goal: Students will show an understanding of the use of electric fields in solving electrostatics problems.

Objectives: Upon completion of the reading, questions, and problems, students will, on oral or written tests:

22:1	P/K	define an electric field; give the direction of the field; distinguish between the field and field lines.
22:2	K/P/S	relate electric field to the force on a test charge; solve problems involving the force due to a point charge.
22:3	K/P	define the difference in electric potential in terms of work done in moving a unit charge; understand the units of potential difference; distinguish potential from potential difference.
22:4	P/K/S	relate electric potential to gravitational potential; solve problems involving uniform electric fields.
22:5	K/S/P	understand the use of electric fields by Millikan to determine the charge of the electron.
22:6	P/K	demonstrate an understanding of the role of energy in the sharing of charge; define grounding; relate charge sharing to grounding.
22:7	P/K	display an understanding of the location of charges on solid and hollow conductors; recognize the relation between conductor shape and electric field near the conductor.
22:8	P/S/K	define capacitance; recognize the principle of the capacitor; solve problems involving charge, potential difference, and capacitance.
	S/A	Students will use laboratory materials in the prescribed manner when conducting lab investigations.

Upon completion of the reading and practice problems, students will exhibit an interest in physics by:

	A/S	expanding on an answer to one or more of the questions or problems at the end of the chapter.
	A/S	read and report on Millikan's life and work, especially his role

in establishing charge quantization.

A   reading unassigned literature related to the ideas presented in the chapter.

Solutions to Problems

Page 370.

1. $E = \dfrac{F}{q'} = \dfrac{0.060 \text{ N}}{2.0 \times 10^{-8} \text{ C}} = 3.0 \times 10^6 \text{ N/C}$

2. $E = \dfrac{F}{q'} = \dfrac{2.5 \times 10^{-4} \text{ N}}{5.0 \times 10^{-4} \text{ C}} = 0.50 \text{ N/C}$

Page 371.

3. $E = \dfrac{F}{q'} = \dfrac{4.0 \times 10^{-3} \text{ N}}{8.0 \times 10^{-5} \text{ C}} = 5.0 \times 10^1 \text{ N/C}$

4. Since $F \times \dfrac{1}{r^2}$ at twice the distance

$F' = \dfrac{F}{4}$

$F' = \dfrac{4.0 \times 10^{-3} \text{ N}}{4} = 1.0 \times 10^{-3} \text{ N}$

Page 373.

5. $V = Ed = (8000 \text{ N/C})(0.05 \text{ m}) = 400 \text{ J/C} = 400 \text{ V}$

6. $V = Ed$

$E = \dfrac{V}{d} = \dfrac{500 \text{ V}}{0.02 \text{ m}} = 25\,000 \text{ N/C} = 3 \times 10^4 \text{ N/C}$

7. $V = Ed = (2.50 \times 10^3 \text{ N/C})(0.500 \text{ m}) = 1.25 \times 10^2 \text{ J/C}$
   $= 1250 \text{ V}$

8. $V = Ed$

$d = \dfrac{V}{E} = \dfrac{5 \times 10^3 \text{ V}}{1 \times 10^6 \text{ N/C}} = 5 \times 10^{-3} \text{ m} = 5 \text{ mm}$

Page 374.

9. $W = qV = (5.0 \text{ C})(1.5 \text{ V}) = 7.5 \text{ CV} = 7.5 \text{ J}$

10. a. $W = qV = (50 \text{ C})(110 \text{ V}) = 5500 \text{ J} = 6000 \text{ J}$

b. $P = \dfrac{W}{t} = \dfrac{6000 \text{ J}}{5.0 \text{ s}} = 1200 \text{ W} = 1.2 \text{ kW}$

Page 376.

11. a. $F = mg$ and $F = Eq$

$q = \dfrac{F}{E} = \dfrac{1.9 \times 10^{-15} \text{ N}}{6.0 \times 10^3 \text{ N/C}} = 3.2 \times 10^{-19} \text{ C}$

b. $\# \text{ electrons} = \dfrac{q}{q_e} = \dfrac{3.2 \times 10^{-19} \text{ C}}{1.6 \times 10^{-19} \text{ C/electron}} = 2 \text{ electrons}$

12. a. $F = Eq$

$q = \dfrac{F}{E} = \dfrac{6.4 \times 10^{-13} \text{ N}}{4.0 \times 10^6 \text{ N/C}} = 1.6 \times 10^{-19} \text{ C}$

b. $\# \text{ electrons} = \dfrac{q}{1.6 \times 10^{-19} \text{ C/electron}} = 1 \text{ electron}$

13. $E = \dfrac{F}{q} = \dfrac{6.4 \times 10^{-13} \text{ N}}{(4)(1.6 \times 10^{-19} \text{ C})} = 1.0 \times 10^6 \text{ N/C}$

14. a.

b. $slope = \dfrac{y}{x} = \dfrac{5.6 \times 10^{-14} \text{ N} - 1.7 \times 10^{-14} \text{ N}}{3.5 \times 10^5 - 1.1 \times 10^5 \text{ N}}$

$= 1.6 \times 10^{-19} \text{ C}$ which represents the charge of an electron

Chapter End Questions

Page 381-382.

1. See Section 22:1 for detailed drawings.

2. The direction of an electric field is the direction of the force on a positive charge placed in the field. This would be away from a positive object and toward a negative object.

3. Volt is work per charge on which work is done; $V = W/q$.

4. $V = W/q = 120 \text{ V}$

5. Charge is shared with an extremely large object, such as Earth.

6. The table is an insulator, or at least a very poor conductor.

7. A capacitor is a device that can store charge. The larger the capacitance, the larger the charge that can be put on it for the same increase in the potential of the capacitor.

8. A ten-cm diameter sphere.

Problems A

Page 382.

1. **a.** $E = \dfrac{F}{q} = \dfrac{8.0 \times 10^{-4} \text{ N}}{2.0 \times 10^{-4} \text{ C}} = 4.0 \text{ N/C}$

   b. It is toward the negative charge.

2. $E = \dfrac{F}{q}$

   $q = \dfrac{F}{E} = \dfrac{1.4 \times 10^{-8} \text{ N}}{2.0 \times 10^{-4} \text{ N/C}} = 7.0 \times 10^{-5} \text{ C}$

3. $V = Ed = (1.5 \times 10^3 \text{ N/C})(0.080 \text{ m})$
     $= 1.2 \times 10^2 \text{ V} = 120 \text{ V}$

4. $V = Ed$

   $E = \dfrac{V}{d} = \dfrac{50.0 \text{ V}}{0.020 \text{ m}} = 2500 \text{ V/m} = 2.5 \times 10^3 \text{ N/C}$

5. $W = qV = (0.15 \text{ C})(9.0 \text{ V}) = 1.4 \text{ J}$

6. $W = qV$

   $q = \dfrac{W}{V} = \dfrac{1200 \text{ J}}{12 \text{ V}} = 1.0 \times 10^2 \text{ C}$

7. **a.** $q = \dfrac{F}{E} = \dfrac{8.5 \times 10^{-15} \text{ N}}{5.3 \times 10^3 \text{ N/C}} = 1.6 \times 10^{-18} \text{ C}$

   b. $\# \text{ electrons} = \dfrac{q}{q_e} = \dfrac{1.6 \times 10^{-18} \text{ C}}{1.6 \times 10^{-19} \text{ C/electron}}$
     $= 10 \text{ electrons}$

8. $C = \dfrac{q}{V}$

   $q = CV = (6.8 \times 10^{-6} \text{ F})(15 \text{ V}) = 1.0 \times 10^{-4} \text{ C}$

Problems B

Page 382.

1. **a.** $W = \dfrac{1}{2}CV^2 = \dfrac{1}{2}(10.0 \times 10^{-6} \text{ F})(3.00 \times 10^2 \text{ V})^2$
     $= 0.450 \text{ J}$

Page 383.

2. **a.** $P = \dfrac{W}{t} = \dfrac{0.450 \text{ J}}{30\text{s}} = 2 \times 10^{-2} \text{ W}$

   b. $P = \dfrac{W}{t} = \dfrac{0.450 \text{ J}}{1.0 \times 10^{-4} \text{ s}} = 4.5 \times 10^3 \text{ W} = 4.5 \text{ kW}$

Electric Currents   Chapter 23

Teaching Techniques

Because electrical technology is well developed there are many terms that are difficult to relate to physical concepts. Continue to stress that volts are joules per coulomb and that an ampere is a coulomb per second.

Explain that a current flows because of a source of potential difference (battery or generator). A potential difference or voltage drop across a resistor is the result of the current flow in that device. Thus, depending on the part of the circuit analyzed, current is either the result of, or a cause of potential difference.

The placement of meters in circuits is always a problem for students. Stress that current is measured through a circuit but voltage across a circuit, and thus place the ammeter in series and the voltmeter in parallel.

There are many uses of electric currents in both the home and automobile that should provide examples of interest to students.

Demonstrations

Section 23:1

Make a simple voltaic cell from a lemon, bare copper wire or strip and a zinc coated nail. Cut apart commercial cells to show construction. Use a small generator wired to a low wattage bulb to demonstrate that work must be done to create electric energy.

Section 23:4

Illustrate Ohm's law with large demonstration ammeters and voltmeters along with a few resistors. Assemble a number of lengths of flexible wires with alligator clips on each end to make quick and secure connections. Have students make calculations. Unless the resistors have sufficiently high power ratings take measurements quickly to avoid heating effects. Some devices that do not obey Ohm's law might also be shown, i.e., small lamp, silicon diode, neon light.

Section 23:6

Either a demonstration rheostat or high power potentiometer should be used with the demonstration meters to show current control. Cut apart a commercial potentiometer to show its construction.

Laboratory Investigations

Ohm's Law
Electrical Equivalent of Heat

Performance Objectives

Goal: Students will understand the nature of current as well as current and potential relationships in simple electric circuits.

Objectives: Upon completion of the reading, questions, and problems, students will, on oral or written tests:

23:1   P/K   define an electric current; recognize the need of a potential difference if an electric current is to be maintained.

23:2   K/P   recognize circuits as closed loops; understand the source and use of energy in circuits.

23:3   K/S   define the ampere; explain the definition of power in electric circuits; solve problems involving current and power.

23:4   K/P/S   state Ohm's law; relate potential drop in a device to current flow through it; solve problems using the law.

23:5   P/K/S   diagram simple electric circuits; recognize the correct way to place ammeters and voltmeters.

23:6   S/K   explain the use of resistors in controlling current.

23:7   K/P/S   explain the relationship between electric energy and heat transfer.

23:8   K   describe the reason for the use of high voltage lines in transmitting electric power.

23:9   K/S   define kilowatt hour; solve problems involving the use and cost of electric energy.

S/A   Students will use laboratory materials in the prescribed manner when conducting lab investigations.

Upon completion of the reading and practice problems, students will exhibit an interest in physics by:

A/S   expanding on an answer to one or more of the questions or problems at the end of the chapter.

A/S   making a list of the current flow and power consumption of various household appliances or devices in an automobile.

A   reading unassigned literature related to the ideas presented in the chapter.

Solutions to Problems

Page 388.

1. $P = VI = (120 \text{ V})(0.5 \text{ A}) = 60 \text{ J/s} = 60 \text{ W}$

2. $P = VI = (12 \text{ V})(2.0 \text{ A}) = 24 \text{ W}$

3. $P = VI = (120 \text{ V})(8.0 \text{ A}) = 960 \text{ W}$

4. $P = VI = (120 \text{ V})(1.2 \text{ A}) = 140 \text{ W}$

5. $P = VI \quad I = \dfrac{P}{V} = \dfrac{75 \text{ W}}{120 \text{ V}} = 0.63 \text{ A}$

6. $P = VI = (12 \text{ V})(210 \text{ A}) = 2500 \text{ W}$
    In 10 s, $E = Pt = (2500 \text{ J/s})(10 \text{ s})$
    $= 25000 \text{ J} = 2.5 \times 10^4 \text{ J}$

Page 389.

7. a. $P = VI = (3.0 \text{ V})(1.5 \text{ A}) = 4.5 \text{ W}$
    b. $E = Pt = (4.5 \text{ W})(10 \text{ min})(60 \text{ s/min}) = 3.0 \times 10^3 \text{ J}$

8. a. $P = VI = (120 \text{ V})(0.5 \text{ A}) = 6.0 \times 10^1 \text{ W}$
    b. $E = Pt = (60 \text{ W})(5 \text{ min})(60 \text{ s/min})$
    $= 20000 \text{ J} = 2 \times 10^4 \text{ J}$

Page 390.

9. $I = \dfrac{V}{R} = \dfrac{12 \text{ V}}{30 \text{ }\Omega} = 0.4 \text{ A}$

10. $I = \dfrac{V}{R} = \dfrac{75 \text{ V}}{15 \text{ }\Omega} = 5.0 \text{ A}$

11. a. $I = \dfrac{V}{R}$
    $R = \dfrac{V}{I} = \dfrac{120 \text{ V}}{0.5 \text{ A}} = 240 \text{ }\Omega = 200 \text{ }\Omega$
    b. $P = VI = (120 \text{ V})(0.5 \text{ A}) = 60 \text{ W}$

12. $V = IR = (3.8 \text{ A})(32 \text{ }\Omega) = 120 \text{ V}$

13. $V = IR$
    $R = \dfrac{V}{I} = \dfrac{3 \text{ V}}{2 \times 10^{-4} \text{ A}} = 1.5 \times 10^4 \text{ }\Omega = 2 \times 10^4 \text{ }\Omega$

14. $V = IR = (0.4 \text{ A})(60 \text{ }\Omega) = 24 \text{ V} = 20 \text{ V}$

Page 391.

15. $I = \dfrac{V}{R} = \dfrac{90 \text{ V}}{45 \text{ }\Omega} = 2 \text{ A}$

16. $I = \dfrac{V}{R} = \dfrac{60 \text{ V}}{12.5 \text{ }\Omega} = 4.80 \text{ A} = 5 \text{ A}$

17. $V = IR = (1.75 \text{ A})(16 \text{ }\Omega) = 28 \text{ V}$

Page 393.

18. a. $V = IR$
    $R = \dfrac{V}{I} = \dfrac{120 \text{ V}}{0.5 \text{ A}} = 240 \text{ }\Omega = 200 \text{ }\Omega$
    b. $R_{cold} = \dfrac{1}{5}(200 \text{ }\Omega) = 40 \text{ }\Omega$
    c. $I = \dfrac{V}{R} = \dfrac{120 \text{ V}}{40 \text{ }\Omega} = 3 \text{ A}$

Page 394.

19. **a.** $I = \dfrac{V}{R} = \dfrac{120 \text{ V}}{15 \text{ }\Omega} = 8.0 \text{ A}$

   b. $P = IV = (8.0 \text{ A})(120 \text{ V}) = 960 \text{ W}$
   Energy $= Pt = (960 \text{ W})(30 \text{ s}) = 29000 \text{ J}$
   c. $Q = I^2 Rt = (8.0 \text{ A})^2 (15 \text{ }\Omega)(30 \text{ s}) = 29000 \text{ J}$

20. **a.** $I = \dfrac{V}{R} = \dfrac{60 \text{ V}}{30 \text{ }\Omega} = 2 \text{ A}$

   b. Energy $= PT = IVt = (2\text{A})(60 \text{ V})(5 \text{ min})(60 \text{ s/min})$
   $= 40000 \text{ J} = 4 \times 10^4 \text{ J}$

21. **a.** $E = Pt = (0.2)(100 \text{ J/s})(60 \text{ s}) = 1200 \text{ J}$
   b. $Q = Pt = (0.8)(100 \text{ J/s})(60 \text{ s}) = 4800 \text{ J}$

Page 395.

22. **a.** $I = \dfrac{V}{R} = \dfrac{220 \text{ V}}{11 \text{ }\Omega} = 2.0 \times 10^1 \text{ A}$

   b. Energy $= Pt = IVt = (2.0 \times 10^1 \text{ A})(220 \text{ V})(30 \text{ s})$
   $= 1.3 \times 10^5 \text{ J}$
   c. With $Q = (0.7)(1.3 \times 10^5 \text{ J}) = 9.1 \times 10^4 \text{ J}$
   $Q = mc\Delta T$

   $\Delta T = \dfrac{Q}{mc} = \dfrac{9.1 \times 10^4 \text{ J}}{(1.20 \text{ kg})(4180 \text{ J/kg} \cdot \text{C}°)}$

   $= 18°C$

23. **a.** $Q = Pt$
   $= (5.00 \times 10^2 \text{ W})(30 \text{ min})(60 \text{ s/min}) = 9 \times 10^5 \text{ J}$
   b. $Q = mc\Delta T$

   $\Delta T = \dfrac{Q}{mc} = \dfrac{(0.5)(9 \times 10^5 \text{ J})}{(50.0 \text{ kg})(1100 \text{ J/kg} \cdot \text{C}°)} = 8°C$

24. Energy $= Pt$
   $= (60 \text{ W})(30 \text{ min})(60 \text{ s/min}) = 1.1 \times 10^5 \text{ J}$
   $Q = Pt$
   $= (60 \text{ W})(0.88)(30 \text{ min})(60 \text{ s/min})$
   $= 9.5 \times 10^4 \text{ J}$

Page 398.

25. **a.** $P = IV = (15.0 \text{ A})(120 \text{ V}) = 1800 \text{ W}$
   b. Energy $= (1.8 \text{ kW})(30 \text{ days})(5 \text{ h/day}) = 270 \text{ kWh}$
   c. Cost $= (270 \text{ kWh})(\$0.08/\text{kWh}) = \$21.60$

26. **a.** $I = \dfrac{V}{R} = \dfrac{(115 \text{ V})}{(12000 \text{ }\Omega)} = 9.6 \times 10^{-3} \text{ A} = 9.6 \text{ mA}$

   b. $P = \dfrac{V^2}{R} = \dfrac{(115 \text{ V})^2}{(12000 \text{ }\Omega)} = 1.1 \text{ W}$

   c. Cost $= (1.1 \times 10^{-3} \text{ kW})(\$0.09/\text{kWh})(30 \text{ days})(24 \text{ h/day}) = \$0.07$

Chapter End Questions
Page 399.

1. Answers will vary. Most devices use electricity produced from fossil fuels.

2. The efficiency of a heater and the amount of power consumed are two important factors. Other factors include: rate of air flow, radiation pattern, and recommended area specifications.

3. **a.** 3 A
   b. Increasing the resistance to 8 Ω or decreasing the voltage to 6 V will reduce the current to 1.5 A.

4. resistance and current

Problems A
Page 399.

1. **a.** $P = IV = (200 \text{ A})(12 \text{ V}) = 2500 \text{ J/s}$
   b. $P = 2500 \text{ W}$
   c. Energy $= Pt = (2500 \text{ J/s})(10 \text{ s}) = 3 \times 10^4 \text{ J}$

Page 400.

2. $I = \dfrac{V}{R} = \dfrac{30 \text{ V}}{20 \text{ }\Omega} = 1.5 \text{ A}$

3. $V = IR = (1.5 \text{ A})(4 \text{ }\Omega) = 6 \text{ V}$

4. $V = IR = (8.0 \text{ A})(15 \text{ }\Omega) = 120 \text{ V}$

5. **a.** $I = \dfrac{V}{R} = \dfrac{15 \text{ V}}{6 \text{ }\Omega} = 2.5 \text{ A} = 3 \text{ A}$

   b. $Q = I^2 Rt = (3 \text{ A})^2 (6 \text{ }\Omega)(10 \text{ min})(60 \text{ s/min})$
   $= 3.24 \times 10^4 \text{ J} = 3 \times 10^4 \text{ J}$

6. **a.** $I = \dfrac{P}{V} = \dfrac{30 \text{ W}}{120 \text{ V}} = 0.25 \text{ A}$

   b. $R = \dfrac{V^2}{P} = \dfrac{(120 \text{ V})^2}{30 \text{ W}} = 480 \text{ }\Omega$

7. **a.** $I = \dfrac{V}{R} = \dfrac{120 \text{ V}}{4.0 \text{ }\Omega} = 3.0 \times 10^1 \text{ A}$

   b. Energy $= Pt = \dfrac{V^2 t}{R} = \dfrac{(120 \text{ V})^2 (5.0 \text{ min})(60 \text{ s/min})}{4.0 \text{ }\Omega}$
   $= 1.1 \times 10^6 \text{ J}$
   c. $Q = mc\Delta T$

   $\Delta T = \dfrac{Q}{mc} = \dfrac{(1.1 \times 10^6 \text{ J})}{(20.0 \text{ kg})(4180 \text{ J/kg} \cdot \text{C}°)} = 13°C$

Problems B

Page 400.

1. **a.** $I = \dfrac{V}{R} = \dfrac{110 \text{ V}}{22.0 \ \Omega} = 5.0 \text{ A}$

   b. $E_w = mg\Delta h = (1 \times 10^4 \text{ kg})(9.8 \text{ m/s}^2)(8.0 \text{ m})$
   $= 7.8 \times 10^5 \text{ J} = 8 \times 10^5 \text{ J}$
   $E_m = IVt = (5.0 \text{ A})(110 \text{ V})(3600 \text{ s}) = 2.0 \times 10^6 \text{ J}$

   $Eff = \dfrac{E_w}{E_m} \times 100\% = \dfrac{8 \times 10^5 \text{ J}}{2.0 \times 10^6 \text{ J}} \times 100\% = 40\%$

Page 401.

2. **a.** $P = IV = (0.050 \text{ A})(9.0 \text{ V}) = 0.45 \text{ W} = 4.5 \times 10^{-4} \text{ kW}$
   $Energy = Pt = (4.5 \times 10^{-4} \text{ kW})(300 \text{ h})$
   $= 0.14 \text{ kWh} = 0.1 \text{ kWh}$

$\dfrac{Cost}{kWh} = \dfrac{\$0.90}{0.1 \ \frac{\text{kWh}}{\text{kWh}}} = \$9$

b. $Cost = \dfrac{\$0.08}{kWh}(0.1 \text{ kWh}) = 1 \text{ cent}$

3. **a.** $V = IR = (1 \times 10^{-3} \text{ A})(1 \times 10^5 \ \Omega)$
   $= 1 \times 10^2 \text{ V} = 100 \text{ V}$

   b. $I = \dfrac{V}{R} = \dfrac{100 \text{ V}}{5 \times 10^3 \ \Omega} = 2 \times 10^{-2} \text{ A}$
   $= 20 \text{ mA} \quad \text{loss of muscle control}$

   c. $V = IR = (1 \times 10^{-3} \text{ A})(5 \times 10^3 \ \Omega) = 5 \text{ V}$

Series and Parallel Circuits   Chapter 24

Teaching Techniques

There are several physical concepts introduced in this chapter that deal with the fundamentals of circuits. The chapter forms a good foundation for students who wish to take technical courses in electricity or electronics.

The water analogy is often helpful when comparing series with parallel circuits. In a series circuit the water must flow through each device. The sum of individual voltage (energy) drops equals the total drop. If one resistor stops the flow, none have any flow. In a parallel circuit the voltage drop across each resistor is the same. The sum of the individual currents is the total flow in the circuit. If current in any resistive path stops, only that path is affected.

Try to stress the trends in working with effective resistance. Adding more series resistors always increases the resistance. Adding more parallel resistors decreases the resistance. The voltage divider provides many applications for a simple two resistor series circuit. House wiring is a good example of the use of parallel circuits.

Demonstrations

Use large demonstration voltmeters and ammeters to show currents and potential drops in series and parallel circuits. It is particularly difficult for students to figure out how to place a real ammeter in a parallel circuit. The fact that circuits must be opened and the meter inserted is easier to see on paper than on the bench. Work this out with the class.

Lamps of different powers provide demonstrations with good visual effects. Build series and parallel circuits, using commercial duplex outlets in metal boxes. Screw lamps into adapters that can be plugged into the sockets. First show the relative brightness of 25-W and 100-W lamps in parallel, then place them in series. Discuss and calculate currents and power in these two cases.

Laboratory Investigations

Series Circuits
Parallel Circuits
Series-Parallel Circuits

Performance Objectives

Goal: Students will obtain an understanding of the fundamentals of series and parallel circuits.

Objectives: Upon completion of the reading, questions, and problems, students will, on oral or written tests:

24:1	K/P/S	describe a series circuit; define effective resistance; state how the effective series resistance is calculated; find the current in a series circuit.
24:2	K/P/S	use Ohm's law to calculate voltage drops in series circuits; use in problems; define a voltage divider; use in solving problems.
24:3	K/P/S	describe a parallel circuit; state how the effective parallel resistance is calculated; find the current in a parallel circuit.
24:4	K	state the important characteristics of parallel circuits.
24:5	K/P/S	describe a series-parallel circuit; state how effective resistance is found using Ohm's law.
24:6	K/P	distinguish between ammeters

and voltmeters; state the important characteristics of each; describe how each is wired into a circuit.

A   Students will use laboratory materials in the prescribed manner when conducting lab investigations.

Upon completion of the reading and practice problems, students will exhibit an interest in physics by:

A/S   expanding on an answer to one or more of the questions or problems at the end of the chapter.

A/S   constructing a lemon galvanic cell, measuring and graphing voltage as a function of current flow, and determining the internal resistance from the voltage divider equation.

A   reading unassigned literature related to the ideas presented in the chapter.

Solutions to Problems

Page 404.

1. **a.** $R = 20\ \Omega + 20\ \Omega + 20\ \Omega = 60\ \Omega$

   b. $I = \dfrac{V}{R} = \dfrac{120\ V}{60\ \Omega} = 2\ A$

Page 405.

2. **a.** $R = 10\ \Omega + 15\ \Omega + 5\ \Omega = 30\ \Omega$

   b. $I = \dfrac{V}{R} = \dfrac{90\ V}{30\ \Omega} = 3\ A$

3. **a.** $R = \dfrac{V}{I} = \dfrac{120\ V}{0.6\ A} = 200\ \Omega$

   b. $R = \dfrac{200\ \Omega}{10} = 20\ \Omega$

4. **a.** $I = \dfrac{V}{R} = \dfrac{15\ V}{10\ \Omega} = 1.5\ A = 2\ A$

   b. $R = \dfrac{V}{I} = \dfrac{15\ V}{0.5\ A} = 30\ \Omega$

   $R = 30\ \Omega - 10\ \Omega = 20\ \Omega$

Page 406.

5. **a.** $R = 20.0\ \Omega + 30.0\ \Omega = 50.0\ \Omega$

b. $I = \dfrac{V}{R} = \dfrac{110\ V}{50.0\ \Omega} = 2.2\ A$

c. $V_{20} = IR_{20} = (2.2\ A)(20.0\ \Omega) = 44\ V$
$V_{30} = IR_{30} = (2.2\ A)(30.0\ \Omega) = 66\ V$

d. $V = V_{20} + V_{30} = 44\ V + 66\ V = 110\ V$

Page 407.

6. **a.** $R = 30.0\ \Omega + 30.0\ \Omega + 30.0\ \Omega = 90.0\ \Omega$

   b. $I = \dfrac{V}{R} = \dfrac{135\ V}{90.0\ \Omega} = 1.50\ A$

   c. $V = IR = (1.50\ A)(30.0\ \Omega) = 45.0\ V$

   d. $V_{total} = 45.0\ V + 45.0\ V + 45.0\ V = 135\ V$

7. **a.** $R = 3\ \Omega + 5\ \Omega + 4\ \Omega = 12\ \Omega$

   b. $I = \dfrac{V}{R} = \dfrac{12\ V}{12\ \Omega} = 1.0\ A$

   c. $V_3 = IR = (1.0\ A)(3\ \Omega) = 3\ V$
   $V_5 = IR = (1.0\ A)(5\ \Omega) = 5\ V$
   $V_4 = IR = (1.0\ A)(4\ \Omega) = 4\ V$

   d. $V = V_3 + V_4 + V_5 = 3\ V + 4\ V + 5\ V = 12\ V$

8. **a.** $R = \dfrac{V}{I} = \dfrac{12\ V}{0.6\ A} = 20\ \Omega$

   $20\ \Omega = R_v + 10.0\ \Omega$
   $R_v = 10\ \Omega$

   b. $V = IR = (0.6\ A)(10\ \Omega)$
   $V_{10} = V_R = 6\ V$

9. **a.** $I = \dfrac{V}{R_T} = \dfrac{9.0\ V}{(500\ \Omega + 400\ \Omega)} = 0.01\ A$

   $V_2 = IR_2 = (0.01\ A)(400\ \Omega) = 4\ V$

   b. $I = \dfrac{V}{R_T} = \dfrac{9.0\ V}{(500\ \Omega + 4.0 \times 10^3\ \Omega)} = 2 \times 10^{-3}\ A$

   $V_2 = IR_2 = (2 \times 10^{-3}\ A)(4.0 \times 10^3\ \Omega) = 8\ V$

   c. $I = \dfrac{V}{R_T} = \dfrac{9.0\ V}{(500\ \Omega + 4.0 \times 10^5\ \Omega)} = 2 \times 10^{-5}\ A$

   $V_2 = IR_2 = (2 \times 10^{-5}\ A)(4.0 \times 10^5\ \Omega) = 8\ V$

Page 408.

10. $V_2 = \dfrac{V}{R_1 + R_2} R_2$

   $R_2 = \dfrac{V_2(R_1 + R_2)}{V}$

   $R_2 - \dfrac{V_2 R_2}{V} = \dfrac{V_2 R_1}{V}$

   $R_2\left(1 - \dfrac{V_2}{V}\right) = \dfrac{V_2 R_1}{V}$

   $R_2 = \dfrac{V_2 R_1}{V\left(1 - \dfrac{V_2}{V}\right)} = \dfrac{(4.0\ V)(100\ \Omega)}{(12\ V)\left(1 - \dfrac{4\ V}{12\ V}\right)} = 50\ \Omega$

Page 410.

11. a. $\dfrac{1}{R} = \dfrac{1}{15\ \Omega} + \dfrac{1}{15\ \Omega} + \dfrac{1}{15\ \Omega} = \dfrac{3}{15\ \Omega}$

$R = \dfrac{15\ \Omega}{3} = 5.00\ \Omega$

b. $I = \dfrac{V}{R} = \dfrac{30.0\ V}{5.00\ \Omega} = 6.00\ A$

c. $I = \dfrac{V}{R_{15}} = \dfrac{30.0\ V}{15.0\ \Omega} = 2.00\ A$

12. a. $\dfrac{1}{R} = \dfrac{1}{10.0\ \Omega} + \dfrac{1}{10.0\ \Omega} = \dfrac{2}{10\ \Omega}$

$R = \dfrac{10\ \Omega}{2} = 5.0\ \Omega$

b. $I = \dfrac{V}{R} = \dfrac{15\ V}{5.0\ \Omega} = 3.0\ A$

c. $I = \dfrac{V}{R_{10}} = \dfrac{15\ V}{10\ \Omega} = 1.5\ A$

13. a. $\dfrac{1}{R} = \dfrac{1}{120.0\ \Omega} + \dfrac{1}{60.0\ \Omega} + \dfrac{1}{40.0\ \Omega}$

$\dfrac{1}{R} = 0.05\dfrac{1}{\Omega}$

$R = \dfrac{1}{0.05\ \Omega} = 20.0\ \Omega$

b. $I = \dfrac{V}{R} = \dfrac{120.0\ V}{20.0\ \Omega} = 6.0\ A$

c. $I_1 = \dfrac{V}{R_1} = \dfrac{120.0\ V}{120.0\ \Omega} = 1.0\ A$

$I_2 = \dfrac{V}{R_2} = \dfrac{120.0\ V}{60.0\ \Omega} = 2.0\ A$

$I_3 = \dfrac{V}{R_3} = \dfrac{120.0\ V}{40.0\ \Omega} = 3.0\ A$

14. a. $I_1 = \dfrac{V}{R_1} = \dfrac{36\ V}{6.0\ \Omega} = 6.0\ A$

$I_2 = \dfrac{V}{R_2} = \dfrac{36\ V}{18\ \Omega} = 2.0\ A$

$I_3 = \dfrac{V}{R_3} = \dfrac{36\ V}{90.0\ \Omega} = 0.40\ A$

b. $I = I_1 + I_2 + I_3 = 6.0\ A + 2.0\ A + 0.40\ A = 8.4\ A$

c. $\dfrac{1}{R} = \dfrac{1}{R_1} + \dfrac{1}{R_2} + \dfrac{1}{R_3} = \dfrac{1}{6.0\ \Omega} + \dfrac{1}{18\ \Omega} + \dfrac{1}{90.0\ \Omega} = 0.23\dfrac{1}{\Omega}$

$R = \dfrac{1}{0.23\ \Omega} = 4.3\ \Omega$

15. a. $I_1 = \dfrac{V}{R_1} = \dfrac{150\ V}{75\ \Omega} = 2.0\ A$

b. $I_2 = \dfrac{V}{R_2} = \dfrac{150\ V}{150\ \Omega} = 1.0\ A$

c. $I = I_1 + I_2 = 2.0\ A + 1.0\ A = 3.0\ A$

d. $\dfrac{1}{R} = \dfrac{1}{R_1} + \dfrac{1}{R_s} = \dfrac{1}{75\ \Omega} + \dfrac{1}{150\ \Omega} = \dfrac{3}{150\ \Omega}$

$R = \dfrac{150}{3}\ \Omega = 5.0 \times 10^1\ \Omega$

e. $I = \dfrac{V}{R} = \dfrac{150\ V}{50\ \Omega} = 3.0\ A$, yes it agrees with the current found in part c.

Page 414.

16. a.

b. $\dfrac{1}{R} = \dfrac{1}{60\ \Omega} + \dfrac{1}{60\ \Omega} = \dfrac{2}{60\ \Omega}$

$R = \dfrac{60\ \Omega}{2} = 30\ \Omega$

c. $R_{eff} = 30\ \Omega + 30\ \Omega = 60\ \Omega$

d. $I = \dfrac{V}{R} = \dfrac{120\ V}{60\ \Omega} = 2\ A$

e. $V_3 = IR_3 = (2\ A)(30\ \Omega) = 60\ V$
f. $V = IR = (2\ A)(30\ \Omega) = 60\ V$

g. $I = \dfrac{V}{R_1} = \dfrac{V}{R_2} = \dfrac{60\ V}{60\ \Omega} = 1\ A$

17. a.

b. $\dfrac{1}{R} = \dfrac{1}{15\ \Omega} + \dfrac{1}{15\ \Omega} + \dfrac{1}{15\ \Omega} = \dfrac{3}{15\ \Omega}$

$R = \dfrac{15\ \Omega}{3} = 5.0\ \Omega$

c. $R_{eff} = 5\ \Omega + 10\ \Omega = 15\ \Omega$

d. $I = \dfrac{V}{R_{eff}} = \dfrac{45 \text{ V}}{15 \text{ }\Omega} = 3.0 \text{ A}$

e. $V = IR = (3.0 \text{ A})(10 \text{ }\Omega) = 30 \text{ V}$

f. $V = IR = (3.0 \text{ A})(5.0 \text{ }\Omega) = 15 \text{ V}$

g. $I = \dfrac{V}{R} = \dfrac{15 \text{ V}}{15 \text{ }\Omega} = 1.0 \text{ A}$

Page 415.

18. **a.** Three resistors in parallel have an equivalent resistance of

$$\dfrac{1}{R_e} = \dfrac{1}{15 \text{ }\Omega} + \dfrac{1}{15 \text{ }\Omega} + \dfrac{1}{15 \text{ }\Omega} = \dfrac{3}{15 \text{ }\Omega}$$

$$R_e = \dfrac{15 \text{ }\Omega}{3} = 5.0 \text{ }\Omega$$

The two parallel sets in series have a total resistance of
$R = 5 \text{ }\Omega + 5 \text{ }\Omega = 1.0 \times 10^1 \text{ }\Omega$

b. $I = \dfrac{V}{R} = \dfrac{12 \text{ V}}{1.0 \times 10^1 \text{ }\Omega} = 1.2 \text{ A}$

c. The current through each of the three 15 Ω resistors in parallel will be equal.

$$I_{15} = \dfrac{1}{3}(1.2 \text{ A}) = 0.40 \text{ A}$$

Chapter End Questions

Pages 417-418.

1. **a.** No current will flow in the resistor.

   b. The current in the resistor will remain the same.

2. In a series circuit, the current is opposed by each resistance in turn. The total resistance is the sum. In a parallel circuit each resistance provides an additional path for current flow. The result is a decrease in the total resistance.

3. The 30-Ω resistors can be used in parallel. Three 30-Ω resistors in parallel will give a 10-Ω resistance. Two 30-Ω resistors in parallel will give a 15-Ω resistance. This is a common but wasteful practice.

4. **a.** series **b.** series **c.** parallel
   d. series **e.** parallel **f.** series
   g. series **h.** parallel **i.** parallel

5. The purpose of a fuse is to prevent conductors from being overloaded with current and, through the resulting heating effect, cause fires. A fuse is simply a short length of wire which will melt due to the same heating effect if the current is over a certain maximum.

6. A short circuit has extremely low resistance. A short circuit is dangerous because a low resistance across any potential difference will draw a large current. The heating effect can then cause a fire. A person standing in water who touches a conductor or light switch can also present the potential difference with a short circuit, which can produce disastrous results.

7. An ammeter must have low resistance because it is placed directly in the circuit. If its resistance were high, it would change the total resistance of the circuit and, thus, serve to reduce the current flowing in the circuit, thereby defeating its own purpose.

8. A voltmeter is placed in parallel with the portion of the circuit across which it is to measure the difference in potential. It must have very high resistance for the very same reason that an ammeter has low resistance. If the voltmeter had low resistance, it would lower the resistance of the portion of the circuit it is across and increase the current in the circuit. This would produce a higher voltage drop across the part of the circuit where the voltmeter is located and the meter would be defeating its own purpose.

Problems A

Page 418.

1. **a.** $R = R_1 + R_2 = 5 \text{ }\Omega + 7 \text{ }\Omega = 12 \text{ }\Omega$

   b. $I_1 = \dfrac{V}{R_1} = \dfrac{12 \text{ V}}{12 \text{ }\Omega} = 1.0 \text{ A}$

   c. The current passes through both resistors since they are in series.
   $I_1 = I_2 = 1.0 \text{ A}$

   d. $V_1 = IR_1 = (1.0 \text{ A})(5 \text{ }\Omega) = 5 \text{ V}$
   $V_2 = IR_2 = (1.0 \text{ A})(7 \text{ }\Omega) = 7 \text{ V}$

2. **a.** $R = R_1 + R_2 + R_3 = 6 \text{ }\Omega + 6 \text{ }\Omega + 3 \text{ }\Omega = 15 \text{ }\Omega$

   b. $I = \dfrac{V}{R} = \dfrac{6.0 \text{ V}}{15 \text{ }\Omega} = 0.40 \text{ A}$

   c. $V_1 = IR_1 = (0.40 \text{ A})(6.0 \text{ }\Omega) = 2.4 \text{ V}$
   $V_1 = V_2 = 2.4 \text{ V}$
   $V_3 = IR_3 = (0.40 \text{ A})(3.0 \text{ V}) = 1.2 \text{ V}$

3. $R = \dfrac{V}{I} = \dfrac{6.0 \text{ V}}{0.50 \text{ A}} = 12 \text{ }\Omega$

   $R = 2 \text{ }\Omega + R_V$
   $R_V = R - 2.0 \text{ }\Omega = 12 \text{ }\Omega - 2.0 \text{ }\Omega = 1 \times 10^1 \text{ V}$

4. $R = \dfrac{V}{I} = \dfrac{60.0 \text{ V}}{4.0 \text{ A}} = 15 \text{ }\Omega$

   $R = 8 \text{ }\Omega + R_s$
   $R_s = 15 \text{ }\Omega - 8 \text{ }\Omega = 7 \text{ }\Omega$

Page 419.

5. $R = \dfrac{V}{I} = \dfrac{120 \text{ V}}{0.75 \text{ A}} = 160 \text{ }\Omega$

   The total resistance, R, is the sum of the ten identical lights, or just $(10)(R_1)$, where R_1 is the resistance of one light.
   $10 R_1 = 160 \text{ }\Omega$
   $R_1 = 16 \text{ }\Omega$

6. **a.** $R = R_1 + R_2 = 20 \text{ }\Omega + 5 \text{ }\Omega = 25 \text{ }\Omega$

   b. $I = \dfrac{V}{R} = \dfrac{50 \text{ V}}{25 \text{ }\Omega} = 2 \text{ A}$

c. $V_1 = IR_1 = (2\ A)(20\ \Omega) = 40\ V$
$V_2 = IR_2 = (2\ A)(5\ \Omega) = 10\ V$

d. $P_1 = IV_1 = (2\ A)(40\ V) = 80\ W$
$P_2 = IV_2 = (2\ A)(10\ V) = 20\ W$

7. a. $\dfrac{1}{R} = \dfrac{1}{R_1} + \dfrac{1}{R_2} = \dfrac{1}{20.0\ \Omega} + \dfrac{1}{5.0\ \Omega} = \dfrac{1}{20.0\ \Omega} + \dfrac{4}{20\ \Omega} = \dfrac{5}{20\ \Omega}$

$R = \dfrac{20\ \Omega}{5} = 4.0\ \Omega$

b. $I = \dfrac{V}{R} = \dfrac{50.0\ V}{4.0\ \Omega} = 13\ A$

c. $I_1 = \dfrac{V}{R_1} = \dfrac{50.0\ V}{20.0\ \Omega} = 2.50\ A$

$I_2 = \dfrac{V}{R_2} = \dfrac{50.0\ V}{5.0\ \Omega} = 1.0 \times 10^1\ A$

d. $V_1 = I_1R_1 = (2.5\ A)(20.0\ \Omega) = 5.0 \times 10^1\ V$
$V_2 = I_2R_2 = (1.0 \times 10^1\ A)(5.0\ \Omega) = 5.0 \times 10^1\ V$

e. $P_1 = I_1V_1 = (2.5\ A)(5.0 \times 10^1\ V) = 130\ W$
$P_2 = I_2V_2 = (1.0 \times 10^1\ A)(5.0 \times 10^1\ V)$
$= 5.0 \times 10^2\ W$

f. With the same potential difference, two resistors in parallel consume much more power than if they were wired in series.

8. a. $\dfrac{1}{R} = \dfrac{1}{R_1} + \dfrac{1}{R_2} = \dfrac{1}{16.0\ \Omega} + \dfrac{1}{20.0\ \Omega}$

$R = \dfrac{1}{0.1125\ \Omega} = 8.89\ \Omega$

b. $I = \dfrac{V}{R} = \dfrac{40\ V}{8.89\ \Omega} = 4.50\ A$

c. $I_1 = \dfrac{V}{R_1} = \dfrac{40.0\ V}{16.0\ \Omega} = 2.50\ A$

9. a. $\dfrac{1}{R} = \dfrac{1}{240\ \Omega} + \dfrac{1}{240\ \Omega} + \dfrac{1}{240\ \Omega} + \dfrac{1}{240\ \Omega} = \dfrac{4}{240\ \Omega}$

$R = \dfrac{240\ \Omega}{4} = 6.0 \times 10^1\ \Omega$

$I = \dfrac{V}{R} = \dfrac{120\ V}{6.0 \times 10^1\ \Omega} = 2.0\ A$

b. $\dfrac{1}{R} = \dfrac{6}{240\ \Omega}$

$R = \dfrac{240\ \Omega}{6} = 4.0 \times 10^1\ \Omega$

$I = \dfrac{V}{R} = \dfrac{120\ V}{4.0 \times 10^1\ \Omega} = 3.0\ A$

c. $\dfrac{1}{R} = \dfrac{1}{4.0 \times 10^1} + \dfrac{1}{10.0\ \Omega} = \dfrac{5}{40\ \Omega}$

$R = \dfrac{40\ \Omega}{5} = 8.0\ \Omega$

$I = \dfrac{V}{R} = \dfrac{120\ V}{8.0\ \Omega} = 15\ A$

10. The equivalent resistance of the three 30.0 Ω resistors in parallel is

$\dfrac{1}{R} = \dfrac{1}{30.0\ \Omega} + \dfrac{1}{30.0\ \Omega} + \dfrac{1}{30.0\ \Omega} = \dfrac{3}{30.0\ \Omega}$

$R = \dfrac{30.0\ \Omega}{3} = 10.0\ \Omega$

$R_{Total} = 10.0\ \Omega + 10.0\ \Omega = 20.0\ \Omega$

$I_1 = \dfrac{V}{R_{Total}} = \dfrac{45.0\ V}{20.0\ \Omega} = 2.25\ A$

$V_1 = (I_1)(10\ \Omega) = (2.25\ A)(10\ \Omega) = 22.5\ V$
An ammeter has an internal resistance of zero, so
$V_2 = V_3 = 45.0\ V - 22.5\ V = 22.5\ V$

$I_2 = \dfrac{V_2}{R_2} = \dfrac{22.5\ V}{30.0\ \Omega} = 0.750\ A$

Page 420.

11. The three 15 Ω resistors in parallel have an equivalent resistance of

$\dfrac{1}{R} = \dfrac{1}{15.0\ \Omega} + \dfrac{1}{15.0\ \Omega} + \dfrac{1}{15.0\ \Omega} = \dfrac{3}{15.0\ \Omega}$

$R = \dfrac{15.0\ \Omega}{3} = 5.00\ \Omega$

The equivalent resistance of the 40.0 Ω and 60.0 Ω in parallel is

$\dfrac{1}{R} = \dfrac{1}{60.0\ \Omega} + \dfrac{1}{40.0\ \Omega} = \dfrac{2}{120\ \Omega} + \dfrac{3}{120\ \Omega} = \dfrac{5}{120\ \Omega}$

$R = \dfrac{120\ \Omega}{5} = 24.0\ \Omega$

The total resistance in the circuit is
$R_{Total} = 10.0\ \Omega + 5.0\ \Omega + 6.0\ \Omega + 24.0\ \Omega = 45.0\ \Omega$
The total current passing through the circuit is I_3,

$I_3 = \dfrac{V}{R_{Total}} = \dfrac{90.0\ V}{45.0\ \Omega} = 2.00\ A$

$V_1 = I_3R = (2.00\ A)(10.0\ \Omega) = 20.0\ V$
$V_2 = I_3R = (2.00\ A)(6.00\ \Omega) = 12.0\ V$
I_3 divides itself equally in the three 15.0 Ω resistors,

so $I_1 = \dfrac{I_3}{3} = \dfrac{2.00\ A}{3} = 0.667\ A$

The voltage drop across the 15.0 Ω is
$V = IR = (2.00\ A)(5.00\ \Omega) = 10.0\ V$
The sum of the voltage drops across the resistors in the circuit is 90.0 V
$90.0\ V = V_1 + 10.0\ V + V_2 + V_3 = 20.0\ V + 10.0\ V + 12.0\ V + V_3$
$V_3 = 48.0\ V$

$I_2 = \dfrac{V_3}{R} = \dfrac{48.0\ V}{60.0\ \Omega} = 0.800\ A$

12. In the 10 Ω resistor,
$P_1 = I_1V_1 = (2.25\ A)(22.5\ V) = 50.6\ W$
In each of the 30 Ω resistors the power will be equal
$P = IV = (0.750\ A)(22.5\ V) = 16.9\ W$

Problems B

Page 420.

1. a.

b. $\Delta Q = mc\Delta T = (100.0\text{ g})(4.2\text{ J/g}\cdot\text{C}°)(75°\text{C}) = 32\,000\text{ J}$
$\Delta Q = mLv = (100.0\text{ g})(2300\text{ J/g}) = 230\,000\text{ J}$
$\Delta Q_{Total} = 32\,000\text{ J} + 230\,000\text{ J} = 260\,000\text{ J}$
Energy is provided at the rate of
$P = IV = (5.0\text{ A})(50.0\text{ V}) = 250\text{ J/s}$

The time required is t $= \dfrac{260\,000\text{ J}}{250\text{ J/s}} = 1.0 \times 10^3\text{ s}$

2. a. $R = 0.25\ \Omega + 0.25\ \Omega + 240.00 = 240.50\ \Omega$

b. $I = \dfrac{V}{R} = \dfrac{120\text{ V}}{240.50\ \Omega} = 0.50\text{ A}$

$P = IV = (0.50\text{ A})(120\text{ V}) = 60\text{ W}$
c. $V = IR = (0.50\text{ A})(0.50\ \Omega) = 0.25\text{ V}$

Page 421.

3. a. $\dfrac{1}{R} = \dfrac{1}{240.00\ \Omega} + \dfrac{1}{6.0\ \Omega} = 0.17\ \Omega$

$R = \dfrac{1}{0.17}\ \Omega = 5.9\ \Omega$

$R_{eff} = 5.9\ \Omega + 0.25\ \Omega + 0.25\ \Omega = 6.4\ \Omega$

b. $I = \dfrac{V}{R} = \dfrac{120\text{ V}}{6.4\ \Omega} = 19\text{ A}$

c. $V = IR = (19\text{ A})(0.50\ \Omega) = 9.5\text{ V}$
d. $V = 120\text{ V} - 9.5\text{ V} = 110\text{ V}$ remains
This will cause a momentary dimming.

Magnetic Fields   Chapter 25

Teaching Techniques

Students have probably studied characteristics of magnets in previous science courses. Begin with a brief review of these characteristics before going into magnetic fields.

Both the SI unit of magnetic induction, tesla, and its equivalent dimensions, newton per ampere-meter are used in this chapter.

The electric field exerts forces on static changes; magnetic fields exert forces on moving charges. This chapter contains less arithmetic material than most, as left hand rules are used to predict the direction of forces and fields. The concepts and processes developed in this chapter are important for the remaining material on electromagnetism and for the study of the atom.

Demonstrations

Section 25:1

Demonstrate field patterns with bar magnets and iron filings. You can do this for all to see using an overhead projector and a thin sheet of glass. Place the magnets on the projector under the glass and sprinkle the filings on the glass.

Chapter 25

Section 25:2

Demonstrate field patterns using direct current and iron filings. Connect a wire to a dry cell or power supply and run current through the wire. Place filings on cardboard over the wire and observe the concentric circles.

Section 25:3

Construct a similar apparatus, but with a coil of wire threaded through the cardboard.

Section 25:4

Domain alignment can be aided by mechanical shock. Magnetize a piece of soft steel by induction, placing it on the end of a strong magnet. Show that the steel can pick up a paper clip only when it is on the magnet. While it is touching the magnet strike the steel sharply with a hammer. It now should retain some magnetism. Throwing it violently on the floor will demagnetize it, as demonstrated by different (unmagnetized) paper clips. Note that this method can also be used to remagnetize old bar magnets.

Section 25:6

Arrange a piece of flexible wire between the poles of a strong magnet. Use a 6-V battery to produce a current in the wire and have students observe the resulting motion. Similarly, two long, flexible, current carrying wires in parallel about 2 cm apart will either attract or repel each other, depending on the relative direction of current flow.

Sections 25:8 and 25:9

You should have some old broken meters and motors partially dismantled to show their construction.

Section 25:10

Bringing a magnet near the face of an oscilloscope demonstrates the force of a field on a beam of electrons. Have students use the left-hand rule to predict the direction of the force.

Laboratory Investigations

Magnetic Fields Around Magnets
Current and Field Strength
Magnetic Fields Around a
*   Current-Carrying Wire*

Performance Objectives

Goal: Students will learn how magnetic fields are produced, the forces they exert on moving charges, and applications of these effects.

Objectives: Upon completion of the reading, questions, and problems, students will, on oral or written tests:

25:1	K	list the properties of magnets.
25:2	K/P	describe the magnetic fields around permanent magnets and the field lines between like and unlike poles.
25:3	K/P	recognize that electric currents produce magnetic fields; describe the field around a current carrying wire; explain the use of the left-hand rule in finding the direction of this field.
25:4	K/P	explain the magnetic field due to several loops of wire; apply the left-hand rule to determine the direction.
25:5	K/P	state the origin of magnetism in materials.
25:6	K/P	define magnetic induction; display an understanding of direction of the force on a current-carrying wire in a magnetic field.
25:7	P/S/K	list the factors that determine the force on a wire; solve problems involving force, current, field strength, and length.

25:8	K/P	explain the design and operation of the galvanometer.
25:9	K/P	explain the design and operation of the electric motor.
25:10	K/P/S	demonstrate an ability to follow the derivation of the equation $F = qvB$. Use the equation to solve typical problems.
	S/A	Students will use laboratory materials in the prescribed manner when conducting lab investigations.

Upon completion of the reading and practice problems, students will exhibit an interest in physics by:

A/S	expanding on an answer to one or more of the questions or problems at the end of the chapter.
A/S	constructing an electric motor and demonstrating its applications of physical principles.
A	reading unassigned literature related to the ideas presented in the chapter.

Solutions to Problems

Page 426.

1. The induced north pole of the filing is located in the direction of the field lines.
2. **a.** repulsive   **b.** attractive

Page 427.

3. **a.** From north to south   **b.** west
4. **a.** Between the two wires.
   b. Along a plane that is equal in distance from each wire.
   c. Along a plane that is equal in distance from each wire.

Page 429.

5. It will point toward the bottom of the page.

Page 433.

6. $F = BIL$

   $$B = \frac{F}{IL} = \frac{0.04 \text{ N}}{(2.0 \text{ A})(0.10 \text{ m})} = 0.20 \text{ T}$$

7. $F = BIL = (0.40 \text{ N/A} \cdot \text{m})(8.0 \text{ A})(0.5 \text{ m}) = 1.6 \text{ N}$

Page 434.

8. $F = BIL$

   $$B = \frac{F}{IL} = \frac{0.6 \text{ N}}{(6.0 \text{ A})(0.75 \text{ m})} = 0.13 = 0.1 \text{ T}$$

9. $F = BIL$

$$B = \frac{F}{IL} = \frac{0.35 \text{ N}}{(6.0 \text{ A})(0.4 \text{ m})} = 0.145 \text{ N/A} \cdot \text{m} = 0.1 \text{ T}$$

10. $F = BIL$

$$I = \frac{F}{BL} = \frac{1.8 \text{ N}}{(0.40 \text{ T})(6.0 \text{ m})} = 0.75 \text{ A}$$

11. **a.** $F = BIL$

$$\frac{F}{L} = BI = (5 \times 10^{-5} \text{ N/A} \cdot \text{m})(2.0 \times 10^2 \text{ A}) = 1 \times 10^{-2} \text{ N/m}$$

b. Down toward the earth.

c. No, it is small compared to the weight of the line.

Page 438.

12. $F = Bqv = (6.0 \times 10^{-2} \text{ T})(1.6 \times 10^{-19} \text{ C})(2.5 \times 10^7 \text{ m/s}) = 2.4 \times 10^{-13} \text{ N}$

13. $F = Bqv = (0.50 \text{ T})(1.6 \times 10^{-19} \text{ C})(4.0 \times 10^6 \text{ m/s}) = 3.2 \times 10^{-13} \text{ N}$

14. $F = Bqv = (9.0 \times 10^{-2} \text{ T})(2)(1.6 \times 10^{-19} \text{ C})(3.0 \times 10^4 \text{ m/s}) = 8.64 \times 10^{-16} \text{ N} = 8.6 \times 10^{-16} \text{ N}$

15. $F = Bqv = (4.0 \times 10^{-2} \text{ T})(3)(1.6 \times 10^{-19} \text{ C})(9.0 \times 10^6 \text{ m/s}) = 1.7 \times 10^{-13} \text{ N}$

16. $F = Bqv = (5.0 \times 10^{-2} \text{ T})(2)(1.6 \times 10^{-19} \text{ C})(4.0 \times 10^4 \text{ m/s}) = 6.4 \times 10^{-16} \text{ N}$

17. $F = Bqv = (0.6 \text{ T })(1.6 \times 10^{-19} \text{ C})(2.5 \times 10^7 \text{ m/s}) = 2.4 \times 10^{-12} \text{ N}$

18. $F = ma$

$$a = \frac{F}{m} = \frac{2.4 \times 10^{-12} \text{ N}}{9.0 \times 10^{-31} \text{ kg}} = 2.7 \times 10^{18} \text{ m/s}^2$$

Chapter End Questions

Pages 439-440.

1. Like poles repel, unlike poles attract.

2. Iron, cobalt, and nickel.

3. A permanent magnet is usually a steel or iron-alloy bar that maintains its magnetic properties for some time. A temporary magnet is a magnet that will display magnetic properties only while under the influence of a strong magnetic field.

4. See text page 425.

5. See text page 425.

6. See text page 426.

7. Grasp wire with left hand keeping thumb pointing in the direction of the electron flow. Fingers will encircle wire and point in the direction of the field.

8. Grasp coil with left hand keeping fingers encircling coil in the direction of the current flow through the loops. Thumb of left hand will point at the north-seeking pole of the electromagnet.

9. Point fingers of left hand in direction of magnetic field. Point thumb in direction of electron flow in wire. Palm of hand then faces in direction of force on wire.

10. Induction of the field B (field strength), the magnitude of the current in the wire, and the length of the wire that is in the field.

Problems A

Page 440.

1. $B = \dfrac{F}{IL} = \dfrac{0.40 \text{ N}}{8.0 \text{ A} \times 0.50 \text{ m}} = 0.10 \text{ N/A} \cdot \text{m} = 0.10 \text{ T}$

2. $F = BIL = (0.30 \text{ N/A} \cdot \text{m})(6.0 \text{ A})(0.25 \text{ m}) = 0.45 \text{ N}$

3. $B = \dfrac{F}{IL} = \dfrac{0.60 \text{ N}}{10.0 \text{ A} \times 1.50 \text{ m}} = 0.040 \text{ N/A} \cdot \text{m}$

$$= 4.0 \times 10^{-2} \text{ T}$$

4. $F = BIL = (0.60 \text{ N/A} \cdot \text{m})(5.0 \text{ A})(0.80 \text{ m}) = 2.4 \text{ N}$

5. $I = \dfrac{F}{BL} = \dfrac{0.12 \text{ N}}{(5 \times 10^{-5} \text{ N/A} \cdot \text{m})(0.80 \text{ m})} = 3 \times 10^3 \text{ A}$

6. $L = \dfrac{F}{BI} = \dfrac{3.6 \text{ N}}{(0.80 \text{ N/A} \cdot \text{m})(7.5 \text{ A})} = 0.60 \text{ m}$

7. $v = F/qB = \dfrac{4.1 \times 10^{-13} \text{ N}}{(0.61 \text{ N/A} \cdot \text{m})(1.6 \times 10^{-19} \text{ C})}$

$$= 4.2 \times 10^6 \text{ m/s}$$

8. $F = Bqv \qquad q = F/Bv$

$$\text{particles} = q\left(\frac{\text{charges}}{1.6 \times 10^{-19} \text{ C}}\right) = \frac{F}{Bv}\left(\frac{\text{charges}}{1.6 \times 10^{-19} \text{ C}}\right)$$

$$= \frac{(5.78 \times 10^{-16} \text{ N})(\text{charges})}{(3.2 \times 10^{-2} \text{ T})(5.65 \times 10^4 \text{ m/s})(1.6 \times 10^{-19} \text{ C})}$$

$$= 2 \text{ charges}$$

9. $B = \dfrac{F}{qv} = \dfrac{(5.00 \times 10^{-12} \text{ N})}{(4.21 \times 10^7 \text{ m/s})(1.6 \times 10^{-19} \text{ C})}$

$$= 7.4 \times 10^{-1} \text{ T}$$

10. $a = \dfrac{F}{m} = \dfrac{(5.00 \times 10^{-12} \text{ N})}{(1.88 \times 10^{-28} \text{ kg})} = 2.7 \times 10^{16} \text{ m/s}^2$

Problems B

Page 440.

1. a. $F = Bqv = (0.10 \text{ T})(1.6 \times 10^{-19} \text{ C})(3.0 \times 10^7 \text{ m/s})$
$= 4.8 \times 10^{-13} \text{ N}$

b. $F = \dfrac{mv^2}{r}$

$r = \dfrac{mv^2}{F} = \dfrac{(1.67 \times 10^{-27} \text{ kg})(3.0 \times 10^7 \text{ m/s})^2}{4.8 \times 10^{-13} \text{ N}}$

$= 3.1 \text{ m}$

2. a. P_2 to P_1

b. $E = (20\,000 \text{ J/C})(1.6 \times 10^{-19} \text{ C}) = 3.2 \times 10^{-15} \text{ J}$

$E = \dfrac{1}{2}mv^2$

$v = \sqrt{\dfrac{2E}{m}} = \sqrt{\dfrac{(2)(3.2 \times 10^{-15} \text{ J})}{(9.0 \times 10^{-31} \text{ kg})}} = 8.4 \times 10^7 \text{ m/s}$

c. Using the left-hand rule it will move clockwise.

3. The spring will oscillate up and down. Current will cause the coils to attract each other, raising the coil from the mercury.

Electromagnetic Induction   Chapter 26

Teaching Techniques

The generation of electric current by changing magnetic fields is described. Alternating current is discussed. The close relationships between electric and magnetic fields is described.

Stress that the term "electromotive force" is misleading because it is not a force but a potential, or an energy increase per coulomb of charge. Point out that EMF could be applied to batteries as well. Ask students what would happen if they drove into a gas station and asked someone to "check the seat of EMF," i.e., the battery voltage.

Demonstrations

Section 26:1

Connect a length of wire to a sensitive galvanometer and move the wire through the poles of a strong magnet. Show that the needle moves only when the wire moves and that the faster the motion, the greater the deflection. Show that the direction of the deflection depends on the direction of wire motion, and, by inverting the magnet, the direction of the field. Gathering loops of wire will show the effects of the length of wire in the field, as well as number of turns for later sections.

Sections 26:3 and 26:5

Connect a simple motor (St. Louis type) to a battery and demonstrate the transfer of electrical to mechanical energy. Then disconnect the battery and connect a galvanometer to the wires. Flip the armature and show the transfer of mechanical to electrical energy. By varying the speed with which a small hand-generator is turned, you can easily demonstrate that the current generated is proportional to the speed with which the wire moves through the field. An oscilloscope can be used to view the alternating current generated.

Section 26:8

There are many commercial devices to demonstrate transformer action. Show the effect of the core. Stress the connection between number of turns and length of wire in the field.

Films

Magnetic Fields and Electric Currents,
Parts 1 and 2 (BFA-Ealing film)

Laboratory Investigations

Induced Current and Lenz's Law
The DC Generator—The DC Motor
Energy Transfer by an Electric Motor

Performance Objectives

Goal: Students will gain knowledge of the origin and character of induced current and its applications.

Objectives: Upon completion of the reading, questions, and problems, students will, on oral or written tests:

26:1	K/P	explain the process by which a changing magnetic field produces a force on electrons and thus a current; apply the left hand rule correctly.
26:2	K/P/S	define EMF; state the meaning of the terms BLv which describe the magnitude of the EMF; understand the limitations of this equation; apply to the solution of problems.
26:3	K/P	explain the generation of current by a rotating armature in an electric generator.

26:4	K/P/S	explain the difference between peak and effective current and voltage and use in solving problems.
26:5	K	compare generators and motors.
26:6	K/P	state Lenz's law; explain back-EMF and its relation to energy transfer in motors and generators.
26:7	K/P	explain the nature of self-inductance and its effects in AC and DC circuits.
26:8	K/P/S	describe the transformer; explain the effect of the ratio of turns in the primary and secondary; solve transformer problems.
	S/A	Students will use laboratory materials in the prescribed manner when conducting lab investigations.

Upon completion of the reading and practice problems, students will exhibit an interest in physics by:

A/S	expanding on an answer to one or more of the questions or problems at the end of the chapter.
A/S	dismantle an old transformer, rewinding it with specific turn ratios, and measuring voltage on primary and secondary.
A	reading unassigned literature related to the ideas presented in the chapter.

Solutions to Problems

Page 446.

1. a. $EMF = BLv = (0.4 \text{ N/A} \cdot \text{m})(0.5 \text{ m})(20 \text{ m/s}) = 4 \text{ V}$
  b. $V = IR$

$$I = \frac{V}{R} = \frac{4 \text{ V}}{6.0 \text{ }\Omega} = 0.7 \text{ A}$$

2. a. $EMF = BLv = (5.0 \times 10^{-5} \text{ N/A} \cdot \text{m})(2.0 \times 10^1 \text{ m})(120 \text{ m/s})$
    $= 0.12 \text{ V}$
  b. $V = IR$

$$I = \frac{V}{R} = \frac{0.12 \text{ V}}{3.0 \times 10^2 \text{ }\Omega} = 0.40 \text{ mA}$$

3. Using the left-hand rule, the north pole is at the top.

4. $EMF = BLv = (2.0 \times 10^{-2} \text{ T})(0.100 \text{ m})(5.0 \text{ m/s})$
    $= 1.0 \times 10^{-2} \text{ V}$
  $V = IR$

$$I = \frac{V}{R} = \frac{1.0 \times 10^{-2} \text{ V}}{0.10 + 0.80 \text{ }\Omega} = 1.1 \times 10^{-2} \text{ A}$$

Page 447.

5. a. $EMF = BLv = (1.0 \text{ N/A} \cdot \text{m})(30.0 \text{ m})(2.0 \text{ m/s})$
    $= 6.0 \times 10^1 \text{ V}$
  b. $V = IR$

$$I = \frac{V}{R} = \frac{60 \text{ V}}{15.0 \text{ }\Omega} = 4.0 \text{ A}$$

Page 450.

6. a. $V_{eff} = (0.707) V_{max} = (0.707)(170 \text{ V}) = 120 \text{ V}$
  b. $I_{eff} = (0.707) I_{max} = (0.707)(0.70 \text{ A}) = 0.49 \text{ A}$

7. a. $V_{max} = \dfrac{V_{eff}}{0.707} = \dfrac{117 \text{ V}}{0.707} = 165 \text{ V}$

  b. $I_{max} = \dfrac{I_{eff}}{0.707} = \dfrac{5.5 \text{ A}}{0.707} = 7.8 \text{ A}$

8. a. $V_{eff} = (0.707) V_{max} = (0.707)(425 \text{ V})$
    $= 3.00 \times 10^2 \text{ V}$
  b. $V = IR$

$$I = \frac{V}{R} = \frac{3.00 \times 10^2 \text{ V}}{5.00 \times 10^2 \text{ }\Omega} = 0.600 \text{ A}$$

Page 455.

9. a. $\dfrac{V_P}{V_S} = \dfrac{N_P}{N_S}$

$$V_S = \frac{V_P N_S}{N_P} = \frac{(120 \text{ V})(1500)}{50} = 3600 \text{ V}$$

  b. $V_P I_P = V_S I_S$

$$I_P = \frac{V_S I_S}{V_P} = \frac{(3600 \text{ V})(3.0 \text{ A})}{120 \text{ V}} = 9.0 \times 10^1 \text{ A}$$

  c. $V_P I_P = (120 \text{ V})(9.0 \times 10^1 \text{ A}) = 10\ 800 \text{ W} = 11\ 000 \text{ W}$
    $V_S I_S = (3600 \text{ V})(3.0 \text{ A}) = 10\ 800 \text{ W} = 11\ 000 \text{ W}$

10. a. $\dfrac{V_P}{V_S} = \dfrac{N_P}{N_S}$

$$V_S = \frac{V_P N_S}{N_P} = \frac{(3600 \text{ V})(50)}{(1500)} = 120 \text{ V}$$

  b. $V_P I_P = V_S I_S$

$$I_S = \frac{V_P I_P}{V_S} = \frac{(3600 \text{ V})(3.0 \text{ A})}{120 \text{ V}} = 9.0 \times 10^1 \text{ A}$$

11. a. $\dfrac{V_P}{V_S} = \dfrac{N_P}{N_S}$

$$V_S = \frac{V_P N_S}{N_P} = \frac{(60.0 \text{ V})(90\ 000)}{300} = 1.80 \times 10^4 \text{ V}$$

  b. $V_P I_P = V_S I_S$

$$I_P = \frac{V_S I_S}{V_P} = \frac{(1.80 \times 10^4 \text{ V})(0.50 \text{ A})}{60.0 \text{ V}} = 1.5 \times 10^2 \text{ A}$$

12. **a.** $\dfrac{V_P}{V_S} = \dfrac{N_P}{N_S}$

$V_S = \dfrac{V_P N_S}{N_P} = \dfrac{(7200 \text{ V})(125)}{7500} = 120 \text{ V}$

b. $V_P I_P = V_S I_S$

$I_P = \dfrac{V_S I_S}{V_P} = \dfrac{(120 \text{ V})(36 \text{ A})}{7200 \text{ V}} = 0.60 \text{ A}$

Page 456.

13. **a.** $\dfrac{V_P}{V_S} = \dfrac{N_P}{N_S}$

$V_S = \dfrac{V_P N_S}{N_P} = \dfrac{(1.20 \times 10^2 \text{ V})(1000)}{1} = 1.20 \times 10^5 \text{ V}$

b. $V_P I_P = V_S I_S$

$I_S = \dfrac{V_P I_P}{V_S} = \dfrac{(1.20 \times 10^2 \text{ V})(1.00 \times 10^2 \text{ A})}{(1.20 \times 10^5 \text{ V})}$

$= 0.100 \text{ A}$

14. **a.** $\dfrac{N_P}{N_S} = \dfrac{V_P}{V_S} = \dfrac{1200 \text{ V}}{240000 \text{ V}} = \dfrac{1}{200}$

b. $V_P I_P = V_S I_S$

$I_S = \dfrac{V_P I_P}{V_S} = \dfrac{(1200 \text{ V})(40.0 \text{ A})}{240000 \text{ V}} = 0.20 \text{ A}$

15. $\dfrac{V_P}{V_S} = \dfrac{N_P}{N_S}$

$N_S = \dfrac{N_P V_S}{V_P}$

a. $N_S = \dfrac{(150)(6.0 \times 10^2 \text{ V})}{120 \text{ V}} = 750$

b. $N_S = \dfrac{(150)(3.0 \times 10^1 \text{ V})}{120 \text{ V}} = 37.5 = 38$

c. $N_S = \dfrac{(150)(6.0 \text{ V})}{120 \text{ V}} = 7.5$

Chapter End Questions

Pages 457-458.

1. A current is generated by moving the wire through the magnetic field of the magnet.
2. The current will move in opposite directions.
3. This is not answered directly in the text and will be a test of the student's reasoning powers. Once an electron in a wire is moved, it constitutes a small electric current which will immediately have a magnetic field associated with it. It is the interaction between the magnetic field about the electron and the external magnetic field that produces the force. *All forces result from field interactions.*
4. EMF is the energy imparted to each unit of charge.

5. $EMF = Blv = (\text{N/A} \cdot \text{m})(\text{m})(\text{m/s})$

$= \dfrac{\text{N}}{\text{A} \cdot \text{m}} \left| \dfrac{\text{m}}{} \right| \dfrac{\text{m}}{\text{s}} \left| \dfrac{1 \text{ A}}{1 \text{ C/s}} \right| \dfrac{1 \text{ J}}{1 \text{ N} \cdot \text{m}} = 1 \text{ J/C} = 1 \text{ V}$

6. See text page 449.
7. Current is induced in an armature (several wire loops) as it rotates in the magnetic field.
8. See text page 450.
9. Multiplying the maximum value of the current by 0.707 is one answer. A better answer is that the alternating current is compared to a direct current and evaluated accordingly.
10. EMF is determined by intensity of the magnetic field, the length of wire in the field, and the speed at which the wire moves through the field. $EMF = Blv$
11. An induced current always acts in such a direction that its magnetic properties oppose the change by which the current is induced.
12. This is due to Lenz's law. Once the motor starts turning, it behaves as a generator and will generate current in opposition to the current being put into the motor.
13. An alternating current is always changing magnitude and direction. Therefore, self-induction is a constant factor. A direct current becomes steady quite rapidly and so there is no changing magnetic field after a short time.
14. The ratio of number of turns of wire in the primary to the number of turns of wire in the secondary determines the EMF ratio.
15. The bulb will light because the current flows in the secondary circuit. This will happen whenever the primary current changes; it will glow both when the switch is closed and open.

Problems A

Page 458.

1. $EMF = BLv = (4.0 \times 10^{-2} \text{ T})(0.30 \text{ m})(15.0 \text{ m/s})$
   $= 0.18 \text{ V}$

2. **a.** $EMF = BLv$
   $= (0.30 \text{ T})(0.75 \text{ m})(16 \text{ m/s}) = 3.6 \text{ V}$
   b. $V = IR$
   $I = \dfrac{V}{R} = \dfrac{3.6 \text{ V}}{4.5 \ \Omega} = 0.80 \text{ A}$

3. $EMF = BLv = (0.50 \text{ T})(20.0 \text{ m})(4.0 \text{ m/s}) = 4.0 \times 10^1 \text{ V}$

4. **a.** $V_{eff} = 0.707 \, (V_{max}) = 0.707 \, (150 \text{ V}) = 106 = 110 \text{ V}$
   b. $I_{eff} = 0.707 \, (I_{max}) = 0.707 \, (30.0 \text{ A}) = 21.2 \text{ A}$

5. **a.** $V_{max} = \dfrac{V_{eff}}{0.707} = \dfrac{220 \text{ V}}{0.707} = 310 \text{ V}$
   b. $V = IR$
   $I = \dfrac{V}{R} = \dfrac{220 \text{ V}}{11 \ \Omega} = 2.0 \times 10^1 \text{ A}$

6. $V_{eff} = 0.707 \, (V_{max}) = 0.707 \, (565 \text{ V}) = 399 \text{ V}$

Page 459.

7. **a.** $\dfrac{V_P}{V_S} = \dfrac{N_P}{N_S}$

$$V_S = \frac{V_P N_S}{N_P} = \frac{(120 \text{ V})(1200)}{80} = 1800 \text{ V}$$

b. $V_P I_P = V_S I_S$

$$I_P = \frac{V_S I_S}{V_P} = \frac{(1800 \text{ V})(2.0 \text{ A})}{120 \text{ V}} = 3.0 \times 10^1 \text{ A}$$

c. $V_P I_P = (120 \text{ V})(3.0 \times 10^1 \text{ A}) = 3600 \text{ W}$
$V_S I_S = (1800 \text{ V})(2.0 \text{ A}) = 3600 \text{ W}$

Problems B

Page 459.

1. **a.** The left-hand rule will show the current moving right.
    b. up

2. **a.** $EMF = BLv$

$$L = \frac{EMF}{Bv} = \frac{12 \text{ V}}{(5.0 \times 10^{-5} \text{ T})(72.0 \times 10^3 \text{ m/h})(1/3600 \text{ s/h})}$$

$$= 1.2 \times 10^4 \text{ m}$$

b. $V = IR$

$$I = \frac{V}{R} = \frac{12 \text{ V}}{(2.6 \times 10^{-4} \ \Omega/\text{m})(1.2 \times 10^4 \text{ m})} = 3.8 \text{ A}$$

Electric and Magnetic Fields   Chapter 27

Teaching Techniques

First experiments using separated electric and magnetic fields are described. These provided many of the experimental facts on which the models of the atom were built. Note that Thomson found the electron mass, not from Millikan's experiment which was done 8 years later, but from electrochemical experiments by Davies and Faraday. The mass spectrograph (often called an MS) is often mentioned in the science press because of its ability to detect extremely small residuals of specific chemicals.

The second topic is the unification of electric and magnetic fields which produces electromagnetic waves, including light. The treatment is qualitative, but make sure the students grasp the concepts. This can be much more difficult than plugging numbers into an equation.

Demonstrations

Section 27:1

A commercial apparatus could be used or the principles demonstrated with a cathode ray tube as found in an oscilloscope.

Section 27:3

A large electromagnet with an iron core should be powered by an AC voltage. Construct a coil of about 20 turns of wire terminated with a small light bulb. If you place the coil on the end of the iron core, mutual inductance (transformer action) should make the bulb light. Now lift the coil off the core; energy is being transmitted through space. You can put your hand between, or even put a beaker of water on the core and drop the coil in.

Section 27:4

Use a pendulum to remind students of the mechanical energy relationships and to demonstrate resonance. A pair of tuning forks on sounding boxes is also useful. Display different coils and capacitors to show the relation between size and electrical characteristics.

Films

Mass of the Electron (university rental, PSSC film)

Laboratory Investigations

Measurement of Magnetic Field Strength
Charge to Mass Ratio of the Electron

Performance Objectives

Goal: Students will learn about the effects of separated electric and magnetic fields on charged particles as well as the nature, production, and detection of electromagnetic waves, including light.

Objectives: Upon completion of the reading, questions, and problems, students will, on oral or written tests:

27:1	K/P/S	describe Thomson's experiment measuring the mass to charge ratio of the electron; solve problems associated with this experiment.
27:2	K/P/S	display an understanding of the mass spectrograph as an analytical tool; use data provided to solve problems.

27:3   K/P   describe the coupling of electric and magnetic fields which produce electromagnetic waves; recognize the frequency or wavelength of many common waves.

27:4   K/P   describe the generation of electromagnetic waves; appreciate the use of resonance in many forms; recognize the necessity of accelerating charges to produce waves.

27:5   K/P   explain the principles of the detection of electromagnetic waves.

27:6   K   describe the nature of X rays.

S/A   Students will use laboratory materials in the prescribed manner when conducting lab investigations.

Upon completion of the reading and practice problems, students will exhibit an interest in physics by:

A/S   expanding on an answer to one or more of the questions or problems at the end of the chapter.

A/S   studying the generation of microwaves, their use in cooking, and possible harmful effects to people.

A   reading unassigned literature related to the ideas presented in the chapter.

Solutions to Problems

Page 464.

1. $Bqv = Eq$

$$v = \frac{E}{B} = \frac{4.5 \times 10^3 \text{ N/C}}{0.6 \text{ T}} = 7.5 \times 10^3 = 8 \times 10^3 \text{ m/s}$$

2. $Bqv = \frac{mv^2}{r}$

$$r = \frac{mv}{Bq} = \frac{(1.7 \times 10^{-27} \text{ kg})(7.5 \times 10^3 \text{ m/s})}{(0.6 \text{ T})(1.6 \times 10^{-19} \text{ C})} = 1.3 \times 10^{-4} \text{ m} = 1 \times 10^{-4} \text{ m}$$

3. $Bqv = Eq$

$$v = \frac{E}{B} = \frac{3.0 \times 10^3 \text{ N/C}}{6.0 \times 10^{-2} \text{ T}} = 5.0 \times 10^4 \text{ m/s}$$

4. $Bqv = \frac{mv^2}{r}$

$$r = \frac{mv}{Bq} = \frac{(9.11 \times 10^{-31} \text{ kg})(5.0 \times 10^4 \text{ m/s})}{(6.0 \times 10^{-2} \text{ T})(1.6 \times 10^{-19} \text{ C})} = 4.7 \times 10^{-6} \text{ m}$$

Page 465.

5. $Bqv = \frac{mv^2}{r}$

$$r = \frac{mv}{Bq} = \frac{(1.7 \times 10^{-27} \text{ kg})(5.4 \times 10^4 \text{ m/s})}{(6.0 \times 10^{-2} \text{ T})(1.6 \times 10^{-19} \text{ C})} = 9.6 \times 10^{-3} \text{ m}$$

6. $Bqv = \frac{mv^2}{r}$

$$v = \frac{Bqr}{m} = \frac{(0.36 \text{ T})(1.6 \times 10^{-19} \text{ C})(0.2 \text{ m})}{(1.7 \times 10^{-27} \text{ kg})} = 6.77 \times 10^6 = 7 \times 10^6 \text{ m/s}$$

7. a. $Bqv = \frac{mv^2}{r}$

$$v = \frac{Bqr}{m} = \frac{(4.0 \times 10^{-3} \text{ T})(1.6 \times 10^{-19} \text{ C})(2.0 \times 10^{-2} \text{ m})}{9.11 \times 10^{-31} \text{ kg}} = 1.4 \times 10^7 \text{ m/s}$$

   b. $Bqv = Eq$
   $E = Bv = (4.0 \times 10^{-3} \text{ T})(1.4 \times 10^7 \text{ m/s}) = 5.6 \times 10^4 \text{ N/C}$

Page 467.

8. a. $Bqv = Eq$

$$v = \frac{E}{B} = \frac{6.0 \times 10^2 \text{ N/C}}{1.5 \times 10^{-3} \text{ T}} = 4.0 \times 10^5 \text{ m/s}$$

b. $Bqv = \dfrac{mv^2}{r}$

$$m = \frac{Bqr}{v} = \frac{(0.18 \text{ T})(1.6 \times 10^{-19} \text{ C})(0.165 \text{ m})}{4.0 \times 10^5 \text{ m/s}}$$

$$= 1.2 \times 10^{-26} \text{ kg}$$

9. $m = \dfrac{B^2 r^2 q}{2V}$

$$= \frac{(5.0 \times 10^{-2} \text{ T})^2 (0.106 \text{ m})^2 (2)(1.6 \times 10^{-19} \text{ C})}{2(66 \text{ V})}$$

$$= 6.8 \times 10^{-26} \text{ kg}$$

10. $m = \dfrac{B^2 r^2 q}{2V}$

$$= \frac{(7.2 \times 10^{-2} \text{ T})^2 (0.085 \text{ m})^2 (1.6 \times 10^{-19} \text{ C})}{2(110 \text{ V})}$$

$$= 2.7 \times 10^{-26} \text{ kg}$$

Chapter End Questions

Pages 474-475.

1. The top plate should be charged positively.
2. The magnetic field would be directed into the plane of the paper.
3. The magnetic field would be directed out the plane of the paper.
4. The electric field lines are located in a plane that is parallel to the antenna, and the magnetic field lines are located in a plane that is perpendicular to the antenna.
5. Electric fields are vertical and magnetic fields are horizontal.
6. Channel 2 requires a longer antenna, as length is directly proportional to wavelength.
7. Channel 2.

Problems A

Page 475.

1. $m = \dfrac{B^2 r^2 q}{2V}$

$$= \frac{(8.0 \times 10^{-2} \text{ T})^2 (0.077 \text{ m})^2 (2)(1.6 \times 10^{-19} \text{ C})}{2(156 \text{ V})}$$

$$= 3.9 \times 10^{-26} \text{ kg}$$

2. a. $v = f\lambda$

$$\lambda = \frac{v}{f} = \frac{3.0 \times 10^8 \text{ m/s}}{85 \times 10^6 \text{ Hz}} = 3.5 \text{ m}$$

b. $Length = \dfrac{\lambda}{2} = \dfrac{3.5}{2} = 1.8 \text{ m}$

3. $E = (4.0 \times 10^5 \text{ J/C})(1.6 \times 10^{-19} \text{ C}) = 6.4 \times 10^{-14} \text{ J}$

Problems B

Page 475.

1. a. $Bqv = \dfrac{mv^2}{r}$

$$v = \frac{Bqr}{m} = \frac{(2.0 \text{ T})(2)(1.6 \times 10^{-19} \text{ C})(0.15 \text{ m})}{6.6 \times 10^{-27} \text{ kg}}$$

$$= 1.5 \times 10^7 \text{ m/s}$$

b. $KE = \dfrac{mv^2}{2}$

$$= \frac{(6.6 \times 10^{-27} \text{ kg})(1.5 \times 10^7 \text{ m/s})^2}{2} = 7.4 \times 10^{-13} \text{ J}$$

c. $KE = qV$

$$V = \frac{KE}{q} = \frac{7.4 \times 10^{-13} \text{ J}}{2(1.6 \times 10^{-19} \text{ C})} = 2.3 \times 10^6 \text{ V}$$

2. a. $E = (1.00 \times 10^4 \text{ J/C})(1.6 \times 10^{-19} \text{ C}) = 1.6 \times 10^{-15} \text{ J}$

b. $E = hf$

$$f = \frac{E}{h} = \frac{1.6 \times 10^{-15} \text{ J}}{4(6.6 \times 10^{-34} \text{ J/Hz})} = 6.1 \times 10^{17} \text{ Hz}$$

Quantum Theory   Chapter 28

Teaching Techniques

The basic phenomena of quantum physics are introduced in this chapter. The photoelectric effect is discussed quantitatively and determination of Planck's constant is developed. The Compton effect is also presented as an aspect of the particle nature of electromagnetic radiation.

The remainder of Chapter 28 presents the wave nature of particles. This presentation complements the particle nature of waves. Students should be impressed with the symmetry displayed.

Demonstrations

The photoelectric effect, especially the existence of threshold frequency, can be demonstrated easily, but most of the other topics are best shown through films.

Films

Matter Waves (university rental, PSSC film)
Photons (university rental, PSSC film)

Laboratory Investigations

A Model for the Quantum Concept

Performance Objectives

Goal: Students will learn how the fact that energy is quantized leads to the particle nature of electromagnetic radiation, including light, and the wave nature of particles.

Objectives: Upon completion of the reading, questions, and problems, students will, on oral or written tests:

28:1	K/P	display an understanding of the spectrum emitted by a hot body and the basics of the theory that explains this spectrum.
28:2	K/P/S	define the photoelectric effect; recognize the fact that wave theory cannot explain this phenomenon but the quantum theory can; use equations in the text to solve problems involving the work function of materials, frequency of incident light, and kinetic energy of photoelectrons.
28:3	K/P	explain the Compton effect in terms of the particle-like photon

colliding elastically with an electron.

28:4	K/P/S	explain the results of the wave nature of matter and solve problems using equations in the text.
28:5	A/P/S	recognize the dual nature of both electromagnetic radiation and matter and the impact of the Heisenberg uncertainty principle.
	S/A	Students will use laboratory materials in the prescribed manner when conducting lab investigations.

Upon completion of the reading and practice problems, students will exhibit an interest in physics by:

A/S	expanding on an answer to one or more of the questions or problems at the end of the chapter.
A/S	read and report on the history of the development of quantum ideas, biographies of one or more of the people involved, or the implications of these ideas on art, literature, or music.
A	reading unassigned literature related to the ideas presented in the chapter.

Solutions to Problems

Page 483.

1. $KE = qV_o = (1.6 \times 10^{-19} \text{ C})(3.2 \text{ J/C}) = 5.1 \times 10^{-19} \text{ J}$

2. $KE = qV_o = (1.6 \times 10^{-19} \text{ C})(5.7 \text{ J/C}) = 9.1 \times 10^{-19} \text{ J}$

3. **a.** $c = f\lambda$

$$f_o = \frac{c}{\lambda} = \frac{3.00 \times 10^8 \text{ m/s}}{310 \times 10^{-9} \text{ m}} = 9.7 \times 10^{14} \text{ Hz}$$

b. $W = hf_o = (6.6 \times 10^{-34} \text{ J/Hz})(9.7 \times 10^{14} \text{ Hz}) = (6.4 \times 10^{-19} \text{ J})(1 \text{ eV}/1.6 \times 10^{-19} \text{ J}) = 4.0 \text{ eV}$

c. $KE_{max} = \dfrac{hc}{\lambda} - hf_o = \dfrac{(6.6 \times 10^{-34} \text{ J/Hz})(3.00 \times 10^8 \text{ m/s})(1 \text{ eV}/1.6 \times 10^{-19} \text{ J})}{240 \times 10^{-9} \text{ m}} - 4.0 \text{ eV} = 5.16 \text{ eV} - 4.0 \text{ eV} = 1.2 \text{ eV}$

Page 486.

4. **a.** $KE = qV$

$$\frac{1}{2}mv^2 = qV$$

$$v = \sqrt{\frac{2qV}{m}} = \sqrt{\frac{(2)(1.6 \times 10^{-19} \text{ C})(250 \text{ V})}{9.11 \times 10^{-31} \text{ kg}}} = 9.4 \times 10^6 \text{ m/s}$$

b. $\lambda = \dfrac{h}{mv} = \dfrac{6.6 \times 10^{-34} \text{ J/Hz}}{(9.11 \times 10^{-31} \text{ kg})(9.4 \times 10^6 \text{ m/s})} = 7.7 \times 10^{-11} \text{ m}$

Chapter End Questions

Pages 487-488.

1. **a.** The rod glowing bright orange.
   b. The higher the frequency the higher the temperature.
2. **a.** Blue has a lower frequency; tungsten has a higher threshold frequency.
   b. Tungsten has a higher work function.
3. Each photon ejects a photoelectron. More intense light has more photons per second, thus it ejects more photoelectrons per second.
4. Each photon lacks the energy needed to eject an electron.
5. Elastic collisions transfer both momentum and energy. Only if photons have momentum can the equations be satisfied.
6. No. Momentum would be zero.
7. The size of the baseball is about 0.10 m, whereas the de Broglie wavelength is 10^{-34} m, a factor of 10^{35} difference.
8. Diffraction and interference.

Problems A

Page 488.

1. $KE = qV$
   $= (1.6 \times 10^{-19} \text{ C})(3.8 \text{ J/C}) = 6.1 \times 10^{-19} \text{ J}$

2. **a.** $c = f\lambda$
   $$\lambda = \frac{c}{f} = \frac{3.0 \times 10^8 \text{ m/s}}{1.2 \times 10^{15} \text{ Hz}} = 2.5 \times 10^{-7} \text{ m}$$
   b. $W = hf_o$
   $= (6.6 \times 10^{-34} \text{ J/Hz})(1.2 \times 10^{15} \text{ Hz})$
   $= (7.9 \times 10^{-19} \text{ J})(1 \text{ eV}/1.6 \times 10^{-19} \text{ J}) = 5.0 \text{ eV}$
   c. $KE_{max} = \dfrac{hc}{\lambda} - hf_o$
   $$= \frac{(6.6 \times 10^{-34} \text{ J/Hz})(3.0 \times 10^8 \text{ m/s})}{(167 \times 10^{-9} \text{ m})(1.6 \times 10^{-19} \text{ J/eV})} - 5.0 \text{ eV}$$
   $= 7.4 \text{ eV} - 5.0 \text{ eV} = 2.4 \text{ eV}$

3. **a.** $W = \dfrac{hc}{\lambda}$
   $$\lambda = \frac{hc}{W}$$
   $$= \frac{(6.6 \times 10^{-34} \text{ J/Hz})(3.0 \times 10^8 \text{ m/s})}{(4.7 \text{ eV})(1.6 \times 10^{-19} \text{ J/eV})} = 2.6 \times 10^{-7} \text{ m}$$
   b. $KE = \dfrac{hc}{\lambda} - W$
   $$= \frac{(6.6 \times 10^{-34} \text{ J/Hz})(3.0 \times 10^8 \text{ m/s})}{(2.6 \times 10^{-7} \text{ m})(1.6 \times 10^{-19} \text{ J/eV})} = 4.7 \text{ eV}$$
   $= 0 \text{ J}$

4. $\lambda = \dfrac{h}{mv} = \dfrac{6.6 \times 10^{-34} \text{ J/Hz}}{(3.3 \times 10^{-27} \text{ kg})(2.5 \times 10^4 \text{ m/s})} = 8.0 \times 10^{-12} \text{ m}$

5. **a.** $KE = qV_o$
   $$\frac{1}{2}mv^2 = qV_o$$
   $$v = \sqrt{\frac{2qV}{m}} = \sqrt{\frac{(2)(1.6 \times 10^{-19} \text{ C})(54 \text{ V})}{9.1 \times 10^{-31} \text{ kg}}}$$
   $= 4.4 \times 10^6 \text{ m/s}$
   b. $\lambda = \dfrac{h}{mv} = \dfrac{6.6 \times 10^{-34} \text{ J/Hz}}{(9.1 \times 10^{-31} \text{ kg})(4.4 \times 10^6 \text{ m/s})}$
   $= 1.6 \times 10^{-10} \text{ m}$

6. **a.** $KE = \dfrac{1}{2}mv^2$
   $$v = \sqrt{\frac{2KE}{m}} = \sqrt{\frac{(2)(0.025 \text{ eV})(1.6 \times 10^{-19} \text{ J/eV})}{1.67 \times 10^{-27} \text{ kg}}}$$
   $= 2.2 \times 10^3 \text{ m/s}$
   b. $\lambda = \dfrac{h}{mv} = \dfrac{6.6 \times 10^{-34} \text{ J/Hz}}{(1.67 \times 10^{-27} \text{ kg})(2.2 \times 10^3 \text{ m/s})}$
   $= 1.8 \times 10^{-10} \text{ m}$

7. $\lambda = \dfrac{h}{mv} = \dfrac{6.6 \times 10^{-34} \text{ J/Hz}}{(1.67 \times 10^{-27} \text{ kg})(1.0 \times 10^6 \text{ m/s})}$
   $= 4.0 \times 10^{-13} \text{ m}$

Problems B

Page 489.

1. **a.** $E = (3000 \text{ h})(3600 \text{ s/h})(1 \text{ J/m}) = 1 \times 10^7 \text{ J/m}^2$
   b. $Area = \dfrac{4 \times 10^{11} \text{ J}}{(0.2)(1 \times 10^7 \text{ J/m})} = 2 \times 10^5 \text{ m}^2$

2. **a.** $KE = \dfrac{1}{2}mv^2$
   $$v = \sqrt{\frac{2 \ KE}{m}} = \sqrt{\frac{(2)(13.65 \text{ eV})(1.60 \times 10^{-19} \text{ J/eV})}{9.11 \times 10^{-31} \text{ kg}}}$$
   $= 2.19 \times 10^6 \text{ m/s}$
   b. $\lambda = \dfrac{h}{mv} = \dfrac{6.6 \times 10^{-34} \text{ J/Hz}}{(9.1 \times 10^{-31} \text{ kg})(2.19 \times 10^6 \text{ m/s})}$
   $= 3.3 \times 10^{-10} \text{ m}$
   c. $5.19 \text{ nm} = 51.9 \times 10^{-10} \text{ m}$
   $$\frac{3.3 \times 10^{-10}}{51.9 \times 10^{-10}} = \frac{1}{16} \text{ the radius of the atom}$$

3. **a.** $\lambda = \dfrac{h}{mv}$
   $$v = \frac{h}{m\lambda} = \frac{6.6 \times 10^{-34} \text{ J/Hz}}{(9.1 \times 10^{-31} \text{ kg})(400 \times 10^{-9} \text{ m})}$$
   $= 2 \times 10^3 \text{ m/s}$
   b. $KE = \dfrac{1}{2}mv^2 = \dfrac{(9.1 \times 10^{-31} \text{ kg})(2 \times 10^3 \text{ m/s})^2}{(2)(1.6 \times 10^{-19} \text{ J/eV})}$
   $= 1 \times 10^{-5} \text{ eV}$

c. $\lambda = \dfrac{h}{mv}$

$v = \dfrac{h}{m\lambda} = \dfrac{6.6 \times 10^{-34} \text{ J/Hz}}{(9.1 \times 10^{-31} \text{ kg})(20 \times 10^{-9} \text{ m})}$

$= 3.6 \times 10^4 \text{ m/s}$

$KE = \dfrac{1}{2}mv^2 = \dfrac{(9.1 \times 10^{-31} \text{ kg})(3.6 \times 10^4 \text{ m/s})^2}{2(1.6 \times 10^{-19} \text{ J/eV})}$

$= 4 \times 10^{-3} \text{ eV}$

The Atom   Chapter 29

Teaching Techniques

In this chapter the work of Rutherford and Bohr that determined the model of the atom are explained. Stress the difference between a model, such as those developed by Rutherford and Bohr and a complete theory, represented by the present quantum theory.

The laser is presented as application of atomic theory.

Demonstrations

Section 29:3

Use either a prism or diffraction grating spectrometer to show the difference between continuous and line spectra. A simple absorption spectrum can be shown by crushing leaves in alcohol. The chlorophyll solution will absorb at both ends of the spectrum.

Films

The Laser Beam (Handel film)
Light: Wave and Quantum Theory (university rental, Indiana University film)

Laboratory Investigations

The Spectra of Elements

Performance Objectives

Goal: Students will gain an understanding of the Rutherford and Bohr models of the atom. They will recognize the importance of these models in relation to our understanding of the structure of the atom and atomic interactions.

Objectives: Upon completion of the reading, questions, and problems, students will, on oral or written tests:

29:1	K/P	explain the method used by Rutherford and co-workers to determine the structure of the atom; describe the Rutherford model.
29:2	K/P	describe the experimental results that suggested the existence of the neutron; contrast the proton with the neutron.
29:3	K/P	distinguish continuous from line spectra; contrast emission and absorption spectra; list some uses of spectroscopy.
29:4	K/P	list the assumption used by Bohr to develop his atomic model; define energy levels and ground and excited states; display an understanding of the connection between photon energy and atomic energy changes.
29:5	A/K/P	describe fluorescence and phosphorescence in terms of excited states of atoms.
29:6	K/P/S	by reference to the text only, use the orbital radius and energy level equations to solve problems using the Bohr model.
29:7	K/P	display an appreciation of the contributions of the Bohr model and its shortcomings; describe the wave model of the atom.
29:8	K/P	describe a laser and the properties of laser light; display an understanding of the processes involved in the operation of the laser.
	S/A	Students will use laboratory materials in the prescribed manner when conducting lab investigations.

Upon completion of the reading and practice problems, students will exhibit an interest in physics by:

	A/S	expanding on an answer to one or more of the questions or problems at the end of the chapter.
	A/S	reading biographies of the people involved in the development of atomic theory.
	A	reading unassigned literature related to the ideas presented in the chapter.

Solutions to Problems

Page 503.

1. $r = n^2k$, where $k = 5.3 \times 10^{-11}$ m
   $r^2 = (2)^2(5.3 \times 10^{-11}$ m$) = 2.1 \times 10^{-10}$ m
   $r^3 = (3)^2(5.3 \times 10^{-11}$ m$) = 4.8 \times 10^{-10}$ m
   $r^4 = (4)^2(5.3 \times 10^{-11}$ m$) = 8.5 \times 10^{-10}$ m

2. $E = \dfrac{-13.6 \text{ eV}}{n^2}$

   $E_2 = \dfrac{-13.6 \text{ eV}}{(2)^2} = -3.4$ eV

   $E_3 = \dfrac{-13.6 \text{ eV}}{(3)^2} = -1.5$ eV

   $E_4 = \dfrac{-13.6 \text{ eV}}{(4)^2} = -0.85$ eV

3. $E_3 - E_2 = (-1.5 \text{ eV}) - (-3.4 \text{ eV}) = 1.9$ eV
   $E_4 - E_3 = (-0.85 \text{ eV}) - (-1.5 \text{ eV}) = 0.65$ eV

Page 504.

4. **a.** $E = E_3 - E_2$
   $\quad = 1.9$ eV
   $E = hf$

   $f = \dfrac{E}{h} = \dfrac{(1.9 \text{ eV})(1.6 \times 10^{-19} \text{ J/eV})}{6.6 \times 10^{-34} \text{ J/Hz}}$

   $\quad = 4.6 \times 10^{14}$ Hz

   $\lambda = \dfrac{c}{f} = \dfrac{3.0 \times 10^8 \text{ m/s}}{4.6 \times 10^{14} \text{ Hz}} = 6.5 \times 10^{-7}$ m

   b. $E = E_4 - E_3 = 0.65$ eV
   $E = hf$

   $f = \dfrac{E}{h} = \dfrac{(0.65 \text{ eV})(1.6 \times 10^{-19} \text{ J/eV})}{6.6 \times 10^{-34} \text{ J/Hz}}$

   $\quad = 1.6 \times 10^{14}$ Hz

   $\lambda = \dfrac{c}{f} = \dfrac{3.0 \times 10^8 \text{ m/s}}{1.6 \times 10^{14} \text{ Hz}}$

   $\quad = 1.9 \times 10^{-6}$ m

5. $E_4 - E_1 = (-0.85 \text{ eV}) - (-13.6 \text{ eV}) = 12.8$ eV

6. $E = hf$

   $f = \dfrac{E}{h} = \dfrac{(12.8 \text{ eV})(1.6 \times 10^{-19} \text{ J/eV})}{6.6 \times 10^{-34} \text{ J/Hz}}$

   $\quad = 3.1 \times 10^{15}$ Hz

   $\lambda = \dfrac{c}{f} = \dfrac{3.0 \times 10^8 \text{ m/s}}{3.1 \times 10^{15} \text{ Hz}}$

   $\quad = 9.7 \times 10^{-8}$ m

Chapter End Questions

Pages 509-510.

1. He directed a beam of charged alpha particles at a thin metal sheet and measured the number of particles deflected into various angles.

2. Neutrons and protons are approximately equal in mass. Protons are positively charged, whereas neutrons are uncharged.

3. It collapses immediately; it has no discrete spectral lines.

4. **a.** Energy levels are quantized.
   b. Electrons do not radiate while they are in an allowed energy level.
   c. Photons are emitted or absorbed when an electron changes energy levels. Energy of a photon is equal to the difference in energy levels.

5. Photon wavelengths are determined by the difference in energies of allowed levels.

6. Six lines are possible. They are E_2-E_1, E_3-E_1, E_4-E_1, E_3-E_2, E_4-E_2, E_4-E_3. E_4-E_1 has highest energy level.

7. The Bohr model has fixed orbital radii; the present model gives a probability of finding an electron at a location. The Bohr model allows for calculation of only hydrogen atoms; the present model can be used for all elements.

8. **a.** Lasers are directional and coherent.
   b. Blue light has a higher frequency and, therefore, higher energy.

Problems A

Page 510.

1. $r = n^2k$, where $k = 5.3 \times 10^{-11}$ m
   $r = (5)^2(5.3 \times 10^{-11}$ m$) = 1.3 \times 10^{-9}$ m
   $r = (6)^2(5.3 \times 10^{-11}$ m$) = 1.9 \times 10^{-9}$ m

2. $E_2 = \dfrac{-13.6 \text{ eV}}{n^2} = \dfrac{-13.6 \text{ eV}}{(2)^2} = -3.4$ eV

   $E_3 = \dfrac{-13.6 \text{ eV}}{(3)^2} = -1.5$ eV

   $E_4 = \dfrac{-13.6 \text{ eV}}{(4)^2} = -0.85$ eV

   $E_5 = \dfrac{-13.6 \text{ eV}}{(5)^2} = -0.54$ eV

   $E_6 = \dfrac{-13.6 \text{ eV}}{(6)^2} = -0.38$ eV

3. **a.** $E_6 - E_5 = (-0.38 \text{ eV}) - (-0.54 \text{ eV}) = 0.16$ eV
   b. $E_6 - E_3 = (-0.38 \text{ eV}) - (-1.50 \text{ eV}) = 1.12$ eV
   c. $E_4 - E_2 = (-0.85 \text{ eV}) - (-3.40 \text{ eV}) = 2.6$ eV
   d. $E_5 - E_2 = (-0.54 \text{ eV}) - (-3.40 \text{ eV}) = 2.86$ eV
   e. $E_5 - E_3 = (-0.54 \text{ eV}) - (-1.50 \text{ eV}) = 0.96$ eV

4. **a.** $E = hf$
   $hf = E_6 - E_5 = 0.16$ eV

   $f = \dfrac{(0.16 \text{ eV})(1.6 \times 10^{-19} \text{ J/eV})}{6.6 \times 10^{-34} \text{ J/Hz}}$

   $\quad = 3.9 \times 10^{13}$ Hz

   b. $hf = E_6 - E_3 = 1.12$ eV

   $f = \dfrac{(1.12 \text{ eV})(1.6 \times 10^{-19} \text{ J/eV})}{6.6 \times 10^{-34} \text{ J/Hz}}$

   $\quad = 2.7 \times 10^{14}$ Hz

c. $hf = E_4 - E_2 = 2.55$ eV

$$f = \frac{(2.55 \text{ eV})(1.6 \times 10^{-19} \text{ J/eV})}{6.6 \times 10^{-34} \text{ J/Hz}}$$

$$= 6.1 \times 10^{14} \text{ Hz}$$

d. $hf = E_5 - E_2 = 2.86$ eV

$$f = \frac{(2.86 \text{ eV})(1.6 \times 10^{-19} \text{ J/eV})}{6.6 \times 10^{-34} \text{ J/Hz}}$$

$$= 6.9 \times 10^{14} \text{ Hz}$$

e. $hf = E_5 - E_3 = 0.96$ eV

$$f = \frac{(0.96 \text{ eV})(1.6 \times 10^{-19} \text{ J/eV})}{6.6 \times 10^{-34} \text{ J/Hz}}$$

$$= 2.3 \times 10^{14} \text{ Hz}$$

5. a. $\lambda = \dfrac{c}{f} = \dfrac{3.0 \times 10^8 \text{ m/s}}{3.9 \times 10^{13} \text{ Hz}} = 7.7 \times 10^{-6}$ m

b. $\lambda = \dfrac{c}{f} = \dfrac{3.0 \times 10^8 \text{ m/s}}{2.7 \times 10^{14} \text{ Hz}} = 1.1 \times 10^{-6}$ m

c. $\lambda = \dfrac{c}{f} = \dfrac{3.0 \times 10^8 \text{ m/s}}{6.1 \times 10^{14} \text{ Hz}} = 4.9 \times 10^{-7}$ m

d. $\lambda = \dfrac{c}{f} = \dfrac{3.0 \times 10^8 \text{ m/s}}{6.9 \times 10^{14} \text{ Hz}} = 4.3 \times 10^{-7}$ m

e. $\lambda = \dfrac{c}{f} = \dfrac{3.0 \times 10^8 \text{ m/s}}{2.3 \times 10^{14} \text{ Hz}} = 1.3 \times 10^{-6}$ m

6. $E = 6.67$ eV $+ 2.15$ eV $= 8.82$ eV which is E_9

7. $E = 8.81$ eV $- 6.67$ eV $= 2.14$ eV

Problems B

Page 511.

1. a. $r = \dfrac{h^2}{4\pi^2 Kmq^2} n^2$ when $n = 1$, $r = 5.3 \times 10^{-11}$ m
when $n = 3$, $r = 4.8 \times 10^{-10}$ m

b. $F = \dfrac{Kq^2}{r^2} = 1.01 \times 10^{-9}$ N

c. $a = \dfrac{F}{m} = \dfrac{1.01 \times 10^{-9} \text{ N}}{9.11 \times 10^{-31} \text{ kg}} = 1.11 \times 10^{21}$ m/s^2

d. $a = \dfrac{v^2}{r}$; $v = \sqrt{ar} = 7.3 \times 10^5$ m/s or 0.2% of c

2. a. Yes, the atom is ionized.

$$\frac{13.65 \text{ eV}}{n^2} = \frac{13.65}{4} \text{ eV} = 3.4 \text{ eV}$$

$$E = hf = hc/\lambda = 6.0 \times 10^{-19} \text{ J} = 3.7 \text{ eV}$$

b. 3.7 eV $- 3.4$ eV $= 0.3$ eV $= 4.8 \times 10^{-20}$ J

The Nucleus　　Chapter 30

Teaching Techniques

This chapter gives an introduction to the physics of the nucleus. Students should become competent in working with nuclear equations. The mass-energy relations presented are also important.

The section on fundamental particles and the quark theory of nucleons is meant to give students the flavor of the status of the field in early 1985.

Demonstrations

Demonstrations depend primarily on the equipment and radioactive sources available. You should do the experiments yourself.

Sections 30:3 and 30:9

If a geiger counter is available decay of radioactive materials can be detected. Some counters can separate betas from gammas by absorbing the betas in a metallic cover. Few have windows thin enough to detect alphas.

If you can detect both betas and gammas, use aluminum sheets and lead sheets to show that betas are stopped by aluminum but lead is required to stop gammas.

A cloud chamber is excellent for showing the tracks of alphas and cosmic rays.

Chapter 30

Laboratory Investigations

Half-Life Simulation

Performance Objectives

Goal: Students will learn the elements of nuclear structure, decay, and reactions, the equipment used to obtain this information, and an outline of the present theory of the strong nuclear force.

Objectives: Upon completion of the reading, questions, and problems, students will, on oral or written tests:

30:1	K	define atomic number and mass number; find the charge and mass of the nucleus.
30:2	K/S/P	define an isotope and a nuclide; calculate the numbers of neutrons, protons, and electrons in an isotope.
30:3	K/P	describe the three modes of radioactive decay; calculate the changes in atomic number and mass number accompanying each mode of decay.
30:4	K/S	write equations for the three forms of decay.

30:5 K/P/S define half-life; calculate the amount of material and its activity remaining after a certain time.

30:6 K/S balance nuclear equations describing the result of nuclear reactions.

30:7 K describe the operation of a linear accelerator.

30:8 K describe the operation of a synchrotron.

30:9 K describe the operation of different radiation detectors.

30:10 K/P list the two families of fundamental particles; describe the difference between fundamental particles and force carriers.

30:11 K/S/P describe anti-particles; calculate the energy of gamma rays emitted when particles annihilate with their anti-particles.

30:12 K/P follow the description of the quark model of the nucleon; understand the place of additional quark and leptons in the quark model.

S/A Students will use laboratory materials in the prescribed manner when conducting lab investigations.

Upon completion of the reading and practice problems, students will exhibit an interest in physics by:

A/S expanding on an answer to one or more of the questions or problems at the end of the chapter.

A/S reading and reporting on the present status of the quark model.

A reading unassigned literature related to the ideas presented in the chapter.

Solutions to Problems

Page 515.

1. $15 - 8 = 7$ neutrons

2. $A - Z$ = neutrons
   $234 - 92 = 142$ neutrons
   $235 - 92 = 143$ neutrons
   $238 - 92 = 146$ neutrons

3. $200 - 80 = 120$ neutrons

4. $^{1}_{1}H$, $^{2}_{1}H$, $^{3}_{1}H$

Page 518.

5. $^{234}_{92}U \rightarrow ^{230}_{90}Th + ^{4}_{2}He$

6. $^{230}_{90}Th \rightarrow ^{226}_{88}Ra + ^{4}_{2}He$

7. $^{226}_{88}Ra \rightarrow ^{222}_{86}Rn + ^{4}_{2}He$

8. $^{214}_{82}Pb \rightarrow ^{214}_{83}Bi + ^{0}_{-1}e$

9. $^{214}_{83}Bi \rightarrow ^{214}_{84}Po + ^{0}_{-1}e$

Page 519.

10. $^{210}_{84}Po \rightarrow ^{206}_{82}Pb + ^{4}_{2}He$

11. $^{56}_{24}Cr \rightarrow ^{56}_{25}Mn + ^{0}_{-1}e$

Page 520.

12. 24.6 years = 2(12.3 years) which is 2 half-lives

$(1.0 \text{ g})\left(\frac{1}{4}\right) = 0.25$ g remaining

13. 7 days is 3.5 half-lives
Looking at the graph showing the decay of $^{238}_{93}Np$ about

$\left(\frac{3}{4}\right)\left(\frac{1}{8}\right)$ (4 g) = 0.38 g remains.

14. The half-life of $^{210}_{84}Po$ is 138 days.

There are 273 days which is about 2 half-lives between September 1 and June 1.
So the activity is

$= \left(2 \times 10^6 \frac{\text{decays}}{\text{s}}\right)\left(\frac{1}{2}\right)\left(\frac{1}{2}\right) = 5 \times 10^5 \frac{\text{decays}}{\text{s}}$

15. The half-life of tritium is 12.3 years.

Six years is about $\frac{1}{2}$ half-life.

In $\frac{1}{2}$ half-life about $\frac{3}{4}$ activity remains so the brightness

is $\frac{3}{4}$ original brightness.

Page 528.

16. a. $E = mc^2 = (1.67 \times 10^{-27} \text{ kg})(3.00 \times 10^8 \text{ m/s})^2 = 1.50 \times 10^{-10}$ J

b. $E = \frac{1.50 \times 10^{-10} \text{ J}}{1.60 \times 10^{-19} \text{ J/eV}} = 9.38 \times 10^8 \text{ eV} = 938 \text{ MeV}$

c. The pair will be (2)(938 MeV) = 1.88 GeV

Chapter End Questions

Page 532.

1. Transmutation is the change of one element into another by means of a nuclear reaction caused by radioactive decay or nuclear bombardment.
$$^{238}_{92}U \longrightarrow \,^{234}_{90}Th + \,^{4}_{2}He$$

2. $A \longrightarrow A-4, Z \longrightarrow Z-2$

3. $A \longrightarrow A, Z \longrightarrow Z+1$

4. $A \longrightarrow A, Z \longrightarrow Z-1$

5. **a.** $^{1}_{1}p$ or $^{1}_{1}H$ **b.** $^{1}_{0}n$ **c.** $^{0}_{1}e\ (e^{+})$
   d. e^{-} or $^{0}_{1}e$ **e.** $\propto$ or $^{4}_{2}He$

6. $(1/2)^{3} = 1/8$

7. It would annihilate with an equivalent amount of matter, producing an extremely large amount of energy.

8. Since each u quark has a charge of $+2/3$, uuu $= 3 \cdot (+2/3) = +2$ elementary charges.

9. $u + \bar{d} = +2/3 + (-(-1/3)) = +1$ elementary charge

10. **a.** $u + \bar{u} = +2/3 + (-(+2/3)) = 0$ charge
    b. $d + \bar{u} = -1/3 + (-(+2/3)) = -1$ charge
    c. $d + \bar{d} = -1/3 + (-(-1/3)) = 0$ charge

Problems A

Page 532.

1. 12 neutrons
2. 8 neutrons
3. **a.** $112 - 48 = 64$
   b. $209 - 83 = 126$
   c. $208 - 83 = 125$
   d. $80 - 35 = 45$

e. $1 - 1 = 0$
f. $40 - 18 = 22$
g. $132 - 54 = 78$

4. $^{25}_{13}Al + \,^{4}_{2}He \rightarrow \,^{1}_{0}n + \,^{28}_{15}P$

5. $^{2}_{1}H + \,^{2}_{1}H \rightarrow \,^{3}_{2}He + \,^{1}_{0}n$

   $^{1}_{0}n$ is produced.

6. $4^{1}_{1}H \rightarrow \,^{4}_{2}He + 2\,^{0}_{1}e$

Problems B

Page 532.

1. 280 years is 10 half-lives. $(\frac{1}{2})^{10}$ is equal to 9.8×10^{-4} or approximately $9.8 \times 10^{-2}\%$.

2. **a.** 48 h is two half-lives, therefore 24 h is one half-life.
   b. Determine the slope (at 24 hours) of the line of a graph of remaining nuclei versus time.

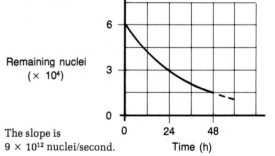

Remaining nuclei $(\times 10^{4})$

Time (h)

The slope is 9×10^{12} nuclei/second.

Nuclear Applications   Chapter 31

Teaching Techniques

This chapter surveys the applications of nuclear physics. It also gives students additional practice in working with nuclear reactions.

It might be possible to contact a local hospital regarding the use of nuclear medicine for analysis or treatment. If a tour cannot be arranged, perhaps a specialist can speak to the class. Similarly, a tour of a nearby nuclear power reactor might be arranged.

Films

Fusion (university rental, PSSC film)

Laboratory Investigations

Simulation of Nuclear Collisions

Performance Objectives

Goal: Students will learn a survey of applications of nuclear physics.

Objectives: Upon completion of the reading, questions, and problems, students will, on oral or written tests:

31:1	K/P	recognize the role and nature of the strong force; define the nucleon and binding energy.
31:2	K/P/S	define mass defect; calculate mass defects and binding energies of various isotopes.
31:3	K/S/P	define artificially produced radioactive isotopes; describe their medical uses; solve nuclear

equations involving formation and decay of radioactive isotopes.

31:4   K/P   define nuclear fission and chain reaction; understand the source of energy in fission.

31:5   K/P   describe the operation of one or more types of nuclear reactors; understand the formation of plutonium in a reactor.

31:6   K/P   describe the fusion process and the formation of helium in the sun.

31:7   K/P   describe two approaches to controlled nuclear fusion.

S/A   Students will use laboratory materials in the prescribed manner when conducting lab investigations.

Upon completion of the reading and practice problems, students will exhibit an interest in physics by:

A/S   expanding on an answer to one or more of the questions or problems at the end of the chapter.

A/S   reading and reporting on the present status of obtaining energy from nuclear fusion.

A   reading unassigned literature related to the ideas presented in the chapter.

Solutions to Problems

Page 537.

1. **a.**   6 protons = (6)(1.007825 amu) =   6.046950 amu
       6 neutrons = (6)(1.008665 amu) =   6.051990 amu

       total   12.098940 amu
       mass of carbon nucleus $-$ 12.000000 amu

       mass defect   0.098940 amu

    b.   (0.098940 amu)(931 MeV/amu) = 92.1 MeV

2. **a.**   1 proton = 1.007825 amu
            1 neutron = 1.008665 amu

            2.016490 amu
       mass of hydrogen nucleus $-$ 2.0140   amu

       mass defect   0.00249 amu

    b.   (0.00249 amu)(931 MeV/amu) = 2.32 MeV

3. **a.**   7 protons = (7)(1.007825 amu) =   7.054775 amu
       8 neutrons = (8)(1.008665 amu) =   8.069320 amu

       total   15.124095 amu
       mass of nitrogen nucleus $-$ 15.00011   amu

       mass defect =   0.123985 amu
                =   0.12399   amu

    b.   (0.12399 amu)(931 MeV/amu) = 115 MeV

4. **a.**   8 protons = (8)(1.007825 amu) =   8.062600 amu
       8 neutrons = (8)(1.008665 a.m.u.) =   8.069320 amu

       total   16.131920 amu
       mass of oxygen nucleus $-$ 15.99491   amu

       mass defect   0.13701 amu

    b.   (0.13701 amu)(931 MeV) = 128 MeV

Page 540.

5. **a.** $^{14}_{6}\text{C} \rightarrow {}^{14}_{7}\text{N} + {}^{0}_{-1}e$

    b. $^{55}_{24}\text{Cr} \rightarrow {}^{55}_{25}\text{Mn} + {}^{0}_{-1}e$

6. $^{238}_{92}\text{U} \rightarrow {}^{234}_{90}\text{Th} + {}^{4}_{2}\text{He}$

7. $^{214}_{84}\text{Po} \rightarrow {}^{210}_{82}\text{Pb} + {}^{4}_{2}\text{He}$

8. **a.** $^{210}_{82}\text{Pb} \rightarrow {}^{210}_{83}\text{Bi} + {}^{0}_{-1}e$

    b. $^{210}_{83}\text{Bi} \rightarrow {}^{210}_{84}\text{Po} + {}^{0}_{-1}e$

    c. $^{234}_{90}\text{Th} \rightarrow {}^{234}_{91}\text{Pa} + {}^{0}_{-1}e$

    d. $^{239}_{93}\text{Np} \rightarrow {}^{239}_{94}\text{Pu} + {}^{0}_{-1}e$

9. $^{7}_{3}\text{Li} + {}^{1}_{1}\text{H} \rightarrow 2\,{}^{4}_{2}\text{He}$

10. **a.** $^{30}_{15}\text{P} \rightarrow {}^{30}_{14}\text{Si} + {}^{0}_{+1}e$

    b. $^{205}_{82}\text{Pb} \rightarrow {}^{205}_{81}\text{Tl} + {}^{0}_{+1}e$

11. **a.** $^{21}_{11}\text{Na} \rightarrow {}^{21}_{10}\text{Ne} + {}^{0}_{+1}e$

    b. $^{49}_{24}\text{Cr} \rightarrow {}^{49}_{23}\text{V} + {}^{0}_{-1}e$

12. **a.** $^{14}_{7}\text{N} + {}^{4}_{2}\text{He} \rightarrow {}^{18}_{9}\text{F}$

    b. $^{27}_{13}\text{Al} + {}^{4}_{2}\text{He} \rightarrow {}^{31}_{15}\text{P}$

13. **a.**   **a.** $^{65}_{29}\text{Cu} + {}^{1}_{0}n \rightarrow {}^{65}_{28}\text{Ni} + {}^{1}_{1}\text{H}$

    b. $^{14}_{7}\text{N} + {}^{1}_{0}n \rightarrow {}^{14}_{6}\text{C} + {}^{1}_{1}\text{H}$

14. **a.**   Lithium

    b.   **a.** $^{10}_{5}\text{B} + {}^{1}_{0}n \rightarrow {}^{7}_{3}\text{Li} + {}^{4}_{2}\text{He}$

Chapter End Questions

Page 547.

1. Sum of mass constituents less mass of the nucleus. It is related to binding energy through $E = mc^2$.

2. The incoming binding energy is less than the outgoing binding energy and, therefore, the reaction does go.

3. Not true. Iron is the most tightly bound element, and thus the most stable nucleus. It cannot decay by either fission or fusion.

4. A naturally radioactive material is one which is found to exist normally in ores and which displays radiations. Artificially radioactive material displays radiations only after being subjected to bombardment by particles.

5. This refers to breeder reactors. Students should explain that fissionable plutonium in a reactor produces more plutonium than is used.

6. Plasma confinement by magnetic fields and inertial confinement or laser implosion are being studied.

Problems A

Page 548.

1. **a.** gold
   b. a. $^{200}_{80}Hg + ^2_1H \rightarrow ^{198}_{79}Au + ^4_2He$

2. **a.**
$$
\begin{array}{lr}
\text{7 protons} = (7)(1.007825 \text{ amu}) = & 7.054775 \text{ amu} \\
\text{7 neutrons} = (7)(1.008665 \text{ amu}) = & 7.060655 \text{ amu} \\
\hline
\text{total} & 14.11543 \text{ amu} \\
\text{mass of nitrogen nucleus} & -14.00307 \text{ amu} \\
\hline
\text{mass defect} & 0.11236 \text{ amu}
\end{array}
$$
   b. $(0.11236 \text{ amu})(931 \text{ MeV/amu}) = 105 \text{ MeV}$

3. $Energy = \dfrac{105 \text{ MeV}}{14 \text{ nucleons}} = 7.5 \text{ MeV/nucleon}$

4. **a.**
$$
\begin{array}{lr}
\text{6 protons} = (6)(1.007825 \text{ amu}) = & 6.046950 \text{ amu} \\
\text{7 neutrons} = (7)(1.008665 \text{ amu}) = & 7.060655 \text{ amu} \\
\hline
\text{total} & 13.107605 \text{ amu} \\
\text{mass of nucleus} & -13.00335 \text{ amu} \\
\hline
\text{mass defect} & 0.104255 \text{ amu} \\
= & 0.10426 \text{ amu}
\end{array}
$$
   b. $(0.10426 \text{ amu})(931 \text{ MeV/amu}) = 97.1 \text{ MeV}$

5. $F = K\dfrac{qq'}{d^2} = 9.0 \times 10^9 \text{ N·m}^2/\text{C}^2 \dfrac{(1.6 \times 10^{-19} \text{ C})(1.6 \times 10^{-19} \text{ C})}{(2.0 \times 10^{-15} \text{ m})^2} = 58 \text{ N}$

7. When a large atom, such as uranium, undergoes fission, the mass of the products is less than that of the original nucleus. An amount of energy equivalent of the difference in mass is released. However, when small nuclei fuse into a larger nucleus, the mass of the more tightly bound large nucleus is less, and the extra mass appears as energy.

8. fission of 1 uranium nucleus = 200 MeV
   fusion of 4 hydrogen nuclei = 50 MeV
   b. Although the fission on one uranium nucleus produces more energy than the fission of two hydrogen nuclei, there are over 100 times as many deuterium nuclei in a kilogram than there are uranium nuclei. Therefore the fusion of a kilogram of deuterium produces much more energy.
   c. see answer to **b.**

9. The water in the heat exchanger is radioactive; that used to generate steam is not.

10. No, plutonium is produced at the expense of uranium.

Problems B

Page 548.

1. **a.** $2 (2.01410 \text{ amu}) - 4.00263 \text{ amu} = 0.02557 \text{ amu}$
   b. $23.8 \text{ MeV/molecule} \times 6.02 \cdot 10^{23} \text{ molecules/mole} \times 1.60 \cdot 10^{-19} \text{ J/eV} \times 10^6 \text{ eV/MeV}$
   $= 2.29 \times 10^{12} \text{ J/mole}$
   c. $\dfrac{2.29 \times 10^{12} \text{ J}}{2.9 \times 10^6 \text{ J/mole}} = 7.9 \times 10^5 \text{ moles}$

2. **a.** $\dfrac{6.02 \times 10^{23} \text{ atoms/mole}}{0.235 \text{ kg/mole}} = 2.56 \times 10^{24} \text{ atoms/kg}$
   b. $2.56 \cdot 10^{24} \text{ atoms/kg} \times 2.0 \cdot 10^2 \text{ MeV/atoms} \times 1.6 \cdot 10^{-19} \text{ J/eV} \times 10^6 \text{ eV/MeV}$
   $= 8.2 \times 10^{13} \text{ J/kg}$
   c. $\dfrac{3.0 \times 10^9 \text{ J/s}}{8.2 \times 10^{13} \text{ J/kg}} = 3.7 \times 10^{-5} \text{ kg/s}$
   d. $3.7 \cdot 10^{-5} \text{ kg/s} \times 3.15 \cdot 10^7 \text{ s/y} = 1.2 \times 10^3 \text{ kg/y}$

Appendix A: Relativity

Teaching Techniques

It is most likely that this appendix will be read by individual students. While it gives an introduction that is complete in itself, this appendix can be supplemented by many sources. Biographies of Einstein, especially those describing his scientific work, are interesting. Many books have described "relativity for the layman". Some are better than others, but all can be read profitably.

Emphasize that relativity is the basis on which all modern physics is built. However, relativity is still being tested by many experiments. Every experiment has confirmed its validity. For example, a recent laser experiment repeated at the Michelson-Morley experiment, establishing the null effect to a precision of (2 parts in 10^5), and another verified time dilation to a precision of (4 parts in 10^4).

Performance Objectives

Goal: Students will learn the basic elements of relativity theory, their origins, and results:

Objectives: Upon completion of the reading, and questions, students will, on oral or written tests:

A:1	K/A/P	understand the use of techniques of Chapter 7 to the description of mechanics from moving frames of reference.
A:2	K/A/P	recognize that electromagnetism did not work in moving frames; understand the problem posed by the Michelson-Morley experiment.
A:3	K/P	state Einstein's two postulates.
A:4	K/P/S	state the new meaning of time; define time dilation; recognize the resolution of the twin paradox.
A:5	K/P/S	display an understanding of the contraction of moving bodies.
A:6	K/P	recognize how the muon experiment tests both time dilation and length contraction.
A:6	K/P/S	use Einstein's method of adding velocities and recognize how it solves the problem of the limiting speed of light.
A:7	K/P/S	understand the nature of the increase in mass of rapid-moving matter.
A:8	K/A:	recognize the origin and significance of the mass-energy equivalence.
A:9	K/A	recognize the realm in which relativistic effects are important and the importance of relativity to our approach to physics.

Students will exhibit an interest in physics by:

A   reading unassigned literature related to the ideas presented in the chapter.

Questions

Page 555.

1. a. 0 m/s
   b. 200 m/s

2. a. 4.0 m/s
   b. 34 m/s, 26 m/s

3. $t_e = \dfrac{t_s}{\sqrt{1 - v^2/c^2}}$

 $= \dfrac{2.6 \times 10^{-8} \text{ s}}{\sqrt{1 - (0.80\,c)^2/c^2}}$

 $= 4.3 \times 10^{-8}$ s

4. $m_e = \dfrac{m_s}{\sqrt{1 - v^2/c^2}}$

 $= \dfrac{2.49 \times 10^{-28}}{\sqrt{1 - (0.80\,c)^2/c^2}}$

 $= 4.2 \times 10^{-28}$ kg

5. $v' = \dfrac{v + u}{1 + uv/c^2}$

 $= \dfrac{0.80\,c + 0.50\,c}{\dfrac{1 + (0.80\,c)(0.50\,c)}{c^2}}$

 $= \dfrac{1.30\,c}{1.40} = 0.93\,c$

6. None. The relative velocity of the astronaut and the measuring devices is zero.

7. $L_e = L_s \sqrt{1 - v^2/c^2}$
   $= (20.0 \text{ m}) \sqrt{1 - (0.50\,c)^2/c^2}$
   $= 17$ m

8. $L_{e''} = L_{s''} \sqrt{1 - v^2/c^2}$
   $= (100.0 \text{ m}) \sqrt{1 - (0.50\,c)^2/c^2}$
   $= 87$ m

9. $t = d/v = \dfrac{(30.0 \text{ y})(c)}{\frac{1}{2}\,c}$

 $= 60.0$ y

10. $t_e = \dfrac{t_s}{\sqrt{1 - v^2/c^2}}$

 $t_s = t_e \sqrt{1 - v^2/c^2}$
 $= (60.0 \text{ y}) \sqrt{1 - (0.50\,c)^2/c^2}$
 $= 52$ y

5 6 7 8 9 10 11 12 13 14 15—92 91 90 89 88

Teacher Questionnaire

Perhaps one the best ways to ensure that effective educational materials are produced is to let authors and publishers know how you feel concerning the texts you are using. Please help us plan revisions and new programs to meet your needs. Complete and return the form found on the next page. Please attach any additional comments to the questionnaire form. After removing the questionnaire from the book, fold and staple it so that the address label shows. We would certainly appreciate hearing from you.

Physics: Principles & Problems

Circle the number which corresponds to your opinion of each of the following items for the Merrill Physics Program. Please also star (*) those three factors which most influence your evaluation or choice of a text.

Student Text	Excellent	Very Good	Satisfactory	Fair	Poor	Comments
1. Readability	5	4	3	2	1	_____
2. Approach	5	4	3	2	1	_____
3. Organization	5	4	3	2	1	_____
4. Factual accuracy	5	4	3	2	1	_____
5. Coverage of physics principles	5	4	3	2	1	_____
6. Concept development	5	4	3	2	1	_____
7. Visual impact	5	4	3	2	1	_____
8. Chapter end materials	5	4	3	2	1	_____
9. Tables	5	4	3	2	1	_____
10. Illustrations	5	4	3	2	1	_____
11. "Dimensions" features	5	4	3	2	1	_____
12. Graphs	5	4	3	2	1	_____
13. Student notes	5	4	3	2	1	_____
14. Example problems	5	4	3	2	1	_____
15. Appendices	5	4	3	2	1	_____
16. Glossary	5	4	3	2	1	_____

Teacher's Annotated Edition

	Excellent	Very Good	Satisfactory	Fair	Poor	
1. Teachability	5	4	3	2	1	_____
2. Effective program use	5	4	3	2	1	_____
3. Demonstrations	5	4	3	2	1	_____
4. Chapter suggestions	5	4	3	2	1	_____
5. Planning guide	5	4	3	2	1	_____
6. Chapter end answers	5	4	3	2	1	_____
7. Audiovisual aids	5	4	3	2	1	_____
8. Annotations	5	4	3	2	1	_____

Supplements

	Excellent	Very Good	Satisfactory	Fair	Poor	
1. Teacher Resource Book for *Physics: Principles & Problems*	5	4	3	2	1	_____
2. *Evaluation Program for Physics; Principles & Problems*	5	4	3	2	1	_____
3. *Laboratory Physics*	5	4	3	2	1	_____
4. *Laboratory Physics, TAE*	5	4	3	2	1	_____

Circle the appropriate information:

1. Grade level of your students   10   11   12

2. Average number of students in your
   physics classes   5-10   11-20   21-30   31-40   40+

3. Total number of students enrolled in
   physics   under 50   51-100   101-200   200+

4. Total school enrollment   under 200   201-500   501-1000   1000+

5. Locale of the school   rural   small town   suburban   city

6. Ability level of students   below avg   average   above avg

7. Appropriateness of the text for your
   class   easy   about right   difficult

8. Number of years the text will be used   1   2   3   4   5

---

9. May we quote you?   yes   no

Please feel free to attach an additional sheet to make further comments.

Name _____ Date _____

School _____ City _____ State _____ Zip _____

PHYSICS
Principles & Problems

AUTHORS

James T. Murphy
Formerly Science Department
Chairperson
Reading Memorial High School
Reading, Massachusetts

James Max Hollon
Physics and Chemistry Teacher
North High School
Evansville, Indiana

Paul W. Zitzewitz
Physics Professor
University of Michigan-Dearborn
Dearborn, Michigan

Consultant

Robert C. Smoot
Science Department Chairperson
McDonogh School
McDonogh, Maryland

Content Consultants

Robert F. Neff
Physics Teacher
Suffern High School
Suffern, New York

Douglas A. Johnson
Physics Teacher
James Madison Memorial High School
Madison, Wisconsin

Charles E. Merrill Publishing Company
A Bell & Howell Company
Columbus, Ohio

Toronto • London • Sydney

A Merrill Science Program

Physics: Principles & Problems
Physics: Principles & Problems, Teacher's Annotated Edition
Physics: Principles & Problems, Teacher Resource Book
Physics: Principles & Problems, Evaluation Program
Laboratory Physics
Laboratory Physics, Teacher's Annotated Edition

About the Authors and Consultants

James T. Murphy was formerly the Chairperson of the Science Department at Reading Memorial High School in Reading, Massachusetts. He received his B.S. and M.Ed. from Massachusetts State University and his M.S. in physics from Clarkson College of Technology. Mr. Murphy taught biology, chemistry, physics, electronics, and general science at the junior and senior high school levels and authored numerous professional articles.

James Max Hollon is presently a physics and chemistry teacher at North High School in Evansville, Indiana, and the director of the Tri-State Regional Science Fair for the University of Evansville. He received his B.S. in mathematics and chemistry from Oakland City College and M.A. in education from the University of Evansville. Mr. Hollon has 20 years of teaching experience at the secondary level.

Paul W. Zitzewitz is professor of physics at the University of Michigan-Dearborn. He received his B.A. from Carleton College and M.A. and Ph.D. from Harvard University, all in physics. Dr. Zitzewitz has 14 years teaching experience and has published more than 50 research papers in the field of atomic physics.

Robert C. Smoot is a chemistry teacher and Chairperson of the Science Department at the McDonogh School, McDonogh, Maryland. He received his B.S. in chemical engineering from Pennsylvania State University and his M.A.T. from Johns Hopkins University. Mr. Smoot is author of Merrill's *Chemistry: A Modern Course.*

Robert F. Neff is completing his twentieth year as a physics teacher at Suffern High School, Suffern, New York. He received his B.S. from Kenyon College and his M.S.T. from Cornell University. For seven years Mr. Neff has presented programs of physics demonstrations to colleagues across the country.

Douglas A. Johnson is a physics teacher at James Madison Memorial High School in Madison, Wisconsin. He received his B.S. in physics from Augsburg College and his M.S.T. from the University of Wisconsin at Superior.

Reviewers

Gayle M. Ater, LSU Laboratory School, Baton Rouge, Louisiana
Dr. Judith L. Doyle, Newark High School, Newark, Ohio
Craig Kramer, Bexley High School, Bexley, Ohio
Michael McGuire, Norwell, Massachusetts
Dr. Willa D. Ramsay, Gompers Secondary School, San Diego, California
Ruth E. R. Spear, San Marcos High School, San Marcos, Texas
Nathan A. Unterman, Von Steuben Metropolitan Science Center, Chicago, Illinois

Cover Photography: The motion of a tennis ball and its interaction with the racquet can be explained by a few laws of physics. Photography by Leonard Kamsler

Project Editor: Robert A. Roth; **Editor:** Madelaine Meek; **Design:** Patrick J. McCarthy; **Project Artist:** David L. Gossell; **Artists:** Jeffrey A. Clark, Brent Good; **Illustrators:** Don Robison, Jim Shough; **Photo Editor:** Kristy Schooler; **Production Editor:** Janice E. Wagner

ISBN 0-675-07069-4

Published by
Charles E. Merrill Publishing Company
A Bell & Howell Company
Columbus, Ohio 43216

Copyright 1986, 1982, 1977, 1972 by Bell & Howell Company

Printed in the United States of America

Preface

A study of physics and its applications is basic and vital to all students whatever their educational goals. *Physics: Principles & Problems* appeals to students with a wide range of interests and can be used successfully for both classroom and individual study.

Physics: Principles & Problems provides a clear and straightforward presentation of the basic concepts of physics. These concepts are developed in an orderly manner so as to present a unified, logical sequence. Excessive detail has been omitted where it would obscure or confuse the main idea.

Mechanics, needed to interpret most phenomena, is the first concept presented. It is used to develop models for heat and matter. Wave phenomena are introduced as models for sound and light. Electromagnetic waves are developed from electricity and magnetism. Atomic and nuclear physics complete the text with an expanded discussion of quantum and elementary particle physics.

An understanding of the nature of measurements and mathematics is necessary in physics. To make the text self-sustaining, a brief review of algebra, trigonometry, and graphing using physical quantities is provided in Chapter 2. Thus, use of outside resources has been eliminated.

The authors have written this text in a manner that bridges the gap between the understanding of a principle and the application of that principle to the solution of problems. Explanations are keyed to experiments and actual experiences, and lead students to an awareness of how physical laws operate in everyday phenomena. Photographs and artwork are used extensively throughout the text to illustrate principles and their applications.

Physics: Principles & Problems reflects the consensus of recent recommendations made by curriculum committees, by teachers using this material, and by students. Following these guidelines, the authors have designed a physics program that is both manageable and realistic in terms of its expectations of students.

The authors wish to express their gratitude to the many physics students, teachers, and science educators who have made suggestions for changes based on their use of the previous editions of *Physics: Principles & Problems*.

To the Student

This physics textbook presents you with the basic physics concepts and principles that will form a foundation for most of your studies of science and technology. These concepts are developed clearly and logically with applications from everyday experiences. Certain features of your textbook are designed to make the time you spend studying physics especially interesting and rewarding.

Each chapter is introduced with a photograph and a few sentences that present the theme of the chapter. A *Goal Statement* appears in the margin at the beginning of each chapter and gives you an overall purpose for studying the chapter. Each chapter is divided into numbered sections that provide an outline of the chapter. Each chapter contains photographs and artwork that illustrate the concepts being presented. In some chapters, information is organized in tables and graphs.

Margin notes are carefully positioned throughout the text to highlight important terms and ideas. You can use these notes in organizing information for study and review. New terms are printed in boldface type and defined within the text when introduced.

Example Problems with step-by-step solutions are provided throughout the text to provide you with a model for solving problems. More complex problems are developed as combinations of fundamental concepts. Each *Example Problem* emphasizes the thinking process involved in setting up a logical solution. These *Example Problems* are immediately followed by *Review Problems*. Answers to the odd-numbered *Review Problems* are provided as blue annotations within the text. Thus, you can immedi-

ately check your understanding of the material just studied.

Some chapters contain a *Physics Focus*. This special feature provides a visual presentation of a current topic in physics research and application.

An extensive *Summary* at the end of each chapter provides you with a chapter overview. Comprehensive sets of *Questions* and *Problems* are also included at the end of each chapter to provide further opportunity for you to check your knowledge and understanding of concepts.

The *Readings* section at the end of each chapter has been thoroughly revised to include readings from many new and popular scientific periodicals. These sections provide you with an opportunity to expand your knowledge beyond the limitations necessarily placed upon a textbook.

The *Appendices* consist of a feature on relativity, a section on the laws of sines and cosines, reference tables, a listing of important physics equations according to sections, and a feature on physics-related careers. The reference tables include trigonometric tables, the elements, physical constants, and important equations. The career appendix includes descriptions and educational requirements for a variety of physics-related careers.

A *Glossary* provides you with a ready reference for the definitions of new terms. An *Index* has been included to provide the page number where an item may be found.

Learning to use all the features of your textbook *Physics: Principles & Problems* will contribute to your success in the study of physics.

Contents

30 The Nucleus 512

Appendices

31 Nuclear Applications 534

Science is the result of curiosity about the universe. Through the ages, people have observed phenomena which occur over and over. Using systematic methods of analyzing these observations, people have attempted to gain a better understanding of their world. We now know that there are a few fundamental laws that govern our universe. What are these laws? How do they affect you? Your study of physics will help you answer these questions.

Physics: A Mathematical Science

Chapter 1 introduces the International System (SI) of measurement and defines fundamental and derived units. Scientific notation is discussed. Accuracy, precision, and significant digits and their operations are also introduced.

What is science? What do scientists do? Scientists are inquisitive people who look carefully at the world around them. Their observations lead them to ask searching questions about the causes of what they see. What makes the sun shine? How do the planets move? Of what is matter made? Perhaps the scientist can begin to explain what he or she has seen, but these explanations usually lead to more questions and experiments. The observations, explanations, experiments, results, and predictions must all be analyzed critically. Explanations should be able to describe more than one thing; they must be general and must lead to a better understanding of the universe.

GOAL: You will gain understanding of the objectives of physics, the SI system of measurements, and the nature of measured quantities.

1:1 Physics: The Search for Understanding

Physics is the branch of science that involves the study of physical phenomena in order to establish patterns. Physicists investigate everything from atoms to galaxies, from toys to toasters, and from music to plumbing. They study the relationships between matter and energy, particles and waves.

Physics is the science that studies the nature of matter, energy, and their relationships.

Some physicists conduct their research in laboratories. Often they must design their own equipment before they can perform their experiments. Equally important research is carried out by physicists who do not work in a laboratory. Theoretical physicists construct a framework of theory based on experimental data. The combined efforts of the experimental and theoretical physicists have led to the present state of our knowledge about the physical universe. Some experimental results are not yet understood theoretically, and some theories predict results that have not yet been seen. There is still much about matter and energy that is not understood.

Physics involves both theory and experiment.

3

FIGURE 1-1. A mirror reflects light from one end of a helium-neon laser tube. The laser was developed both from theory and experimentation.

Have students name famous physicists and determine whether their work is primarily theoretical, experimental, or applied.

Other sciences use the results of physics.

FIGURE 1-2. Professor Stephen Hawking (a), an astrophysicist, is currently studying black holes. Astronaut Sally Ride was chosen as the first woman to take part in a space shuttle mission (b).

Physics is important to all other sciences. Biology, geology, chemistry, and astronomy use applications of physics. Engineers apply physics to help solve problems. Technology, or applied science, affects the lives of all people more and more each year. Citizens need an understanding of physics, as well as the other sciences, to make informed decisions about problems created by our rapidly changing society.

a

b

a

b

FIGURE 1-3. Much of your knowledge of physics will be gained in the laboratory through experimentation (a). The scientific method of studying events was developed by Galileo (b).

Perhaps the most surprising aspect of physics is that its experiments and theories can be explained by a small number of relationships, or laws, and that these laws can often be expressed using mathematics. The language of physics is mathematics. For that reason, we begin the study of physics with a review of how measurements are made and how mathematics can be used to describe physical relationships.

1:2 Measurement and the Scientific Method

Starting in the fourth and fifth centuries B.C., Greek philosophers tried to determine what the world was made of. Their method was to observe nature and fit their observations into a logical framework. Doing experiments was not part of their method. One of the most famous of the Greek philosophers was Aristotle, who lived in the fourth century B.C.

Galileo was one of the first modern scientists.

During the fifteenth and sixteenth centuries, Europeans accepted Arabic translations of the writings of the early Greeks as truth without verification. One of the first European scientists to claim publicly that knowledge must be based on observations and experiment rather than ancient books was Galileo Galilei (1564-1642). He questioned the belief that the earth is the center of the universe. He doubted Aristotle's views on physics, especially the idea that objects of large mass fall faster than objects of small mass. To prove Aristotle wrong, Galileo developed a systematic method of observation, experimentation, and analysis.

This method for studying natural events is known today as the scientific method. It is based on systematic experimentation with careful measurement and analysis of results. From the analyses, conclusions are drawn. These conclusions are then subjected to additional tests to find out if they are valid. Since Galileo's time, scientists all over the world have used this method to gain a better understanding of the universe.

1:3   Metric System

The metric system of measurement was created by French scientists in 1795. The metric system is convenient to use because units of different sizes are related by powers of 10. However, in the time since the original metric system was introduced, many versions of it have appeared. In order to have a standardized world system, the International System (SI) has been established by international agreement. SI is now the standard language of measurement. SI units will be emphasized throughout this text. The National Bureau of Standards keeps official national standards for the units of length, mass, volume, and time for the United States.

The standard unit of time is the **second** (s). The second was first defined as 1/86 400 of the mean solar day. A mean solar day is the average length of the day over a period of one year. In 1967, the second was redefined in terms of one type of radiation emitted by cesium-133.

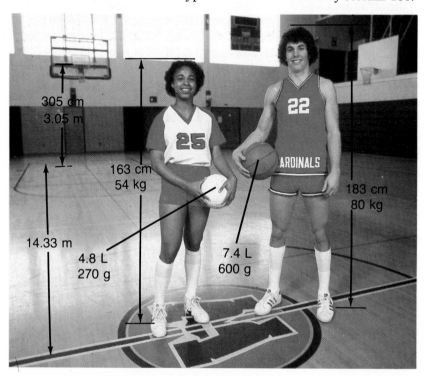

FIGURE 1-4. You can use common objects to form concepts of metric measurements.

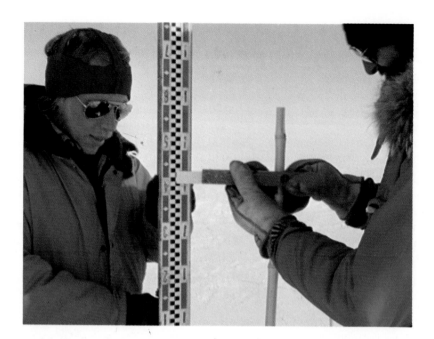

FIGURE 1-5. Scientists, such as these polar geologists, make observations and measurements in studies conducted in the field as well as in the laboratory.

The standard SI unit of length is the **meter** (m). The meter was first defined as one ten-millionth (10^{-7}) of the distance from the north pole to the equator as measured along a line passing through Lyons, France.

The meter is defined as the distance travelled by light in a certain length of time.

The SI unit of length is the meter.

In the 20th century, physicists found that light could be used to make very precise measurements of distances. In 1960 the meter was redefined as a multiple of a wavelength of light emitted by krypton-86. However, by 1982 a more precise length measurement defined the meter as the distance light travels in 1/299 792 458 second.

The third standard unit measures the mass of an object, the quantity of matter it contains. The **kilogram** is the only unit not defined in terms of the properties of atoms. It is the mass of a platinum-iridium metal cylinder kept near Paris.

The SI unit of the quantity of matter is the kilogram.

Other standard SI units will be formally introduced later in this text.

1:4 Prefixes Used with SI Units

One advantage of the metric system is that it is a decimal system. Prefixes are used to change SI units by powers of ten. Thus, one tenth of a meter is a decimeter, one hundredth of a meter is a centimeter, and one thousandth of a meter is a millimeter. Each of these divisions can be found on a meter stick. Ten meters is a dekameter, one hundred meters is a hectometer, and one thousand meters is a kilometer. Metric units for other quantities use the same prefixes. One thousandth of a gram is a milligram, and one thousand grams is a kilogram. To use SI units effectively, it is important to know the meanings of the prefixes in Table 1-1.

Metric units differ from one another by factors of ten.

TABLE 1-1

Prefixes are used to designate divisions and multiples of SI units.

Prefix	Symbol	Fractions	Example
				Prefixes Used with SI Units
deci	d	1/10 or 10^{-1}	decimeter (dm)
centi	c	1/100 or 10^{-2}	centimeter (cm)
milli	m	1/1 000 or 10^{-3}	milligram (mg)
micro	μ	1/1 000 000 or 10^{-6}	microgram (μg)
nano	n	1/1 000 000 000 or 10^{-9}	nanometer (nm)
pico	p	1/1 000 000 000 000 or 10^{-12}	picometer (pm)
		Multiples	
deka	da	10 or 10^{1}	dekagram (dag)
hecto	h	100 or 10^{2}	hectometer (hm)
kilo	k	1 000 or 10^{3}	kilometer (km)
mega	M	1 000 000 or 10^{6}	megagram (Mg)
giga	G	1 000 000 000 or 10^{9}	gigameter (Gm)

EXAMPLE

Conversion Between Units

What is 500 nanometers equivalent to in meters?

Solution: From Table 1-1, we see the conversion factor is

$$1 \text{ nanometer} = 1 \times 10^{-9} \text{ meter}$$

Therefore,

$$(500 \text{ nm}) (1 \times 10^{-9} \text{ m/nm}) = 500 \times 10^{-9} \text{ m}$$
$$= 5 \times 10^{-7} \text{ m}$$

Problems

1. Convert each of the following length measurements to its equivalent in meters.

   a. 1.1 cm   **b.** 76.2 pm   **c.** 2.1 km   **d.** 0.123 Mm

2. Rank the following mass measurements from smallest to largest.

   11.6 mg, 1021 μg, 0.6 cg, 0.31 mg   0.31 mg, 1021 μg, 0.6 cg, 11.6 mg

1. a. 0.011m
   b. 7.62 × 10^{-11} m
   c. 2.1 × 10^{3} m
   d. 1.23 × 10^{5} m

FIGURE 1-6. The meter stick contains decimeter, centimeter, and millimeter divisions.

1:5 Fundamental and Derived Units

In the study of motion, the first topic we will investigate, three fundamental quantities are used. These quantities are mass, length, and time. These quantities are commonly expressed in units of kilogram, meter, and second respectively. All other quantities relating to motion can be expressed in terms of mass, length, and time. For example, speed is found by dividing distance (length) by time. The speed of an object that travels 6 m in 2 s is 3 m/s. Meter per second is a derived unit.

In the same way, other quantities are defined in terms of fundamental quantities. Volume for rectangular solids is length times width (a length) times height (a length). The SI unit for volume is m^3, but a common unit is the liter. One liter (L) is 1000 cm^3 or 1 dm^3 or 0.001 m^3. One milliliter (mL) is 1 cm^3.

The quantity density is calculated by dividing mass by volume.

$$\text{density} = \frac{\text{mass}}{\text{volume}} = \frac{\text{mass}}{(\text{length})^3}$$

The SI unit for density is kilogram per cubic meter (kg/m^3), which is a derived unit.

The fundamental quantities and their units are mass (kilogram), length (meter), and time (second).

Derived quantities are combinations of fundamental quantities.

1:6 Scientific Notation

Scientists often work with very large and very small measurements. For example, the mass of the earth is about

    6 000 000 000 000 000 000 000 000 kilograms

and the mass of an electron is

    0.000 000 000 000 000 000 000 000 000 000 911 kilograms.

In this form, the measurements take up much space and are difficult to use in calculations. To work with such measurements more easily, we can write them in a shortened form by expressing decimal places as powers of ten. This method of expressing numbers is called exponential notation. Scientific notation is based on exponential notation. In scientific notation, the numerical part of a measurement is expressed as the product of a number between 1 and 10 and a whole-number power of 10.

$$\boxed{M \times 10^n}$$

In this expression, $1 \le M < 10$ and n is an integer. For example, two kilometers can be expressed as 2×10^3 m. The mass of a softball is about 1.8×10^{-1} kg.

To write measurements using scientific notation, move the decimal point until only one digit appears to the left of the decimal point. Count the number of places the decimal point was moved and use that number as the exponent of ten. Thus, the mass of the earth can also be

Scientific notation is used to write very small and very large quantities.

A value expressed in scientific notation consists of a number between 1 and 10 followed by 10 raised to a power.

expressed as 6×10^{24} kg. Note that the exponent becomes larger as the decimal point is moved to the left.

$$1\ 000\ 000 \text{ m} = 1 \times 10^6 \text{ m}$$

$$96\ 000 \text{ kg} = 9.6 \times 10^4 \text{ kg}$$

$$365 \text{ s} = 3.65 \times 10^2 \text{ s}$$

To write the mass of the electron in scientific notation, the decimal point is moved 31 places to the right. Thus, the mass of the electron can also be written as 9.11×10^{-31} kg. Note that the exponent becomes smaller as the decimal point is moved to the right.

$$0.000\ 63 \text{ m} = 6.3 \times 10^{-4} \text{ m}$$

$$0.007 \text{ kg} = 7 \times 10^{-3} \text{ kg}$$

$$0.000\ 000\ 95 \text{ s} = 9.5 \times 10^{-7} \text{ s}$$

Problems

Express the following measurements in scientific notation.

3. a. 5800 m   **c.** 302 000 000 m
  b. 450 000 m   **d.** 86 000 000 000 m

4. a. 0.000 508 kg   **c.** 0.0036 kg
  b. 0.000 000 45 kg   **d.** 0.004 kg

5. a. 300 000 000 s   **b.** 186 000 s   **c.** 93 000 000 s

6. a. 0.0073 m   **b.** 0.000 87 m   **c.** 0.0032 m

7. a. 5 000 000 000 000 000 000 000 000 m   **c.** 2 033 000 000 m
  b. 0.000 000 000 000 000 000 166 m   **d.** 0.000 000 103 0 m

Have students practice converting to and from scientific notation.

4. a. 5.08×10^{-4} kg
   b. 4.5×10^{-7} kg
   c. 3.6×10^{-3} kg
   d. 4×10^{-3} kg

6. a. 7.3×10^{-3} m
   b. 8.7×10^{-4} m
   c. 3.2×10^{-3} m

3. a. 5.8×10^3 m
   b. 4.5×10^5 m
   c. 3.02×10^8 m
   d. 8.6×10^{10} m

5. a. 3×10^8 s
   b. 1.86×10^5 s
   c. 9.3×10^7 s

7. a. 5×10^{24} m
   b. 1.66×10^{-19} m
   c. 2.033×10^9 m
   d. 1.030×10^{-7} m

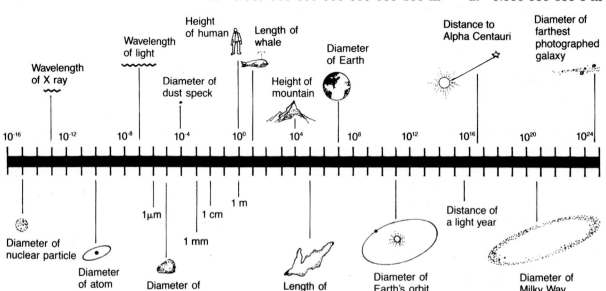

FIGURE 1-7. The magnitude of a measurement is usually expressed as a multiple of a standard unit.

8. a. 650 000 kg   **b.** 5 000 000 s   **c.** 226 m   **d.** 4500 s

9. a. 0.025 m   **c.** 0.0006 s

   b. 0.000 25 m   **d.** 0.000 000 000 000 19 s

9. a. 2.5×10^{-2} m
b. 2.5×10^{-4} m
c. 6×10^{-4} s
d. 1.9×10^{-13} s

1:7 Addition and Subtraction in Scientific Notation

Suppose you need to add or subtract measurements expressed in scientific notation ($M \times 10^n$). If they have the same exponent, you simply add or subtract the values of M and keep the same n.

Quantities to be added or subtracted must have equal exponents.

8. a. 6.5×10^5 kg
b. 5×10^6 s
c. 2.26×10^2 m
d. 4.5×10^3 s

EXAMPLE

Adding and Subtracting with Like Exponents

   a. 4×10^8 m $+ 3 \times 10^8$ m $= 7 \times 10^8$ m

   b. 4×10^{-8} m $+ 3 \times 10^{-8}$ $= 7 \times 10^{-8}$ m

   c. 8.1×10^6 m $- 4.2 \times 10^6$ m $= 3.9 \times 10^6$ m

   d. 6.2×10^{-3} m $- 2.8 \times 10^{-3}$ m $= 3.4 \times 10^{-3}$ m

If the powers of ten are not the same, they must be made the same before the numbers are added or subtracted. Move the decimal points until the exponents are the same.

EXAMPLE

Adding and Subtracting with Unlike Exponents

   a. 4.0×10^6 m $+ 3 \times 10^5$ m   **c.** 4.0×10^{-6} kg $- 3 \times 10^{-7}$ kg
     $= 4.0 \times 10^6$ m $+ 0.3 \times 10^6$ m $= 4.0 \times 10^{-6}$ kg $- 0.3 \times 10^{-6}$ kg
     $= 4.3 \times 10^6$ m $= 3.7 \times 10^{-6}$ kg

   b. 4.0×10^6 cm $- 3 \times 10^5$ cm
     $= 4.0 \times 10^6$ cm $- 0.3 \times 10^6$ cm
     $= 3.7 \times 10^6$ cm

Problems

Solve the following problems. Express your answers in scientific notation.

10. a. 5×10^7 m $+ 3 \times 10^7$ m

   b. 6×10^8 m $+ 2 \times 10^8$ m

   c. 4.2×10^4 m $+ 3.6 \times 10^4$ m

   d. 1.8×10^9 m $+ 2.5 \times 10^9$ m

11. a. 5×10^{-7} kg $+ 3 \times 10^{-7}$ kg

   b. 4×10^{-3} kg $+ 3 \times 10^{-3}$ kg

   c. 1.66×10^{-19} kg $+ 2.30 \times 10^{-19}$ kg

   d. 7.2×10^{-12} kg $- 2.6 \times 10^{-12}$ kg

10. a. 8×10^7 m
b. 8×10^8 m
c. 7.8×10^4 m
d. 4.3×10^9 m

11. a. 8×10^{-7} kg
b. 7×10^{-3} kg
c. 3.96×10^{-19} kg
d. 4.6×10^{-12} kg

12. a. 2×10^8 cm
    b. 1.9×10^{12} cm
    c. 3.0×10^9 cm
    d. 1.75×10^4 cm

13. a. 2×10^{-8} m²
    b. -1.5×10^{-11} m²
    c. 3.0×10^{-9} m²
    d. 4.6×10^{-19} m²

14. a. 6.4×10^8 kg
    b. 7.2×10^4 kg
    c. 3.4×10^5 kg
    d. 5.6×10^{11} kg

15. a. 5.4×10^{-7} cg
    b. 6.2×10^{-3} cg
    c. 3.2×10^{-14} cg
    d. 4.6×10^{-12} cg

16. a. 4.6×10^{-7} L
    b. 5.8×10^{-3} L
    c. 2.8×10^{-14} L
    d. 7.8×10^{-16} L

17. a. 9×10^8 m
    b. 5.8×10^4 m
    c. 5.6×10^8 m
    d. 1.0×10^6 m

18. a. 5.2×10^{-8} g
    b. 2.0×10^7 g
    c. 5.4×10^{-8} g
    d. 1.4×10^{12} g

12. a. 6×10^8 cm $- 4 \times 10^8$ cm
   b. 3.8×10^{12} cm $- 1.9 \times 10^{12}$ cm
   c. 5.8×10^9 cm $- 2.8 \times 10^9$ cm
   d. 6.25×10^4 cm $- 4.50 \times 10^4$ cm

13. a. 6×10^{-8} m² $- 4 \times 10^{-8}$ m²
   b. 3.8×10^{-12} m² $- 1.9 \times 10^{-11}$ m²
   c. 5.8×10^{-9} m² $- 2.8 \times 10^{-9}$ m²
   d. 2.26×10^{-18} m² $- 1.80 \times 10^{-18}$ m²

14. a. 6.0×10^8 kg $+ 4 \times 10^7$ kg
   b. 7.0×10^4 kg $+ 2 \times 10^3$ kg
   c. 4×10^4 kg $+ 3.0 \times 10^5$ kg
   d. 6.0×10^{10} kg $+ 5.0 \times 10^{11}$ kg

15. a. 5.0×10^{-7} cg $+ 4 \times 10^{-8}$ cg
   b. 6.0×10^{-3} cg $+ 2 \times 10^{-4}$ cg
   c. 3.0×10^{-14} cg $+ 2 \times 10^{-15}$ cg
   d. 4.0×10^{-12} cg $+ 6.0 \times 10^{-13}$ cg

16. a. 5.0×10^{-7} L $- 4 \times 10^{-8}$ L
   b. 6.0×10^{-3} L $- 2 \times 10^{-4}$ L
   c. 3.0×10^{-14} L $- 2 \times 10^{-15}$ L
   d. 8.2×10^{-16} L $- 3.8 \times 10^{-17}$ L

17. a. 6×10^8 m $+ 3 \times 10^8$ m
   b. 2.2×10^4 m $+ 3.6 \times 10^4$ m
   c. 5.0×10^8 m $+ 6.0 \times 10^7$ m
   d. 9.8×10^5 m $+ 2.0 \times 10^4$ m

18. a. 8.4×10^{-8} g $- 3.2 \times 10^{-8}$ g
   b. 5.4×10^7 g $- 3.4 \times 10^7$ g
   c. 6.0×10^{-8} g $- 6.0 \times 10^{-9}$ g
   d. 2.2×10^{12} g $- 8.0 \times 10^{11}$ g

The product of two numbers expressed in scientific notation is the product of the values of M times ten raised to the sum of their exponents.

1:8   Multiplication and Division in Scientific Notation

Measurements expressed in scientific notation can be multiplied whether or not the exponents are the same. Multiply the values of M. Then add the exponents.

EXAMPLE
Multiplication Using Scientific Notation

   a. $(3 \times 10^6 \text{ m})(2 \times 10^3 \text{ m}) = 6 \times 10^{6+3} \text{ m}^2 = 6 \times 10^9 \text{ m}^2$

   b. $(2 \times 10^{-5} \text{ m})(4 \times 10^9 \text{ m}) = 8 \times 10^{9-5} \text{ m}^2 = 8 \times 10^4 \text{ m}^2$

c. $(4 \times 10^3 \text{ kg}) (5 \times 10^{11} \text{ m})$
    $= 20 \times 10^{3+11} \text{ kg} \cdot \text{m} = 2 \times 10^{15} \text{ kg} \cdot \text{m}$

Measurements expressed in scientific notation can also be divided whether or not the exponents are the same. Divide the values of M, and subtract the exponent of the divisor from the exponent of the dividend.

The quotient of two numbers expressed in scientific notation is the quotient of the values of $\acute{M}$ times ten raised to the difference of their exponents.

EXAMPLE
Division Using Scientific Notation

a. $\dfrac{8 \times 10^6 \text{ m}}{2 \times 10^3 \text{ s}} = 4 \times 10^{6-3} \text{ m/s} \quad = 4 \times 10^3 \text{ m/s}$

b. $\dfrac{8 \times 10^6 \text{ kg}}{2 \times 10^{-2} \text{ m}^3} = 4 \times 10^{6-(-2)} \text{ kg/m}^3 = 4 \times 10^8 \text{ kg/m}^3$

Problems
Find the value of each of the following problems.

19. a. $(2 \times 10^4 \text{ m}) (4 \times 10^8 \text{ m})$
  b. $(3 \times 10^4 \text{ m}) (2 \times 10^6 \text{ m})$
  c. $(6 \times 10^{-4} \text{ m}) (5 \times 10^{-8} \text{ m})$
  d. $(2.5 \times 10^{-7} \text{ m}) (2.5 \times 10^{16} \text{ m})$

19. a. 8×10^{12} m²
    b. 6×10^{10} m²
    c. 3×10^{-11} m²
    d. 6.3×10^9 m²

20. a. $\dfrac{6 \times 10^8 \text{ kg}}{2 \times 10^4 \text{ m}^3}$ **c.** $\dfrac{6 \times 10^{-8} \text{ m}}{2 \times 10^4 \text{ s}}$

  b. $\dfrac{6 \times 10^8 \text{ kg}}{2 \times 10^{-4} \text{ m}^3}$ **d.** $\dfrac{6 \times 10^{-8} \text{ m}}{2 \times 10^{-4} \text{ s}}$

20. a. 3×10^4 kg/m³
    b. 3×10^{12} kg/m³
    c. 3×10^{-12} m/s
    d. 3×10^{-4} m/s

21. a. $\dfrac{(3 \times 10^4 \text{ kg})(4 \times 10^4 \text{ m})}{6 \times 10^4 \text{ s}}$ **b.** $\dfrac{(2.5 \times 10^6 \text{ kg})(6 \times 10^4 \text{ m})}{5 \times 10^{-2} \text{ s}^2}$

21. a. 2×10^4 kg•m/s
    b. 3×10^{12} kg•m/s²

1:9 Uncertainties of Measurements

Several scientists often measure the same quantities and compare the data they obtain. Each scientist must know how trustworthy the data are. For that reason the knowledge of how well a measurement was made is very important.

a

b

FIGURE 1-8. A parallax example is shown when a car's gasoline gauge is viewed from the passenger's seat (a) and the driver's seat (b). Note the apparent difference in readings.

a

b

FIGURE 1-9. The micrometer (a) and analytical balance (b) are used to obtain very precise measurements of length and mass, respectively.

All measurements are subject to uncertainties.

When measuring, keep in mind that every measurement is subject to uncertainty. The length of a ruler can change with changes of temperature. An electric measuring device is affected by magnetic fields near it. In one way or another, all instruments are subject to external influence. Uncertainties in measurement are to be expected.

In addition to uncertainties due to external causes, accuracy of measurement depends on the person making the reading. Measuring devices must be read by looking at the scales straight on. In a car, the passenger's reading of the gas gauge and the driver's reading of the same gauge can be quite different. From the passenger's seat, the gauge may read empty. From the driver's seat, the gauge may read one-quarter full. The driver's reading is the more correct one. The difference in the readings is parallax error. **Parallax** (PAR uh laks) is the apparent shift in the position of an object when it is viewed from various angles. It is the reference points behind the object that differ. Thus, the object appears as if it has moved. When sitting next to the driver, your eyes line up the gauge needle near the empty mark. But if you move to the driver's seat, the needle will almost line up with the one-quarter-full mark. Laboratory instruments would be read at eye level and straight on to avoid parallax errors. (See Figure 1-8)

Parallax is a common cause of uncertainty in measurements.

1:10 Accuracy and Precision

The precision of a measurement describes how exactly it was measured.

Precision is the degree of exactness with which a quantity is measured. For example, after several trials, a student might determine the speed of light to be 3.001×10^8 m/s. As part of this experiment, it was found that several values differed from 3.001×10^8 m/s by 0.001×10^8 m/s. According to the student, the speed of light might range from 3.000×10^8 m/s to 3.002×10^8 m/s. The precision of the measurement is then 0.001×10^8 m/s.

Accuracy is the extent to which a measured value agrees with some predetermined standard value of a quantity. In the example above, the accuracy is the difference between the student's measurement and the defined value, quoted to the same precision: 2.998×10^8 m/s. Thus, the accuracy is 3.001×10^8 m/s $- 2.998 \times 10^8$ m/s $= 0.003 \times 10^8$ m/s. Note that precision need not be an indication of accuracy.

The precision of a measuring device is limited by the finest division on its scale. The smallest division on a meter stick is a millimeter. Thus, a measurement of any smaller length with a meter stick can be only an estimate. There is a limit to the precision of even the best instruments.

The accuracy of a measuring device depends upon how well a measurement made using that instrument agrees with the currently accepted value. Thus, when a measurement is made, the measuring device should first be checked for accuracy. This can be done by using the instrument to measure quantities whose values are accurately known. The measured values are then compared with accepted values. Uncertainties in measurement affect the accuracy of a measurement. However, the precision is not affected since readings are still stated in terms of the smallest division on the instrument.

> The accuracy of a measurement describes how well the result agrees with a standard value.

> The finest division of a scale on a measuring device limits its precision.

> The National Bureau of Standards is responsible for determining the accuracy of instruments used in the USA.

> Discuss examples of measurements which are precise without being accurate, and vice versa. How could accuracy be described if there is no standard value?

1:11 Significant Digits

Because the precision of all measuring devices is limited, the number of digits that are valid for any measurement is also limited. When making a measurement, read the instrument to its smallest division and estimate the fraction of the next division. The figures that you write down for the measurements are called significant digits. Significant digits are all the digits of a measurement that you are sure of plus the estimated digit.

Suppose you want to measure the length of a strip of metal with a meter stick. The metal strip in Figure 1-10 is somewhat longer than 5.6

> Significant digits are all the digits of a measurement that are certain plus one estimated digit.

metal strip

5.6 cm — 5.64 cm

FIGURE 1-10. The accuracy of any measurement depends on both the instrument used and the observer. After a calculation, keep only those digits that truly reflect the accuracy of the original measurement.

centimeters. Looking closely at the scale, you can see that the end of the metal strip is about four-tenths of the way between 5.6 centimeters and 5.7 centimeters. Therefore, the length of the strip is best stated as 5.64 centimeters. The last digit is an estimate. Either 5.6 centimeters or 5.7 centimeters would be more in error than 5.64 centimeters. The readings of 5.6 centimeters and 5.7 centimeters are at least 0.03 centimeter and probably 0.04 centimeter in error. It is not likely that a reading of 5.64 centimeters is more than 0.01 centimeter in error.

Suppose that the end of the metal strip is exactly on the 5.6 centimeter mark. In this case, you can write the measurement as 5.60 centimeters. The zero indicates that the strip is not 0.01 centimeter more or less than 5.6 centimeters. Therefore, the zero is a significant digit, for it has meaning. It is the uncertain digit because you are estimating it. The last digit written down for any measurement is the uncertain digit. All nonzero digits in a measurement are significant.

Zeros are often a problem. The zero mentioned in 5.60 centimeters is significant. However, a zero that only serves to locate the decimal point is not significant. Thus the value of 0.0026 kilogram contains two significant digits. The measurement of 0.002060 kilogram contains four significant digits. The final zero indicates a probable value.

There is no way to tell how many of the zeros in the measurement 186 000 m are significant. The 6 may have been the estimated digit and the three zeros may be needed only to place the decimal point. Or, all three zeros may be significant because they were measured. To avoid this problem, such measurements are written in scientific notation. In the number that appears before the power of ten, all the digits are significant. Thus, 1.860×10^5 m has four significant digits. To summarize, the following rules are used to determine the number of significant digits.

1. Nonzero digits are always significant.
2. All final zeros used after the decimal point are significant.
3. Zeros between two other significant digits are always significant.
4. Zeros used solely for spacing the decimal point are not significant.

The final digit in a measurement is the estimated digit.

Discuss the error in this advertising statement "Net weight before cooking 4 oz (113.4 g)"

Write results in scientific notation to indicate clearly which zeros are significant.

Problems

22. State the number of significant digits in each measurement.

a. 2804 m   **c.** 0.0029 m   **e.** 4.6×10^5 m
b. 2.84 m   **d.** 0.003 068 m   **f.** 4.06×10^5 m

23. State the number of significant digits for each measurement.

a. 75 m   **c.** 0.007 060 kg   **e.** 1.008×10^8 m
b. 75.00 cm   **d.** 1.87×10^6 m   **f.** 1.20×10^{-4} m

22. a. 4   d. 4
    b. 3   e. 2
    c. 2   f. 3

23. a. 2   c. 4   e. 4
    b. 4   d. 3   f. 3

1:12 Operations Using Significant Digits

The results of any mathematical operation with measurements cannot be more precise than the least precise measurement involved. Assume that you must add the lengths 6.48 meters and 18.2 meters. The length 18.2 meters is precise only to a tenth of a meter. Therefore, the sum of the two lengths can be precise only to a tenth of a meter. First add 6.48 meters to 18.2 meters to get 24.68 meters. Then round off the sum to the nearest tenth of a meter. The correct value is 24.7 meters. Subtraction is handled the same way. To add or subtract measurements, first perform the operation and then round off the result to correspond to the least precise value involved.

The sum or difference of two values is as precise as the least precise value.

EXAMPLE

Significant Digits—Addition

Add 24.686 m + 2.343 m + 3.21 m

Solution: 24.686 m   Note that 3.21 m is the least precise
        2.343 m   measurement. Round off the result to
        3.21 m   the nearest hundredth of a meter.
    30.239 m = 30.24 m

To multiply or divide two measurements, perform the operation before rounding. Then, keep in the product or quotient only as many significant digits as are in the factor with the lesser number of significant digits.

The number of significant digits in a product or quotient is the number in the factor with the lesser number of significant digits.

EXAMPLE

Significant Digits—Multiplication

Multiply 3.22 cm by 2.1 cm.

Solution: 3.2 ② cm
      2.① cm
     ③②②
  6 4 ④
  6 ⑦⑥② cm² This is correctly stated as 6.8 cm².

Note that each circled digit is doubtful, either because it is an estimated measurement or is multiplied by an estimated measurement. Since the 7 in the product is doubtful, the 6 and 2 are certainly not significant. The answer is best stated as 6.8 cm². Recall also that the least precise factor, 2.1 cm, contains two significant digits.

EXAMPLE

Significant Digits—Division

Divide 36.5 m by 3.414 s.

Solution:

$$\frac{36.5 \text{ m}}{3.414 \text{ s}} = 10.69 \text{ m/s}$$ This is correctly stated as 10.7 m/s.

FIGURE 1-11. When using a calculator in answering problems, it is important to note that your answers cannot be more precise than the least precise quantity involved.

Generally the uncertainty in the estimated significant digit is one unit, i.e.

$$34 \pm 1 \text{ g}$$
$$34.6 \pm 0.1 \text{ g}$$

It may be even larger, as in 15.56 ± 0.02 cm³. The ± 0.02 indicates that the value can be as high as 15.58 or as low as 15.54. Student answers should therefore be allowed to vary by at least ± 1 in the last place.

Avoid reporting all the digits given by a calculator. Only report significant digits.

24. 26.3 cm

25. 78.5 m

26. 71.7 kg

27. 362.1 m

28. 2.5 g

29. 17.30 mL

30. 48.2 kg

31. a. 3.0×10^2 cm²
    b. 15 cm²
    c. 13.6 km²

32. a. 2.73 cm/s
    b. 0.253 cm/s
    c. 4.73 m/s

33. 69.2 m²

Whenever the measurements made during an experiment are recorded, it is important to write these measurements with the correct number of significant digits. In this way, each stated value can be communicated to other scientists in a way showing the precision of the measurement. This information must be considered when judging the validity of experimental results.

In both the laboratory and the classroom, you will be making calculations based on measurements. When using a calculator, be particularly careful to observe the proper use of significant digits.

Problems

24. Add 6.201 cm, 7.4 cm, 0.68 cm, and 12.0 cm.

25. Add 28.662 m, 32.34 m, and 17.5 m.

26. Add 26.38 kg, 14.531 kg, and 30.8 kg.

27. The sides of a quadrangular plot of land are measured. Their lengths are found to be 132.68 m, 48.3 m, 132.736 m, and 48.37 m. What is the perimeter of the plot of land as can best be determined from these measurements?

28. Subtract 8.264 g from 10.8 g.

29. Subtract 26.82 mL from 44.12 mL.

30. A water tank has a mass of 3.64 kg when empty and a mass of 51.8 kg when filled to a certain level. What is the mass of the water in the tank?

31. Perform the following multiplications.
    a. 131 cm $\times$ 2.3 cm
    b. 6.87 cm $\times$ 2.2 cm
    c. 3.2145 km $\times$ 4.23 km

32. Perform the following divisions.
    a. 20.2 cm $\div$ 7.41 s
    b. 3.1416 cm $\div$ 12.4 s
    c. 64.39 m $\div$ 13.6 s

33. A rectangular floor has a length of 15.72 m and a width of 4.40 m. Calculate the area of the floor to the best possible value using these measurements.

Summary

1. Physics is the study of physical events in order to establish patterns.   1:1
2. Physics is basic to all other sciences.   1:1
3. Engineers and technologists use the results of physics.   1:1
4. A knowledge of physics makes us, as citizens, better able to make decisions about questions related to science and technology.   1:1
5. The language of physics is mathematics.   1:1
6. Galileo Galilei was one of the first modern experimenters in physics.   1:2
7. The second, meter, and kilogram are the fundamental units of time, distance, and mass in the SI system.   1:3
8. SI units of different sizes are related by powers of ten.   1:4
9. Derived units are a combination of fundamental units.   1:5
10. Large and small measurements, which are often used in physics, are easily dealt with using scientific notation.   1:6
11. All measurements are subject to some uncertainty.   1:9
12. Precision is the degree of exactness with which a quantity is measured.   1:10
13. Accuracy is the extent to which the measured and accepted values of a quantity agree.   1:10
14. For a given measurement, the number of significant digits is limited by the precision of the measuring device.   1:11
15. The last digit in a reading is always an estimate. Only one estimated digit is significant.   1:11

Detailed answers to all Questions and Problems are given in the Teacher's Guide at the front of this book.

Questions

1. Define physics.
2. What differences are there between fundamental units and derived units?
3. What are the fundamental units used in a study of motion?
4. Express speed in terms of fundamental units.
5. What is the importance of the International System of Units?
6. Give the proper name for each multiple of the meter listed.
    a. 1/100 m   **b.** 1/1000 m   **c.** 1000 m
7. **a.**   What is mass?
    b.   What is the standard unit of mass in SI?

8. How does the last digit differ from the other digits of a measurement?

9. What determines the precision of a measurement?

10. a. Why is it difficult to tell how many significant digits are in a measured value such as 76 000?

   b. How can the number of significant digits in such a number be made clear?

Problems–A

1. a. 3 b. 4 c. 1 d. 5

1. State the number of significant digits in each of these measurements.

   a. 248 m   **b.** 64.01 m   **c.** 0.000 03 m   **d.** 80.001 m

2. a. 3 b. 1 c. 3

2. State the number of significant digits in the following measurements.

   a. 2.40×10^6 kg   **b.** 6×10^8 kg   **c.** 4.07×10^{16} m

3. a. 34.7 m
b. 25.022 m
c. 46.00 cm²
d. 3.1 kg

3. Add or subtract the following as indicated.

   a. 16.2 m + 5.008 m + 13.48 m
   b. 5.006 m + 12.0077 m + 8.0084 m
   c. 78.05 cm² − 32.046 cm²
   d. 15.07 kg − 12.0 kg

4. a. 1.7 cm²
b. 21 m²
c. 188 cm²
d. 12.0 cm³
e. 36 cm²
f. 3.2 × 10¹⁵ m²
g. 1.5 × 10⁻⁶ m

4. Multiply the following.

   a. 1.42 cm × 1.2 cm   **e.** 4.3 cm × 8.26 cm
   b. 6.8 m × 3.145 m   **f.** $(2.0 \times 10^8$ m$)$ $(1.6 \times 10^7$ m$)$
   c. 74.0 cm × 2.54 cm   **g.** 0.000 50 m/s × 0.0030 s
   d. 8.002 cm² × 1.50 cm

5. 2.4 × 10² m³

5. The length of a room is 16.40 m, its width is 4.5 m, and its height is 3.26 m. What volume of air does the room contain?

Problems–B

1. 29 cent difference

1. Tony's Pizza Shop ordered new 23-cm pizza pans (9-inch pans). By mistake, 26-cm (10-inch) pans were delivered. Tony says that the difference is too small to worry about. As Tony's accountant, what would you say knowing materials cost about .25 cents per square centimeter?

2. 27 km

2. Studies have shown that nuclear matter is unbelievably dense. Neutrons have a density of about 2.0×10^{14} grams per cubic centimeter (more than 200 000 000 tons per cubic centimeter). Pulsars are thought to be the compact remnants of old stars that have collapsed due to gravity. These stars form rapidly spinning, spherical bodies consisting entirely of neutrons. Let us assume that our sun is sufficiently large to form a pulsar. Calculate the diameter in kilometers of the pulsar formed from our sun if it were to collapse completely so that its density equaled that of neutrons. The mass of the sun is about 2.0×10^{30} kg.

3. Make a table in which you list the surface areas and volumes of cubes having sides that measure 1 m, 2 m, 3 m, 4 m, 5 m, and 6 m respectively. Add a third column in which you list the ratio of the surface area to volume for each cube. (For example, the first ratio is six to one.) Suppose that you are a member of a building committee in charge of designing a new high school building for a town that has cold winters. Part of the committee is in favor of a one-floor building consisting of many wings. A second group wants a cube-shaped building of several stories. You know that heating is a major cost in the operation of a school and that heat loss takes place through the walls, ceilings, and floors of buildings. How would you cast your vote on this matter? Explain.

3. See Teacher's Guide.

4. On the basis of what you have found in regard to the ratios of surface areas to volumes in Problem B-3, explain the following facts.
   a. Elephants like to wallow in cool streams.
   b. Elephants have large ears containing many veins.
   c. Hummingbirds (one of the smallest of birds) eat almost constantly from sunrise to sunset.
   d. A shrew (one of the smallest mammals) will attack and kill animals much larger than itself to satisfy its tremendous appetite.

4. See Teacher's Guide.

Readings

Cole, K. C., "Beyond Measurement." *Discover*, October, 1983.

Day, Richard, "Metric Makes Planking Easy." *Popular Science*, May, 1984.

Hildebrandt, Stefon, *Mathematics and Optimal Form.* Scientific American Books, New York, N.Y., 1984.

Robinson, Heilier, J., "A Theorist's Philosophy of Science." *Physics Today*, March, 1984.

Zimmerer, Robert, "The Measurement of Mass." *The Physics Teacher*, September, 1983.

During a baseball game, millions of events occur. We see bats, ball, players, and fans move; we hear the crack of the bat and the cheers of the crowd; we feel the warmth of the sun and the cool breeze. These events can be measured and quantified. They then can be related and expressed as mathematical relationships. It is from these relationships that we can develop the fundamental laws of physics.

Mathematical Relationships

Chapter 2 stresses the role of mathematical relationships in physics and contains a brief review of algebra and graphing as well as a presentation of the basic trigonometry that the students will need for the course.

Mathematics does not involve just numbers, but also relationships between quantities. For example, in the game of baseball, the distance a ball is hit is related to the speed of the pitch, the mass of the bat, the speed the batter gives the bat, etc. If you have played baseball, you can name even more relationships. We can often express relationships like these either by using equations or by drawing graphs. In this chapter you will learn how to use both methods.

GOAL: You will review basic algebra, graphing, and trigonometry to solve problems associated with this course.

Equations and graphs are both means of expressing relationships among variables.

2:1 Solving Equations Using Algebra

The fundamental laws of physics are often stated as equations. Suppose that you need to find the value of a in the equation

$$F = ma$$

To do this, the equation must be solved for a. Remember that when an operation is performed on one side of an equation, the same operation must also be done on the other side of the equation. In the present example, we first divide both sides of the equation by m. This operation gives us the equation

$$\frac{F}{m} = \frac{ma}{m} \quad \text{or} \quad \frac{F}{m} = a$$

This expression should be rewritten

$$a = \frac{F}{m}$$

If an equation contains several factors, the same process is followed until the unknown is isolated on the left side of the equation.

The quantity in an equation which is required is the unknown.

Algebraic equations are manipulated by performing the same operation on each side of the equation.

Solve equations for the unknown, placing it on the left-hand side of the equal sign.

23

EXAMPLE

Solving Equations

Solve the following equation for x. $\dfrac{ay}{x} = \dfrac{cb}{s}$

Solution:

Multiply both sides by x. $ay = \dfrac{cbx}{s}$

Multiply both sides by s. $ays = cbx$

Divide both sides by cb and rewrite with x on the left. $x = \dfrac{ays}{cb}$

In problems such as 2(c) and 7(d) the physical significance of the sign is addressed in Chapter 3.

Problems

1. You know that $2 = \dfrac{8}{4}$. Use the method described above to isolate the following integers on the left side of the equation.
  a. 8   **b.** 4

1. a. $8 = 2 \times 4$
   b. $4 = 8/2$

2. Solve the following equations for v.

  a. $d = vt$ **b.** $t = \dfrac{d}{v}$ **c.** $a = \dfrac{v^2}{2d}$ **d.** $\dfrac{v}{a} = \dfrac{b}{c}$

2. a. $v = d/t$ c. $v = \pm\sqrt{2ad}$
   b. $v = d/t$ d. $v = ab/c$

3. Solve the equation $d = \dfrac{at^2}{2}$ for t^2, a, and 2.

3. $t^2 = 2d/a$, $a = 2d/t^2$, $2 = at^2/d$

4. Solve each of these equations for E.

  a. $f = \dfrac{E}{s}$ **b.** $m = \dfrac{2E}{v^2}$ **c.** $\dfrac{E}{c^2} = m$

4. a. $E = fs$ c. $E = mc^2$
   b. $E = \frac{1}{2}mv^2$

5. Solve the equation $P = Fv$ for v and F.

5. $v = P/F$, $F = P/v$

6. Solve the equation $v^2 = 2da$ for d and a.

6. $d = v^2/2a$, $a = v^2/2d$

7. Solve each of these equations for x.

  a. $w = fx$ **b.** $g = \dfrac{f}{x}$ **c.** $n = \dfrac{x}{y}$ **d.** $d = \dfrac{ax^2}{2}$

7. a. $x = w/f$
   b. $x = f/g$
   c. $x = ny$
   d. $x = \pm\sqrt{2\,d/a}$

2:2   Units and Equations

All terms in an equation must have the same units.

In mathematics, you learned not to mix units if you wanted meaningful answers to problems. To find the area of a rectangle, you should not multiply length by width if the two sides are measured in different units. To multiply 12 meters by 60 centimeters, you first change the units so they are all the same. Thus, our example might be written 12 meters × 0.60 meters. An answer of 7.2 square meters is obtained. Similar quantities must be expressed in the same units in calculations.

Always include units with values in equations.

When substituting values into an equation in physics, you must state the units as well as the numerical values. The units can be treated mathematically as factors. This practice often suggests a solution to a problem, as well as serving as a check on mathematical operations.

EXAMPLE

Correct Unit Equation

mass = (density)(volume)

$$kg = \frac{kg}{m^3}(m^3)$$

kg = kg

Note that the units on the right do agree with those on the left. By inspecting the units, you will be able to tell when the equation is incorrect.

Units provide a useful way of checking the correctness of an equation.

Stress the utility of using units to check equations.

Problems

8. Find the answers to these problems using consistent units.

   a. Find the area of a rectangle 2 mm by 30 cm.
   b. Find the perimeter of a rectangle 25 cm by 2.00 m.

8. a. 6 cm²
   b. 4.50 m

9. Substitute suitable units into the following equations and state which are correct.

   a. area = (length)(width)(height)
   b. time = $\dfrac{distance}{speed}$
   c. distance = (speed)(time)²

9. a. m³, incorrect
   b. s, correct
   c. ms, incorrect

The independent variable is controlled by the experimenter.

2:3 Graphs

Quantitative experiments are done to learn what relationships exist between measured quantities. During an experiment, one quantity called the **independent variable** is carefully changed. The value of

FIGURE 2-1. The mathematical relationship between two or more variables can be programmed on a computer (a). Computer-aided graphing is prevalent in research and industry (b).

a

b

another quantity called the **dependent variable** is measured for each measurement of the independent variable. The values of the independent variable are plotted horizontally (x-axis). *The values of the dependent variable are plotted vertically (y-axis).* The curve that best fits the plotted points is then drawn.

Graphs are valuable because they can often show the relationship between two variables that substituting numbers into an equation cannot. A graph shows a dynamic, changing picture; an equation gives a static one.

Often, the shape of the curve of a graph clearly shows the mathematical relationship that exists between the dependent and independent variables. A straight line shows that the dependent variable y varies directly with the independent variable x. A hyperbola shows that the dependent variable varies inversely with the independent variable. A parabola shows that the dependent variable varies with the square of the independent variable.

2:4   Linear Relationships

The most general form for a linear equation is

$$y = mx + b$$

where m and b are constants. The graph of a linear equation is a straight line. For example, the graph of the equation $y = 3x + 2$ is shown in Figure 2-2. The values used to plot this graph are given with the graph.

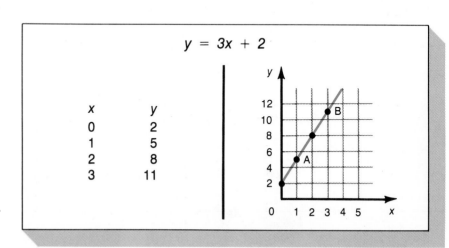

FIGURE 2-2. The graph of a linear equation is a straight line.

The constants m and b are called the slope and y-intercept, respectively. Each constant is obtained from the graph. The slope, m, is the ratio of the vertical change to the corresponding horizontal change. The vertical change, or rise, Δy, is the difference in the vertical values of points *A* and *B*. The horizontal change, or run, Δx, is the difference in the horizontal values of points *A* and *B*. The slope of the graph can be calculated as

$$m = \frac{\text{rise}}{\text{run}} = \frac{\Delta y}{\Delta x} = \frac{11 - 5}{3 - 1} = \frac{6}{2} = 3$$

> The slope (*m*) of a graph is $\Delta y / \Delta x$.

The *y*-intercept, *b*, is the point at which the line crosses the *y*-axis, and is the vertical value when the value of *x* is zero. In this case, when x is zero, the value of *y* is 2.

> The *y*-intercept is the point where the curve crosses the *y*-axis.

When the *y*-intercept equals zero, the equation becomes

$$y = mx$$

The graph of this equation is always a straight line passing through the origin.

> For maximum precision, determine slope using the largest possible Δx.

A good example of direct variation is provided by a law discovered by Sir Robert Hooke (1635-1703). Hooke's law states that the elongation or the stretching of a spring varies directly with the force acting on the spring. Thus, if a force of 1.0 newton (N)* causes a spring to stretch 1.5 centimeters, a force of 2.0 newtons will cause it to stretch 3.0 centimeters, and a force of 3.0 newtons will cause it to stretch 4.5 centimeters.

> This is a graphing example, not meant to teach force or Hooke's law.

In a test of this law, the force acting on a spring was varied and the resulting changes in length were measured. The data are shown in the table in Figure 2-3.

By plotting the independent variable *F* (force) on the x-axis, and the dependent variable *l* (elongation) on the y-axis, we obtain the linear relationship shown in Figure 2-3. The line in Figure 2-3 passes through the origin. Therefore, the elongation varies directly with the applied

Elongation versus Force

Force (N)	Elongation (cm)
0	0.0
1	0.7
2	1.5
3	2.1
4	2.7
5	3.5

FIGURE 2-3. A straight-line graph passing through the origin shows a direct variation.

---

*A newton is a unit of force and will be formally defined in Chapter 5.

force. The equation for the line is

$$l = \frac{\Delta y}{\Delta x} \cdot F = \frac{2.7 \text{ cm} - 0.7 \text{ cm}}{4 \text{ N} - 1 \text{ N}} \cdot F$$

$$l = (0.7 \text{ cm/N}) \cdot F$$

The b term is not written since the y-value is zero at $x = 0$.

2:5   Parabolic Relationships

When one quantity varies as the square of another, the graph of the relationship will be a parabola. The general equation for a parabolic relationship is

$$\boxed{y = kx^2}$$

where k is a constant.

Figure 2-4 shows the position-time graph for a uniformly accelerated object starting from rest. The graph shows only half a parabola, since negative values for time have no meaning for us.

A parabola results when one variable depends on the square of another.

Position versus Time

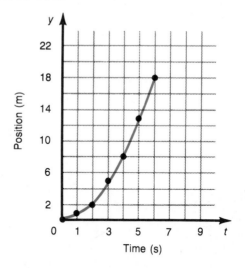

FIGURE 2-4. A graph showing a parabolic relationship indicates one quantity varies as the square of another.

2:6   Inverse Variation

When one quantity varies inversely with another, the second quantity will decrease as the first increases and increase as the first decreases. The general equation for an inverse relationship is

$$y = \frac{k}{x} \quad \text{or} \quad \boxed{xy = k} \quad \text{where } k \text{ is a constant.}$$

In inverse variation the product of the two variables is a constant.

The relationship between the pressure and volume of a fixed amount of gas shows an inverse variation. An example of a fixed amount of gas is a bicycle pump with a plugged hose. When the pressure on the gas is increased by pressing on the pump handle, the volume of the gas is reduced. When the pressure is doubled, the volume will be reduced to one-half its original volume. This relationship is an inverse variation. Within limits, further increases in pressure cause corresponding decreases in volume. This relationship between pressure and volume is called Boyle's law.

Figure 2-5 displays data collected during an experiment with a gas. The graph is a hyperbola, not a straight line.

A hyperbola results when one variable depends on the inverse of the other.

Volume versus Pressure

FIGURE 2-5. The graph of an inverse relationship is a hyperbola.

Remind students that over small variations in x both paraboli and hyperboli look like straight lines. The independent variable must be changed by a larger amount to determine the true nature of the relationship.

2:7 Trigonometry of Right Triangles

Physics is concerned with motion in more than one dimension. Suppose a baseball is hit into the upper deck of the ball park. The upper deck is 84 m from home plate and 21 m high. One way to describe the

FIGURE 2-6. The distance a baseball is hit into the upper deck of a ball park can be described in terms of its horizontal distance and vertical distance from home plate.

FIGURE 2-7. The distance a baseball is hit into the upper deck can also be described as the hypotenuse of a right triangle.

Trigonometry is the study of the relationships among sides and angles of right triangles.

The three most important trigonometric functions are the sine, cosine, and tangent.

Many inexpensive calculators provide these three functions. If students have such calculators, help them learn to use these features.

path is that the ball travels 84 m horizontally and 21 m vertically. The hit can also be described by a single distance and an angle above the horizontal. In this case, the length of the hit is 87 m at an angle of 14° above the horizontal.

The answer above was found using **trigonometry** (trig uh NAHM uh tree), which deals with the relations between angles and sides of triangles. A right triangle is shown in Figure 2-8. A right triangle is one that contains a 90.0° angle. In Figure 2-8, the angles are labeled A, B, and C. The sides opposite angles A, B, and C are b, and c respectively.

The common functions of an angle are cal' d the sine (sin), cosine (cos), and tangent (tan). For angle A, these unctions are expressed as

$$\text{sine } A = \frac{\text{opposite side}}{\text{hypotenuse}} \quad \text{ r} \quad \sin A = \frac{a}{c}$$

$$\text{cosine } A = \frac{\text{adjacent side}}{\text{hypotenuse}} \quad \text{or} \quad \cos A = \frac{b}{c}$$

$$\text{tangent } A = \frac{\text{opposite side}}{\text{adjacent side}} \quad \text{or} \quad \tan A = \frac{a}{b}$$

A table of numerical values for trigonometric functions is given in Table C-6 of the Appendix.

FIGURE 2-8. The angles and sides of a right triangle are related by trigonometric functions.

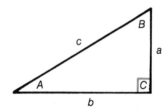

EXAMPLE

Length of Sides on a Triangle

Angle A in Figure 2-8 is 30.0°. The hypotenuse is 8.0 cm. What is the length of side a and of side b? (The sine and cosine of 30.0° are found in Table C-6 of the Appendix.)

Given: angle (A) = 30.0°   **Unknowns:** sides a and b

hypotenuse (c) = 8.0 cm

Solution:

Side a: $\sin A = \dfrac{a}{c}$ Side b: $\cos A = \dfrac{b}{c}$

$a = c \sin A$ $b = c \cos A$

= 8.0 cm × 0.500   = 8.0 cm × 0.866

= 4.0 cm   = 6.9 cm

Two right triangles, a 30°-60°-90° triangle and a 45°-45°-90° triangle, are often used. The relationships between their sides are summarized in Figure 2-9.

 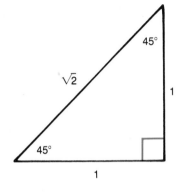

FIGURE 2-9. It is useful to learn the ratios of the sides of a 30°-60°-90° triangle and the sides of a 45°-45°-90° triangle.

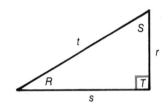

FIGURE 2-10. Use with Problem 10.

Problems

10. Refer to Figure 2-10.
    a. Which side of the triangle is opposite angle R?
    b. Which side is adjacent to angle R?
    c. Write the equations for the sine, cosine, and tangent of angle R.

11. Find the size of the angles associated with each trigonometric function below. The greek letter theta, θ, is used to designate the unknown angle.
    a. $\sin \theta = 0.500$ **e.** $\tan \theta = 1.00$
    b. $\sin \theta = 0.985$ **f.** $\tan \theta = 0.364$
    c. $\cos \theta = 0.707$ **g.** $\tan \theta = 2.050$
    d. $\sin \theta = 0.707$ **h.** $\cos \theta = 0.866$

12. One angle of a right triangle is 20.0°. The length of the hypotenuse is 6.00 cm.
    a. Draw the triangle to scale and measure the lengths of the other two sides.
    b. Use trigonometry to calculate the lengths of these two sides.

13. One angle of a right triangle is 35°. The length of the side opposite the angle is 14 cm. Use the tangent of 35° to calculate the length of the side adjacent to the angle.

14. Show the calculations to obtain the solution to the baseball problem in Section 2:7, page 29.

10. a. r
    b. s
    c. sine $R = r/t$
       cosine $R = s/t$
       tangent $R = r/s$

11. a. 30.0°   e. 45.0°
    b. 80.0°   f. 20.0°
    c. 45.0°   g. 64.0°
    d. 45.0°   h. 30.0°

12. a. the lengths should agree with answer b.
    b. opposite side = 2.05 cm
       adjacent side = 5.64 cm

13. 2.0×10^1 cm

14. See Teacher's Guide.

Summary

2:1   **1.** The laws of physics are often stated as equations involving variables.

2:2   **2.** Units should always be included when solving problems. The units must be equivalent on each side of the equation. If they are not, the equation will be wrong.

2:3   **3.** Graphs are plotted to show the relationship between two variables. The independent variable is the variable changed by the experimenter and is plotted on the x- or horizontal axis. The dependent variable is plotted on the y- or vertical axis.

2:4, 5, 6   **4.** A straight line graph indicates that one quantity varies directly as the other. A parabola indicates that one quantity varies as the square of the other. A hyperbola indicates that one quantity varies inversely as the other.

2:4   **5.** The slope, m, of a graph is the vertical change divided by the corresponding horizontal change.

2:7   **6.** Trigonometry deals with the relationships between the sides and angles of triangles.

2:7   **7.** The most-used trigonometric functions are the sine, cosine, and tangent.

Detailed answers to all Questions and Problems are given in the Teacher's Guide at the front of this book.

Questions

1. How may units be used to check if an equation is written correctly?

2. During a laboratory experiment, one quantity is varied and the resulting change in the value of the second quantity is measured. What is the first quantity called? What is the second quantity called?

3. When plotting a graph,
   a. what quantity is plotted horizontally?
   b. what quantity is plotted vertically?

4. Define the slope of a graph.

5. Think of a relationship between two variables—for example, in baseball, the distance the ball is hit and the speed of the pitch. Now, determine which is the independent variable and which is the dependent variable. In this example, the speed of the pitch is the independent variable. Choose your own relationship. If you can, think of other possible independent variables for the same dependent variable.

6. Aristotle wrote (presumably without performing any experiments) that the quickness of a falling object varies inversely with the density of the medium in which it is falling. What would this mean in terms of an object falling through a vacuum? Based on this, why did Aristotle write that there could be no such thing as a vacuum?

7. A relationship between the independent variable x and the dependent variable y can be written using the equation $y = ax^2$, where a is a constant. **a.** What is the shape of the graph of y versus x? **b.** If $z = x^2$ what would be the shape of the graph $y = az$?

Problems–A

1. Gold has a density of 19.3 g/cm³. A cube of gold measures 4.23 cm on each edge.
   a. What is the volume of the cube?
   b. What is its mass?

1. a. 75.7 cm³
   b. 1460 g

2. One cubic centimeter of silver has a mass of 10.5 g.
   a. What is the mass of 65.0 cm³ of silver?
   b. When placed on a beam balance, the 65.0-cm³ piece of silver is shown to have a mass of only 616 g. What volume of the piece is hollow?

2. a. 683 g
   b. 6.4 cm³

3. Substitute any suitable and consistent units into each of the following equations and then state which are correct and which are incorrect equations.

   a. $\text{speed} = \dfrac{\text{distance}}{\text{time}}$ **c.** $\text{distance} = \dfrac{\text{speed}}{\text{time}}$

   b. $\text{area} = \dfrac{\text{height}}{\text{volume}}$ **d.** $\text{time} = \dfrac{\text{length}}{\text{length/time}^2}$

3. a. m/s, correct
   b. 1/m², incorrect
   c. m/s², incorrect
   d. s², incorrect

4. During a laboratory experiment, a student measured the mass of 10.0 cm³ of water. The student then measured the mass of 20.0 cm³ of water. In this way, the data in Table 2-1 were collected.
   a. Plot the values given in the table and draw the curve that best fits all points.
   b. Describe the resulting curve.
   c. According to the graph, what is the relationship between the volume of the water and the mass of the water?

4. a. student graph
   b. straight line passing through the origin
   c. The mass of the water varies directly with its volume.

5. During a science demonstration, an instructor placed a 1-kg mass on a horizontal table that was nearly frictionless. The instructor then applied various horizontal forces to the mass and measured the rate at which the mass gained speed (was accelerated) for each force applied. The results of the experiment are shown in Table 2-2.
   a. Plot the values given in the table and draw the curve that best fits all points.

5. a. a straight line

b. According to the graph, what is the relationship between the force applied to a mass and the rate at which it gains speed?

6. The teacher who performed the experiment in Problem 5 then changed the procedure. The mass was varied while the force was kept constant. The rate at which each mass gained speed was then recorded. The results are shown in Table 2-3.

   a. Plot the values given in Table 2-3 and draw the curve that best fits all points.

   b. Describe the resulting curve.

   c. According to the graph, what is the relationship between mass and the acceleration produced by a constant force?

Use the data in the tables that follow to answer Problems 4, 5, and 6.

TABLE 2-1		TABLE 2-2		TABLE 2-3	
Volume (cm³)	Mass (g)	Force (N)	Acceleration (m/s²)	Mass (kg)	Acceleration (m/s²)
10.0	10.0	5.0	4.9	1.0	12.0
20.0	20.1	10.0	9.8	2.0	5.9
30.0	29.8	15.0	15.2	3.0	4.1
40.0	40.2	20.0	20.1	4.0	3.0
50.0	50.3	25.0	25.0	5.0	2.5
		30.0	29.9	6.0	2.0

7. Find the angle associated with these trigonometric functions.

   a. $\sin \theta = 0.0872$ **d.** $\cos \theta = 0.9816$ **g.** $\tan \theta = 0.3640$
   b. $\sin \theta = 0.5150$ **e.** $\cos \theta = 0.7771$ **h.** $\tan \theta = 1.000$
   c. $\sin \theta = 0.3090$ **f.** $\cos \theta = 0.2588$ **i.** $\tan \theta = 3.0777$

8. One angle of a right triangle is 26°. The hypotenuse is 11 cm. Calculate the lengths of the other two sides.

9. One angle of a right triangle is 50.0°. The length of the side opposite the 50.0° angle is 8.50 cm. Calculate the length of the adjacent side and the hypotenuse.

====== Problems–B ======

1. The average distance between the earth and the sun is 1.50×10^8 km.

   a. Calculate the average speed , in km/h, of the earth along its circular orbital path.

   b. Convert your answer from km/h to m/s. Show all units.

2. During a preliminary survey of a future bridge site, an engineer measures 2. 1.20×10^2 m
the distance across a river by laying a baseline 30.0 m in length along the
shoreline. One end of the baseline, end A, is directly across from a tree on
the opposite shoreline. Using a sighting instrument, the engineer finds that
a line from the tree to the other end of the baseline, end B, would form an
angle of 76.0° with the baseline. What is the distance across the river?

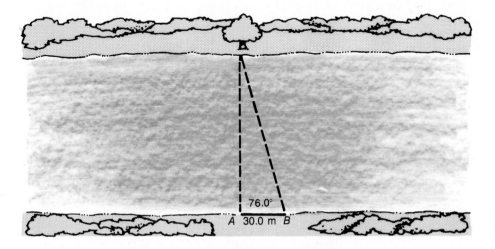

76.0°

A 30.0 m B

FIGURE 2-11. Use with Problem B-2.

Readings

Bak, Per, "Doing Physics with Microcomputers." *Physics Today*, December, 1983.

Friberg, Joran, "Numbers and Measures in the Earliest Written Records." *Scientific American*, February, 1984.

Gardner, Martin, "Slicing π Into Million." *Discover*, January, 1985.

McCorduck, Pamela, "The Conquering Machine." *Science*, November, 1984.

Stepler, Richard, "The House That Computers Built." *Popular Science*, April, 1984.

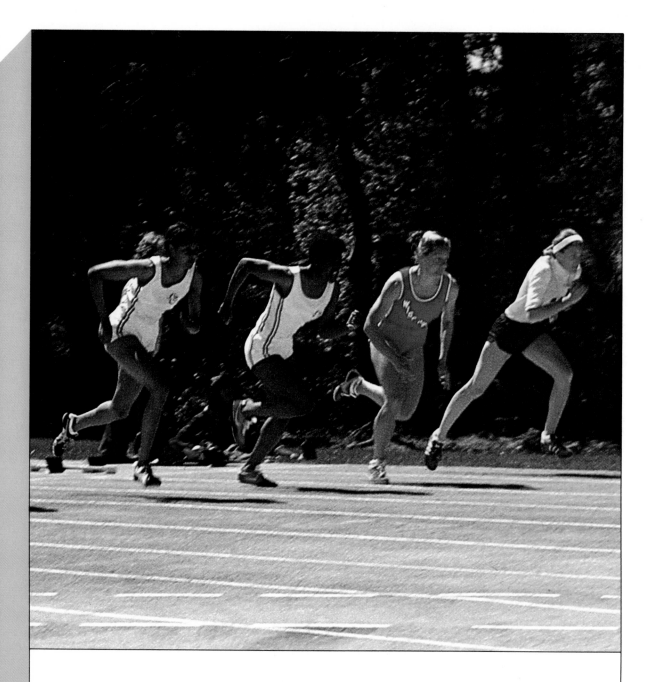

Whenever you think of the words speed and acceleration, a race probably comes to mind. The motion of the sprinters, as well as other moving objects, can be described in terms of displacement, velocity, acceleration, and time. Consider your motion every day traveling from home to school and from class to class. How do displacement, velocity, acceleration, and time describe your motion?

Motion in a Straight Line

Chapter 3 introduces one-dimensional vectors and the quantities used to describe rectilinear motion. Equations are developed to describe motion for constant velocity and for uniformly accelerated motion.

Many things on earth move. People walk, run, and ride bicycles. Automobiles and planes carry people rapidly from place to place. We move with the earth as it spins once a day and revolves about the sun each year. The sun is moving in the Milky Way galaxy as the galaxy itself is in motion within its group of galaxies. It might seem impossible to find a simple way to describe and understand the motions of all these objects. However, this is just what physicists have done! A few simple equations apply to all motions. They are basic to everything the physicist studies. The amazing thing about physics is that the laws of nature tend to be simple, not complex. An understanding of physics begins with an understanding of motion.

GOAL: You will gain knowledge and understanding of the fundamental quantities of motion: distance, time, velocity, and acceleration.

Emphasize the simplicity and universality of the material in this chapter.

3:1 Motion

An object is in motion if its position changes. When you are running, skiing, or riding a bicycle, you are in motion. The terms speed and velocity indicate how fast your motion is. If you ride 10 km in 10 minutes, you have a greater speed than if it takes you 20 minutes to move the same distance.

Speed and velocity describe the change in position through time.

If you move faster or slower, your speed and velocity change. The rate at which the velocity changes in an interval of time is called acceleration. By learning how to work with speed, velocity, and acceleration, you can describe all motion, no matter how complicated. The mathematical description of motion is called **kinematics**. In this chapter, we will concentrate on motion in a straight line. In Chapter 7, motion along a curved path will be discussed.

Acceleration describes the change in velocity through time.

37

FIGURE 3-1. The motion of a bi-cyclist can be described in terms of measured quantities.

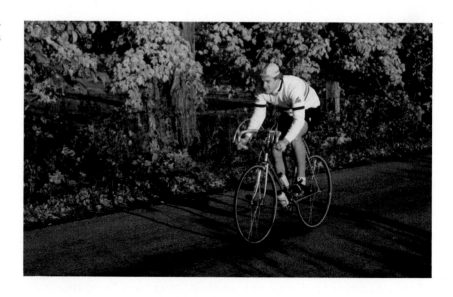

3:2   Scalar and Vector Quantities

A change in position might be described by measuring only the distance moved. For example, a bicyclist moved a distance of 10 km. The quantity 10 km is a scalar quantity. A **scalar quantity** is completely described by its size or **magnitude**. Distance, mass, and volume are scalar quantities. Examples of scalar quantities are 10 km, 8 kg, and 18 L.

A change of position can be described more completely by giving the direction of the motion as well as the distance moved. The bicyclist moved 10 km due east. The quantity 10 km due east is a vector quantity. A **vector quantity** is completely described by its magnitude and direction.

Scalar quantities are added according to the rules of the ordinary arithmetic. Thus, 2 liters plus 3 liters is 5 liters. However, the sum of two vector quantities depends on their directions as well as their magnitudes.

In this book, symbols for vector quantities will be printed in boldface type, for example, A. When vector quantities are written, an arrow is placed over the symbol as in $\vec{A}$. Sometimes only the magnitude of the quantity is being discussed. The magnitude of vector A or $\vec{A}$ will be denoted as A.

3:3   Vector Addition—Graphical Method

A vector quantity can be represented by an arrow-tipped line segment. The length of the arrow drawn to scale represents the magnitude of the quantity. The direction of the arrow represents the direction of the quantity. This arrow-tipped line segment is called a vector.

A scalar quantity is described completely by its magnitude.

A vector quantity requires both direction and magnitude.

When you write a vector quantity, place an arrow over the symbol.

A vector quantity can be represented by an arrow of specific length, called a vector.

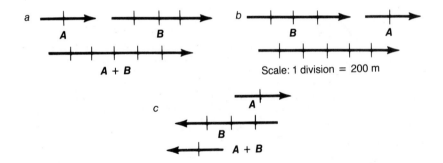

FIGURE 3-2. Vector addition can be shown graphically for **A** + **B** (a), **B** + **A** (b), and **A** + **B** when the directions are opposite (c).

The sum of any two vectors can be found graphically. Consider a person who walks 200 m east, and then continues 400 m east. To find the total change in position of the person, the vector quantities must be added. In Figure 3-2, **A** and **B** represent the two vectors. The vectors are added by placing the tail of one vector at the head of the other vector. Neither the direction nor the length of either vector is changed. A third vector is drawn connecting the tail of the first vector to the head of the second vector. This vector represents the sum of the two vectors. This third vector is called the **resultant** of **A** and **B**. The resultant is always drawn from the tail of the first vector to the head of the second vector.

> Two vectors are added by placing them head to tail.

In both algebraic and geometric vector addition, the order of addition does not matter. The tail of **A** could have been placed at the head of **B**. Figure 3-2 shows that the same sum would result.

To find the magnitude of the resultant, measure its length using the same scale used to draw **A** and **B**. In this situation, the total change in position is 200 m, east + 400 m, east = 600 m, east. If the person had stopped after moving 200 m, east and walked 400 m, west, the change of position of the person would have been 200 m, east + 400 m, west or 200 m, west. Note that in both cases the vectors are added head to tail and their directions are not changed.

> A vector can be moved without changing its magnitude or direction.

3:4 Distance and Displacement

Distance and displacement are not the same. Suppose you leave your home and walk 4 km due east and then turn and walk 3 km due west. You will have walked a distance of 7 km. However, you will not be 7 km

Scale: 1 division = 1 km

FIGURE 3-3. A vector representing 4 km due east added to one of 3 km due west has a resultant of 1 km due east.

from your home, but only 1 km. **Distance**, the length moved, is a scalar quantity. It is the scalar sum of the actual paths traveled. In this case, the distance is 7 km. **Displacement** is the length and direction of the change in position measured from the starting point. In the example above, the displacement is 1 km east. Displacement is a vector quantity and can be quite different from distance. Figure 3-3 shows the walk as two displacements, one 4 km, east, and the other 3 km, west. These are vectors. The resultant displacement is their vector sum, 1 km, east.

3:5 Instantaneous Speed and Velocity

The **speed** of a moving object is the distance it travels per unit time. The **instantaneous speed** of a moving object is the speed at which it is moving at any given instant. For a bicycle or car, this speed is the reading of the speedometer at a given moment. Speed may be stated in kilometers per hour or meters per second. The direction is not stated. Speed is a scalar quantity.

The **instantaneous velocity** of an object is its instantaneous speed in the direction that it is moving. For example, the instantaneous velocity of a car is 25 km/hr, west. Note that in stating velocity, both magnitude and direction are given. Velocity is a vector quantity. Speed is the magnitude of the velocity at any given instant.

3:6 Average Speed and Velocity

Often an object in motion does not move at a constant speed. During even a short trip, a biker may speed up and slow down many times. The motion of the biker for the whole trip can be described by an average speed. The **average speed** of an object during a time interval can be calculated with the equation

$$\bar{v} = \frac{d}{t}$$

FIGURE 3-4. One of the first high-speed photographs was taken in 1878. The vertical lines are 68 cm apart. The time between exposures is 1/25 second. What is the average speed of the horse in m/s? 17 m/s

Here, $\bar{v}$ (v-bar) is the average speed, d is the distance traveled, and t is the time spent traveling. If the object moves exactly the same distance every second, its speed is constant. The instantaneous speed and average speed in this case are the same.

A bar over a symbol means average.

EXAMPLE

Average Speed

A bicycle rider travels 22 kilometers in 3.25 hours. What is the average speed of the bicycle rider?

Given: distance (d) = 22 km   **Unknown:** average speed ($\bar{v}$)

time interval (t) = 3.25 h   **Basic equation:** $\bar{v} = \dfrac{d}{t}$

Solution: $\bar{v} = \dfrac{d}{t}$ = 22 km/3.25 h

$\bar{v}$ = 6.8 km/h

The calculation of the **average velocity** closely follows that of the average speed. The average velocity is found by the equation

Average velocity is the displacement divided by the time interval.

$$\boxed{\bar{v} = \frac{d}{t}}$$

Here, $\bar{v}$ is the average velocity, d is the displacement, and t is the time interval during which the displacement is made.

EXAMPLE

Average Velocity

A high-speed train shown in Figure 3-5 takes 2.00 hours to travel from Paris 454 km due south to Lyons. What is the average velocity of the train?

Given: displacement   **Unknown:** average velocity ($\bar{v}$)
(d) = 454 km, S
                                 Basic equation: $\bar{v} = \dfrac{d}{t}$
time interval

(t) = 2.00 h

Solution: $\bar{v} = \dfrac{d}{t}$ = 454 km/2.00 h

A vector quantity requires that the direction be indicated, even though the direction is not used in the calculation.

$\bar{v}$ = 227 km/h, S

Note: *Only the magnitudes of vectors are used in these calculations.*
A quantity given in km/h can be expressed in m/s. To make this conversion, we must change kilometers to meters and hours to seconds. In algebra, you learn that if a quantity is multiplied by 1, its value does not change. Any quantity divided by its equivalent equals one. Since 1000 m = 1 km and 3600 s = 1 h,

Always include units with quantities when solving problems.

$$\frac{1000 \text{ m}}{1 \text{ km}} = 1 \qquad \frac{1 \text{ h}}{3600 \text{ s}} = 1$$

FIGURE 3-5. This high speed French train travels commercially at speeds close to 305 km/h. The train moves as a single unit giving it an exceptionally smooth ride. Japanese and German railroads are working on magnetically-suspended trains which can reach speeds of 480 km/h.

Therefore, to change 227 km/h to m/s, first multiply by a distance factor equivalent to 1 and then by a time factor equivalent to 1.

$$\frac{227 \ \text{km}}{1 \ \text{h}} \times \frac{1000 \ \text{m}}{1 \ \text{km}} \times \frac{1 \ \text{h}}{3600 \ \text{s}} = 63.1 \ \text{m/s}$$

Units can be converted by multiplying by a factor of unit magnitude.

This method of converting one unit to an equivalent unit is called the factor-label method of unit conversion. Note that unit labels are treated as factors and can be divided out. If the final units do not make sense, check your factors. You may find that a factor has either been inverted or stated incorrectly.

Problems

1. 6.5 km/h
   1.8 m/s
2. 8.20 m/s
   29.5 km/h
3. a. 0.4500 s
   b. 2592 km/h, E.
4. 4.0 × 10⁴ km/h
   11 000 m/s
5. 1.5 × 10⁸ km

1. A boy walks 13 km in 2.0 h. What is his speed in km/h and m/s?

2. A high school athlete runs 1.00×10^2 m in 12.20 s. What is her speed in m/s and km/h?

3. A bullet is shot from a rifle with a speed of 720.0 m/s.
   a. What time is required for the bullet to strike a target 3240.0 m to the east ?
   b. What is the velocity of the bullet in km/h?

4. A rocket launched into outer space travels 240 000 km during the first 6.0 h after the launching. What is the average speed of the rocket in km/h and m/s?

5. Light from the sun reaches the earth in 8.3 min. The speed of light is 3.00×10^8 m/s. In kilometers, how far is the earth from the sun?

6. On a baseball diamond, the distance from home plate to the pitcher's mound is 18.5 m. If a pitcher is capable of throwing a ball at 38.5 m/s, how much time does it take a thrown ball to reach home plate?

7. A car is driven 60 km west in 40 min and then 70 km east in 50 min. What is the average speed and average velocity of the car in km/h?

8. The French train in the example problem is traveling 301 km/h. When it is 360 m from a road crossing, the engineer blows the whistle. If the speed of sound is 330 m/s, how many seconds after the whistle is heard at the crossing will the train cross there?

6. 0.481 s

7. 90 km/h
   7 km/h east

8. 3.2 s

3:7 Acceleration

Whenever the velocity of an object changes, the object is accelerating. For example, if an automobile starts from rest and speeds up to 50 km/h, it is accelerating. **Acceleration** is the rate of change of velocity. Thus, the interval of time over which a change in speed takes place is important. If one car takes four seconds to reach 50 km/h from rest while a second car requires six seconds to reach the same speed from rest, the first car has a greater acceleration.

Just as velocity is the rate at which the position of an object changes, acceleration is the rate at which velocity changes. We define acceleration as the change in velocity divided by the interval (t) during which the change takes place. The change in velocity is the final velocity (v_f) minus the initial velocity (v_i). Acceleration is

Acceleration is the change in velocity divided by the interval of time in which the change occurs. The unit of acceleration is m/s².

An object can be accelerating even if its instantaneous velocity is zero.

$$a = \frac{v_f - v_i}{t}$$

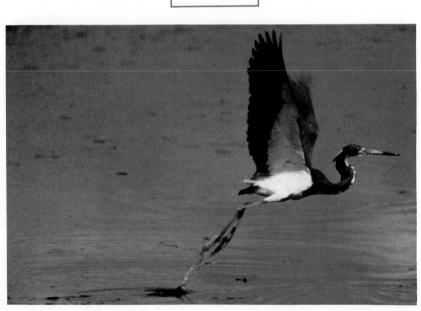

FIGURE 3-6. The heron must maintain an acceleration in order to reach the necessary velocity for flight.

The unit of velocity is meter per second, m/s. Therefore, the unit by which acceleration is measured is (m/s)/s or m/s/s. This unit is read "meter per second per second." The unit of acceleration is sometimes written in the equivalent form m/s^2, read "meter per second squared."

EXAMPLE

Acceleration

The velocity of an automobile increases from 0 to 14 m/s, E, in 3.5 s. What is its acceleration?

Given: initial velocity
(v_i) = 0 m/s
final velocity
(v_f) = 14 m/s, E
time interval (t) = 3.5 s

Unknown: acceleration (a)

Basic equation: $a = \dfrac{v_f - v_i}{t}$

Solution: $a = \dfrac{v_f - v_i}{t}$

$$= \frac{14 \text{ m/s} - 0 \text{ m/s}}{3.5 \text{ s}}$$

$$a = 4.0 \text{ m/s}^2, \text{ E}$$

Describe the related fact that the velocity can be nonzero even if the displacement at one instant is zero. Have students give examples of nonzero velocity and acceleration.

An acceleration of 4.0 m/s^2 means that the velocity increases 4.0 m/s each second. After one second the velocity of the car is 4.0 m/s, E, after two seconds it is 8.0 m/s, E, and after three seconds the velocity is 12.0 m/s, E. This is true only if the acceleration is constant, or uniform. In this chapter, only uniform acceleration will be considered.

Be careful not to confuse acceleration and velocity. The two are not the same. An object moving with constant velocity has zero acceleration. On the other hand, an object can have zero velocity while it is accelerating. The automobile accelerating from rest in the above example is such a case.

Deceleration, or negative acceleration, occurs when an object slows down.

When an object slows down, its velocity decreases. For example, suppose the driver of the car in the preceding example applies the brakes and slows the car from 14 m/s to 7 m/s. The final velocity is less than the initial velocity, so the change in velocity is negative. Therefore, the acceleration is negative. Negative acceleration is sometimes called deceleration, but it is simply another example of acceleration.

EXAMPLE

Negative Acceleration

An automobile slows from 14.0 m/s, E, to 7.0 m/s, E, in 2.0 s. Find its acceleration.

Given: initial velocity (v_i) = 14.0 m/s, E

final velocity (v_f) = 7.0 m/s, E

time interval (t) = 2.0 s

Unknown: acceleration (a)

Basic equation: $a = \dfrac{v_f - v_i}{t}$

Solution: $a = \dfrac{v_f - v_i}{t}$

$= \dfrac{7.0 \text{ m/s} - 14.0 \text{ m/s}}{2.0 \text{ s}}$

$a = -3.5 \text{ m/s}^2$, E (slowing down)

Problems

9. What is the acceleration of a racing car if its velocity is increased uniformly from 44 m/s, S, to 66 m/s, S, over an 11-s period?

9. 2.0 m/s², S

10. What is the acceleration of a racing car moving south if its velocity is decreased uniformly from 66 m/s to 44 m/s over an 11-s period?

10. −2.0 m/s², S

11. A train moving west at a velocity of 15 m/s is accelerated uniformly to 17 m/s over a 12-s period. What is its acceleration?

11. 0.2 m/s², W

12. A plane starting from rest $(v_i = 0)$ is accelerated uniformly to its takeoff velocity of + 72 m/s during a 5.0-s period. What is the plane's acceleration?

12. +14 m/s²

13. In a vacuum tube, an electron is accelerated uniformly from rest to a velocity of + 2.6 × 10⁵ m/s during a time period of 6.5 × 10⁻⁷ s. Calculate the acceleration of the electron.

13. +4.0 × 10¹¹ m/s²

3:8 Final Velocity After Uniform Acceleration

When the uniform acceleration is known, the final velocity of an object at the end of an acceleration interval can be calculated. The equation for acceleration is solved for v_f.

$$a = \frac{v_f - v_i}{t}$$

$$v_f - v_i = at$$

$$\boxed{v_f = v_i + at}$$

Final velocity can be found from the initial velocity, acceleration, and time interval.

EXAMPLE

Final Velocity After Uniform Acceleration

A ball rolling down an incline for 5.0 s undergoes a uniform acceleration of 4.2 m/s². If the ball has an initial velocity of 2.0 m/s when it starts down the incline, what is its final velocity?

Given: time interval   **Unknown:** final velocity (v_f)
$(t) = 5.0$ s
acceleration   **Basic equation:** $a = \dfrac{v_f - v_i}{t}$
$(a) = 4.2$ m/s²

initial velocity $(v_i) = 2.0$ m/s, down the incline

Solution: $a = \dfrac{v_f - v_i}{t}$

$v_f = v_i + at$

$\quad = 2.0$ m/s $+ (4.2$ m/s² $\times 5.0$ s$)$

$v_f = 2.0$ m/s $+ 21$ m/s $= 23$ m/s, down the incline

Problems

14. A car is uniformly accelerated at the rate of $+ 1.2$ m/s² for 12 s. If the original velocity of the car is $+ 8.0$ m/s, what is its final speed?

15. An airplane flying at 95 m/s, E, is accelerated uniformly at the rate of 0.50 m/s², E, for 10.0 s. What is its final velocity in m/s and km/h?

16. A race car traveling at 45 m/s east is slowed uniformly at the rate of $- 1.5$ m/s² for 9.8 seconds. What is its final velocity in m/s?

14. $+22$ m/s

15. 1.0×10^2 m/s, E
3.6×10^2 km/h, E

16. 3.0×10^1 m/s, E

3:9 Displacement During Uniform Acceleration

The displacement of an object during any time interval can be calculated from the average velocity of the object during that time.

$$d = \bar{v}t$$

This equation is valid for both an object traveling at a constant velocity and for an object undergoing acceleration.

Consider a car accelerating uniformly from 15 m/s, N, to 25 m/s, N, for 3.0 seconds. The car will pass smoothly through the whole set of velocities between 15 m/s and 25 m/s. The middle velocity is 20 m/s, N. Half of the velocities will be less than 20 m/s, half greater than 20 m/s. The average velocity is just the middle velocity, 20 m/s, N. The average velocity of a uniformly accelerated object is always the middle velocity.

The middle velocity of the car can be found by adding the final velocity and the initial velocity and dividing the sum by two. This expression can be written

$$\boxed{\bar{v} = \dfrac{v_f + v_i}{2}}$$

The average velocity of a uniformly accelerating object is the middle velocity.

Thus, the average velocity of the car in the example is

$$\bar{v} = \dfrac{25 \text{ m/s} + 15 \text{ m/s}}{2} = \dfrac{40 \text{ m/s}}{2} = 20 \text{ m/s, N}$$

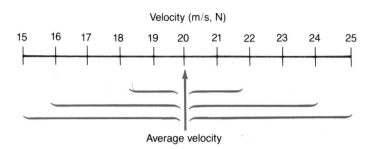

Velocity (m/s, N)

Average velocity

FIGURE 3-7. The average velocity of a uniformly accelerated object is the middle velocity.

To find the displacement of an accelerating object during a time interval, substitute the expression for average velocity into the equation $d = \bar{v}t$. This expression becomes

The displacement of an object can be found from its initial and final velocities and the time interval.

$$d = \frac{v_f + v_i}{2}\, t$$

In three seconds, the car will undergo a displacement of 60 m, N.

EXAMPLE

Displacement During Uniform Acceleration

What is the displacement of a train as it is accelerated uniformly from 22 m/s to 44 m/s, west in a 20.0 s interval?

Given: initial velocity   **Unknown:** displacement (d)
(v_i) = 22 m/s, W
final velocity   **Basic equation:** $d = \frac{v_f + v_i}{2}\, t$
(v_f) = 44 m/s, W
time interval (t) = 20.0 s

Solution: $d = \frac{v_f + v_i}{2}\, t$

$$= \frac{44 \text{ m/s} + 22 \text{ m/s}}{2}\,(20.0 \text{ s})$$

$$d = 6.6 \times 10^2 \text{ m, W}$$

Problems

17. A race car starts from rest ($v_i = 0$) and is accelerated uniformly to +41 m/s in 8.0 s. What distance does the car travel?

17. 1.6×10^2 m

18. A race car traveling south at 44 m/s is uniformly decelerated to a velocity of 22 m/s, S, over an 11-s interval. What is its displacement during this time?

18. 360 m, S

19. 1700 m

20. a. 41 s
b. 1200 m

The displacement can also be found from the initial velocity, acceleration, and time interval.

Give examples that show how the two displacements add. Include both negative initial velocities and negative acceleration.

19. A rocket traveling at $+88$ m/s is accelerated uniformly to $+132$ m/s over a 15-s interval. What distance in meters does the rocket travel during this time?

20. An engineer is to design a runway to accommodate airplanes that must gain ground speed of $+61$ m/s before they can take off. These planes are capable of being accelerated uniformly at the rate of $+1.5$ m/s^2.

   a.   How long will it take them to achieve take-off speed?
   b.   What must be the minimum length of the runway?

   Often the acceleration and the initial velocity of an object are known. The displacement of the object during a time interval can be calculated by combining equations already used. The final velocity of a uniformly accelerated object is $v_f = v_i + at$. The displacement of an object with uniform acceleration is

$$d = \tfrac{1}{2}(v_f + v_i)\, t$$

Substituting the final velocity from the first equation into the second yields

$$d = \tfrac{1}{2}[(v_i + at) + v_i]\, t$$
$$= \tfrac{1}{2}(2\, v_i + at)\, t$$
$$\boxed{d = v_i t + \tfrac{1}{2}\, at^2}$$

This equation can be thought of as expressing two displacements during the same time interval. The first term gives the displacement of the object moving with constant velocity (v_i). The second term gives the displacement of the object moving with uniform acceleration. The addition of these two terms gives the displacement of an object with uniform acceleration and an initial velocity.

EXAMPLE

Calculating Displacement From Acceleration and Time

   A car starting from rest is accelerated at 6.1 m/s^2, S. What is the car's displacement during the first 7.0 s of acceleration?

Given: initial velocity   **Unknown:**   displacement (d)
          (v_i) $= 0$ m/s   **Basic equation:** $d = v_i t + \tfrac{1}{2}at^2$
          acceleration
          (a) $= 6.1$ m/s^2, S
          time interval (t) $= 7.0$ s

Solution: $d = v_i t + \tfrac{1}{2}\, at^2$

$$= (0 \text{ m/s})(7.0 \text{ s}) + \tfrac{1}{2}(6.1 \text{ m/s}^2)(7.0 \text{ s})^2$$
$$d = 0 + \tfrac{1}{2}(6.1 \text{ m/s}^2)(49 \text{ s}^2) = 150 \text{ m, S}$$

Problems

21. An airplane starts from rest and undergoes a uniform acceleration of $+3.0$ m/s² for 30.0 s before leaving the ground. What is its displacement during the 30.0 s?

21. 1400 m

22. A jet plane traveling at 88 m/s, N, lands on a runway and is decelerated uniformly to rest in 11 s.
   a. Calculate its acceleration.
   b. Calculate the distance it travels.

22. a. −8.0 m/s²
    b. 480 m

23. The Tokyo Express is uniformly accelerated from rest at $+1.0$ m/s² for 1.0 min. How far does it travel during this time?

23. 1800 m

24. Starting from rest, a racing car has displacement of 201 m, S, in the first 5.0 s of uniform acceleration. What is the car's acceleration?

24. 16 m/s², S

25. In an emergency, a driver brings a car to a full stop in 8.0 s. The car is traveling at a rate of $+21$ m/s when braking begins.
   a. What is the car's acceleration?
   b. How far does it travel before stopping?

25. a. −2.6 m/s²
    b. +84 m

26. A stone is dropped from an airplane at a height of 490 m. The stone required 10.0 s to reach the ground. At what rate does gravity accelerate the stone? (Assume downward is negative.)

26. −9.8 m/s²

27. A bicyclist approaches the crest of a hill at $+4.5$ m/s. She accelerates down the hill at a rate of $+0.40$ m/s² for 12 s. How far does she move down the hill during this time interval?

27. 83 m

The basic equations for final velocity and displacement can be combined to form an equation that is independent of time. As you recall,

Since vector multiplication and division are beyond the scope of this text, only the magnitudes of vectors are used in making calculations involving these operations.

$$d = \tfrac{1}{2}\,(v_i + v_f)t \text{ and } v_f = v_i + at$$

If the second equation is solved for t and substituted in the first, the result is

$$d = \frac{(v_f + v_i)}{2} \cdot \frac{(v_f - v_i)}{a}$$

$$d = \frac{v_f^2 - v_i^2}{2a}$$

Solving for v_f^2 yields

$$\boxed{v_f^2 = v_i^2 + 2\ ad}$$

The final velocity of a moving object is related to its acceleration, displacement, and initial velocity. This equation can be solved without knowing the time interval during which the object has moved.

Final velocity can also be found from the initial velocity, acceleration, and distance travelled.

EXAMPLE

Calculating Acceleration From Displacement and Velocity

   An airplane must achieve a velocity of $+71$ m/s for takeoff. If the runway is 1.0×10^3 m long, what must the acceleration be?

Given: initial velocity   **Unknown:** acceleration (a)
$(v_i) = 0$ m/s   **Basic equation:** $v_f^2 = v_i^2 + 2ad$
final velocity
$(v_f) = +71$ m/s
displacement $(d) = 1.0 \times 10^3$ m

Solution: $v_f^2 = v_i^2 + 2ad$

$$a = \frac{v_f^2 - v_i^2}{2d}$$

$$= \frac{(71 \text{ m/s})^2 - (0 \text{ m/s})^2}{2 \times 1.0 \times 10^3 \text{ m}}$$

$$\boldsymbol{a} = +2.5 \text{ m/s}^2$$

In the preceding example problem, we found that a plane starting from rest accelerated at a rate of $+2.5$ m/s² to reach a takeoff velocity of $+71$ m/s. During this acceleration, it traveled 1.0×10^3 m. Consider the reverse of this problem. A plane initially traveling at 71 m/s decelerates at a rate of -2.5 m/s² to a stop. The displacement is given by

$$\boldsymbol{d} = \frac{v_f^2 - v_i^2}{2a}$$

> The displacement is the same if initial and final velocities are exchanged and acceleration is changed to deceleration.

Substituting the value into the equation yields

$$d = \frac{(0 \text{ m/s})^2 - (71 \text{ m/s})^2}{2 \times (-2.5 \text{ m/s}^2)} = +1.0 \times 10^3 \text{ m}$$

Note that the displacement in both problems is the same. These problems are said to be symmetrical. That is, even though the conditions stated in the problem were reversed, the solutions are equivalent. We will see that other problems in accelerated motion are also symmetrical.

> Stress the value of symmetry. Compare to a movie run in reverse.

Problems

> 28. 56 m/s

28. A plane is accelerated from a speed of 2.0 m/s at the constant rate of 3.0 m/s² over a distance of 530 m. What is its speed after traveling this distance?

> 29. 88 m/s

29. Decelerating a plane at the uniform rate of 8.0 m/s² ($a = -8.0$ m/s²), a pilot stops the plane in $+484$ m. How fast was the plane going before braking began?

> 30. 25 m/s

30. A box falls off the tailgate of a truck and slides along the street for a distance of 62.5 m. Friction decelerates the box at 5.0 m/s². At what speed was the truck moving when the box fell?

3:10 Acceleration Due to Gravity

All freely falling objects that are close to the surface of the earth gain speed toward the earth at the same rate (disregarding any frictional effects of air). Hence, it is worthwhile for you to memorize the value of

a

b

FIGURE 3-8. Before opening his parachute, a sky diver's downward speed increases by about 10 m/s each second.

All freely falling bodies accelerate at the same rate.

The acceleration of a freely falling body is -9.80 m/s². (toward the earth).

Students should learn this value. Stress the modeling process used here. Solutions of this simplified model provide a guide to solving problems where g varies and air resistance is important.

Emphasize the symmetry in this example.

Acceleration is the same whether the velocity is positive, negative, or zero.

gravitational acceleration. Acceleration due to gravity near the earth's surface is −9.81 m/s². All equations discussed in this chapter can be applied to gravitational acceleration. It is usual to replace the a used in acceleration equations with g when working with the acceleration of gravity. Hence,

$$v_f = v_i + gt, \quad v_f^2 = v_i^2 + 2gd, \text{ and } d = v_it + \tfrac{1}{2}gt^2$$

At the earth's surface, the acceleration of gravity is always approximately − 9.81 m/s² (toward the earth). It does not depend on whether an object is moving up or down. Suppose an object is shot straight up. It slows at the rate of 9.81 m/s². At its highest point, the object will momentarily come to rest but will still be accelerating down at the same rate. As it returns to earth, it will increase its velocity at the same rate of 9.81 m/s². Suppose an arrow is shot from an archer's bow with a speed of 49 m/s straight up. The acceleration of gravity causes the speed of the arrow to decrease 9.81 m/s for every second of flight. After 5.0 seconds, the arrow has a speed of 0 m/s. For an instant, it is at rest. Then the arrow moves downward, just as any object starting from rest and falling toward the earth. The arrow falls for just 5.0 seconds before reaching the point from which it left the bow. At that point, it has a speed of 49 m/s (5.0 s × 9.81 m/s²). The arrow spends 10 seconds in the air. It rises the same distance during the first five seconds as it falls during the final five seconds. The equation for uniformly accelerated motion is symmetrical.

EXAMPLE

Acceleration Due to Gravity—1

A brick falls freely from a high scaffold. **a.** What is its velocity after 4.0 s? **b.** How far does the brick fall during the first 4.0 s?

Given: acceleration of gravity

$(g) = -9.81$ m/s² (downward)

$(v_i) = 0$ m/s

$t = 4.0$ s

Unknowns: a. v_f
                b. d

Basic equations: a. $v_f = v_i + gt$
                       b. $d = v_i t + \frac{1}{2}gt^2$

Solution: a. $v_f = v_i + gt$

$= 0$ m/s $+ (-9.81$ m/s²$)(4.0$ s$)$

$v_i = -39$ m/s (downward)

b. $d = v_i t + \frac{1}{2}gt^2$

$= 0 + \frac{1}{2}(-9.81$ m/s²$)(4.0$ s$)^2$

$= \frac{1}{2}(-9.81$ m/s²$)(16$ s²$)$

$d = -78$ m (downward)

EXAMPLE

Acceleration Due to Gravity—2

A tennis ball is thrown straight up with an initial speed of $+22.5$ m/s. **a.** How long does the ball remain in the air? **b.** How high does the ball rise?

Given: $v_i = +22.5$ m/s
            (upward)

$g = -9.81$ m/s²

Unknowns: a. t
                b. d

Basic equations: a. $v_f = v_i + gt$
                       b. $d = v_i t + \frac{1}{2}gt^2$

Solution:

Negative values of *g*, *v_f*, and *d* indicate a downward direction.

a. Symmetry requires that the speed when the ball reaches the ground will be the same as the initial speed. The direction will be reversed, so the signs of the velocities will be opposite. Therefore, $v_f = -22.5$ m/s (downward).

$$v_f = v_i + gt$$

$$t = \frac{v_f - v_i}{g}$$

$$t = \frac{-22.5 \text{ m/s} - (22.5 \text{ m/s})}{-9.81 \text{ m/s}^2} = 4.59 \text{ s}$$

b. Symmetry indicates that the time for the ball to rise will be one-half the total time it is in the air. At the end of its upward displacement, it will come to rest for a brief moment. Therefore, $v_f = 0$ m/s, $t = 2.30$ s.

$$d = \frac{1}{2}(v_i + v_f)t = \frac{1}{2}(22.5 \text{ m/s} + 0 \text{ m/s})(2.30 \text{ s})$$

$$d = +25.9 \text{ m}$$

Note the positive sign indicates the ball has undergone an upward displacement.

3:11 Solving Physics Problems

Table 3-1 summarizes the equations introduced in this chapter.

Write this table on the chalkboard and have students follow Steps 1-4

Table 3-1   for all problems in order to give them practice in following this procedure.

Equation	Quantities Related
$v_f = v_i + at$	$v_i,$ $a,$ $v_f,$ t
$d = \frac{1}{2}(v_f + v_i)t$	$v_i,$ $d,$ $v_f,$ t
$d = v_it + \frac{1}{2}at^2$	$v_i,$ $d,$ $a,$ t
$v_f^2 = v_i^2 + 2ad$	$v_i,$ $a,$ $d,$ v_f

FIGURE 3-9. A juggler's ball experiences constant acceleration. As the ball rises its speed decreases, which can be seen as smaller intervals of distance traveled, and as it falls its speed increases.

When solving physics problems, an orderly procedure should be followed.

1. Read the problem carefully.
2. Identify the quantities that are given in the problem.
3. Identify the quantity that has to be found.
4. Identify the equation that contains these quantities.
5. Solve the equation for the unknown quantity.
6. Substitute the values given in the problem, along with their proper units, into the equation and solve it.
7. Check to see if the answer will be in the correct units.
8. Check your answer to see if it is reasonable.

Each of the equations developed in this chapter has one quantity missing.

In order to solve problems in which you must choose the equation to be solved, follow this procedure.

EXAMPLE

Finding Displacement When Velocities and Times Are Known

Determine the displacement during constant acceleration of an airplane that is accelerated from +66.0 m/s to +88.0 m/s in 12.0 s.

Given: $v_i = +66.0$ m/s   **Unknown: d**

$v_f = +88.0$ m/s

$t = 12.0$ s

The equation that contains d, v_f, v_i, and t is $d = \frac{1}{2}(v_f + v_i)t$

Solution: $d = \frac{1}{2}(v_f + v_i)t$

$= \frac{1}{2}(66.0 \text{ m/s} + 88.0 \text{ m/s})(12.0 \text{ s})$

$d = +924$ m

Problem

31. A spacecraft traveling at a speed of +1210 m/s is uniformly accelerated at the rate of −150 m/s². If acceleration lasts for 1.8 seconds, what is the final speed of the craft?

31. 940 m/s

Summary

3:1   **1.** All motion can be described in terms of velocity and acceleration.

3:2   **2.** A scalar quantity is described completely by its magnitude.

3:2   **3.** A vector quantity requires both magnitude and direction.

3:3   **4.** Vectors can be added graphically by placing the tail of one at the head of the other.

3:4   **5.** Distance is a scalar quantity that indicates how far an object has traveled.

3:4   **6.** Displacement is a vector quantity that indicates the magnitude and direction of an object's change of position.

3:5   **7.** Speed is a scalar quantity. Velocity is a vector quantity whose magnitude is speed.

3:5   **8.** Instantaneous speed is the speed of an object at any given instant. Instantaneous velocity is the instantaneous speed of an object and the direction that the object is moving.

3:6   **9.** Average speed is the distance traveled divided by the elapsed time. Average velocity is the displacement divided by the elapsed time.

3:7   **10.** Acceleration is the rate of change of velocity.

3:7   **11.** When an object has an increasing velocity, its acceleration is positive. When it has a decreasing velocity, its acceleration is negative. A negative acceleration is sometimes called a deceleration.

3:7   **12.** Constant acceleration is called uniform acceleration.

3:9   **13.** The average velocity of an object undergoing uniform acceleration is always its middle velocity. The average velocity is found by adding the initial and final velocities and dividing by two.

3:10   **14.** The acceleration of gravity is -9.80 m/s^2 near the earth. The acceleration of gravity is treated the same way as any other acceleration.

Urge the students to write a summary table and use it in setting up and solving problems.

Detailed answers to all Questions and Problems are given in the Teacher's Guide at the front of this book.

Questions

1. Write a summary of the equations for displacement, velocity, and time of a body experiencing uniformly accelerated motion.

2. Four cars are started from rest. Car A is accelerated at 6.0 m/s^2. Car B is accelerated at 5.4 m/s^2. Car C is accelerated at 8.0 m/s^2, and Car D speeds up at 12 m/s^2. In the first column of a table, show the speed of each car at the end of 2.0 s. In the second column, show the distance each car travels during the same two seconds. What conclusion do you reach about the speed attained and the distance traveled by a body starting from rest at the end of the first two seconds of acceleration?

3. An object shot straight up rises for 7.0 s before gravity brings it to a halt. A second object falling from rest takes 7.0 s to reach the ground. Compare the distances traveled by the objects.

4. Explain why an aluminum ball and a steel ball of similar size, dropped from the same height, reach the ground at the same time.

5. Describe the changes in the speed of the ball thrown straight up into the air. Now describe the changes in its acceleration.

Problems–A

1. You are driving down a street in a car at 55 km/h. Suddenly a child runs into the street. If it takes you 0.75 s to react and apply the brakes, how many meters will you have moved before you begin to slow down?

   1. 11 m

2. A race car can be slowed with a deceleration of -11 m/s².
   a. If it is going $+55$ m/s , how many meters will it take to stop?
   b. Repeat for a car going 110 m/s.

   2. a. 140 m
   b. 550 m

3. An astronaut dropped a feather from 1.2 m above the surface of the moon. If the acceleration of gravity on the moon is 1/6 that of the earth, how long did it take to hit the surface?

   3. 1.2 s

4. Find the uniform acceleration that will cause an object's speed to change from 32 m/s to 96 m/s in an 8.0-s period.

   4. 8.0 m/s²

5. A rocket traveling at $+155$ m/s is decelerated at a rate of -31.0 m/s².
   a. How long will it take before the instantaneous speed is 0 m/s?
   b. How far will it travel during this time?
   c. What will be its velocity after 8.00 s?

   5. a. 5.00 s
   b. 388 m
   c. -93 m/s

6. A car with a velocity of 22 m/s, E, is accelerated uniformly at the rate of 1.6 m/s², E, for 6.8 s. What is its final velocity?

   6. 33 m/s, E

7. Determine the final speed of a proton that has an initial speed of 2.35×10^5 m/s and then is decelerated uniformly in an electric field at the rate of 1.10×10^{12} m/s² for 1.50×10^{-7} s.

   7. 7.0×10^4 m/s

8. A supersonic jet flying at 2.0×10^1 m/s is accelerated uniformly at the rate of 23.1 m/s² for 20.0 s.
   a. What is its final speed?
   b. The speed of sound is 331 m/s in air. How many times the speed of sound is the plane's final speed?

   8. a. 482 m/s
   b. 1.46 times

9. 920 m, S

9. Determine the displacement of a plane that is uniformly accelerated from 66 m/s, S, to 88 m/s, S, in 12 s.

10. 1700 m

10. How far does a plane fly while being decelerated uniformly from 145 m/s to 75 m/s in 15 s?

11. 2×10^5 m/s²

11. If a bullet leaves the muzzle of a rifle with a speed of 600 m/s, and the barrel of the rifle is 0.9 m long, at what rate is the bullet accelerated while in the barrel?

12. 290 m

12. A car comes to rest after uniform deceleration at the rate of 9.0 m/s² for 8.0 s. What distance does it travel during this time?

13. 71 m/s

13. A plane travels a distance of $+5.0 \times 10^2$ m while being accelerated uniformly from rest at the rate of $+5.0$ m/s². What final speed does it attain?

14. a. -78 m/s, (down)
    b. -310 m, (down)

14. A stone falls freely from rest for 8.0 s.
   a. Calculate its final velocity.
   b. What distance does the stone fall during this time?

15. a. 276 m
    b. 7.5 s

15. A weather balloon is floating at a constant height above the earth when it releases a pack of instruments.
   a. If the pack hits the ground with a speed of -73.5 m/s, how far does the pack fall?
   b. How long does the pack fall?

16. 240 m; no, the distance is the same but the displacement is different.

16. Consider the objects in Question 3. The first object has an initial upward velocity of 69 m/s. Calculate the displacement of each object. Do your results support your answer to Question 3?

17. Falls 44 m.
    Rises 44 m.

17. During a baseball game, a batter hits a long fly ball. If the ball remains in the air for 6.0 s, how high does it rise?   (Hint: Calculate the second half of the trajectory.)

18. 15 m/s

18. A student drops a rock from a bridge to the water 12.0 m below. With what speed does the rock strike the water ?

19. a. 150 m
    b. 42 m/s

19. Just as a traffic light turns green, a waiting car starts off with a constant acceleration of $+6.0$ m/s². At the instant the car begins to accelerate, a truck with a constant velocity of $+21$ m/s passes in the next lane.
   a. How far will the car travel before it overtakes the truck?
   b. How fast will the car be traveling when it overtakes the truck?

Problems–B

1. a. -14 m/s
   b. 20 m

1. A wrench falls from a helicopter that is rising steadily at $+6.0$ m/s. After 2.0 s,
   a. what is the velocity of the wrench?
   b. how far below the helicopter is the wrench?

2. Now that you know about acceleration, test your reaction time. Ask a friend to hold a ruler just even with the top of your fingers. Then have your friend drop the ruler. Taking the number of centimeters that the ruler falls before you can catch it, calculate your reaction time. An average of several trials will give more accurate results. The reaction time for most people is more than 0.15 seconds.

2. Students should use $d = \frac{1}{2} gt^2$ and solve for t.

3. **a.** A driver of a car going 90.0 km/h suddenly sees the lights of a barrier 40.0 m ahead. It takes the driver 0.75 s to apply the brakes, and the maximum deceleration during braking is -10.0 m/s². Determine if the car hits the barrier.

   b. What is the maximum speed at which the car could be moving and not hit the barrier 40.0 m ahead? Hint: The distance traveled at constant speed plus the distance decelerating equals the total distance traveled.

3. a. It hits the barrier.
   b. 22 m/s

Problem 3(b) requires use of the quadratic equation.

4. You plan a trip on which you want to average 9.0×10^1 km/h. You cover the first half of the distance at an average speed of only 5.0×10^1 km/h.

   a. What must your average speed be in the second half of the trip to meet your goal? Note that the velocities are based on half the distance, not half the time.

   b. Is this a reasonable speed?

4. a. 450 km h
   b. no

Readings

Engel, Chuck, "Motorcycle Physics." *Science Teacher*, January, 1983.

Goodman, Danny, "All About Automotive Navigation Systems." *Radio Electronics*, July, 1983.

Hammer, Signe, "The Riddle of Turbulence." *Science Digest*, May, 1984.

Taubes, Gary, "The Mathematics of Chaos." *Discover*, September, 1984.

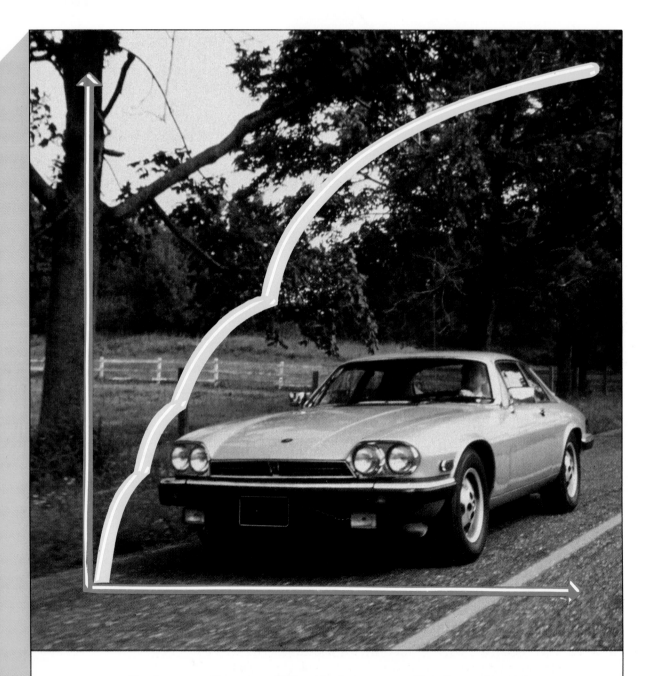

Graphs are used to analyze relationships between quantities. By graphing data relative to the design and performance of a car, designers and engineers can build more efficient automobiles. In this chapter, you will use graphs to study the basic relationships among `position, velocity, acceleration, and time. Of what value are these relationships in the designing of a new car? How might graphs be useful to you in understanding motion?

Graphical Analysis of Motion

Chapter 4 introduces the use of graphs to describe rectilinear motion. The chapter serves to reinforce material presented in Chapter 3.

Overhead transparencies can be helpful with this material.

Graphs are one of our most useful tools. We use them to determine relationships between quantities. For instance, a straight line indicates that one quantity varies directly with another. The parabola always means that one quantity varies as the square of the other. The straight line and parabola are curves that you will see as you study motion graphs. By interpreting the curves of motion graphs, you will be able to determine the relationships between displacement, velocity, acceleration, and time.

GOAL: You will gain knowledge and understanding of the uses of graphs and the relationship between variables the shape of the curve indicates.

4:1 Position-Time Graph for Constant Velocity

An object moving at a constant velocity has the same displacement during each second of motion. The equation describing this motion is $d = vt$. The equation indicates that the displacement (change of position) varies directly with the elapsed time. A graph of position as a function of time for an object moving with a constant velocity is a straight line. The straight line will pass through the origin if the displacement of the object is zero at a time reading of zero.

When velocity is constant displacement varies directly with time.

Consider an airplane flying in a straight line at a constant velocity of 6.0×10^1 m/s. Figure 4-1 lists the position of the plane at various times during a 5-second interval and shows a plot of the data. The curve is a straight line passing through the origin.

59

Position versus Time

Time (s)	Position (m)
0	0
1	60
2	120
3	180
4	240
5	300

4:2   Velocity from a Position-Time Graph

The slope of a graph is $\Delta y/\Delta x$.

As you recall from Chapter 2, the slope of the curve of a graph is the rise (Δy) divided by the run (Δx). On a position-time graph, the rise of the line is the change of position of the object, that is, the displacement. The run is the time interval during which the displacement is made.

$$\text{slope} = \frac{\text{rise}}{\text{run}} = \frac{\Delta y}{\Delta x} = \frac{d}{t}$$

When finding the slope use the line rather than data points and use the largest possible triangles to increase precision.

For example, the slope of the line between points A and D in Figure 4-1 is

$$\text{slope} = \frac{\text{rise}}{\text{run}} = \frac{\Delta y}{\Delta x} = \frac{240 \text{ m} - 60 \text{ m}}{4 \text{ s} - 1 \text{ s}} = \frac{180 \text{ m}}{3 \text{ s}} = 60 \text{ m/s}$$

The slope of a curve on a position-time graph is the velocity.

Note that the unit of the slope is meter per second, a velocity unit. The slope of a position-time graph is the velocity.

4:3   Position-Time Graph for a Complete Trip

The position-time graph in Figure 4-2 represents a short car trip. During the first 10 seconds, a car travels +200 meters from its point of origin. Thus, the average velocity of the car for these 10 seconds is

$$\text{slope} = \frac{d}{t} = \frac{200 \text{ m}}{10 \text{ s}} = 20 \text{ m/s}$$

Between points B and C, the car is at rest. Its position from its point of origin does not change. Since $d = 0$ m, the slope d/t must also be 0 m/s. Thus, the velocity of the car between the tenth and twentieth seconds of the trip is 0 m/s.

FIGURE 4-2. A position-time graph for an object traveling at varying velocities.

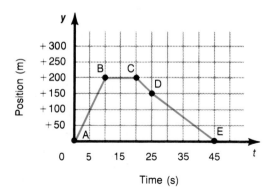

A steep slope of a position-time graph indicates high velocity. When the slope is zero the object is at rest.

Between points C and D, the position of the car from the point of origin decreases. Thus, d is negative. Therefore, the slope d/t is also negative. A negative slope indicates the car is traveling in a direction opposite to its original direction. Between points C and D, the velocity is

A negative slope on a position-time graph shows that the object is moving in the direction opposite to its original direction.

$$\text{slope} = \frac{d}{t} = \frac{-50 \text{ m}}{5 \text{ s}} = -10 \text{ m/s}$$

Following point D, the slope of the line is less steep. Between points D and E the velocity is

$$\text{slope} = \frac{d}{t} = \frac{-150 \text{ m}}{20 \text{ s}} = -7.5 \text{ m/s}$$

Note that at point E the car is back at its origin. The displacement of the car from point A to point E is zero m; that is, the final position minus the initial position is equal to zero.

Suppose the line DE of the graph extended below the t-axis. This would indicate that the car had passed its starting point and was moving in a direction opposite to that of its motion during the first 10 seconds of the trip. The displacement and the velocity would be negative.

A negative value on a position-time graph indicates a negative displacement.

4:4   Velocity-Time Graph for Constant Velocity

Consider a plane flying at a constant velocity of 6.0×10^1 m/s, east. Figure 4-3 is a plot of its velocity as a function of time. Because the velocity is constant, every point on the line has the same vertical value. Therefore, the line through these points is parallel to the t-axis. The slope of the line in this case is equal to 0 m/s². Because the velocity is constant, the acceleration is equal to 0 m/s².

A velocity-time graph is useful because the area between the curve and the t-axis represents the displacement, d, of the object. For

FIGURE 4-3. The velocity-time graph for an object moving with constant velocity.

Velocity versus Time

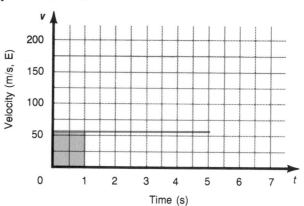

The velocity-time graph of a constant velocity is a line parallel to the *t*-axis.

The area under a velocity-time graph is displacement.

example, note the shaded area under the line in Figure 4-3. The vertical side of this area is the velocity, $v = 6.0 \times 10^1$ m/s. The horizontal side is the time interval, $t = 1.0$ second. The area of this rectangular box is vt, 6.0×10^1 m/s $\times 1.0$ s, or 6.0×10^1 m. This quantity, 60 meters, is the displacement of the plane in 1.0 second.

At the end of 3.0 seconds, the area under the line would be $vt = 6.0 \times 10^1$ m/s $\times 3.0$ s $= 180$ m. The area under the curve of a velocity-time graph represents the displacement.

The displacement increases linearly with time. As seen above, the curve of a position-time graph for constant velocity motion is a straight line.

Problems

1. A plane flies in a straight line with a constant velocity of $+5.0 \times 10^1$ m/s.

   a. Construct a table showing the position or total displacement of the plane at the end of each second for a 10-s period.
   b. Use the data from the table to plot a position-time graph.
   c. Show that the slope of the line gives the velocity of the plane. Use at least two different sets of points along the graph.
   d. Plot a velocity-time graph of the plane's motion for the first 6 s of the 10-s interval.
   e. Find the displacement of the plane between the seventh and tenth seconds.

2. Use the position-time graph in Figure 4-4 to find

   a. how far the object travels between $t = 0$ s and $t = 40$ s.
   b. how far it travels between $t = 40$ s and $t = 70$ s.
   c. how far it travels between $t = 90$ s and $t = 100$ s.

3. Use Figure 4-4 to find

   a. the velocity of the object during the first 40 s.

1. a.

t(s)	d(m)
0	0
1	50
2	100
3	150
...	...
10	500

b. straight line
c. about 50 m/s
d. horizontal straight line
e. 150 m

2. a. 400 m
   b. 0 m
   c. 200 m

3. a. 10 m/s

Position versus Time

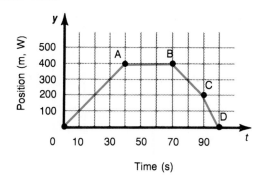

Position (m, W)

Time (s)

FIGURE 4-4. Use with Problems 3, 4, and 5.

4. $t(s)$	$v(m/s)$
0	0
10	10
20	10
30	10
40	10
50	0
60	0
70	0
80	−10
90	−10
100	−20

b. the velocity of the object between $t = 40$ s and $t = 70$ s.
c. the velocity of the object between $t = 70$ s and $t = 90$ s.
d. the velocity of the object between $t = 90$ s and $t = 100$ s.

3. b. 0 m/s
   c. −10 m/s
   d. −20 m/s

4. Use the position-time graph, Figure 4-4, to construct a table showing the average velocity of the object during each 10-s interval over the entire 100 s.

5. Plot a velocity-time graph using the table from Problem 4.

5. graph

6. A car moves along a straight road at a constant velocity of 4.0×10^1 m/s, south.

   a. Plot its position-time graph for a ten-second interval.
   b. Find the slope of the curve using two different points along the line.
   c. Plot a velocity-time graph for the car. What does the area under the curve of the graph represent?
   d. Calculate the area under the curve of the graph between the fifth and sixth seconds. What does this area represent?

6. a. a straight line
   b. $\Delta y/\Delta x = 40$ m/s
   c. horizontal straight line, The area under the curve is vt and thus represents total distance.
   d. 40 m, the distance traveled during one second

7. A cyclist maintains a velocity of 5.0 m/s, south. She is located 250 m north of location A.

   a. Plot a position-time graph of her location from point A for 10.0-s intervals for 60.0 s.
   b. What is her position at 60.0 s?
   c. What is her displacement from her original position for the 60.0-s interval?

7. a. graph
   b. 5.0×10^1 m south of location A
   c. 3.0×10^2 m

4:5 Velocity-Time Graph for Uniform Acceleration

   Consider a jet plane that starts from rest on a runway. It is accelerated uniformly at the rate of 20 m/s². Figure 4-5 lists the velocity of the plane at several times over 5 seconds and shows a plot of these velocities against time. The velocity-time graph for uniformly accelerated motion starting from rest is a straight line passing through the origin. During

FIGURE 4-5. A velocity-time graph for uniformly accelerated motion.

FIGURE 4-5. A velocity-time graph for uniformly accelerated motion.

uniform acceleration, the velocity varies directly with time. The equation that describes the velocity of an object (starting from rest) as a function of time is $v = at$.

For uniform acceleration, the slope of a velocity-time graph is constant along its entire length. The slope gives the acceleration of the object. Between points A and B

The velocity-time graph of constant acceleration is a straight line which passes through the origin.

$$\text{slope} = \frac{\Delta y}{\Delta x} = \frac{v_f - v_i}{t} = \frac{40 \text{ m/s} - 0 \text{ m/s}}{2 \text{ s}} = 20 \text{ m/s}^2$$

The acceleration of an object is the slope of the curve of a velocity-time graph.

The slope of the curve of a velocity-time graph is the acceleration.

In Section 4:3 you found that, for a moving object with constant velocity, the area under the curve of a velocity-time graph gives the displacement (change of position) of the object. This is also true of an object undergoing uniform acceleration. In fact, the area under any velocity-time curve gives the displacement, regardless of the type of motion.

Look at the shaded area under the curve between points A and B. The shaded area is a triangle. The altitude of the triangle is 40 m/s. This value is the velocity attained by the jet plane when it is accelerated from rest at the rate of 20 m/s² for 2 seconds. This velocity can be expressed as the product of its acceleration and the time interval, or $v = at$. Thus, the altitude of the triangle is at. The base of the triangle is the time interval, t, during which the acceleration is taking place. The area of a triangle can be found by multiplying the product of the altitude and the base by one half. Therefore, the area under the curve of the graph is $\frac{1}{2}(at)(t)$, or $\frac{1}{2}at^2$. This quantity is the displacement of an object undergoing uniform acceleration from rest. The area under the curve of a velocity-time graph represents the displacement of the object.

4:6 Position-Time Graph for Uniform Acceleration

Now let us plot a position-time graph for the jet plane discussed in Section 4:5. The position of the plane at the end of each second can be found in two ways. It can be calculated with the equation

$$d = v_i t + \frac{1}{2}at^2$$

It can also be found by determining the area under the velocity-time curve of Figure 4-5. The results are given in Figure 4-6. The data from the table is used to plot a position-time graph.

Position versus Time

Time (s)	Position (m)
0	+0
1	+10
2	+40
3	+90
4	+160
5	+250

FIGURE 4-6. A position-time graph for uniformly accelerated motion.

The curve of the position-time graph is half a parabola. A parabola shows that one quantity varies directly with the square of another.

The slope of any position-time graph yields the velocity. When the velocity is constant, the position-time graph is a straight line. Figure

The curve of a position-time graph of constant acceleration has the shape of a parabola.

FIGURE 4-7. A jet aircraft undergoes a large horizontal displacement during its rapid acceleration.

4-1 shows how to find the slope of the line. However, when an object is accelerating from rest, it travels a greater distance each second than it did the second before. The steepness of the curve constantly increases. The resulting smooth curve is a parabola. The slope of this curve is more difficult to find than the slope of a straight line. It is found by drawing a line tangent to the curve at the point where the slope is wanted. The slope of the tangent line gives the instantaneous velocity at the point on the curve that the tangent line touches. In Figure 4-8, a tangent line is drawn at point P. The slope of the tangent line at this point is

$$\frac{\Delta y}{\Delta x} = \frac{d}{t} = \frac{150 \text{ m} - 30 \text{ m}}{4 \text{ s} - 2 \text{ s}} = \frac{120 \text{ m}}{2 \text{ s}} = 60 \text{ m/s}$$

Point P coincides with the velocity after 3 seconds of travel. The velocity at the end of 3 seconds for an object that accelerates at 20 m/s² from rest is 60 m/s. Note also that this is the velocity shown on the velocity-time graph for the same object after 3 seconds.

Position versus Time

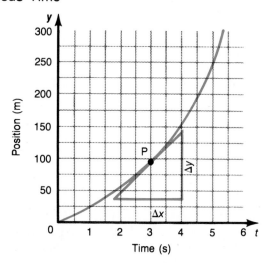

4:7   Acceleration-Time Graph for Uniform Acceleration

Acceleration that does not change with time is called uniform acceleration. If the acceleration is constant, an acceleration-time graph is a line parallel to the t-axis.

In Figure 4-9, the acceleration of the jet plane of Section 4:5 is plotted against time. As expected, the acceleration-time curve is a straight line parallel to the t-axis.

Note that the area under the curve of the acceleration-time graph represents the change in velocity of the plane. Because the plane

Acceleration versus Time

FIGURE 4-9. An acceleration-time graph for uniformly accelerated motion.

started from rest, $v_i = 0$ m/s. The area represents the plane's final velocity. At any point along the t-axis, the area under the line is a rectangle with sides a and t. Therefore, the area of the rectangle is at. This area gives the final velocity, since $v_f = at + v_i$. For example, at the end of 3 seconds, the velocity of the plane is 60 m/s (20 m/s² × 3 s).

The area under an acceleration-time graph represents velocity.

Lasers as Measurement Tools

Physics Focus

The speed of light was long thought to be infinite. But in 1894, a French physicist, Armand Fizeau, rigged a device that let him calculate the speed at 313 000 km/s. Since 1849, several scientists have refined this technique. In 1926, the American Albert Michelson calculated a speed of 299 793 km/s. Further refinements have yielded a speed of 299 792 km/s. For all practical purposes, the speed can be considered to be 300 000 km/s.

In recent years, scientists have been able to focus light in a narrow beam, a laser, that can be used for precise measurement. Light pulses from a laser in one position are reflected from a mirrored surface in another position. From travel times of the pulses, distance between the two positions can be calculated very accurately.

Light from Earth-based lasers bouncing off reflectors left on the moon by Apollo astronauts has been used to measure distance from the earth to the moon to within 2 cm. Laser light reflecting off satellites measures the rate of continental drift. Lasers directed across the San Andreas fault measure distortion along the fault and can help in predicting earthquakes. The applications of laser measurement are virtually limitless.

Summary

Introduction.
1. Many graphs have characteristic shapes. From these shapes, certain relationships often can be recognized.

4:1
2. The position-time graph for an object moving with constant velocity is a straight line that may pass through the origin.

4:2
3. The slope of a position-time graph is the velocity of the object.

4:3
4. If the curve of the position-time graph is parallel to the t-axis, the slope is zero. A zero slope indicates zero velocity.

4:4
5. For an object moving at a constant velocity, the velocity-time graph is a line parallel with the t-axis.

4:4
6. The area under the curve of a velocity-time graph represents the displacement.

4:5
7. The velocity-time graph for uniformly accelerated motion is a straight line.

4:6
8. In a position-time graph for uniformly accelerated motion, the curve is a half parabola. This curve indicates that displacement varies with the square of time. The slope of a tangent to the curve at any point yields instantaneous velocity.

4:7
9. When uniform acceleration is plotted against time, the acceleration-time curve is a straight line parallel to the t-axis. The area under the curve represents the velocity of the accelerating object.

Detailed answers to all Questions and Problems are given in the Teacher's Guide at the front of this book.

Questions

1. What does the slope of a position-time graph indicate?
2. What quantity is represented by the area under a velocity-time curve?
3. What does the slope of a velocity-time graph indicate?
4. If a velocity-time curve is a straight line parallel to the t-axis, what can be said about the acceleration?
5. What quantity is represented by the area under an acceleration-time curve?
6. Figure 4-10 shows a velocity-time graph for an automobile on a test track. Describe the changes in velocity with time.
7. Study Figure 4-10. During what interval is the acceleration largest? During what interval is it smallest?

Velocity versus Time

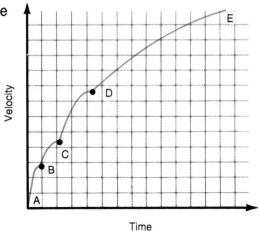

FIGURE 4-10. Use with
questions 6 and 7.

Time

Problems–A

1. The velocity of an automobile changes over an 8-s time period as shown in
   Table 4-1 below.
   a. Plot the velocity-time graph of the motion.
   b. Determine the distance the car travels during the first 2.0 s.
   c. What distance does the car travel during the first 4.0 s?
   d. What distance does the car travel during the entire 8.0 s?
   e. Find the slope of the line between $t = 0$ s and $t = 4.0$ s. What does
      this slope represent?
   f. Find the slope of the line between $t = 5.0$ s and $t = 7.0$ s. What does
      this slope indicate?

2. The total distance a steel ball rolls down an incline at the end of each
   second of travel is given in Table 4-2.

1. a. student graph
   b. 8.0 m
   c. 32 m
   d. 110 m
   e. 4.0 m/s², acceleration
   f. 0 m/s², constant velocity

TABLE 4-1

Time (s)	Velocity (m/s)	Time (s)	Velocity (m/s)
0.0	0.0	5.0	20.0
1.0	4.0	6.0	20.0
2.0	8.0	7.0	20.0
3.0	12.0	8.0	20.0
4.0	16.0		

TABLE 4-2

Time (s)	Distance (m)
0.0	0.0
1.0	2.0
2.0	8.0
3.0	18.0
4.0	32.0
5.0	50.0

2. a. student graph
   b. parabola
   c. 9.7 m
   d. 12 m/s represents
      the speed at the
      end of 3.0 s.

a.   Make a distance-time graph of the motion of the ball. When setting up
the axes use five divisions for each 10 m of travel on the d-axis. Use five
divisions for each second of time on the t-axis.

b.   What type of curve is the line of the graph?

c.   What distance has the ball rolled at the end of 2.2 s?

d.   Find the slope of the line at t = 3.0 s. What does this slope show?

Velocity versus Time

FIGURE 4-11. Use with Problems A-3 and A-4.

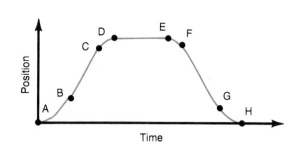

FIGURE 4-12. Use with Problem A-5.

3. a. 6 m/s²
   b. 0 m/s²
   c. −2 m/s²
   d. −4 m/s²
4. a. 75 m
   b. 150 m
   c. 125 m
   d. 500 m
5. A-B = acceleration
   B-C = constant velocity
   C-D = deceleration
   D-E = rest
   E-F = acceleration in
         opposite direction
   F-G = constant velocity
   G-H = deceleration
6. a. student graph
   b. The area represents
      the displacement of the
      object (−123 m).

7. a. t(s)   d(m)
      1   4.9
      2   19.6
      3   44.1
      4   78.4
      5   123
   b. parabola
   c. 20 m/s and 39 m/s

3. Use Figure 4-11 to find the acceleration of the moving object

a.   during the first 5 s of travel.

b.   during the second 5 s of travel.

c.   between the tenth and the fifteenth s of travel.

d.   between the twentieth and twenty-fifth s of travel.

4. Refer to Figure 4-11 to find the distance the moving object travels

a.   between t = 0 and t = 5 s.

b.   between t = 5 s and t = 10 s.

c.   between t = 10 s and t = 15 s.

d.   between t = 0 and t = 25 s.

5. Use the intervals marked on the graph in Figure 4-12 to describe the motion
of the object.

6. Make a table of the velocities of an object at the end of each second for the
first 5 s of free-fall from rest.

a.   Use the data in your table to plot a velocity-time graph.

b.   What does the total area under the curve represent?

7. a.   Compute the total distance the object in Problem 6 has fallen at the end
of each second.

b.   Use the distances calculated in Part a to plot a position-time graph.

c.   Find the slope of the curve at the end of 2 and 4 s. What are the
approximate slopes? Do these values agree with the table of speeds in
Problem 6?

8. Use the data prepared in Problem 7 to plot a distance versus time squared graph.
   a. What type of curve is obtained?
   b. Find the slope of the curve at any point. Explain the significance of the value you obtain.
   c. Does this curve agree with the equation $d = \frac{1}{2}gt^2$?

8. a. a straight line through the origin
   b. The slope will be 4.9 m/s² which is the proportionality constant between d and t^2 or $\frac{1}{2}g$.
   c. yes, since d = $\frac{1}{2}gt^2$

FIGURE 4-13.

FIGURE 4-14.

FIGURE 4-15.

FIGURE 4-16.

FIGURE 4-17.

9. Look at Figure 4-13.
   a. What kind of motion does this graph represent?
   b. What does the slope of the graph represent?

9. a. constant velocity
   b. velocity

10. Look at Figure 4-14.
    a. What kind of motion does this graph represent?
    b. What does the area under the curve of the graph represent?

10. a. constant velocity
    b. displacement

11. Look at Figure 4-15.
    a. What kind of motion does this graph represent?
    b. What does the slope of the line represent?
    c. What does the area under the curve represent?

11. a. uniform acceleration
    b. the acceleration
    c. displacement

12. Look at Figure 4-16. What does the area under the curve of this graph represent?

12. velocity

13. Look at Figure 4-17, which is a position-time graph of uniform acceleration.
    a. What type of curve does this graph represent?
    b. What does the slope of the line taken at any point represent?
    c. How would slopes taken at higher points on the line differ from those taken at lower points?

13. a. parabola
    b. instantaneous velocity
    c. The slopes would be larger at higher points indicating larger velocities

| Problems–B |

1. To accompany each of the graphs shown below, draw

   a. a velocity-time graph.

   b. an acceleration-time graph.

FIGURE 4-18. Use with problem B-1.

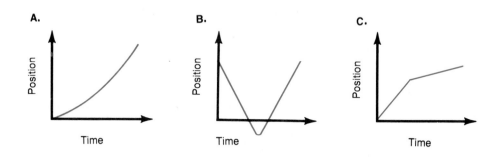

A.   B.   C.

2. a. Draw velocity-time and position-time graphs for the car and truck of Problem 19, page 56, Chapter 3.

   b. Do the graphs confirm the answers you calculated for Problem 19?

3. An express train, traveling at 36.0 m/s, is accidentally sidetracked onto a local train track. The express engineer spots a local train exactly 100 m ahead on the same track and traveling in the same direction. The engineer jams on the brakes and slows the express at a rate of 3.00 m/s. The local engineer is unaware of the situation. If the speed of the local is 11.0 m/s, will the express be able to stop in time or will there be a collision? To solve this problem take the position of the express when it first sights the local as a point of origin. Next, keeping in mind that the local has exactly a 100-m lead, calculate how far each train is from this point at the end of the 12.0 s it would take the express to stop.

   a. On the basis of your calculations, would you conclude that there is or is not a collision?

   b. The calculations you made in Part **a** do not allow for the possibility that a collision might take place before the end of the twelve seconds required for the express to come to a halt. To check on this, take the position of the express when it first sights the local as the point of origin and calculate the position of each train at the end of each second after sighting. The local will always be 100 + (11 t) meters from the origin while the express will be

$$\frac{v_f + v_i}{2} \times t \text{ meters from the origin.}$$

   Make a table showing the distance of each train from the origin at the end of each second. Plot these positions on the same graph and draw two lines.

   c. Use your graph to answer Part *a*.

4. The velocity-time graph of Figure 4-19 can be used to find both the acceleration and the displacement of the car.

   a. Carefully read the graph and calculate the acceleration of the car at several different times. Choose three times in the first ten seconds, and three more in the next 20 seconds. Note the small level places on the graph where the driver shifted gears.

      Now make an acceleration-time graph. At what times is the acceleration largest and smallest? Do your answers agree with those of Question 7, page 68?

   b. Sketch the position-time graph of Figure 4-19.

4. a. See Teacher's Guide.
   b. See Teacher's Guide.

FIGURE 4-19. Use with problem B-4.

 Velocity versus Time

Readings

Bartusiak, Marcia, "Mapping The Sea Floor From Space." *Popular Science,* February, 1984.

Gardner, Martin, "The Computer As Scientist." *Discover,* June, 1983.

McKean, Kevin, "Whiz Kids in the Fast Lane." *Discover,* May, 1983.

Silk, Joseph, "The Large-Scale Structure of the Universe." *Scientific American,* October, 1983.

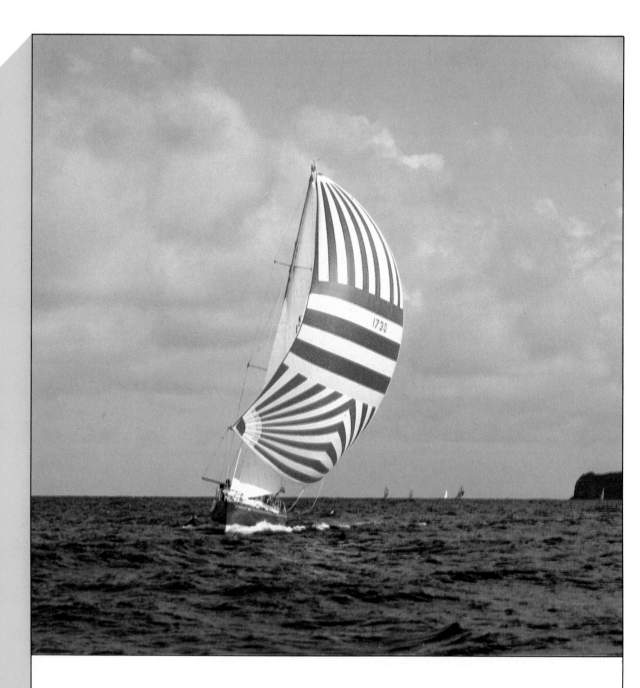

The motion of any object can be described in terms of forces acting on it. Dynamics deals with the cause of motion. A thorough understanding of forces and motion is necessary to design and sail these boats. What forces cause the forward motion? What forces does the water exert on the boat? How can a skillful sailor use these forces effectively? How do forces affect you?

Forces

Chapter 5 introduces Newton's laws of motion and stresses their application for describing all motion. Friction and the distinction between mass and weight are discussed.

Dynamics is the study of the effects of forces on matter. The relationship between force and matter is the most basic of all scientific concepts. Any time two or more objects interact, forces are the cause of the interaction. There are no exceptions. A baseball leaves a bat after impact due to forces. Blood flows through your veins due to forces. The planets orbit the sun due to forces. All changes in motion are the result of forces.

Isaac Newton (1642-1727) was born in the same year that Galileo died. By the age of eighteen, Newton had discovered the binomial theorem. He later discovered the law of universal gravitation and explained the motions of the planets, comets, and the moon. Newton also explained the nature of light and invented a system of calculus. Few scientists have contributed as much to science as has Sir Isaac Newton.

About the year 1665, Sir Isaac Newton stated three laws that are now known as Newton's laws of motion. The three laws are basic to the science of physics. Anytime forces act on matter, these laws are followed.

GOAL: You will gain an understanding of the use of Newton's laws of motion to determine the motion of bodies that have forces acting on them.

5:1 Forces

Forces can be classified as one of four kinds. These forces are gravitational, electromagnetic, and strong and weak nuclear. Gravitational and electromagnetic forces cause most of the observable interactions. Interactions caused by nuclear forces are rarely observed because the forces exist only inside the nuclei of atoms.

Gravitational force is a force of attraction that exists between all masses. The earth exerts a gravitational force on objects that causes them to accelerate toward the earth. The moon exerts a gravitational force on the earth that causes tides. Even though the gravitational force is a major influence on our daily lives, it is the weakest of the three forces.

Electromagnetic forces are forces between charged particles. Electric forces exist between stationary charged particles. "Mechanical" or "frictional" forces are examples of electric forces between surface atoms of materials in contact. Moving charged particles produce magnetic forces. Electric and magnetic forces are related because each involves charged particles. Electromagnetic forces are very large compared to gravitational forces. A discussion of electric and magnetic forces will appear later in the book.

Nuclear forces are much stronger than any of the other forces. The **strong nuclear force** holds the nucleus of an atom together despite the large electric force of repulsion between particles in the nucleus.

A second force exists inside the nucleus. This force is called the **weak force** and is actually a form of the electromagnetic force. It acts mainly within the particles inside the nucleus. The weak force is involved in the breaking apart of some nuclei.

5:2   Newton's First Law of Motion

Galileo demonstrated that a ball rolling down an inclined ramp gained velocity uniformly. From this, he developed the concept of acceleration. He also noticed that the ball lost very little speed as it

Stress the importance of Newton's laws of motion to all physics.

FIGURE 5-1. Galileo studied acceleration due to gravity by rolling metal balls down smooth ramps and timing them with a water clock.

a

b

c

FIGURE 5-2. A quick snap of a finger can knock a card out from under a coin allowing the coin to drop into the glass.

rolled from the end of the ramp and across the stone floor. From his experiments, he reasoned that if the floor were perfectly smooth and endless, the ball would never stop rolling. This line of reasoning led Galileo to believe there is a tendency for any object to resist change in its state of motion. **Inertia** is the tendency for an object to remain in the same state of motion.

Inertia is the resistance to change in motion of an object.

Newton was the first scientist to state formally the relationships that are basic to the study of motion. From his studies, he derived the laws of motion.

Note that giving this tendency the name "inertia" does not explain it!

The following statement is the **first law of motion**. *An object continues in its state of rest, or of uniform motion in a straight line, unless it is acted upon by an unbalanced force.* This law means that an object has a tendency to maintain its motion. Recall that the property of matter that resists a change in its motion is inertia. The first law of motion makes the function of force clear. An unbalanced force can change the state of motion of an object.

Newton's first law states that unless an unbalanced force acts on an object, the velocity of the object does not change.

We can perform a simple experiment that demonstrates Newton's first law of motion. Lay an index card over a drinking glass. Place a flat object such as a penny on the card, centered over the glass. Hold the glass with one hand and with a flick of a finger give the card a large horizontal velocity. The horizontal force on the penny is not large enough to overcome its inertia and move it from its original position. Due to the unbalanced force, the force of gravity, the penny falls to the bottom of the glass.

Newton's first law of motion implies that there is no fundamental difference between an object at rest and one that is moving with constant velocity. Consider the two sailboats in Figure 5-4. One

FIGURE 5-3. On a perfectly smooth floor, a ball will regain the height from which it was rolled. With no incline it will continue in motion in a straight line at a constant speed.

FIGURE 5-4. When forces are balanced, there is no acceleration.

sailboat is at rest while the other is moving in a straight line at a constant velocity of 10 km/h, east. Two forces are shown acting on the boat at rest. The weight of the boat pulls it downward. The buoyant force of the water pushes it upward. The two forces acting on the boat have equal magnitudes but opposite directions. The vector sum of the forces is zero and the boat remains at rest.

Four forces are shown acting on the sailboat moving at a constant velocity. In the vertical direction, the same two balanced forces are present that act on the boat at rest. In the horizontal direction, the force of the wind on the sails pushes the boat forward while the water exerts a force on the boat that opposes the forward motion. The vector sum of these forces is zero, and the boat travels at a constant velocity. The boat at rest and the boat moving at a constant velocity will both maintain their present states of motion unless acted on by an unbalanced force. If the forward force of the wind on the sails of the moving boat should lessen, the boat would decelerate. An unbalanced force would then be acting on the boat and its state of motion would change.

5:3 Newton's Second Law of Motion

Newton's second law says that an unbalanced force causes acceleration.

Newton was the first to recognize that an unbalanced force always causes acceleration and not just motion. Newton then formulated his **second law of motion**. *When an unbalanced force acts on an object, the object will be accelerated. The acceleration will vary directly with the unbalanced force applied and will be in the same direction as the applied force. It will vary inversely with the mass of the object.* The mathematical expression of Newton's second law is

$$a = \frac{F}{m}$$

More often, Newton's second law of motion is written

$$\boxed{F = ma}$$

The most familiar form of the second law is **F = ma.**

Force is a vector quantity. The acceleration caused by an applied force will be in the direction of the applied force.

5:4 Units of Force

A force is measured in terms of the acceleration it gives a standard mass. Suppose a 1.00-kg mass is located on a frictionless, horizontal surface. The force that will cause this 1.00-kg mass to accelerate at 1.00 m/s² is defined as one newton (N). The equation below shows how Newton's second law is used to define mathematically one newton.

A force of one newton will accelerate a one kilogram mass at a rate of one meter per second per second.

$$F = ma$$
$$= (1.00 \text{ kg})(1.00 \text{ m/s}^2)$$
$$= 1.00 \text{ kg} \cdot \text{m/s}^2$$
$$F = 1.00 \text{ N}$$

The newton is the SI unit of force.

EXAMPLE

Using Newton's Second Law to Find Force

An unbalanced force gives a 2.00 kg mass an acceleration of 5.00 m/s². What is the force applied to the object?

Given: mass (m) = 2.00 kg   **Unknown:** force (**F**)

a = +5.00 m/s²   **Basic equation:** $F = ma$

Solution: $F = ma$
$$= (2.00 \text{ kg})(5.00 \text{ m/s}^2)$$
$$= 10.0 \text{ kg} \cdot \text{m/s}^2$$
$$F = 10.0 \text{ N (in the direction of motion)}$$

FIGURE 5-5. The expanding gases exert forces on the car causing it to accelerate.

EXAMPLE

Using Newton's Second Law to Find Mass

An unbalanced force of 20 N gives a stone an acceleration of 4.0 m/s². What is the mass of the stone?

Given: $F = +20$ N   **Unknown:** m

$a = +4.0$ m/s²   **Basic equation:** $F = ma$

Solution: $F = ma$

$$m = \frac{F}{a}$$

$$= \frac{+20 \text{ N}}{4.0 \text{ m/s}^2} = \frac{20 \text{ kg} \cdot \text{m/s}^2}{4.0 \text{ m/s}^2}$$

$$m = 5 \text{ kg}$$

Problems

1. An unbalanced force of 25 N, E, is applied to a 12-kg mass. What is the acceleration given to the mass?

2. An unbalanced 16-N force is applied to a 2-kg mass. What is the acceleration of the mass?

3. A shot-putter exerts an unbalanced force of 140 N on a shot giving it an acceleration of 19 m/s². What is the mass of the shot?

4. A 1.5-kg mass accelerates across a smooth table at 16 m/s². What is the unbalanced force applied to it?

5. An object moving with a constant velocity has an unbalanced force applied to it. If the unbalanced force is − 20.0 N and the mass of the object is 3.75 kg, what is the acceleration of the object while this force is acting?

6. An unbalanced force of 965 N causes an object to accelerate at 54.5 m/s². What is the mass of the object?

7. Determine the acceleration that an unbalanced force of 25 N gives to a 4.0-kg mass.

8. A racing car undergoes a uniform acceleration of 8.00 m/s². If the unbalanced force causing the acceleration is 6.00 × 10³ N, what is the mass of the racing car?

9. A racing car has a mass of 710 kg. It starts from rest and travels 120 m in 3.0 s. The car undergoes uniform acceleration during the entire 3.0 s. What unbalanced force is applied to it?

10. An artillery shell has a mass of 55 kg. The shell is fired from the muzzle of a gun with a speed of 770 m/s. The gun barrel is 1.5 m long. What is the average force on the shell while it is in the gun barrel?

1. 2.1 m/s², E

2. 8 m/s²

3. 7.4 kg

4. 24 N

5. − 5.33 m/s²

6. 17.7 kg

7. 6.3 m/s²

8. 7.50 × 10² kg

9. 1.9 × 10⁴ N

10. 1.1 × 10⁷ N

5:5 Mass and Weight

It is important to understand clearly the distinction between mass and weight. **Mass** depends upon the amount of matter in an object. From Newton's second law, it follows that a larger force is necessary to give a larger mass the same acceleration as a smaller mass.

More force is necessary to give a truck the same acceleration as a pencil; therefore, the inertia of the truck must be greater than the inertia of the pencil. Mass may be defined as a measure of the inertia of a body.

Consider the force that must act on a 1.00-kg mass allowed to fall freely from some point near the earth's surface. The mass accelerates at the rate of 9.81 m/s². By Newton's second law of motion, the force needed to accelerate a 1.00-kg mass at the rate of 9.81 m/s² is

$$F = ma$$
$$= (1.00 \text{ kg}) (9.81 \text{ m/s}^2)$$
$$= 9.81 \text{ kg} \cdot \text{m/s}^2$$
$$= 9.81 \text{ N}$$

Thus, the earth must exert a force of 9.81 newtons on the 1.00-kilogram mass. If you hang a 1.00-kilogram mass on a spring scale, you will find that it weighs 9.81 newtons. If you hang a 2.00-kilogram mass on the spring scale, you will find that it weighs 19.6 newtons. A force of 19.6 newtons is the force needed to give a 2.00-kilogram mass an acceleration of 9.81 m/s². In the same way, a 3.00-kilogram-mass weights 29.4 N. **Weight** refers to the gravitational force exerted on the object by a very massive body like the earth. Weight is another name for gravitational force. Like other forces, weight is measured in newtons. A medium apple weighs about one newton. As we will see, mass and weight are proportional.

To determine the weight of a mass, Newton's second law may be written in the form

$$\boxed{W = mg.}$$

Here, W represents the weight, m represents the mass, and g represents the acceleration of gravity. The weight of a 5.00-kilogram mass is

$$W = mg$$
$$= (5.00 \text{ kg})(9.81 \text{ m/s}^2)$$
$$= 49.1 \text{ kg} \cdot \text{m/s}^2$$
$$W = 49.1 \text{ N}$$

Weight is a vector quantity. It is a force directed toward the center of the massive object. The weight of an object varies with its location because the acceleration of gravity varies from location to location. An object weighs slightly less in an airplane at ten thousand meters than it does at sea level. An object on the moon weighs one-sixth as much as it does on the earth. However, the mass of an object is always the same. The mass of an object does not change from one location to another.

Mass is the quantity of matter in an object.

The inertia of a body is proportional to its mass.

Note that we are using magnitudes only when discussing the force of gravity and the acceleration due to it.

Suggested demonstrations: Hang kilogram masses on a spring scale calibrated in newtons.

Weight is the gravitational force on an object.

$W = mg$ is the equation for the weight of mass m.

Weight is a vector directed toward the center of the attracting body.

Weight varies with location, mass does not.

FIGURE 5-6. The small force from a jet pack allows an astronaut to move about untethered in space.

EXAMPLE

Finding the Weight of an Object

What is the weight of a 7.2-kg mass on the earth's surface?

Given: g = 9.81 m/s²   **Unknown:** weight (W)

m = 7.2 kg   **Basic equation:** $W = mg$

Solution: $W = mg$

$= (7.2 \text{ kg})(9.81 \text{ m/s}^2)$

$W = 71 \text{ N}$

Problems

Assume the acceleration of gravity is 9.81 m/s² unless indicated otherwise.

11. Determine the weights of these masses.

   a. 14 kg   **b.** 0.43 kg   **c.** 0.7 kg

12. Determine the mass of these weights.

   a. 98 N   **b.** 80 N   **c.** 0.98 N

11. a. 140 N
    b. 4.2 N
    c. 7 N
12. a. 1.0 × 10¹ kg
    b. 8 kg
    c. 0.10 kg

13. How much force is needed to keep a 20-N stone from falling?

14. An economy car has a mass of 800 kg. What is its weight?

15. A car has a mass of 1000 kg. What is its weight?

16. A small yacht weighs 14 700 N. What is its mass?

17. A 7.5-kg object is placed on a spring scale. If the spring scale reads 78.4 N, what is the acceleration of gravity at that location?

18. A car has a mass of 1200 kg. How much would the car weigh on the moon? (The moon's gravitational acceleration is 1.6 m/s².)

13. 20 N

14. 8×10^3 N

15. 1×10^4 N

16. 1.50×10^3 kg

17. 1.0×10^1 m/s², down

18. 1.9×10^3 N

5:6 Two Ways to Measure Mass

There are two fundamentally different methods used to measure the mass of an object. One method is to use a beam balance. An unknown mass is placed on a pan at the end of a beam. Known masses are placed on a pan at the other end of the beam. When the pans balance, the force of gravity is the same on each pan. Then the masses on either side of the balance must also be the same. The mass measured by a beam balance is the gravitational mass. The beam balance method is a method of comparison. The variations of gravitational force from place to place do not affect measurements made in this way. The same result for a measurement by the beam balance method is obtained anywhere.

The second method to determine the mass of an object is quite different. It uses the property of inertia. An object of unknown mass is placed on a frictionless, horizontal surface. A known force is applied to the object and the acceleration of the object is measured. The mass of the object can then be calculated using the equation $m = F/a$. The mass determined by this method is called the inertial mass. This second method is seldom used because it involves both a frictionless surface and a difficult measurement of acceleration. The gravitational method of measuring mass is easier and more widely used.

Gravitational mass and inertial mass are two essentially different concepts. But for a given object, they are always numerically equal. Thus, an important relationship exists between gravitational mass and inertial mass. For a long time, this equivalence was thought to be one of nature's most remarkable coincidences. However, Albert Einstein (1879-1955) recognized that this was more than a coincidence. Einstein used this phenomenon as the foundation for his general theory of relativity.

The beam balance compares the weights of two objects.

A beam balance measures gravitational mass.

The inertial mass of an object can be measured by finding the acceleration caused by a known force.

Inertial mass can also be measured by finding the period of oscillation of a mass hanging on a spring.

Gravitational mass is numerically equal to inertial mass.

Baron Eotvos of Hungary was the first to show experimentally that the two masses are equal.

The equality of the two kinds of mass is called the equivalence principle.

5:7 Friction

Slide your hand across a tabletop. You will feel some opposition to the motion. This opposition is friction. The **force of friction** is the resistance to motion between two objects that are in contact. Friction is an electromagnetic force and results from temporary attractions

Friction is a force that opposes the motion of two objects that are touching each other.

a

b

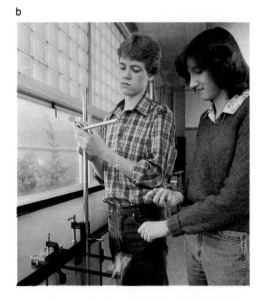

FIGURE 5-7. A beam balance (a) allows you to compare an unknown mass to a known mass. Using an inertial balance (b), you can calculate the mass from the back and forth motion of the mass.

Friction acts in a direction parallel to the surfaces in contact and opposing the motion.

Static friction is always larger than sliding friction.

We will not be calculating static friction.

The coefficient of friction is the ratio of the force of friction (F_f) to the force pressing the surfaces together (F_N).

between the contact points of the two surfaces. The force of friction always acts parallel to the surfaces in contact and in a direction that opposes the motion.

Consider moving a heavy box across the floor. It is harder to start the box moving than to keep it moving. This indicates that the force of friction resisting the start of motion (static friction) is greater than the force resisting existing motion (sliding friction). By analyzing the motion of the box, the force of sliding friction can be studied.

Figure 5-8 shows the horizontal forces acting on the box being pulled at a constant velocity across the floor. Because the box is moving at a constant velocity, the horizontal forces must be balanced. The constant velocity indicates that the force of sliding friction must have the same magnitude as the applied force but must be acting in the opposite direction. By measuring the applied force (F_A), the force of sliding friction (F_f) also can be determined. The force of friction depends only on the nature of the surfaces in contact and the force pushing the surfaces together. Mathematically, the force of friction can be expressed

$$F_f = \mu F_N$$

FIGURE 5-8. Four forces are shown acting on a box moving to the right with a constant horizontal velocity.

In this equation μ (mu), called the coefficient of friction, is a value describing the nature of the surfaces in contact. F_N represents the force pushing the surfaces together and is called the **normal force.** The normal force (F_N) always acts perpendicular to the surfaces in contact. In Figure 5-8, the normal force is numerically equal to the weight of the box (F_W).

In most cases, the coefficient of sliding friction for two surfaces in contact is independent of the surface areas in contact and the velocity of the motion.

Friction does not depend on the areas of the surfaces in contact.

EXAMPLE

Sliding Friction

A smooth wooden block is placed on a smooth wooden tabletop, as shown in Figure 5-9. A force of 14.0 N is necessary to keep the 40.0-N block moving at a constant velocity. **a.** What is the coefficient of sliding friction for the block and table? **b.** If a 20.0-N weight is placed on the block, what force will be required to keep the block and weight moving at a constant velocity across the table?

Given: $F_A = 14.0$ N   **Unknowns:** **a.** coefficient of sliding
$\quad\quad\quad\quad$ $W_1 = 40.0$ N $\quad\quad\quad\quad\quad\quad\quad\quad$ friction (μ)
$\quad\quad\quad\quad$ $W_2 = 20.0$ N $\quad\quad\quad\quad\quad$ **b.** force of friction (F_f)

Basic equation: $F_f = \mu F_N$

Solutions:

a. $\mu = \dfrac{F_f}{F_N} = \dfrac{F}{W_1}$ $\quad$ **b.** $\mu = \dfrac{F_f}{F_N}$

$\quad\quad = \dfrac{14.0 \text{ N}}{40.0 \text{ N}}$ $\quad\quad\quad\quad F_f = \mu F_N = \mu (W_1 + W_2)$

$\quad\quad\quad\quad\quad\quad\quad\quad\quad = 0.350 (40.0 \text{ N} + 20.0 \text{ N})$

$\quad\quad = 0.350$ $\quad\quad\quad\quad\quad F_f = 21.0 \text{ N}$

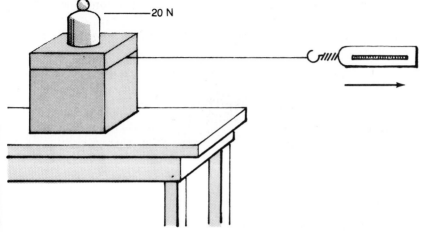

FIGURE 5-9. Use with Example Problem.

FIGURE 5-10. By reducing frictional forces, the hydrofoil boat can maintain higher speeds than an ordinary boat.

FIGURE 5-10. By reducing frictional forces, the hydrofoil boat can maintain higher speeds than an ordinary boat.

Problems

19. 0.35

19. A horizontal force of 18 N is necessary to pull a 52-N sled across a cement sidewalk at constant speed. What is the coefficient of sliding friction between the sidewalk and the metal runners of the sled?

20. 8.4 N

20. The sled in Problem 19 is then placed on packed snow. If a 650-N boy sits on the sled, what will be the force necessary to slide the sled across the snow at a constant speed? The coefficient of sliding friction is 0.012 for the sled runners on packed snow.

5:8 Net Force and Acceleration

An unbalanced force causes a mass to accelerate.

In Newton's second law of motion, $F = ma$, the force, F, which causes the mass to accelerate, is the unbalanced force acting on the mass. Consider a 10-kg mass resting on a frictionless, horizontal surface. If a $+100$-N force is applied horizontally to the mass, then the acceleration is

$$a = \frac{F}{m} = \frac{100 \text{ N}}{10 \text{ kg}} = \frac{100 \text{ kg} \cdot \text{m/s}^2}{10 \text{ kg}} = +10 \text{ m/s}^2$$

Suppose the 10-kg mass rests on a rough surface. When the 100-N force is applied, a friction force will also be present. The resulting acceleration will be caused by an unbalanced force. The unbalanced force is referred to as the net force acting on the mass. The net force is the vector sum of the forces acting on the object. If the force of friction between the 10-kg mass and the table is 20 N, the net force acting in the direction of motion is

The net force is the vector sum of all forces acting on a body.

$$F_{net} = F_{applied} + F_f$$

If the applied force is considered positive, the force of friction is negative.

F_{net} = 100 N + (−20 N)

= 80 N

$$a = \frac{F}{m} = \frac{80 \text{ N}}{10 \text{ kg}}$$

$$= \frac{80 \text{ kg} \cdot \text{m/s}^2}{10 \text{ kg}} = 8 \text{ m/s}^2 \text{ (in the direction of the larger force)}$$

Friction is not the only force preventing the force applied to an object from being the net force acting on it. Consider a 10.0-kg stone lying on the ground. In order to accelerate it upward, a force greater than its weight must be applied to it in an upward direction. The weight of the stone, W, is 98.0 N down. If someone lifts the stone with a force of 148 N up, the net force acting on the stone is

The weight of an object can be one of the forces acting on an object.

$$F_{net} = F_{applied} - W$$
$$= +148 \text{ N} - (98 \text{ N})$$
$$F_{net} = 50 \text{ N}$$

The net force acting on the stone is 50 N upward. The acceleration of the stone can be calculated from Newton's second law.

$$a = \frac{F}{m} = \frac{+50 \text{ N}}{10.0 \text{ kg}} = \frac{+50 \text{ kg} \cdot \text{m/s}^2}{10.0 \text{ kg}} = +5 \text{ m/s}^2$$

The stone will be accelerated upward at a rate of +5 m/s².

F = 148 N

10 kg

W = 98 N

FIGURE 5-11. A mass is accelerated upward if the total force exerted upward is greater than the weight.

Problems

21. A rubber ball weighs 49 N. What is the acceleration of the ball if an upward force of 69 N is applied?

21. 4.0 m/s²

22. a. What is the weight of a 20.0-kg stone?
   b. What force is needed to accelerate the stone upward at 10 m/s²?

22. a. 196 N
    b. 400 N

a

a = 10 m/s²

100 N

μ = 0.0

b

a = 8.0 m/s²

μ = 0.20

F_f

FIGURE 5-12. When acted upon by a 100-N force, the acceleration of a 10-kg mass on a frictionless surface (a) is greater than the acceleration of a 10-kg mass on a rough surface (b).

23. a. 1.0×10^3 kg
    b. 13 800 N, upward

24. 210 N

25. 3.8 m/s²

26. a. 1.50 kg
    b. −3.0 m/s²,
       downward

27. a. 7.4 N
    b. 84 N, upward
    c. 110 m/s², upward

28. a. ~~7.99~~kg 60̄0
    b. 3.25 m/s², upward
    c. 26 m/s, upward

29. a. 49 N
    b. 9.8 m/s², upward
    c. 100 m/s, upward
    d. 49 N, downward
    e. 10 s

FIGURE 5-13. In a vacuum, a coin and feather fall with the same acceleration.

Air   Vacuum

23. A rocket weighs 9800 N.
    a. What is its mass?
    b. What applied force will give an acceleration of 4.0 m/s²?

24. An object with mass of 22.7 kg is placed on a surface. The mass moves horizontally at a constant speed. The coefficient of sliding friction between the two surfaces is 0.94. What is the force of friction?

25. A car moving on a level highway has a mass of 4.0×10^2 kg. The coefficient of friction between the tires and the highway is 0.19. What acceleration will a force of 2250 N produce on the car?

26. A small rocket weighs 14.7 N.
    a. What is its mass?
    b. The rocket is fired from a high platform but its engine fails to burn properly. The rocket gains a total upward force of only 10.2 N. What is the acceleration of the rocket?

27. A force of 91 N is exerted straight up on a stone that has a mass of 0.75 kg. Calculate
    a. the weight of the stone.
    b. the net force acting on the stone.
    c. the acceleration of the stone.

28. A rocket that weighs 7840 N on the earth is fired. The force of propulsion is +10 440 N. Determine
    a. the mass of the rocket.
    b. the acceleration of the rocket.
    c. the velocity of the rocket at the end of 8.0 s.

29. The instruments attached to a weather balloon have a mass of 5.0 kg.
    a. What do the instruments weigh?
    b. The balloon is released on a calm day and exerts an upward force of 98 N on the instruments. At what rate does the balloon with instruments accelerate?
    c. After accelerating for 10 seconds, the weather instruments are released automatically. What is their velocity at that instant?
    d. What net force acts on the instruments after their release?
    e. What time elapses before the instruments begin to fall?

5:9 Free Fall

An object falling toward the earth is said to be in free fall if the only force acting on it is its weight. As was disussed in Chapter 3, the acceleration of falling objects near the earth is 9.81 m/s². However, in most real situations, objects fall through air. As an object falls, it collides with air molecules that exert an upward force on it. The upward force is caused by friction between the air molecules and the

FIGURE 5-14. The structure of the dandelion seeds allows them to reach terminal velocity quickly.

surface of the object. This frictional force is called **air resistance.** The upward force depends on the shape of the object, the number of air molecules the object strikes per second, and how fast it strikes them. When the object strikes a large number of air molecules fast enough, the upward force can equal the object's weight and stop it from accelerating. The body will then fall at a constant velocity called **terminal velocity.**

A feather has a large surface area and a small weight. As a feather falls, its weight is quickly equaled by air resistance. Terminal velocity for a feather or a leaf is only a few centimeters per second. Tiny droplets of water, such as those found in dense fog, have large surface areas and low weights. You can watch them fall slowly and steadily in the beam of an automobile's headlamp. Likewise, small insects have large surface areas and low weights. Thus, an ant can fall from the 50th floor of a tall building and, upon reaching the sidewalk, walk off unharmed. Birds can fly easily because their weights are low and they have large surface areas. On the other hand, a skydiver has a fairly high weight compared to surface area. A falling skydiver must collide at high speed with a large number of air molecules per second to reach terminal velocity, which is usually more than 200 km per hour. When the diver's parachute opens, the surface area greatly increases. The terminal velocity is reduced and the skydiver can land safely.

You have noticed that a leaf, a feather, or a piece of paper does not fall through air quite as fast as a heavier object, such as a brick. If you eliminate air resistance by letting the objects fall through a vacuum, they will all have the same acceleration.

An object in free fall has only the force of gravity acting on it. Its acceleration is equal to g.

The force of air molecules striking a moving object is called air resistance.

If the air resistance equals the weight, the object does not accelerate. It moves at its terminal velocity.

The film loop showing an astronaut dropping a hammer and feather on the moon and on the earth could be shown here.

5:10 Newton's Third Law of Motion

Newton's third law of motion is called the **law of action and reaction.** *Every force is accompanied by an equal but opposite force.* According to this law, there is no situation in which one force acts on a single object. Two magnets repel each other. Two charged objects attract each other. Your hand pushes a ball and the ball exerts a force on your hand. Every interaction involves at least two objects and two equal but opposite forces.

Newton's second law of motion states that when one object exerts a force on another object, the second object accelerates. But a fact often overlooked is that the object being accelerated exerts an equal and opposite force on the first object. The first object is also accelerated. For example, a golf ball is hit with a golf club. While the club is in contact with the ball, the club exerts a force on the ball. The ball accelerates. During this time, the ball also exerts an equal and opposite force on the club. Note that the two forces are equal and opposite, but act on different objects. The club is also accelerated, but in a direction opposite to the ball. The acceleration of the club is opposite to its original direction of motion and the club slows down. The magnitudes of the acceleration differ because the golf ball and the golf club have different masses. In any interaction between objects A and B, A produces a force on B and B exerts an equal and opposite force on A.

FIGURE 5-15. During a golf swing (b), the club exerts a force on the ball and the ball exerts an equal force on the club (a).

a

b

Summary

1. Dynamics is the study of the effects of forces on matter.

2. The four fundamental forces are the gravitational, electromagnetic, and strong and weak nuclear forces.

3. Newton's first law of motion states that an object continues in its state or rest, or of uniform motion in a straight line, unless it is acted upon by an unbalanced force.

4. Inertia is the tendency for an object to remain in the same state of motion.

5. Newton's second law of motion states that when an unbalanced force acts on an object, the object will be accelerated in accordance with the equation $F = ma$.

6. One newton (N) is the force necessary to accelerate a 1-kg mass at the rate of 1 m/s².

7. Mass is a measure of the inertia of a body. Weight is a measure of the gravitational force on a body.

8. Gravitational mass and inertial mass are two essentially different concepts. However, the gravitational and inertial masses of a body are numerically equal.

9. Friction is a force that opposes the motion of two objects in contact.

10. The force of friction is equal to the product of the coefficient of friction and the normal force.

11. The net force is an unbalanced force acting on a body.

12. A freely-falling body reaches terminal velocity when the upward force of the air molecules is equivalent to the body's weight.

13. Newton's third law of motion states that every force is accompanied by an equal but opposite force.

Detailed answers to all Questions and Problems are given in the Teacher's Guide at the front of this book.

Questions

1. A ball is rolled across the top of a table and slowly comes to a stop. Considering Newton's first law of motion, explain why the ball stops. How could the ball have remained in motion?

2. An object on Earth has a mass of 3.0 kg. What would be the mass of the object if it were taken to Jupiter where the acceleration of gravity is 10 times that of Earth?

3. Why do you tend to fall backward on a bus when it accelerates from rest? Why do you tend to fall forward when the driver applies the brakes?

4. Why does a car use more gasoline per mile traveling in a city than it does traveling on an interstate highway?

5. What is the difference between mass and weight?

6. A person weighing 490 N stands on a scale in an elevator.
   a. What is the scale reading when the elevator is at rest?
   b. The elevator starts to ascend and accelerates the person upward at 2.2 m/s². What does the scale read?
   c. What is the reading on the scale when the elevator rises at a constant velocity?
   d. The elevator begins to slow down as it reaches the proper floor. Do the scale readings increase or decrease?
   e. The elevator starts to descend. Does the scale reading increase or decrease?
   f. What is the scale reading when the elevator descends at a constant velocity?
   g. If the cable snapped and the elevator fell freely, what would be the scale reading?

7. A spacecraft is accelerated away from the earth by its rockets. Once the craft reaches a high velocity and is far from the earth, must it continue to fire its rockets to keep moving? Explain.

8. A spacecraft in outer space accelerates by firing rockets. How can the hot gases escaping from the rocket propel the craft if there is nothing in space for these gases to push against?

Problems–A

1. 8.3×10^{-2} m/s²

1. A 12-kg sled is pulled along level ground. The horizontal force exerted on the sled is 10.0 N. Find the acceleration of the sled if the coefficient of friction is 0.0765.

2. 2.09 m/s²

2. The mass of an elevator plus occupants is 752 kg. The tension in the cable is 8950 N. At what rate does the elevator accelerate upward?

3. a. 5 m/s², down
   b. 50 N, down

3. a. Determine the acceleration of the system in Figure 5-16.
   b. Determine the tension in the rope.

5 kg

Frictionless surface

5 kg

FIGURE 5-16. Use with Problem A-3.

4. In Problem 3 the surface is sanded so that the coefficient of friction between the two surfaces is 0.31. Determine the acceleration of the system.   4. 4 m/s², left

Problems–B

1. Safety engineers estimate that an elevator can hold 20 persons of 75-kg average mass. The elevator itself has a mass of 500 kg. Tensile strength tests show that the cable supporting the elevator can tolerate a maximum force of 29 600 N. What is the greatest acceleration that the elevator's motor can produce without breaking the cable?   1. 4.8 m/s²

2. A 2.0-kg mass and a 3.0-kg mass are attached to a lightweight cord that passes over a frictionless pulley. The hanging masses are left free to move.
  a. In what direction will the smaller mass move?
  b. What will be its acceleration?   2. a. upward
                                b. 2.0 m/s²

2.0 kg

3.0 kg

FIGURE 5-17. Use with Problem B-2.

Readings

Brancazio, Peter, "Sir Isaac and the Rising Fast Ball." *Discover*, July, 1984.

Easton, D., "Weightlessness and Free Bodies." *The Physics Teacher*, November, 1983.

Frenkel, Karen A., "The Leading Edge." *Forbes*, December 31, 1984.

Keebler, Jack, "Now: Skid Control Brakes." *Popular Science*, November, 1984.

Shopf, Bruce, "Pivoting Windmill." *Popular Science*, January, 1984.

The motion associated with a tennis serve is quite complex. However, it is possible to break this complex motion into a few simple parts through the use of computers. The movement of each body segment is a part of the total serve. An analysis of these simple movements can show whether or not the server is moving properly to direct the maximum amount of force on the ball. How are vectors related to the motion of the tennis player and the force he exerts on the racquet? How are vectors related to your activities?

Vectors

Chapter 6 introduces vectors in two dimensions. Vectors are added and resolved into component vectors both graphically and mathematically.

Vectors are not easy for students to visualize. Demonstrations, such as those suggested in the Teacher's Guide at the front of this book, may help them gain understanding.

In adding two vectors, place the tail of one vector at the head of the other vector.

In adding two vectors, a third vector is drawn from the tail of the first to the head of the second. This vector, the resultant, is the sum of the two vectors.

Scalar and vector quantities were introduced in Chapter 3. The addition of vectors acting in the same or opposite directions was discussed. In this chapter, additional mathematical operations involving vectors will be introduced.

GOAL: You will gain an understanding of vector quantities and their use in solving physics problems.

Understanding basic vector operations will enable us to analyze complex situations involving vector quantities such as displacement, velocity, and force. By studying the vector nature of forces, the concept of equilibrium will be developed. A study of the forces acting on an object that is in equilibrium is called statics.

A vector quantity can be shown as an arrow-tipped line segment (length indicates magnitude; arrow indicates direction).

6:1 Vector Addition in Two Dimensions

As discussed in Chapter 3, a vector quantity can be represented by an arrow-tipped line segment. The length of the arrow drawn to scale represents the magnitude of the quantity. The direction of the arrow represents the direction of the quantity.

The sum of any two vectors can be found graphically. In Figure 6-1, **A** and **B** represent two displacements of a student who walked 95 m east and 55 m south. The vectors are added by placing the tail of one vector at the head of the other vector. Neither the direction nor the length of either vector is changed. The resultant of **A** and **B** is drawn connecting the tail of the first vector with the head of the second vector. To find the magnitude of the resultant, **R**, measure its length and evaluate it using the same scale used to draw **A** and **B**. Its direction is found by using a protractor. The direction is expressed as an angle measured clockwise from north (0°). In Figure 6-1, the resultant displacement is 110 km at 120°.

FIGURE 6-1. The vector sum of B + A is the same as the vector sum of A + B.

Scale: 1 division = 10 m

95

6:2 Independence of Vector Quantities

Vectors act independently. Consider a motorboat that heads due east at 8.0 m/s across a river flowing due south at 5.0 m/s. The boat will travel 8.0 meters due east in one second. It will also travel 5.0 meters due south in the same second. The southerly velocity cannot change the easterly velocity. Neither can the easterly velocity change the southerly velocity. Each velocity is independent of the other and acts as if it were the only velocity. This concept is known as the independence of velocities. All vector quantities, not only velocity, behave in this manner.

In Figure 6-2, the two velocities of the boat are represented by vectors. When these vectors are added, the resultant velocity, v_R, is 9.4 m/s in the direction of 122°. In one second, this resultant velocity will carry the motorboat 8.0 meters due east and 5.0 meters due south. You can think of the boat as traveling east at 8.0 m/s and south at 5.0 m/s at the same time. You can also think of it as traveling 9.4 m/s in the direction of 122°. Both statements have the same meaning.

Suppose that the river being crossed by the boat is 80 meters wide. Because the boat's velocity is 8 m/s at all times, it will take the boat 10 seconds to cross the river. The boat will also be carried 50 meters downstream during this 10 seconds. However, in no way does the downstream velocity change the river-crossing velocity.

6:3 Vector Addition on Forces

Force vectors are added in the same way as velocity vectors. Forces that act on the same point at the same time are called **concurrent forces.**

In Figure 6-3, a force of 45 N and a force of 65 N act concurrently on point P. The smaller force acts in the direction of 30° and the larger force acts at 90°. The resultant R is the sum of the two forces. Forces A and B are drawn to scale. R is found by moving A parallel to itself until the tail of A is located at the head of B. The resultant is drawn from the tail of the first vector to the head of the second vector. The magnitude of R is interpreted in terms of the scale used. The angle is found with a protractor. In this case, R is 96 N acting in a direction of 66°. In this

Vectors act independently; one vector cannot change the other.

Concurrent forces act on the same point at the same time.

Moving a vector does not change either its magnitude or its direction.

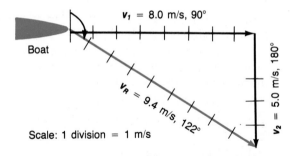

FIGURE 6-2. A boat traveling 9.4 m/s in the direction 122° can also be described as traveling both east at 8.0 m/s and south at 5.0 m/s at the same time.

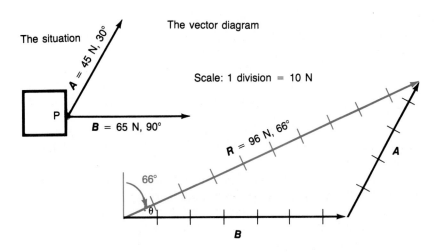

The situation

A = 45 N, 30°

P

B = 65 N, 90°

The vector diagram

Scale: 1 division = 10 N

R = 96 N, 66°

66°

θ

A

B

FIGURE 6-3. The resultant force of two forces acting on a point can be determined graphically.

situation, a force of 96 N acting in a direction of 66° is equivalent to a force of 45 N at 30° and a force of 65 N at 90° acting concurrently.

Problems

Draw vector diagrams to solve each problem.

1. After walking 11 km due north from camp, a hiker then walks 11 km due east.
   a. What is the total distance walked by the hiker?
   b. Determine the total displacement from the starting point.

2. A plane flying due north at 1.00×10^2 m/s is blown due west at 5.0×10^1 m/s by a strong wind. Find the plane's resultant velocity.

3. A motorboat heads due east at 16 m/s across a river that flows due south at 9.0 m/s.
   a. What is the resultant velocity (speed and direction) of the boat?
   b. If the river is 136 m wide, how long does it take the motorboat to reach the other side?
   c. How far downstream is the boat when it reaches the other side of the river?

4. While flying due west at 120 km/h, an airplane is blown due north at 45 km/h by the wind. What is the plane's resultant velocity?

5. A salesperson leaves the office and drives 26 km due north along a straight highway. A turn is made onto a highway that leads in a direction of 60.0°. The driver continues on the highway for a distance of 62 km and then stops. What is the total displacement of the salesperson from the office?

6. Two soccer players kick the ball at exactly the same time. One player's foot exerts a force of 66 N north. The other's foot exerts a force of 88 N east. What is the magnitude and direction of the resultant force on the ball?

1. a. 22 km
   b. 16 km, 45°

2. 110 m/s at 330°

3. a. 18 m/s at 120°
   b. 8.5 s
   c. 77 m

4. 130 km/h at 290°

5. 78 km at 43°

6. 110 N at 53°

7. Two forces of 62 N each act concurrently on a point P. Determine the magnitude of the resultant force acting on point P when the angle between the forces is as follows.

a. 0.0°   **b.** 30.0°   **c.** 60.0°   **d.** 90.0°   **e.** 180°

8. In Problem 7, what happens to the resultant of two forces as the angle between them increases?

9. A weather team releases a weather balloon. The balloon's buoyancy accelerates it straight up at 15 m/s². A wind accelerates it horizontally at 6.5 m/s². What is the magnitude and direction (with reference to the horizontal) of the resultant acceleration?

10. What is the vector sum of a 65-N force acting due east and a 32-N force acting due west?

11. A plane flies due north at 225 km/h. A wind blows it due east at 55 km/h. What is the magnitude and direction of the plane's resultant velocity?

12. A meteoroid passes between the moon and the earth. A gravitational force of 6.0×10^2 N pulls the meteoroid toward the moon. At the same time, a gravitational force of 4.8×10^2 N pulls it toward the earth. The angle between the two forces is 130°. The moon's force acts perpendicularly to the meteoroid's original path. What is the resultant magnitude and direction of the force acting on the meteoroid? State the direction in reference to the meteoroid's original path. (Figure 6-4, below is not a vector diagram. It is intended to show direction only.)

6:4   Vector Addition—Mathematical Method

The vector sum of any two vectors can be determined mathematically. If two vectors are perpendicular, a right angle is formed when the tail of the second vector is placed at the head of the first. The resultant vector, drawn from the tail of the first to the head of the second, is the hypotenuse of a right triangle. The resultant can be calculated using the Pythagorean theorem.

The Pythagorean theorem can be used to find the length of the third side of a right triangle.

$$c^2 = a^2 + b^2$$

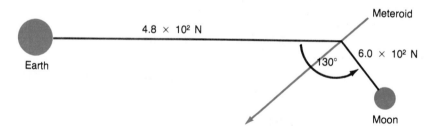

Earth 4.8×10^2 N   Meteroid

130° 6.0×10^2 N

Moon

FIGURE 6-4. Use with Problem 12.

In Figure 6-5, c is the **hypotenuse** (side opposite the right angle) and sides a and b are the legs of a right triangle.

The interior angle, θ, may be found by using the definition of a tangent. The tangent (tan) of an angle is the ratio of the length of the side opposite the angle to the length of the side adjacent to the angle. In Figure 6-5, $\tan \theta = a/b$.

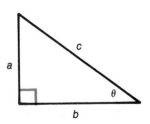

FIGURE 6-5. Some vector sums can be determined using right triangles.

$V_R = 103$ km/h, 61°

$v_2 = 50.0$ km/h, 0°

$v_1 = 90.0$ km/h, 90°

If students have calculators with trig functions, encourage them to solve the problems using the calculator rather than tables.

FIGURE 6-6. A vector diagram can be used to approximate the mathematical solution.

EXAMPLE

Finding the Resultant Mathematically

Consider an airplane that is flying due east at 90.0 km/h and is being blown north at 50.0 km/h. What is the resultant velocity of the plane?

Given: plane velocity (v_1) =
90.0 km/h, 90°

wind velocity (v_2) =
50.0 km/h, 0°

Unknown: resultant velocity (v_R)

Basic equation: $c^2 = a^2 + b^2$

Solution: The vector v_R is the hypotenuse of a right triangle. Its magnitude is given by

$$c = \sqrt{a^2 + b^2}$$
$$c = \sqrt{(90.0 \text{ km/h})^2 + (50.0 \text{ km/h})^2}$$
$$= \sqrt{1.06 \times 10^4} \text{ km/h}$$
$$c = 1.03 \times 10^2 \text{ km/h}$$

The angle, θ, is found by

$$\tan \theta = \frac{\text{opposite side}}{\text{adjacent side}}$$
$$= \frac{50.0 \text{ km/h}}{90.0 \text{ km/h}}$$
$$\tan \theta = 0.566$$

Table C-6 in the Appendix shows that 0.566 is the tangent of 29°. Therefore, θ is 29°. The complementary angle of θ is 61°. The resultant velocity, v_R, is 103 km/h at 61°.

If two vectors are acting at angles other than 90°, one way to determine the resultant mathematically is by using the law of cosines and the law of sines. These are discussed in the Appendix B.

Either the laws of sines and cosines or resolution of vectors into components can be used for these problems.

13. 120 N, 27°

14. a. 9.3 m/s, 24°
       downstream
    b. 13 s

15. a. 4.4 m/s, 30° downstream
    b. 11 s
    c. 24 m

16. 160 km/h, 140°

17. a. 30 N   d. 15 N
    b. 29 N   e. 0 N
    c. 21 N

18. a. 4.1 m/s
    b. 63 s
    c. 1.0 × 10² m

19. a. 110 N   d. 81 N
    b. 110 N   e. 3.0 × 10¹ N
    c. 96 N

Problems

Solve each problem graphically or mathematically depending on your instructor's directions.

13. A 110-N force and a 55-N force act on point P. The 110-N force acts due north. The 55-N force acts due east. What is the magnitude and direction of the resultant force?

14. A motorboat travels at 8.5 m/s. It heads straight across a river 110 m wide.

   a. If the water flows at the rate of 3.8 m/s, what is the boat's resultant velocity?

   b. How much time does it take the boat to reach the opposite shore?

15. A boat heads directly across a river 41 m wide at 3.8 m/s. The current is flowing at 2.2 m/s.

   a. What is the resultant velocity of the boat?

   b. How much time does it take the boat to cross the river?

   c. How far downstream is the boat when it reaches the other side?

16. A 42-km/h wind blows in the direction 215°. What is the resultant velocity of a plane that flies a heading of 125° at 152 km/h?

17. Two 15-N forces act concurrently on point P. Find the magnitude of their resultant when the angle between them is

   a. 0.0°   **b.** 30.0°   **c.** 90.0°   **d.** 120.0°   **e.** 180.0°

18. A boat travels at 3.8 m/s and heads straight across a river 240 m wide. The river flows at 1.6 m/s.

   a. What is the boat's resultant speed with respect to the river bank?

   b. How long does it take the boat to cross the river?

   c. How far downstream is the boat when it reaches the other side?

19. Determine the magnitude of the resultant of a 4.0 × 10¹-N force and a 7.0 × 10¹-N force acting concurrently when the angle between them is

   a. 0.0°   **b.** 30.0°   **c.** 60.0°   **d.** 90.0°   **e.** 180.0°

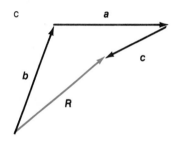

FIGURE 6-7. In (a) the three forces act concurrently on point P. In (b) and (c) the vectors are added graphically. The resultant is the same in both diagrams.

6:5 Addition of Several Vectors

Often three or more forces act concurrently on the same point. To determine the resultant of three or more vectors, follow the same procedure you use to add two vectors. Place the vectors head-to-tail. The order of addition is not important. In Figure 6-7a, the three forces a, b, and c, act concurrently on point P. In Figures 6-7b and 6-7c, the vectors are added graphically. Note that the resultant is the same in both parts although two different orders of addition are used. In placing the vectors head-to-tail, their directions must be maintained.

Solve problems having three or more vectors in the same way you solved problems with two vectors.

The order of vector addition is unimportant.

6:6 Equilibrium

When two or more forces act concurrently on an object and their vector sum is zero, the object is in **equilibrium**. An object in equilibrium has no acceleration. An example of equilibrium is the case in which two equal forces act in opposite directions on point P, as shown in Figure 6-8. The resultant force is zero.

Figure 6-9 shows point P with three concurrent forces acting on it. The 3-N force and the 4-N force are at right angles to each other. When the three vectors are added head-to-tail, they form a closed triangle, Figure 6-9. The vector sum is zero because the length of the resultant is zero. Therefore, the three forces produce no net force on point P. Point P is in equilibrium.

Scale: 1 division = 10 N

FIGURE 6-8. Two 30-N forces exerted in opposite directions on point P produce equilibrium.

Equilibrium occurs when the sum of forces acting at a point is zero.

FIGURE 6-9. Vectors in equilibrium give a resultant of zero.

a

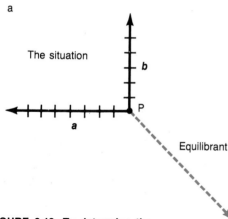

The situation

b

a

P

Equilibrant

b

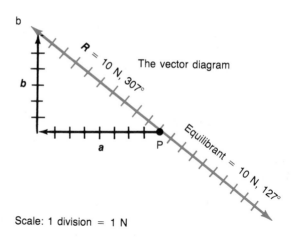

The vector diagram

R = 10 N, 307°

b

a

P

Equilibrant = 10 N, 127°

Scale: 1 division = 1 N

FIGURE 6-10. To determine the equilibrant of two forces acting at an angle of 90° with each other, first find the resultant of the two forces.

An equilibrant force balances the forces acting on a point to produce equilibrium.

The equilibrant is equal in magnitude to the resultant, but opposite in direction.

6:7 The Equilibrant

When two or more forces act on a point and their vector sum is not zero, a force can be found that will produce equilibrium. This force is called the **equilibrant** (ee KWIL uh bruhnt) **force**. The equilibrant force is the single additional force which, when applied at the same point as the other forces, will produce equilibrium. In Figure 6-10, the equilibrant is a 10-N force whose direction is opposite to the direction of the resultant.

To find the equilibrant force of two or more concurrent forces, find the resultant force. The equilibrant force is equal in magnitude to the resultant, but opposite in direction.

Problems

20. 55 N due east

20. A force of 55 N acts due west on an object. What added single force on the object produces equilibrium?

21. a. 1.0×10^2 N, 37°
    b. 1.0×10^2 N, 217°

21. Two forces act concurrently on a point P. One force is 6.0×10^1 N due east. The second force is 8.0×10^1 N due north.
    a. Find the magnitude and direction of the resultant.
    b. What is the magnitude and direction of their equilibrant?

22. a. 120 N, 45°
    b. 120 N, 225°

22. A 62-N force acting at 30.0° and a second 62-N force acting at 60° are concurrent forces.
    a. Determine the resultant force.
    b. What is the magnitude and direction of their equilibrant?

23. 6.0×10^1 N, 278°

23. A 36-N force acts at 225°. A 48-N force acts at 315°. The two forces act on the same point. What is the magnitude and direction of their equilibrant?

24. A 33-N force acting due north and a 44-N force acting at 30° act concurrently on point P. What is the magnitude and direction of a third force that produces equilibrium at point P?

24. 74 N, 197°

6:8 Perpendicular Components of Vectors

Up to this point, we have dealt with two or more vectors acting in different directions from the same point. We have seen that these vectors may be replaced by a single vector, the resultant, which has the same effect as the two vectors.

It is also possible to regard a single vector quantity as the resultant of two vectors each acting in directions other than the original vector. These two vectors are called the **components** of the given vector. Most of the time, we are concerned with the vertical and horizontal components of a given vector.

The process of finding the effective value of a component in a given direction is called **vector resolution**. Consider the sled being pulled in Figure 6-11. A 58-N force is being exerted on a rope held at an angle of 30° with the horizontal. The 58-N force pulls forward on the sled and also upward on the sled. The force that pulls the sled forward is the horizontal component (F_h). The vertical component (F_v) exerts an upward force on the sled.

The value of the horizontal and vertical components of F can be found by first drawing a set of perpendicular axes, Figure 6-12. One axis represents the horizontal direction. The other axis represents the vertical direction. The vector that represents the force (F) in the rope is then drawn to scale at the proper angle with the horizontal axis. To

Point out that physical concerns dictate the directions of the components. Component forces are the result of real agents: ropes, planes, the earth, friction, etc.

Component forces, when added, give the resultant force.

FIGURE 6-11. The force used to pull a sled can be resolved into its vertical and horizontal components.

a

b

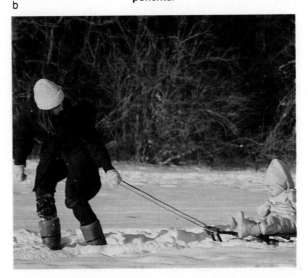

The magnitude of the components depends on the direction of the force.

resolve that force into the components F_v and F_h, draw lines perpendicularly from each axis to the tip of the force vector. The magnitudes of the two components are then found in terms of the scale used for F. (Note that the resultant of F_v and F_h is the original force, F.)

As can be seen in Figure 6-12, F_v and F_h are perpendicular to each other and form a right triangle with F as the hypotenuse. The magnitudes of F_v and F_h can be found by using trigonometry. In this case,

$$\sin \theta = \frac{F_v}{F} \qquad\qquad \cos \theta = \frac{F_h}{F}$$

$$F_v = F \sin \theta \qquad\qquad F_h = F \cos \theta$$

The directions of F_v and F_h can be found from the vector diagram.

The size of the horizontal component is increased when the person pulling the sled lowers the rope. But if the angle between the rope and the horizontal is increased to 60°, the horizontal component is decreased to 29 N. Thus, the magnitude of the components change as the direction of the force changes.

In resolving velocity and displacement vectors, let one axis represent a north-south direction. Let the second axis represent an east-west direction.

Vector resolution can be used to add two or more vectors that are not perpendicular to each other. Each vector is resolved into its vertical and horizontal components. The vertical components of all of the vectors are added together to produce a single vector that acts in the vertical direction. Likewise, all of the horizontal components of the vectors are added together. The resulting vertical vector and horizontal vector can be added together using the methods described in Section 6:4.

In adding nonperpendicular vectors, first find the components of those vectors. Then add the vertical and horizontal components separately. Finally combine the sums vectorially to form the resultant vectors.

a

b

FIGURE 6-12. The horizontal and vertical components of a force depend upon its direction.

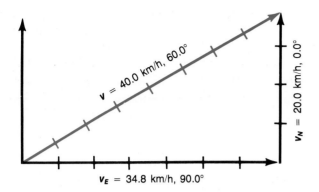

FIGURE 6-13. A velocity vector **V** can be resolved into north and east components.

EXAMPLE

Resolving a Velocity Vector into Its Components

A wind with a velocity of 40.0 km/h blows at 60.0°.   **a.** What is the north component of the wind's velocity?   **b.** What is the east component of the wind's velocity?

Given: v = 40.0 km/h, 60.0°   **Unknowns:** v_N, v_E

Solution:

To find the north component, v_N, use the relation

$$\sin 30.0° = \frac{v_N}{v} \qquad \text{Then, } v_N = (v)(\sin 30.0°)$$

$$v_N = (40.0 \text{ km/h})(0.500) = 20.0 \text{ km/h, } 0.0°$$

To find the east component, v_E, use the relation

$$\cos 30.0° = \frac{v_E}{v} \qquad \text{Then, } v_E = (v)(\cos 30.0°)$$

$$v_E = (40.0 \text{ km/h})(0.866) = 34.6 \text{ km/h, } 90.0°$$

Problems

25. A heavy box is pulled across a wooden floor with a rope. The rope forms an angle of 60° with the floor. A tension of 8.0×10^1 N is maintained on the rope. What force actually is pulling the box across the floor?

25. 4.0×10^1 N

26. An airplane flies 301° at 5.0×10^2 km/h. At what rate is the plane moving?

   a. north   **b.** west

26. a. 260 km/h
    b. 430 km/h

27. By applying a force of 72 N along the handle of a lawnmower, a student can push it across the lawn. Find the horizontal component of this force when the handle is held at an angle with the lawn of

   a. 60.0°   **b.** 40.0°   **c.** 30.0°

27. a. 36 N
    b. 55 N
    c. 62 N

FIGURE 6-14. Use with Problem 28.

28. 7.0 N

29. 2.0 × 10² N

The correct choice of axes to use in inclinded plane problems is the set perpendicular and parallel to the plane.

28. A house address sign is hung from a post with a lightweight rod as shown in Figure 6-14. If the sign weighs 4.5 N, what is the force in the chain?

29. A water skier is towed by a speedboat. The skier moves to one side of the boat in such a way that the towrope forms an angle of 55° with the wake of the boat. The tension on the rope is 350 N. What would be the tension on the rope if the skier were directly behind the boat?

6:9   Gravitational Force and Inclined Planes

The gravitational force acting on an object on an incline is directed toward the center of the earth. This means that the object's weight, W, must act perpendicular to the surface of the earth. The direction of W is vertical or perpendicular to the horizontal.

Figure 6-15 shows a trunk resting on an inclined plane. The weight of the trunk, W, can be resolved into two components perpendicular to each other. One component, $F_\perp$, is called the perpendicular force and acts perpendicular to the incline. The second component, $F_\parallel$, is called the parallel force and acts parallel to and down the incline.

The right triangle formed by the incline and the right triangle formed by W, $F_\perp$, and $F_\parallel$ are similar triangles (corresponding sides are mutually perpendicular). If θ and W are both known, a vector diagram similar to Figure 6-15 may be drawn and the force W resolved into the components $F_\parallel$ and $F_\perp$ by the graphical method. An easier method is to calculate the values of $F_\parallel$ and $F_\perp$ using the trigonometric functions of right triangles. Note that $F_\perp$ is numerically equal to the normal force F_N, that the plane exerts on the trunk.

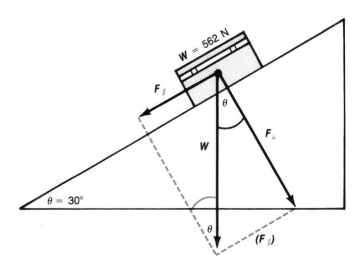

FIGURE 6-15. The weight vector W is resolved into two components. One component acts parallel to the plane. The other acts perpendicular to the plane.

EXAMPLE

Finding F $_\parallel$ and F $_\perp$

A trunk weighing 562 N is resting on a plane inclined at 30.0° from the horizontal.   Find the magnitudes of the parallel and perpendicular components of the weight.

Given: W = 562 N   **Unknowns:** perpendicular force ($F_\perp$),

θ = 30.0°   parallel force ($F_\parallel$)

Solution:

$$\sin \theta = \frac{F_\parallel}{W}$$

$F_\parallel$ = (562 N)(sin 30.0°)
$F_\parallel$ = (562 N)(0.500)
$F_\parallel$ = 281 N

$$\cos \theta = \frac{F_\perp}{W}$$

$F_\perp$ = (562 N)(cos 30.0°)
$F_\perp$ = (562 N)(0.866)
$F_\perp$ = 487 N

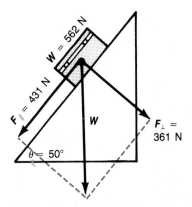

FIGURE 6-16. As the angle of the incline increases, the component of the weight acting parallel to the plane increases. The component that acts perpendicular to the plane decreases.

Note that as the incline in Figure 6-16 becomes steeper, $F_\parallel$ becomes greater and $F_\perp$ becomes less.

Problems

30. A 5.00 × 10²-N trunk is placed on an inclined plane that forms a 66° angle with the horizontal.

  a. Calculate the values of F $_\perp$ and F $_\parallel$.
  b. Compare your results with those given above for the same trunk on a 30° incline.
  c. When the angle of an incline increases, how do the force components acting on the trunk change?

31. A car weighing 12 000 N is parked on a 36° slope.

  a. Find the force tending to cause the car to roll down the hill.
  b. What is the perpendicular force between the car and the hill?

32. In order to slide a 325-N trunk up a 20.0°-inclined plane at a constant speed, a force of 211 N is applied. What is the force of friction acting on the trunk?

30. a. $F_\perp$ = 2.0 × 10² N
       $F_\parallel$ = 460 N
    b. $F_\perp$ = 430 N
       $F_\parallel$ = 250 N
       $F_\parallel$ is less and $F_\perp$ is greater than the example in Part a.
    c. As the angle of the incline increases, $F_\parallel$ increases and $F_\perp$ decreases.

31. a. $F_\parallel$ = 7100 N
    b. $F_\perp$ × 9700 N

32. 1.00 × 10² N

6:10   Nonperpendicular Components of Vectors

In Section 6:8, a single vector was resolved into two components at right angles to each other. However, a vector can be resolved into components that lie in any direction as long as their vector sum is equal

The direction of the component depends on the direction of the object exerting the force.

to the original vector. In some cases, it may be necessary for you to resolve a vector into components that are not at right angles to each other.

A sign that weighs 40 N is supported by ropes A and B, Figure 6-17. Three forces act on the sign. These are the force in rope A, the force in rope B, and the force due to gravity (the weight of the sign). The weight of the sign, 40 N, acts in the direction straight down. Because the sign is in equilibrium, the forces in the two ropes must produce a resultant, R, of 40 N straight up to balance the weight of the sign. Thus, the magnitude and direction of the resultant of the forces in the two ropes is known, although the force in each rope is not known.

Figure 6-17 shows how R can be resolved into two components to find the force in each rope. Three lines are drawn. These are the known, R, and two lines that represent the directions of ropes A and B.

The vector R is then resolved into two components—one in the direction of rope A and one in the direction of rope B. You can resolve R by constructing a parallelogram. The broken lines in this diagram represent the parallel sides that are drawn to complete the parallelogram. These broken lines intersect the lines in the direction of ropes A and B. In so doing, they define the components of R. The two components, a and b, are then interpreted in terms of the scale of the diagram to find the force in each rope.

In this case, the force turns out to be 40 N in each rope. The fact that the component forces in each rope are equal to the weight is due to the choice of angles. At other angles, the forces in the ropes will vary. Note that when a, b, and W are added, as in Figure 6-17, they form a closed triangle. This triangle indicates a vector sum of zero. Thus, the sign hangs in equilibrium.

The situation

The vector diagram

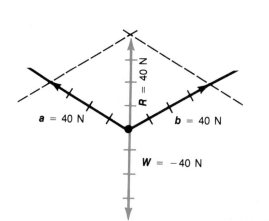

FIGURE 6-17. Resolving the force R into the nonperpendicular components a and b.

Summary

1. Addition of two vectors is done by placing the tail of the second vector at the head of the first vector. The resultant vector is drawn by connecting the tail of the first vector to the head of the second vector.   6:1

2. Vectors act independently of each other.   6:2

3. Vectors may be added graphically or mathematically.   6:3, 6:4

4. When there is no net force acting on an object, it is in equilibrium.   6:6

5. The equilibrant force is the force that produces equilibrium when applied to an object.   6:7

6. A vector can be resolved into two perpendicular components.   6:8

7. The weight of an object on an inclined plane can be resolved into two perpendicular components. One component, $F_{\parallel}$, acts parallel to the plane; the other component, $F_{\perp}$, acts perpendicular to the plane.   6:9

Detailed answers to all Questions and Problems are given in the Teacher's Guide at the front of this book.

Questions

1. What is meant by equilibrium?

2. How are vectors added graphically?

3. When two or more vectors are added graphically, how is the resultant found?

4. What is meant by the term concurrent forces?

5. How does the resultant of two vectors change as the angle between the two vectors increases?

6. A lawnmower is pushed across a lawn. Can the horizontal component of the force be increased without changing the force applied to the handle of the mower? Explain.

7. What is the sum of three vectors that form a triangle? Assuming that the vectors are forces, what does this imply about the object on which the forces act?

8. How can the equilibrant of two or more concurrent forces be found?

9. A gardener may find that it is easier to pull a lawnroller across the lawn than it is to push the same roller across the lawn. Explain.

Problems—A

1. Three people attempt to haul a heavy sign to the roof of a building by means of three ropes attached to the sign. Person A stands directly above the sign and pulls straight up on a rope. Person B and Person C stand on either side   1. 279N

of Person A. Their ropes form 30.0° angles with Person A's rope. A force of 102 N is applied on each rope. What is the net upward force acting on the sign?

2. 1.93 × 10² km,
   2.30 × 10² km

2. A plane travels on a heading of 50.0° for a distance of 3.00 × 10² km. How far north and how far east does the plane travel?

3. a. 65 m/s
   b. 58°

3. A descent vehicle landing on the moon has a vertical velocity toward the surface of the moon of 35 m/s. At the same time it has a horizontal velocity of 55 m/s.

    a. At what speed does the vehicle move along its descent path?
    b. At what angle with the vertical is this path?

4. a. 48 N, 82 N
   b. 82 N, 48 N

4. A lawnmower is pushed across a lawn by applying a force of 95 N along the handle of the mower. The handle makes an angle of 60.0° with the horizontal.

    a. What are the horizontal and vertical components of the force?
    b. The handle is lowered so that it makes an angle of 30.0° with the horizontal. What are the horizontal and vertical components of the force?

5. 65 N, 65 N

5. A force of 92 N is exerted on a heavy box by means of a rope. The rope is held at an angle of 45° with the horizontal. What are the vertical and horizontal components of the 92-N force?

6. a. 3.1 m/s
   b. 6.7 m/s

6. A river flows due south. A riverboat pilot heads the boat 297° and is able to go straight across the river at 6.0 m/s.

    a. What is the velocity of the current?
    b. What is the velocity of the boat?

7. 150 N in each

7. A street lamp weighs 150 N. It is supported equally by two wires that form an angle of 120° with each other. What is the tension of each of these wires?

8. 106 N in each

8. If the angle between the wires in Problem 7 is changed to 90.0°, what is the tension of each of the wires?

9. a. 144 N, 74° up
   b. 144 N, 74° up
   c. They are equivalent

9. Three forces act concurrently on point P. Force **a** has a magnitude of 80.0 N and is directed 30.0°. Force **b** has a magnitude of 70.0 N and is directed due east. Force **c** has a magnitude of 40.0 N and is directed 135°.

    a. Graphically add these three forces in the order **a** + **b** + **c**.

FIGURE 6-18. Use with Problem B-1.

b. Graphically add these three forces in the order **c + b + a**.

c. What is noted about the solutions in each case?

Problems–B

1. A mass, M, starts from rest and slides down the frictionless incline as shown. As it leaves the incline its speed is 24 m/s, (Figure 6-18).

    a. What is the acceleration of the mass while on the incline?

    b. What is the length of the incline?

    c. How long does it take the mass to reach the floor after it leaves the ~~top of the~~ incline?

1. a. 4.9 m/s²
   b. 59 m
   c. 1.0 s

   5.9 *nc* - *Top*

2. Two masses are attached to each other by a rope that passes over a frictionless pulley as shown in Figure 6-19. Find the direction and magnitude of the acceleration of the 2.00 kg mass on the frictionless incline.

2. 0.30 m/s², down the incline

FIGURE 6-19. Use with Problem B-2.

Readings

Browne, Malcolm W., "Slippery Skins for Speedier Subs." *Discover*, April, 1984.

Crane, Richard, "Frisbees, Can Lids, and Gyroscopic Effects." *The Physics Teacher*, May, 1983.

Gilmore, C.P., "Spin Sail Harnesses Mysterious Magnus Effect." *Popular Science*, January, 1984.

Hirsch, Julian, "Record Wear." *Stereo Review*, January, 1985.

MacKeown, P.K., "Gravity is Geometry." *The Physics Teacher*, December, 1984.

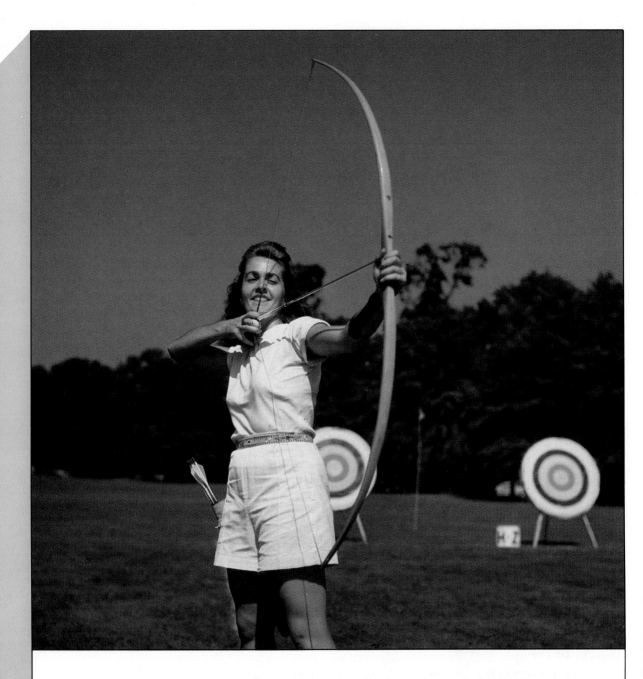

The motion of an arrow is certainly not as simple as that of a falling apple. However, curved motion is similar to motion in a straight line in that it is the result of forces acting on an object. You can understand curved motion more easily if you think of it as motion in two directions at the same time. What are some other examples of curved motion? What do they have in common?

Motion in Two Dimensions

Chapter 7 introduces curvilinear motion and treats the subject in terms of simultaneous linear motion in two dimensions. Uniform circular motion and simple harmonic motion are also discussed.

The velocity of a car moving around a circular racetrack at constant speed changes with time. Velocity is described by magnitude and direction. Even though the speed of the car does not change, the direction changes; therefore, velocity changes. Any change in velocity is caused by an unbalanced force.

All curved motion is the result of a force that causes an object to deviate from its straight-line motion. According to Newton's first law of motion, an object in motion will travel in a straight line unless acted upon by an unbalanced force. From this statement, we can conclude that an object moving in a curved path must be acted upon by a net force. Thus, the curved path followed by an object depends only upon the direction and size of the unbalanced force that acts on the object.

GOAL: You will gain an understanding of motion in two dimensions and its application in studying projectile motion, uniform circular motion, and simple harmonic motion.

7:1 Projectiles

If a baseball is thrown horizontally, it falls toward the ground in a curved path. As an arrow leaves the bow, it moves in a curved path toward the target. Baseballs, arrows, and model rockets are examples of projectiles. A **projectile** is any object that is thrown or otherwise projected into the air. The characteristic path followed by a projectile is a parabola and is called its **trajectory. Projectile motion** describes the movement of a projectile along its trajectory.

Projectile motion is the curved motion of an object that is projected into the air.

The trajectory is the path of a projectile.

113

A frame of reference is the viewpoint of an observer of motion.

The shape of a trajectory depends on the frame of reference of the observer.

The shape of a trajectory depends on the observer. Suppose a passenger in a bus traveling at a constant velocity threw a ball straight up. From the passenger's viewpoint, or **frame of reference,** the ball returned to the same position from which it was thrown. The motion of the ball was straight up and down because the bus, passenger, and ball all had the same horizontal velocity. To a group of students watching the bus go by, the motion of the ball appeared quite different. From their frame of reference, the ball followed a curved path from the time it left the passenger's hand until it was caught. To the stationary observers, the ball had both a vertical and a horizontal velocity. An analysis of projectile motion in terms of independent vertical and horizontal motion will allow us to predict the motion of projectiles.

Consider the two golf balls shown in Figure 7-2. The two balls are released at the same time. One ball is projected horizontally. The other ball is dropped. Strobe photography shows the path followed by each ball. The same vertical force, gravity, is acting on both balls. Therefore, even though the projected ball moves to the right, its vertical position is at all times the same as the vertical position of the dropped ball. Vertically, the projected ball acts as if it has no horizontal velocity and is simply falling. Note also that the projected ball moves the same distance to the right during each time interval. The horizontal velocity of the ball is constant because no unbalanced horizontal force is acting on it. The falling motion does not change the speed at which the ball moves to the right. The horizontal and vertical velocities of the ball act independently. The trajectory of the ball on the right results from the vector sum of the horizontal and vertical motions of the ball.

Horizontal and vertical velocities of a projectile are independent.

The horizontal displacement, d_h, of a projectile that moves while it is falling depends on the horizontal velocity, v_h, and the interval of time that the projectile is in the air. The projectile's initial vertical velocity

FIGURE 7-1. To observer A, the ball falls straight down. To observer B, the path of the ball is a parabola.

FIGURE 7-2. A flash photograph of two golf balls released simultaneously. Both balls were allowed to fall freely, but one was projected horizontally with an initial velocity of 2.00 m/s. The light flashes are 1/30 s apart.

and the acceleration of gravity determine the time interval. The time interval can be found by solving the following equation for *t*.

Horizontal velocity is constant; vertical velocity is constantly changing because of gravity.

$$\boldsymbol{d_v} = \tfrac{1}{2}\boldsymbol{g}t^2 + \boldsymbol{v_i}t$$

Here, $\boldsymbol{v_i}$ is the initial *vertical* velocity. The horizontal displacement is equal to the product of the horizontal velocity and the time of fall.

$$\boldsymbol{d_h} = \boldsymbol{v_h}t$$

EXAMPLE

Projectile Thrown Horizontally

A stone is thrown horizontally at 15 m/s. It is thrown from the top of a cliff 44 m high. **a.** How long does it take the stone to reach the bottom of the cliff? **b.** How far from the base of the cliff does the stone strike the ground? **c.** Sketch the trajectory of the stone.

Given: horizontal velocity   **Unknowns: a.** time interval (*t*)
$(\boldsymbol{v_h})$ = 15 m/s

initial vertical velocity
$(\boldsymbol{v_i})$ = 0 m/s

vertical acceleration $(\boldsymbol{g})$ = -9.8 m/s²

initial height $(\boldsymbol{d_v})$ = 44m

b. horizontal displacement $(\boldsymbol{d_h})$

Point out to students that if an observer moved to the right at the correct speed, the ball projected horizontally could appear to fall straight down. The other would move along a parabola to the left.

FIGURE 7-3. The path of a projectile thrown horizontally.

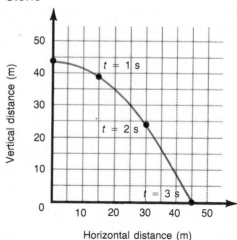

Trajectory of stone

Solution:
If the initial height is 44 m, then the vertical displacement (d_v) is -44 m.

a. $d_v = \frac{1}{2}gt^2 + v_it,\ (v_i = 0\ \text{m/s})$

$$t = \sqrt{\frac{2d_v}{g}}$$

$$= \sqrt{\frac{2 \times -44\ \text{m}}{-9.8\ \text{m/s}^2}}$$

$$t = \sqrt{9.0\ \text{s}^2} = 3.0\ \text{s}$$

b. $d_h = v_h t$
$$= (15\ \text{m/s})(3.0\ \text{s}) = 45\ \text{m}$$

Problems

1. A stone is thrown horizontally at a speed of 10.0 m/s from the top of a cliff 78.4 m high.

    a. How long does it take the stone to reach the bottom of the cliff?
    b. How far from the base of the cliff does the stone strike the ground?

2. A steel projectile is shot horizontally at 20.0 m/s from the top of a 49.0-m high tower. How far from the base of the tower does the projectile hit the ground?

3. A steel ball with a constant velocity of 0.800 m/s rolls off the edge of a table. The table is 0.950 meter high. How far from the edge of the table does the ball land?

1. a. 4.00 s
   b. 40.0 m

2. 63.2 m

3. 0.352 m

4. A person standing on a cliff throws a stone with a horizontal velocity of 15.0 m/s and the stone hits the ground 47 m from the base of the cliff. How far does the stone fall? How high is the cliff? (Remember, vertical displacement is the negative of initial height.)
   - 47 m, 47m

5. A projectile is launched horizontally from the top of a building with a velocity of 12.7 m/s. At what height is the projectile launched if the projectile lands 15.0 meters from the side of the building?

6. An arrow is fired horizontally with a speed of 89 m/s directly at the bull's-eye of a target 60.0 m away. When it is fired, the arrow is 1.0 m above the ground. How far short of the target does it strike the ground? 2.0×10^1 m

7:2 Projectile Motion

When a projectile is fired at an angle above the horizontal, it will be moving both vertically and horizontally along its trajectory. Its vertical motion will depend upon the vertical component of its initial velocity and the acceleration of gravity. Its horizontal motion will depend upon the horizontal component of its initial velocity. Its motion in two dimensions can be analyzed by considering its horizontal and vertical motion independently.

EXAMPLE

Projectile Motion

A golf ball is hit and leaves the tee with a velocity of 25.0 m/s at 35.0° with respect to the horizontal. What is the horizontal displacement of the ball?

Given: v = 25.0 m/s, 35.0°   **Unknown:** d_h

FIGURE 7-4. The path of this diver can be analyzed by treating the diver as a projectile fired at an angle with the horizontal.

The velocity of a projectile is resolved into horizontal and vertical components.

When solving problems, the horizontal and vertical motions are treated separately.

5. 6.83 m

FIGURE 7-5. The flight of a golf ball can be described in terms of horizontal and vertical components.

FIGURE 7-6. Vector diagram for projectile motion in the Example Problem. The space between each mark is 5 m/s.

Solution: As seen in Figure 7-6

$$v_v = (v)(\sin 35.0°) \qquad\qquad v_h = (v)(\cos 35.0°)$$
$$= (25.0 \text{ m/s})(0.574) \qquad\quad = (25.0 \text{ m/s})(0.819)$$
$$v_v = 14.4 \text{ m/s} \qquad\qquad\quad v_h = 20.5 \text{ m/s}$$

The total time the projectile is in motion is equal to the time to rise to zero velocity plus the time to fall again to the initial velocity.

$$t_{down} = \frac{v_f - v_i}{g} = \frac{-14.4 \text{ m/s} - 0}{-9.81 \text{ m/s}^2} = 1.47 \text{ s}$$

$$t = 2(t_{down}) = 2(1.47 \text{ s}) = 2.98 \text{ s}$$

The horizontal displacement is given by

$$d_h = v_h t$$
$$= (20.5 \text{ m/s})(2.94 \text{ s})$$
$$d_h = 60.3 \text{ m}$$

Problems

Assume no frictional effects.

7. A projectile is fired at such an angle from the horizontal that the vertical component of its velocity is 49 m/s. The horizontal component of its velocity is 61 m/s.
   a. How long does the projectile remain in the air?
   b. What horizontal distance does it travel?
   c. What is the initial velocity of the projectile?

8. A projectile is fired with a velocity of 196 m/s at an angle of 60.0° with the horizontal. Calculate
   a. the vertical velocity and the horizontal velocity of the projectile.
   b. the time the projectile is in the air.
   c. the horizontal distance the projectile travels.
   d. The maximum height the projectile reaches.

9. A projectile is fired at an angle of 53° with the horizontal. The speed of the projectile is 2.00 × 10² m/s. Calculate
   a. the time the shell remains in the air.
   b. the horizontal distance it travels.

10. While standing on an open bed of a truck moving at a constant velocity of 22 m/s, an archer sees a duck flying directly overhead. The archer shoots an arrow at the duck and misses. The arrow leaves the bow with a vertical velocity of 98 m/s.
   a. For what time interval does the arrow remain in the air?
   b. Where does the arrow finally land?

7. a. 10.0 s
   b. 610 m
   c. 78 m/s, 39° above the horizontal

8. a. 1.70 × 10²   c. 3390 m
       98.0 m/s   d. 1470 m
   b. 34.6 s

9. a. 33 s
   b. 4.0 × 10³ m

10. a. 2.0 × 10¹ s
    b. It hits the archer.

c. What horizontal distance does the arrow travel while it is in the air?

11. A golf ball is hit at an angle of 45° with the horizontal. If the initial velocity of the ball is 52 m/s, how far will it travel horizontally before striking the ground?

10. c. 4.4 × 10² m

11. 280 m

FIGURE 7-7. The force on a model plane in flight is directed toward the center of the circle.

7:3 Uniform Circular Motion

Uniform circular motion results when a net force, acting on a mass moving at constant speed, changes direction in such a way that the force is always acting at a right angle to the direction in which the mass is moving.

Consider Figure 7-7. A hand-controlled airplane is attached to the ends of the control strings and moves in a horizontal circle. Your hand pulls on the strings and provides an inward radial force that keeps the plane moving in its circular path. This force is called a **centripetal** (sen TRIP uht uhl) **force, F_c.** Centripetal means center-seeking. If the force of the strings is removed, the plane will travel in a straight line from its point of release. This behavior is in accord with the first law of motion. The straight line path is tangent to the circle at the point of release. This line is shown as v_t on Figure 7-8.

Note that the centripetal force always acts at right angles to the instantaneous velocity of the plane. Therefore, the centripetal force cannot change the magnitude of the velocity. However, the force does

A centripetal force is a force directed toward the center of a circle.

FIGURE 7-8. A model airplane would move in a straight path if the strings were cut.

Instantaneous velocity

If motion is circular, the centripetal force is always at right angles to the instantaneous velocity of the object.

Centripetal acceleration, like centripetal force, is always directed toward the center of the circle. This is a result of Newton's laws.

Vectors are subtracted by placing them tail to tail.

change the direction of the velocity. Since velocity is a vector quantity, a change in direction is a change in velocity, Δv. A change in the plane's velocity means that it is being accelerated. According to the second law of motion, acceleration is always in the same direction as the applied force. The force, F_c, acting on the plane is always directed toward the center of the circle. Thus, the acceleration is also directed toward the center of the circle. This acceleration is called **centripetal acceleration**.

By drawing a vector diagram, we can analyze uniform circular motion. That is, we can derive equations for the magnitude of both the centripetal acceleration and the centripetal force.

In Figure 7-9a, A and B are two successive positions of a mass that is moving with uniform circular motion. The radius of the circle is r. The vector v_1 represents the instantaneous velocity of the mass at A. The vector v_2 represents the velocity of the mass at B. Note that v_1 and v_2 are identical in magnitude, but their directions are different.

In Figure 7-9b, v_1 and v_2 have been placed tail to tail. We learned in Chapter 6 that by placing vectors head to tail, we could find their vector sum. By placing two vectors tail to tail, we can find their vector difference. The change in velocity, Δv, can be found by subtracting the two vectors. By drawing the vector, Δv, you can see that the vector v_2 is the resultant of v_1 and Δv. Because

$$v_1 + \Delta v = v_2,$$

it is apparent that

$$\Delta v = v_2 - v_1.$$

Therefore, Δv is the vector difference between v_1 and v_2.

The triangles ABC and DEF are similar triangles because the corresponding sides of angles C and F are perpendicular. Thus,

$$\frac{\Delta v}{v} = \frac{\text{chord } AB}{r}$$

The arc AB is the distance the mass moves during the time interval t. The distance may be expressed as vt. If we choose A and B such that

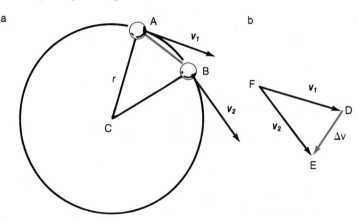

FIGURE 7-9. Vector diagrams can be used to analyze uniform circular motion.

FIGURE 7-10. Friction is the force that holds these people up. Centripetal force keeps them from flying out.

they are very close together, the chord AB and the arc AB are approximately equal. Thus, the chord AB is the displacement and can be expressed as vt. By substituting the value for the chord AB in the above equation,

$$\frac{\Delta v}{v} = \frac{vt}{r}$$

Solving for the centripetal acceleration, $\Delta v/t$, yields

$$a_c = \frac{\Delta v}{t} = \frac{v^2}{r}$$

Centripetal acceleration $a_c = v^2/r$.

Since the magnitude of any force is equal to ma, the magnitude of the centripetal force, F_c, producing the circular motion must be

$$F_c = ma$$

$$\boxed{F_c = \frac{mv^2}{r}}$$

You can show that this equation yields force units by substituting SI units for mass, velocity, and radius in the centripetal force equation.

$$\frac{kg \cdot (m/s)^2}{m} = \frac{kg \cdot m^2/s^2}{m} = kg \cdot m/s^2 = N$$

The direction of the centripetal force acting on a body moving in circular motion is always directed toward the center of the circle.

Emphasize to students that centripetal force always has a causative agent. Have students identify the agent in Figure 7-10 and in other examples such as a car rounding a curve, and in Problems 12-17.

EXAMPLE   Centripetal Acceleration and Force

A 0.25-kg mass is attached to a 1.00-m length of string. The mass completes a horizontal circle in 0.42 s.   **a.** What is the velocity of the mass?   **b.** What is the centripetal force acting on the mass?

Given: $m = 0.25$ kg   **Unknown:** **a.** velocity (v)
$\qquad\quad r = 1.00$ m $\qquad\qquad\qquad$ **b.** centripetal force (F_c)
$\qquad\quad t = 0.42$ s

$\qquad\qquad\qquad$ **Basic Formulas:** $v = d/t = \dfrac{2\pi r}{t}$

$\qquad\qquad\qquad\qquad\qquad\qquad\qquad F_c = \dfrac{mv^2}{r}$

Solution:

a. $v = \dfrac{2\pi r}{t}$ $\qquad\qquad$ **b.** $F_c = \dfrac{mv^2}{r}$

$\quad = \dfrac{2(3.14)(1.00 \text{ m})}{0.42 \text{ s}}$ $\qquad\qquad = \dfrac{(0.25 \text{ kg})(15.0 \text{ m/s})^2}{1.00 \text{ m}}$

$\quad = 15$ m/s $\qquad\qquad\qquad\qquad = \dfrac{(0.25)(225 \text{ m}^2\,\text{s}^2)}{1.00 \text{ m}}$

$\qquad\qquad\qquad F_c = 56$ kg $\cdot$ m/s^2 $= 56$ N (radially inward)

Problems

12. What is the centripetal acceleration of an object moving in a circular path of 20.0 m radius with a speed of 20.0 m/s?

13. A 2.0-kg mass is attached to a string 1.0 m long and swings in a circle parallel to the horizontal. The mass goes around its path once each 0.80 s.
   a.   What is its centripetal acceleration?
   b.   What tension is in the string?

14. It takes a 6.00×10^2-kg racing car 10.0 s to travel at a uniform speed around a circular racetrack of 50.0 m radius.
   a.   What average force must the car's tires exert against the track to maintain its circular motion?
   b.   What is the acceleration of the car?

15. A child twirls a yo-yo about in a horizontal circle. The yo-yo has a mass of 0.20 kg and is attached to a string 0.80 m long.
   a.   If the yo-yo makes one complete revolution each second, what tension must exist in the string?
   b.   If the child increases the speed of the yo-yo to 2 rev/s, what tension must be in the string?
   c.   What is the ratio of the answer in (b) to (a)? Why?

16. A 1.00-kg mass is attached to a string 1.0 m long and completes a horizontal circle in 0.25 s.
   a.   Find the centripetal acceleration of the mass.
   b.   Calculate the centripetal force (the tension in the string).

---

12. 20.0 m/s²

13. a. 62 m/s²
    b. 120 N

14. a. 1.18 × 10⁴ N
    b. 19.7 m/s²

15. a. 6.3 N
    b. 25 N
    c. The ratio is 4:1.

16. a. 630 m/s²
    b. 630 N

FIGURE 7-11. If the cannonball travels 8 km horizontally in 1 s, it will fall the same distance toward Earth as Earth falls from the cannonball.

17. An early major objection to the idea that the earth is spinning on its axis was that the earth would turn so fast (1600 km/h) at the equator that people would be thrown off into space. Show the error in this logic by calculating

  a. the weight of a 1.00×10^2-kg person.
  b. the centripetal force needed to hold the same person in place at the equator. The radius of the earth is about 6400 km.

17. a. 9.81×10^2 N
    b. 3.0 N

7:4 Placing a Satellite in Orbit

Look at Figure 7-11. If you assume the earth is a sphere, you can see that the earth curves away from a line tangent to its surface at a rate of 4.9 meters for every 8.0×10^3 meters. That is, the altitude of the line tangent to the earth at A will be 4.9 m above the earth at B. As you recall from Chapter 3, in one second an object will fall 4.9 m from rest. If the cannonball in Figure 7-11 were given a horizontal velocity so that it could travel from A to B in one second, it would fall 4.9 m and arrive at

FIGURE 7-12. The drawing is from Newton's "Systems of the World." It shows the trajectories of a body projected with different speeds from a high mountain. Newton knew that a projectile would orbit the earth if its speed were great enough. The trajectories from point V to points D, E, F, and G are the paths of objects with greater and greater horizontal velocities.

FIGURE 7-13. An orbiting satellite is acted upon by centripetal force directed toward the center of Earth.

The force of gravity on a satellite, its weight, provides the centripetal force to maintain its circular motion.

C. Take note that the altitude of the cannonball has not changed. The cannonball is falling toward the earth at the same rate that the earth's surface is curving away. An object with a horizontal speed of 8.00×10^3 m/s will maintain the same altitude if air resistance is ignored. The cannonball will continue circling the earth as an artificial satellite.

Most satellites are placed in orbit at a height of more than 320 km above the earth's surface. At such heights, there is very little atmosphere to cause friction and reduce the speed of the satellite. Thus, a launched satellite will orbit the earth for long periods of time.

Notice that the motion of the satellite above the earth is circular motion. Since the satellite circles the earth, it is acted upon by a centripetal force (F_c) that is always directed toward the center of the earth. The gravitational force acting on the satellite, its weight, provides the centripetal force. Thus, the weight of a space capsule is what keeps it in its orbital path.

The equation for centripetal force is $F_c = mv^2/r$. Because it is the weight (mg) of a satellite that provides the necessary centripetal force to keep it in its orbital path,

$$mg = \frac{mv^2}{r}$$

This equation reduces to

$$g = \frac{v^2}{r}$$

Thus, the velocity a satellite must have to orbit the earth is

$$\boxed{v = \sqrt{gr}}$$

A satellite farther from the earth has a larger velocity.

where g is the acceleration of gravity at distance r from the center of the earth and r is the average radius of its orbit from the center of the earth.

Note that the mass of the satellite does not affect its orbital velocity. A more massive satellite requires a greater centripetal force to keep it in orbit. However, a more massive satellite also has a greater weight. The greater weight provides the greater centripetal force. As shown above, the orbital velocity is independent of the mass of the satellite.

The velocity of a satellite is independent of its mass.

Satellites are accelerated to reach an orbital velocity by large rockets such as the Saturn V. The acceleration of any mass follows Newton's second law ($F = ma$). A massive satellite requires a large force to accelerate it to orbital velocity. Thus, the mass of launched satellites is limited by the capabilities of the rocket that is used. Large space platforms could be placed in orbit by using several rockets. Each would carry parts of the platform to be assembled in orbit.

A satellite must be given a large velocity to place it into orbit.

Problems

18. 8.0×10^3 m/s

18. Calculate the velocity at which a satellite must be launched in order to achieve an orbit about the earth. Use 9.8 m/s² as the acceleration of gravity and 6.5×10^3 km as the earth's radius.

19. During the lunar landings, the command module orbited close to the moon's surface while waiting for the lunar module to return from the moon's surface. The diameter of the moon is 3570 km and the acceleration of gravity on the moon is 1.60 m/s².

   a. At what velocity did the command module orbit the moon?
   b. In how many minutes did the module complete one orbit?

20. Calculate the velocity at which a satellite orbits Jupiter. The acceleration of gravity on Jupiter is 5.80×10^3 m/s². The diameter of the planet is 1.422×10^5 km.   642 km/s

19. a. 1.7 km/s
    b. 1.1×10^2 min

In simple harmonic motion the force varies directly with the displacement from equilibrium.

7:5 Simple Harmonic Motion

A swinging pendulum and vibrating guitar string are both examples of vibrational motion. An object in vibrational motion moves back and forth over the same path.

One characteristic of simple harmonic motion (SHM) is that the motion of the object repeats a pattern. This repeated pattern is called a **cycle.** The time to complete one cycle is called the **period,** T, and the number of cycles completed in a given time interval is called the **frequency,** f. The period and frequency are reciprocals and are related by the equation

$$T = \frac{1}{f}$$

The SI units for period and frequency will be discussed later.

Simple harmonic motion is a special kind of vibrational motion. It can best be described in terms of the motion of a mass on a spring. Figure 7-15 shows the equilibrium position of a mass suspended from a spring. The weight of the mass, **W,** is balanced by an upward restoring force, **F_1,** due to the stretch of the spring ($F_1 + W = 0$). An external force, **F,** moves the mass downward to rest at position 2. The mass is again in equilibrium, and the downward force ($F + W$) is balanced by

FIGURE 7-14. Vibrating objects undergo simple harmonic motion.

FIGURE 7-15. Simple harmonic motion can be shown by the vibrating of a mass on a spring.

a $a = 0$ $v = 0$ F_1 W

b $a = 0$ $v = 0$ F_2 $(W + F)$

c $a = \text{max}$ $v = 0$ F_2 W

d $a = 0$ $v = \text{max}$ F_1

e $a = \text{max}$ $v = 0$ $(W + F)$

Vibrational motion is the back and forth movement of an object over the same path.

the upward force, F_2, due to the increased stretch of the spring. If the external force, F, is removed, the restoring force of the spring will cause the mass to accelerate upward. As the mass rises toward the original equilibrium position, the upward force decreases due to less stretch of the spring. The decreasing upward force will cause a decreasing upward acceleration. At the original equilibrium position, the net force acting on the mass will be zero $(F_1 + W = 0)$ and the mass will have a maximum upward velocity. As the mass continues to move upward, it will compress the spring more and more. The increasing compression will cause the spring to exert an increasing downward restoring force. The increasing downward force will give the mass an increasing negative acceleration, causing it to slow down. When the mass comes to rest at its highest point, it will have a maximum downward force acting on it. It will then begin to move back toward its original equilibrium position. The mass will continue to vibrate up and down in simple harmonic motion. In the real world, air resistance eventually will stop the vibrations. It is important to note that in all SHM, the magnitude of the restoring force acting on the mass is proportional to the displacement of the mass from equilibrium and is always directed toward the equilibrium position.

The motion of pendulums is also an example of SHM. Figure 7-16a shows a simple pendulum consisting of a small suspended mass (the bob) that swings back and forth. The amplitude of the swing is the distance from the equilibrium position, E, to the points of greatest

Amplitude is the greatest displacement from the rest position.

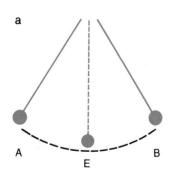

FIGURE 7-16. The motion of a simple pendulum (a). The motion of the pendulum of a clock is an example of simple harmonic motion.

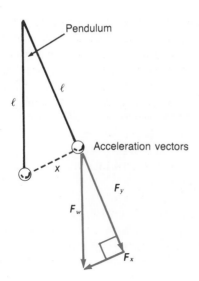

Pendulum

ℓ

ℓ

Acceleration vectors

x

F_y

F_w

F_x

FIGURE 7-17. The gravitational acceleration of a pendulum can be resolved into two components.

displacement, *A* and *B*. The period, *T*, of a pendulum is the time interval for the bob to move from *A* to *B* and back to *A*.

As shown in Figure 7-17, the gravitational force, **F**, is resolved into two components. **F**$_y$ is parallel to the string and opposes the force exerted by the string on the bob. The component **F**$_x$ is at right angles to the direction of the string. Since the motion of the bob is always at a right angle to the direction of the string, **F**$_x$ represents the restoring force that accelerates the bob toward the equilibrium position. For small amplitudes (θ less than 15°), the two triangles of Figure 7-17 are similar triangles. As can be seen, the acceleration of the bob at any moment depends on the magnitude of the displacement at that moment. The acceleration is also always directed toward the equilibrium position. These are the characteristics of SHM.

The period is the time required to finish one complete motion.

A pendulum making small swings undergoes simple harmonic motion.

The period of the simple pendulum of length ℓ is expressed as

$$T = 2\pi \sqrt{\frac{\ell}{g}}$$

Recall that all masses accelerate at the same rate in the same gravitational field. Therefore, the period of a simple pendulum does not depend on the mass of the bob or the amplitude of the swing. In any one location, the period depends only on the length of the pendulum and the acceleration of gravity. For this reason, the pendulum can be used to measure the acceleration of gravity.

The period of a pendulum depends on its length and the acceleration due to gravity, but not on its mass.

Like the period of a simple pendulum, the period of a small object vibrating on a spring does not depend upon the amplitude. However, unlike the pendulum, the period of the SHM is independent of the acceleration of gravity. The period depends upon the mass of the object and the stiffness of the spring.

The period of a mass on a spring depends on its mass and on the stiffness of the spring, but not on the acceleration of gravity.

FIGURE 7-18. A swing is an example of a simple pendulum.

The amplitude of any vibrating object can be greatly increased by applying a small external force at the same frequency as the vibrating object. This effect is called mechanical **resonance**. Your first encounter with resonance probably came at a very young age when you learned to "pump" a swing. You found that the amplitude of the swing (a pendulum) could be increased if you applied a force to it at the right frequency. This frequency is called the natural frequency of the pendulum. Other familiar examples of mechanical resonance are rocking a car to free it from a snow bank or jumping up and down on a trampoline.

FIGURE 7-19. Jumping up and down on a trampoline is an example of mechanical resonance.

Summary

1. Motion in a curved path can be analyzed as motion in two directions at the same time.   7:1

2. The horizontal motion and vertical motion of a projectile are independent of each other.   7:1

3. The trajectory of a projectile fired at an angle depends on the horizontal and vertical components of its initial velocity.   7:1, 7:2

4. Uniform circular motion results when a net force, called the centripetal force, constantly acts at a right angle to the direction in which the mass is moving.   7:3

5. Both the centripetal force and the centripetal acceleration are always directed toward the center of the circle.   7:3

6. The weight of a satellite provides the centripetal force needed to keep it in its orbital path.   7:4

7. The orbital velocity of a satellite depends upon the acceleration of gravity and its distance from the center of the body that it is orbiting.   7:4

8. If the motion of an object's path is repeated in a regular pattern, its motion is called simple harmonic motion (SHM).   7:5

9. Mechanical resonance occurs when the motion of an object undergoing SHM is reinforced by a small unbalanced force applied repeatedly at the correct frequency.   7:5

Detailed answers to all Questions and Problems are given in the Teacher's Guide at the front of this book.

Questions

1. A zoologist standing on a high platform aims a tranquilizer gun at a monkey hanging on a distant tree branch by one hand. The barrel of the gun is parallel to the horizontal. Just as the scientist pulls the trigger, the monkey lets go of the branch and begins to fall. Will the dart hit the monkey?

2. An airplane is flying at a constant velocity parallel to the horizontal, and the pilot drops a flare. Where will the plane be relative to the flare when the flare hits the ground?

3. What relationship must exist between an applied force and a moving mass if uniform circular motion is to result?

4. Distinguish between the period and the amplitude of a pendulum.

5. How is simple harmonic motion distinguished from other types of vibrational motion?

FIGURE 7-20. Use with Question 6.

6. Consider the trajectory of the ball in Figure 7-20.
   a. At which point is the vertical velocity the greatest?
   b. At which point is the horizontal velocity the greatest?
   c. Where is the vertical velocity least?
   d. Name the curve traveled by the ball.

Problems—A

1. 32 m

1. A stone is thrown horizontally at 8.0 m/s from a cliff 78.4 m high. How far from the base of the cliff will the stone strike the ground?

2. 130 m

2. A bridge is 176.4 m above a river. If a lead-weighted fishing line is thrown from the bridge with a horizontal speed of 22 m/s, what horizontal displacement will it travel before striking the water?

3. a. 1.0×10^1 s
   b. 2.0×10^3 m

3. a. If an object falls from a resting height of 490 m, how long will it remain in the air?
   b. If the object had a horizontal velocity of 2.00×10^2 m/s when it began to fall, what horizontal displacement will it travel?

4. a. 0.50 s
   b. 0.80 m/s

4. A toy car moves off the edge of a table that is 1.225 m high. If the car lands 0.40 m from the base of the table,
   a. how long did it take for the car to fall to the floor?
   b. with what horizontal velocity was the car moving?

5. 6.6 m/s

5. Divers at Acapulco dive from a cliff that is 61 m high. If the rocks below the cliff extend outward for 23 m, what is the minimum horizontal velocity a diver must have to clear them?

6. 98.2 km

6. A projectile is fired at an angle of 37.0° with the horizontal. If the initial velocity of the projectile is 1.00×10^3 m/s, what is the horizontal displacement?

7. 108.1 m

7. A baseball is hit at 30.0 m/s at an angle of 53.0° with the horizontal. An outfielder runs 4.00 m/s toward the infield and catches the ball. What was the original distance between the batter and the outfielder?

8. a. 51 m/s²
   b. 360 N

8. An athlete twirls a 7.00-kg hammer tied to the end of a 1.3-m rope in a horizontal circle. The hammer moves at the rate of 1.0 rev/s.
   a. What is the centripetal acceleration of the hammer?
   b. What is the tension in the rope?

Problems—B

1. In a cyclotron, an electromagnet exerts a force of 7.50×10^{-13} N on a beam of protons. Each proton has a mass of 1.67×10^{-27} kg. The electromagnet causes the protons to travel in a circular path of radius 1.20 m. What is the velocity of the proton beam?

2. A 75-kg pilot flies in her plane in a loop and notices that at the top of the loop, where the plane is completely upside-down for an instant, she hangs freely in her seat. The airspeed indicator reads 120 m/s. What is the radius of the plane's loop?

1. 2.32×10^7 m/s

2. 1500 m

Readings

Brancazio, Peter, "Getting a Kick Out of Physics." *Discover*, November, 1984.

Eskow, Dennis, "A Mach 20 Airliner." *Popular Mechanics*, November, 1984.

Greenslade, Thomas, "More Bicycle Physics." *The Physics Teacher*, September, 1983.

Lamb, William, "Bulldozing Your Way Through Projectile Motion." *Science Teacher*, November, 1983.

Rubin, V.C., "The Rotation of Spiral Galaxies." *Science*, June 24, 1983.

At one time, gravity was thought to be a special force which pulls everything to the earth. However, in the seventeenth century, Sir Isaac Newton began to think that all objects might exert gravitational forces on all other objects. He found evidence to support this idea in the motions of heavenly bodies. From experience, we know that this parachutist is being pulled to the ground by the earth's gravitational force. However, does the parachutist also exert a gravitational pull on the earth?

Universal Gravitation

Chapter 8 introduces the law of universal gravitation. It describes how Newton used the observations of Kepler and Brahe to develop the law of universal gravitation. It also describes the method used by Cavendish to test the law in the laboratory. Gravitational fields and Einstein's concepts of qravity are also discussed.

Until Newton's time, gravitational force was thought to be a unique property of the earth. However, Newton suspected that the earth was not unique among the heavenly bodies. He had already found that all motion follows three laws. Perhaps the gravitational force of the earth was only one example of a force that acts between any two bodies.

GOAL: You will gain an understanding of the law of gravitation and how it applies to the motion of the earth and other planets as well as the motion of objects near the earth.

8:1 Kepler's Laws of Planetary Motion

As a boy of fourteen, Tycho Brahe (1546-1601) heard that astronomers had predicted an eclipse of the sun on August 21, 1560. Brahe watched for the eclipse on that date, and it did indeed occur. However, he noticed that the astronomers' prediction of the exact time of the eclipse was 20 minutes in error. He was disturbed by the error in their prediction and thereupon decided to become an astronomer.

Brahe studied at many universities to prepare for his career. In 1576, King Frederick II of Denmark gave Brahe the island of Hveen where Brahe built the finest observatory of its time. Here, for most of his life, he observed the heavens. Night after night, for more than 20 years, he meticulously recorded the positions of the planets and stars. Near the end of Brahe's life, Johannes Kepler (1571-1630) became one of Brahe's students and an assistant. Kepler was an excellent mathematician and

Tycho Brahe made very accurate measurements of the positions of planets and stars before the telescope was invented.

Kepler was driven to find the true paths of planets after finding Tycho's predicitons were wrong by eight minutes of arc (one-fourth the width of the moon).

Kepler's laws are now known to be the result of the conservation of energy and angular momentum.

Actually these laws are applicable to motion in any conic section (ellipse, parabola, hyperbola, as well as circle).

FIGURE 8-2. An imaginary line from Earth to the sun sweeps out equal areas each second whether Earth is close to or far from the sun.

painstakingly worked with Brahe's data for 22 years. Using Brahe's vast amount of data, Kepler formulated three laws of planetary motion.

1. The paths of the planets are ellipses.
2. An imaginary line from a planet to the sun sweeps out equal areas in equal time intervals whether the planet is close to or far from the sun (Figure 8-2).
3. The ratio of the average radius of a planet's orbit about the sun, r, cubed and the planet's period, T, (the time for it to travel about the sun once) squared, is a constant for all the planets. This law can be expressed mathematically as

$$\frac{r^3}{T^2} = k$$

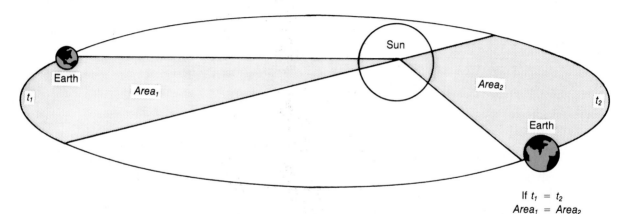

Earth

t_1

$Area_1$

Sun

$Area_2$

t_2

Earth

If $t_1 = t_2$
$Area_1 = Area_2$

8:2   Universal Gravitation

The observations of Tycho Brahe and the calculations of Johannes Kepler provided the basis for Newton's theory of universal gravitation. Legend has it that while watching an apple fall from a tree, Newton recognized that the apple fell because an unbalanced force acted on it (Newton's second law of motion). This force was gravity. Newton wondered if this special force was peculiar to the earth. Did other bodies also have it? Perhaps every body exerts a gravitational force on every other body. Newton looked for a way to describe this force and to determine its magnitude. He reasoned that if gravitational force is found throughout the universe, it might also be the force that keeps the moon in its orbit around the earth and the planets in their orbits around the sun. Kepler's studies revealed two important facts about the planets. First, their elliptical orbits are nearly circular. Thus, the force that causes the planets to move around the sun must conform to the equations for circular motion.

Newton proposed that the force that causes objects to fall to the earth exists between all other bodies, even the sun and planets.

Newton proposed that the motion of the moon around the earth was the result of the gravitational forces between the earth and the moon.

$$F_c = \frac{mv^2}{r}$$

The speed of a moving object is

$$v = \frac{d}{t}$$

The distance the object travels in a single revolution is the circumference of the circle, $2\pi r$. The time it takes the object to move once around the circumference is its period, T. Thus, its speed is

$$v = \frac{2\pi r}{T}$$

This expression for v can be substituted into the equation for centripetal force to yield

$$F_c = \frac{m(2\pi r/T)^2}{r}$$

$$= \frac{m4\pi^2 r}{T^2}$$

The equation for circular motion can be expressed in terms of the radius of the circle and the period of revolution.

Second, r^3/T^2 is a constant, k, for all the planets. Newton knew that this relationship was no accident. It had to be the result of the force keeping the planets in their orbits. Since $r^3/T^2 = k$, $T^2 = r^3/k$. He then substituted r^3/k for T^2 in the equation for the centripetal force acting on the planet.

Newton used Kepler's third law to relate the period of revolution to the radius of the orbit.

$$F_c = \frac{m4\pi^2 r}{T^2}$$

$$= \frac{m4\pi^2 r}{r^3/k}$$

$$= \frac{m4\pi^2 k}{r^2}$$

In this expression, $4\pi^2k$ is considered to be a single factor or constant. The value of each of its components is always the same. Thus $4\pi^2k$ is called K. The equation becomes

$$F_c = \frac{mK}{r^2}$$

The gravitational force varies inversely with the square of the distance between the two bodies.

This result told Newton that the force between any planet and the sun varies inversely with the square of its distance (radius) from the sun. It also told him that the force varies directly with the mass of a planet.

Newton's third law applies to gravitational interactions.

Newton reasoned that if the force between the sun and a planet depends on the mass of the planet, the force must also depend on the mass of the sun. After all, the planet is one mass and the sun is another. Since the sun exerts a force on the planet, then, by the third law of motion, the planet must exert an equal but opposite force on the sun. If the mass of a planet were suddenly doubled, the gravitational force between the planet and the sun would be doubled. If instead the mass of the sun were doubled, the gravitational force between the sun and the planet would still be doubled. If the mass of both the planet and the sun were doubled, the gravitational force between the two would increase by a factor of four. Thus, the gravitational force between any two bodies must increase as the product of their masses, m_1m_2 (Figure 8-3).

The gravitational force is proportional to the mass of each of the two bodies.

FIGURE 8-3. The gravitational force between any two bodies varies directly as the product of their masses and inversely as the square of their distances.

FIGURE 8-4. Gravitational forces hold the stars in their relative positions in this spiral galaxy.

Newton assumed that the gravitational force between any two bodies acts in the same way as the force between a planet and the sun. From this assumption, he developed the law of universal gravitation. This law states that every body in the universe attracts every other body in the universe with a force that varies directly with the product of the masses and inversely with the square of the distance between the centers of the two masses. This law is written

$$F \propto \frac{m_1 m_2}{d^2}$$

In the equation, m_1 and m_2 are the masses of the two bodies, and d is the distance between the centers of the masses.

The law of universal gravitation is valid for any two bodies.

Note that d is the distance between the centers of the objects. It took Newton 20 years to prove that this law was valid for large bodies as well as point particles.

8:3 Newton's Test of the Inverse Square Law

Newton lacked the necessary equipment to make a direct test of the law of universal gravitation. That is, he could not measure the gravitational force between two small masses. However, Newton did know something about the moon and its orbit. Therefore, he applied his law to the moon to determine whether or not it could be gravitational force that keeps it in its orbital path around the earth.

The moon is about 60 earth radii from the earth. Since gravitational force varies inversely with the square of the distance between two masses, Newton reasoned that the gravitational acceleration of the earth on the moon should vary in the same way. The value of the gravitational acceleration of the earth at 60 earth radii should equal the moon's centripetal acceleration. Thus, the gravitational acceleration

Newton tested the law of universal gravitation applied to the motion of the moon about the earth.

Point out that Newton couldn't determine the proportionality constant because the mass of the earth was unknown.

FIGURE 8-5. The moon is held in its orbit around Earth by gravitational force.

given to the moon by the earth should be only $1/(60)^2$ or $1/3600$ of the gravitational acceleration found at the earth's surface. This would be

$$(9.8 \text{ m/s}^2) \, \frac{1}{3600} = 0.0027 \text{ m/s}^2$$

Newton's second law, $F = ma$, states that if the force varies as $1/d^2$, so does the resulting acceleration.

Because Newton knew the distance to the moon and its period, he could calculate its centripetal acceleration. He could compare the moon's centripetal acceleration with the acceleration predicted by the inverse square law. The calculation is

$$a = \frac{v^2}{r}$$

$$= \frac{4\pi^2 r}{T^2}$$

$$a = \frac{4(3.14)^2(3.9 \times 10^8 \text{m})}{(2.3 \times 10^6 \text{ s})^2} = 0.0029 \text{ m/s}^2$$

FIGURE 8-6. Cavendish verified the existence of gravitational forces between masses by using an apparatus similar to that shown.

The actual centripetal acceleration of the moon is in close agreement with the acceleration predicted by the law of universal gravitation. This agreement was strong evidence that the law of universal gravitation, as stated, was correct.

8:4 Cavendish Experiment

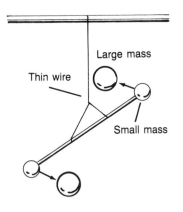

Nearly one hundred years after Newton first proposed his law of universal gravitation, it was experimentally confirmed by Henry Cavendish (1731-1810). Figure 8-6 shows the basic apparatus that Cavendish used. He attached a lead ball to each end of a long rod and suspended the rod by a thin wire. Then he carefully measured the amounts of force required to rotate the wire through given angles. Next he placed two large lead balls close to the small ones as shown. The two small balls were attracted by the two large balls. This caused the wire to twist. By measuring the angle through which the wire turned, Cavendish was able to find the force between the lead masses. He found that the force exactly followed the law of gravitation.

Cavendish measured the masses of the balls and the distances between their centers. Substituting these values for force, mass, and distance into the law of gravitation, he determined the value of G for Newton's law of universal gravitation.

The equation for gravitational force is

$$F_g = G \frac{m_1 m_2}{d^2}$$

If m_1 and m_2 are expressed in kilograms and d is expressed in meters, the value of the proportionality constant G is 6.67×10^{-11} N · m²/kg².

Cavindish tested the law of universal gravitation between small masses on the earth.

Because the law of gravitation is universal, G is the same for any two bodies. Knowing G, Cavendish could determine the mass of the earth.

Cavindish was able to measure, experimentally, the constant G in Newton's law of universal gravitation.

EXAMPLE

Law of Universal Gravitation

Two 3.00-kg lead balls are placed with their centers 7.25 m apart. What gravitational force exists between them?

Given: $m_1 = m_2 = 3.00$ kg   **Unknown:** F

$d = 7.25$ m   **Basic equation:** $F = G \frac{m_1 m_2}{d^2}$

Solution: $F = G \frac{m_1 m_2}{d^2}$

$= 6.67 \times 10^{-11} \frac{N \cdot m^2}{kg^2} \frac{(3.00 \text{ kg}) \times (3.00 \text{ kg})}{(7.25 \text{ m})^2}$

$= 6.67 \times 10^{-11} \frac{N \cdot m^2}{kg^2} \frac{(9.00 \text{ kg}^2)}{(52.6 \text{ m}^2)}$

$F = 1.14 \times 10^{-11}$ N

Note that the gravitational force between these two masses is quite small.

Problems

Assume the distance, d, is between the centers of the two masses.

1. Two balls have their centers 2.0 m apart. One has a mass of 8.0 kg. The other has a mass of 6.0 kg. What is the gravitational force between them?

2. **a.** What is the gravitational force between two 8.00 kg spherical masses that are 5.0 m apart?
   b. What is the gravitational force between them when they are 5.0×10^1 m apart?

1. 8.0×10^{-10} N

2. a. 1.7×10^{-10} N
   b. 1.7×10^{-12} N

3. Two large spheres are suspended close to each other. Their centers are 4.0 m apart. One mass weighs 9.8×10^2 N. The other mass has a weight of 1.96×10^2 N. What is the gravitational force that exists between them?

4. Two satellites of equal mass are put into orbit 30 m apart. The gravitational force between them is 2.0×10^{-7} N.
   a. What is the mass of each satellite?
   b. What is the initial acceleration given to each satellite by this force?

5. The mass of the earth is 6.0×10^{24} kg. If the centers of the earth and moon are 3.9×10^8 m apart, the gravitational force between them is about 1.9×10^{20} N. What is the approximate mass of the moon?

6. Use Newton's second law of motion to find the acceleration given to the moon by the force in Problem 5.

7. The mass of an electron is 9.1×10^{-31} kg. The mass of a proton is 1.7×10^{-27} kg. They are about 1.0×10^{-10} m apart in a hydrogen atom. What force of gravitation exists between the proton and the electron of a hydrogen atom?

8:5 Law of Universal Gravitation and Weight

The force that causes an object to fall toward the earth is the gravitational force between that object and the earth. This force is called weight. The weight of any object follows the law of universal gravitation. The magnitude of the weight of any mass near the earth's surface is

$$W = G\frac{m_o m_e}{d_e^{\,2}}$$

where m_o is the mass of the object, m_e is the mass of the earth, and d_e is the radius of the earth. (Gravitational force is always calculated by using the distances between the centers of two attracting objects.)

Since W also equals $m_o g$, we can rewrite the equation above as

$$m_o g = G\,\frac{m_o m_e}{d_e^{\,2}}$$

which reduces to

$$g = G\,\frac{m_e}{d_e^{\,2}}$$

The acceleration of gravity is the same for all bodies near the earth's surface since G, m_e, and d_e are constants. The acceleration of gravity, g', at any location above the earth's surface is given by

$$g' = G\,\frac{m_e}{d^2}$$

where d is the distance from the center of the earth.

Weight is the gravitational force of the earth on an object.

The acceleration due to gravity, being the result of weight, is independent of the mass of the object.

FIGURE 8-7. This map shows the variations in the force of gravity throughout the United States and Canada. Milligals are units of gravitational acceleration.

The weight of an object above the earth's surface is

$$W' = m_o g' = G \frac{m_o m_e}{d^2}$$

As can be seen, the weight of an object above the earth's surface varies inversely with the square of its distance from the earth's center. Figure 8-8 shows the change in a rocket's weight as the distance between the rocket and the earth increases.

8:6 Gravitational Fields

The gravitational force between the earth and the sun keeps the earth in its orbit even though the earth and sun are millions of kilometers apart. Scientists have never satisfactorily explained how a force could act through such a distance. To describe the effects of forces acting at a distance, the concept of fields was invented. A field describes some effect that an object will experience by being at a certain location. The field does not explain how the effect is produced. The concept of a field was first developed in the study of electromagnetic forces and now is applied to all forces.

According to Newton's law of gravitation, the gravitational force of the earth acting on an object depends on the masses of the earth and of the object as well as the distance the object is from the center of the earth. The acceleration at any location produced by a force acting on a mass is given by

$$g' = \frac{F}{m} = G \frac{m_e}{d^2}$$

Have students calculate their weights at the height of a satellite or at the location of the moon. Discuss the question of weightlessness in satellites.

FIGURE 8-8. The change in gravitational force with distance follows the inverse square law.

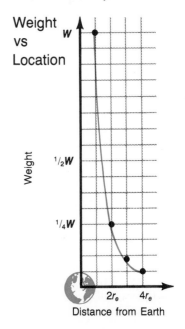

FIGURE 8-9. Vectors can be used to show Earth's gravitational field.

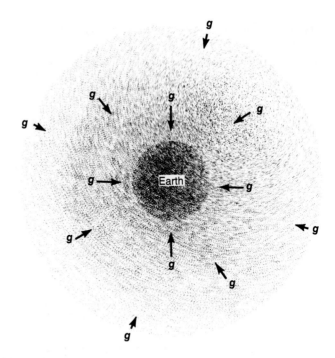

The gravitational field describes the acceleration a body would experience if placed at a certain location.

The field strength varies inversely with the square of the distance from the earth.

The effect of the gravitational force acting on the object is the acceleration of gravity, g', which is independent of the mass of the object. Every location in space has a vector g' associated with it. The magnitude of the vector at that point is the acceleration an object would experience if it were placed there. The direction of the vector g' is always pointed toward the center of the earth. The earth's gravitational field is simply a collection of all of these vectors. The value for g' at any location is called the gravitational field strength. Figure 8-9 represents the gravitational field of the earth. As can be seen, the magnitudes of the vectors decrease with greater distance from the earth. Thus, the strength of the field decreases with greater distance from the earth in the same manner.

8:7 Einstein's Concept of Gravity

Newton's law of universal gravitation allows us to calculate the magnitude of the force that exists between two masses due to their masses. It allows us also to develop the concept of a gravitational field. The law describes how gravitational force varies with mass and distance but does not attempt to explain the nature of gravitational force as such.

The concept of gravity as a peculiarity of space itself was proposed by Albert Einstein (1879-1955) during the early twentieth century. Einstein considered the effect of gravity as a characteristic of the space around a large mass rather than the mass itself. According to Einstein, space is changed in some way due to the presence of mass. The fact that

The gravitational field does not explain *why* a body is accelerated.

astronomers are better able to explain astronomical events when gravitational force is treated as a characteristic of the space around a mass, rather than of the mass itself, has given support to Einstein's theory, which is called the general theory of relativity. At the moment, our understanding is far from complete so it is not possible to explain how this change in space takes place, if indeed we will be able to explain this in the future.

Einstein's concept of gravity agrees with every experimental test.

One way to picture how space is affected by mass is to compare it to a two-dimensional rubber sheet. Each large ball on the sheet represents large massive objects (Figure 8-10). Each will form an indentation. Rolling a marble across the sheet simulates the motion of an object in space. If a marble is moving near a sagging region in the sheet, its path will curve. In the same way, the earth orbits the sun due to the space distortion that is caused by the masses of the two bodies.

Einstein said that a body, like the earth, changes space around it, and the acceleration of another body is a result of the change in space.

Many tests of Einstein's theory have consistently verified his concept of gravity as a property of space.

Perhaps the most interesting prediction is the deflection of light by massive objects. Astronomers have seen light from a distant, bright galaxy bent as it passes by a closer, dark galaxy. The result is two images of the galaxy. In the extreme case light emitted by an object can be bent back to the object. The light never escapes. Such an object, called a black-hole, has been observed due to its effect on nearby stars.

FIGURE 8-10. Matter causes space to curve just as a mass on a rubber sheet curves the sheet around it. Moving bodies, near the mass, follow the curvature of space.

a

b

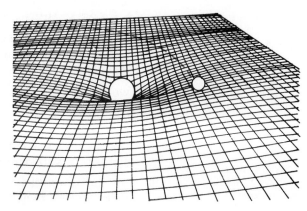

Summary

8:1   **1.** Johannes Kepler used Brahe's data to formulate three laws of planetary motion.

8:2   **2.** Newton showed that all objects exert gravitational forces on all other objects.

8:2   **3.** The law of universal gravitation states that every body in the universe attracts every other body with a force that varies directly with the product of the masses and inversely with the square of the distance between the centers of the masses.

8:3   **4.** Newton tested his inverse square law by calculating the acceleration of the moon and comparing the result with the acceleration predicted by his new law.

8:5   **5.** Using the law of universal gravitation, it can be shown that the acceleration of gravity of the earth depends on the earth and the distance from its center.

8:6   **6.** A gravitational field is a collection of vectors representing the acceleration due to gravity at all locations.

8:7   **7.** Einstein considered gravity as a property of the space around an object rather than of the object itself.

Detailed answers to all Questions and Problems are given in the Teacher's Guide at the front of this book.

Questions

1. An imaginary line from a planet to the sun sweeps out equal areas in equal times. Does the planet move faster along its orbital path when it is close to or far away from the sun?

2. The radius of the earth is about 6.40×10^3 km. A 7.20×10^3-N spacecraft travels away from the earth. What would be the weight of the spacecraft at these distances from the earth's surface?

    a. 6.40×10^3 km   **c.** 1.92×10^4 km   **e.** 3.20×10^4 km

    b. 1.28×10^4 km   **d.** 2.56×10^4 km

3. The force of gravity acting on an object near the earth's surface is proportional to the mass of the object. Why doesn't a heavy object fall faster than a light object?

4. Two 1.00-kg masses are 1.00 m apart. What is the force of attraction between them?

5. The earth and the moon are attracted to each other by gravitational force. Does the more massive earth attract the moon with a greater force than the moon attracts the earth? Explain.

6. How did Cavendish demonstrate that a gravitational force of attraction exists between two small bodies?

7. During space flight, astronauts often refer to forces as multiples of the force of gravity on the earth's surface. What would a force of 5-g mean to an astronaut?

8. Newton assumed that gravitational force acts directly between the earth and the moon. How would Einstein's view of the attraction between the two bodies differ from Newton's view?

Problems–A

1. Two bowling balls each have a mass of 6.8 kg. The spheres are located next to one another with their centers 21.8 cm apart. What gravitational force do they exert on each other?

1. 6.5×10^{-8} N

2. Two spherical balls are placed so their centers are 2.6 meters apart. The force between the two balls is 2.75×10^{-12} N. What is the mass of each ball if one ball is twice the mass of the second ball?

2. 0.37 kg, 0.75 kg

3. Use the following data to compute the gravitational force the sun exerts on Jupiter.

Mass of Earth = 6.0×10^{24} kg

Mass of Sun = 3.3×10^5 times the mass of Earth

Mass of Jupiter = 3.0×10^2 times the mass of Earth

Distance between Jupiter and Sun = 7.8×10^{11} m

3. 3.9×10^{23} N

Problems–B

1. If a small planet were located 8 times as far from the sun as the earth's distance from the sun (1.5×10^{11} m), how many years would it take the planet to orbit the sun? ($r^3/T^2 = 3.35 \times 10^{18}$ m^3/s^2)

1. 23 yrs

2. Using the fact that a 1.0 - kg mass weighs 9.8 N on the surface of the earth and the radius of the earth is roughly 6.4×10^6 m,
   a. calculate the mass of the earth.
   b. calculate the average density of the earth.

2. a. 6.0×10^{24} kg
   b. 5.5×10^3 kg/m^3

Readings

Ferris, Timothy, "Einstein's Wonderful Year." *Science 84*, November, 1984.

Fisher, Arthur, "Testing Einstein Again With a Relativity Satellite." *Popular Science*, August, 1983.

Oppenheimer, Steve, "The Search For Gravity Waves." *Science Digest*, March, 1984.

Spetz, Gary, "Detection of Gravity Waves." *The Physics Teacher*, May, 1984.

All objects in motion have momentum. Momentum is actually a calculated quantity. It is the product of the mass and the velocity of an object. The sum of the momenta of the racket and ball before impact is equal to the sum of the momenta after impact. This relationship is known as the law of conservation of momentum. Would the momentum of a tennis ball hit by a child equal that of a ball hit by an adult? How might the momentum of a tennis ball be increased?

Momentum and Its Conservation

Chapter 9 introduces the momentum form of Newton's second law of motion. The law of conservation of linear momentum is then treated as a restatement of Newton's third law of motion.

The motion produced when an unbalanced force acts on a mass can be very difficult to describe. Physicists trying to solve these problems in the 18th and 19th centuries found that they had great success when they applied conservation laws. In general, a conservation law states that some property will be conserved, or remain constant, during an interaction.

Newton defined the quantity of motion of a body as the product of its mass and velocity. We call this quantity momentum. It is a vector quantity and has the same direction as the velocity. Newton originally stated his laws in terms of the change in momentum of an object with force acting on it. When two bodies collide, the total momentum before the collision is equal to the total momentum after the collision. When a tennis racquet strikes a tennis ball, the ball leaves with a velocity that depends on the force exerted by the racquet and the length of time the racquet and ball are in contact. The total momentum of the ball and racquet before collision is equal to their total momentum after collision.

The law of conservation of momentum is one of the cornerstones of physics. It is a concept that explains much of the behavior of matter and enables us to describe interactions of matter and predict their results.

GOAL: You will gain an understanding of the law of conservation of momentum and its use in analyzing the motion of colliding objects.

9:1 Impulse and Change in Momentum

Consider a large mass and a small mass moving horizontally at the same velocity. We have already learned that a larger force must be applied to the larger mass in order to stop it in the same time interval as the smaller mass. Now consider two equal masses moving horizontally. If one is moving faster than the other, a larger force will have to be

a

b

FIGURE 9-1. A light bowling ball (a) generally has less momentum when it reaches the pins than a heavier ball (b). Notice the difference in pin action between the two photographs.

applied to it to stop it in the same time interval as the slower one. Thus it seems that the velocity and mass of a moving object are important factors in determining what is necessary to change its motion.

We can rewrite Newton's second law of motion in terms of mass and velocity. By substituting the definition of acceleration into Newton's second law equation, we find

$$\boldsymbol{F} = m\boldsymbol{a}$$

$$= \frac{m\Delta\boldsymbol{v}}{t}$$

Multiplying both sides of the equation by t, we now have the equation

$$\boxed{\boldsymbol{F}t = m\Delta\boldsymbol{v}}$$

The product of unbalanced force and the interval of time (t) that is exerted is called the **impulse**. The unit for impulse is the newton · second (N · s). This quantity is equal to the product of the mass and the change in velocity. The direction of the impulse will be in the direction of the force.

Momentum is the product of an object's mass and velocity and is represented by $\boldsymbol{p}$. The equation for momentum is

$$\boxed{\boldsymbol{p} = m\boldsymbol{v}}$$

The unit for momentum is kilogram · meter/second (kg · m/s). If an object has a change in velocity, then the momentum will also change. A change in momentum, $\Delta\boldsymbol{p}$, is the product of the mass and the change of velocity, assuming the mass is constant. The change in momentum equation is written

$$\Delta\boldsymbol{p} = m\Delta\boldsymbol{v}$$

Note that $\boldsymbol{F}t$ and $\Delta\boldsymbol{p}$ are equivalent. That is, the impulse given to an object is equal to its change in momentum.

EXAMPLE

Impulse and Change in Momentum—1

A force of 20 N acts on a 2.0-kg mass for 10 s. Compute **a** the impulse and **b** the change in velocity of the mass.

Given: $F = 20$ N

 $m = 2.0$ kg

 $t = 10$ s

Unknowns: **a.** (Ft)

  b. Δv

Basic equation: $Ft = \Delta p$

Solution:

a. $Ft = (20\text{ N})(10\text{ s})$
 $Ft = 200$ N $\cdot$ s

b. $Ft = \Delta p$
  $= m\Delta v$

$$\Delta v = \frac{Ft}{m} = \frac{200\text{ N}\cdot\text{s}}{2.0\text{ kg}}$$

$$= \frac{(200)(\text{kg}\cdot\text{m/s}^2)(\text{s})}{2.0\text{ kg}}$$

$$\Delta v = 100\text{ m/s, in the direction of }F$$

EXAMPLE

Impulse and Change in Momentum—2

A car that weighs 7840 N is accelerated from rest to a velocity of 25.0 m/s eastward by a force of 1000 N. **a.** What was the car's change in momentum? **b.** How long did the force act to change the car's momentum?

Given: $W = -7840$ N

 $v_f = 25.0$ m/s, E

 $F = 1000$ N

Unknowns: **a.** Δp

  b. t

Basic equation: $Ft = \Delta p$

FIGURE 9-2. A change in the momentum of a baseball occurs when a pitcher exerts a force on the baseball over a period of time.

Solution:

a. $\Delta p = m\Delta v$

$$= \frac{W}{g}(v_f - v_i)$$

$$= \frac{-7840 \text{ N}}{-9.81 \text{ m/s}^2}(25.0 \text{ m/s} - 0)$$

$$= \frac{(7840 \text{ kg m/s}^2)(25.0 \text{ m/s})}{9.81 \text{ m/s}^2}$$

$\Delta p = 2.00 \times 10^4 \text{ kg} \cdot \text{m/s, E}$

b. $Ft = \Delta p$

$$t = \frac{\Delta p}{F}$$

$$= \frac{2.00 \times 10^4 \text{ kg} \cdot \text{m/s}}{1 \times 10^3 \text{ N}}$$

$$= \frac{2.00 \times 10^4 \text{ kg} \cdot \text{m/s}}{1 \times 10^3 \text{ kg} \cdot \text{m/s}^2}$$

$t = 20 \text{ s}$

Problems

1. a. 60.0 N · s
   b. 20.0 m/s

1. A force of 6.00 N acts on a 3.00-kg object for 10.0 s.
   a. What is the object's change in momentum?
   b. What is its change in velocity?

2. 1.21 × 10³ N

2. What force is needed to bring a 1.10×10^3-kg car moving at 22.0 m/s to a halt in 20.0 s?

3. 1.00 × 10² s

3. A net force of 2.00×10^3 N acts on a rocket of mass 1.00×10^3 kg. How long does it take this force to increase the rocket's velocity from 0.0 m/s to 2.00×10^2 m/s?

4. a. 5.50 × 10³ N · s
   b. 91.7 N

4. A snowmobile has a mass of 2.50×10^2 kg. A constant force acts upon it for 60.0 s. The snowmobile's initial velocity is 6.00 m/s and its final velocity is 28.0 m/s.
   a. What is its change in momentum?
   b. What is the magnitude of the force that acts upon it?

5. a. 1.60 × 10³ kg
   b. 3.20 × 10⁴ N · s
   c. 3.20 × 10⁴ N · s
   d. 50.0 s

5. A car weighing 15 680 N and moving at 20.0 m/s is acted upon by a 6.40×10^2 N force until it is brought to a halt.
   a. What is the car's mass?
   b. What is its initial momentum?
   c. What is the change in the car's momentum?
   d. How long does the braking force act on the car to bring it to a halt?

6. a. 2.04 × 10⁴ N · s
   b. 3.00 × 10² N

6. The velocity of a 6.00×10^2-kg mass is changed from 10.0 m/s to 44.0 m/s in 68.0 s by an applied, constant force.
   a. What change in momentum does the force produce?
   b. What is the magnitude of the force?

7. 1.1 × 10² m/s

7. What is the final velocity of a rocket of mass 2.0×10^4 kg, starting from rest, if a net force of 1.5×10^5 N acts upon it for 15.0 s?

9:2 Newton's Third Law and Momentum

Newton's three laws of motion were introduced in Chapter 5. The third law of motion is called the law of action and reaction. It relates the forces that two objects exert on each other. Newton's third law is a way

FIGURE 9-3. When a racquet hits a tennis ball, both the ball and the racquet are accelerated. The forces of the racquet on the ball and the ball on the racquet are evident in the photograph.

of stating the law of conservation of momentum. Newton's second law of motion states that when one object exerts a force on another, the second object accelerates. But, a fact often overlooked is that the object causing the force also accelerates. For example, a tennis ball is hit with a racquet. The ball is accelerated; its momentum increases. Likewise, the racquet is accelerated, but in a direction opposite to the ball. While striking the ball, the racquet slows down; its momentum decreases. The force exerted on the racquet by the ball gives the racquet negative acceleration. According to the third law, exactly equal and opposite forces appear whenever two objects interact. The equal and opposite forces act for the same time; one never exists without the other. Thus the impulse, Ft, given to the ball must be exactly the same as the impulse given to the racquet but in the opposite direction.

Newton's third law is equivalent to the conservation of momentum.

A single force cannot exist. Every force on a body is accompanied by an equal and opposite force on another body.

for Object A		for Object B
Ft	$=$	$-Ft$
$m\Delta v$	$=$	$-m\Delta v$
Δp_A	$=$	$-\Delta p_B$

The momentum gained by one body in an interaction is equal to the momentum lost by the other body.

It follows from this equation that in any interaction a gain in momentum by one object occurs only through the loss of the same amount of momentum by a second object.

9:3 Law of Conservation of Momentum

An isolated system is a system that has no net external force acting on it. The law of conservation of momentum always holds for any isolated system. For this reason, scientists consider this law to be of great importance. It helps them to understand what happens during all

A system is isolated if no net external force acts on it.

collisions. Because all interactions are collisions in one form or another, the law of conservation of momentum is a powerful tool.

The **law of conservation of momentum** can be stated as follows. *The total momentum of an isolated system does not change.* That is, the initial momentum of an isolated system is equal to the final momentum. This follows from Newton's third law of motion. For an isolated system consisting of objects A and B, recall from Section 9:2 that,

$$\Delta p_A = -\Delta p_B$$

If p_A' and p_B' represent the final momenta of A and B

$$p_A' - p_A = -(p_B' - p_A)$$
$$p_A' + p_B' = p_A + p_B$$

The final momentum of the system is equal to the initial momentum of the system.

$$p_A + p_B = p_A' + p_B'$$
$$m_A v_A + m_B v_B = m_A v_A' + m_B v_B'$$

Consider two freight cars A and B of equal mass (3.0×10^5 kg) shown in Figure 9-4. Car A is moving slowly at 2.2 m/s. Car B is at rest. The two cars collide and are coupled together. The law of conservation of momentum will allow us to predict the resulting velocity of the two cars.

Because the masses are equal, $m_A = m_B = m$. Also, since car B is at rest, its velocity, v_B, is zero. The equation for conservation of momentum is

$$p_A + p_B = p_A' + p_B'$$
$$m_A v_A + m_B v_B = m_A v_A' + m_B v_B'$$
$$m v_A = m v_A' + m v_B'$$

After the collision, the coupled cars move with the same velocity $v_A' = v_B' = v'$.   Therefore,

2.2 m/s

A   B

A   B

1.1 m/s

A   B

$$mv_A = mv' + mv'$$
$$mv_A = 2mv'$$
$$v_A = 2v'$$
$$v_i' = \frac{1}{2}v_A$$

After the collision, the two cars move with half the velocity of the moving car (car A) before the collision.

The total momentum of the system does not change, $\Delta p = 0$. The initial momentum of the system consists of the momenta of cars A and B before the collision.

$$p_A + p_B = m_A v_A + m_B v_B$$
$$= (3.0 \times 10^5 \text{ kg})(2.2 \text{ m/s}) + (3.0 \times 10^5 \text{ kg})(0 \text{ m/s})$$
$$p_A + p_B = 6.6 \times 10^5 \text{ kg} \cdot \text{m/s, in the direction of } A\text{'s original motion.}$$

The final momentum consisted of the momenta of cars A and B after the collision.

$$p_A' + p_B' = m_A v_A' + m_B v_B'$$
$$= (3.0 \times 10^5 \text{ kg})(1.1 \text{ m/s}) + (3.0 \times 10^5 \text{ kg})(1.1 \text{ m/s})$$
$$p_A' + p_B' = 6.6 \times 10^5 \text{ kg} \cdot \text{m/s, in the direction of } A\text{'s original motion.}$$

A second consequence of the conservation of momentum is that the change in momentum of one object in a two-object system must yield an equal and opposite change in the momentum of the other. The change in momentum of car A is

$$\Delta p_A = p_A' - p_A = m_A v_A' - m_A v_A$$
$$= (3.0 \times 10^5 \text{ kg})(1.1 \text{ m/s}) - (3.0 \times 10^5 \text{ kg})(2.2 \text{ m/s})$$
$$\Delta p_A = -3.3 \times 10^{-5} \text{ kg} \cdot \text{m/s}$$

The change in momentum of car B is

$$\Delta p_B = p_B' - p_B = m_B v_B' - m_B v_B$$
$$= (3.0 \times 10^5 \text{ kg})(1.1 \text{ m/s}) - (3.0 \times 10^5 \text{ kg})(0 \text{ m/s})$$
$$\Delta p_B = 3.3 \times 10^5 \text{ kg} \cdot \text{m/s}$$

In this case, the momentum "lost" by car A (-3.3×10^5 kg $\cdot$ m/s) is equal to the momentum "gained" by car B ($+3.3 \times 10^5$ kg $\cdot$ m/s).

Momentum is only transferred in a collision. Total momentum is constant.

Note carefully that there are two important aspects of any collision. First, the total momentum of the system is the same before and after the collision.

$$p_1 + p_2 = p_1' + p_2'$$

Second, in any collision within an isolated system, momentum is transferred from one object to another.

$$\Delta p_1 = \Delta p_2$$

However, the total momentum of the system remains constant.

FIGURE 9-5. Momentum is transferred when billiard balls collide. However, some momentum is lost due to friction between the balls and the table. If we consider the billiard balls and table together as a system, momentum is conserved.

EXAMPLE

Conservation of Momentum—1

A steel glider of mass 0.50 kg moves along an air track with a velocity of 0.75 m/s. It collides with a second steel glider of mass 1.0 kg moving in the same direction at a speed of 0.38 m/s. After the collision, the first glider continues with a velocity of 0.35 m/s. What is the velocity of the second glider after the collision?

Given: $m_1 = 0.50$ kg   **Unknown:** v_2'

$v_1 = 0.75$ m/s   **Basic equation:** $p_1 + p_2 = p_1' + p_2'$

$m_2 = 1.0$ kg

$v_2 = 0.38$ m/s

$v_1' = 0.35$ m/s

Solution:

$$p_2' = p_1 + p_2 - p_1'$$

$$m_2 v_2' = m_1 v_1 + m_2 v_2 - m_1 v_1'$$

$$v_2' = \frac{m_1 v_1 + m_2 v_2 - m_1 v_1'}{m_2}$$

$$= \frac{(0.50 \text{ kg})(.75 \text{ m/s}) + (1.0 \text{ kg})(.38 \text{ m/s}) - (0.50 \text{ kg})(.35 \text{ m/s})}{1.0 \text{ kg}}$$

$$= \frac{0.58 \text{ kg} \cdot \text{m/s}}{1.0 \text{ kg}}$$

$$v_2' = 0.58 \text{ m/s}$$

Problems

8. Moving at 20.0 m/s, a car of mass 7.00×10^2 kg collides with a stationary truck of mass 1.40×10^3 kg. If the two vehicles interlock as a result of the collision, what is the velocity of the car-truck system?

9. A bullet of mass 50.0 g strikes a wooden block of mass 5.0 kg and becomes embedded in the block. The block and bullet then flies off at 10.0 m/s. What was the original velocity of the bullet?

10. A 0.50-kg ball traveling at 6.0 m/s collides head-on with a 1.00-kg ball moving in the opposite direction at a velocity of -12.0 m/s. The 0.50-kg ball moves away at -14 m/s after the collision. Find the velocity of the 1.00-kg ball after the collision.

11. A plastic ball of mass 0.200 kg moves with a velocity of 0.30 m/s. This plastic ball collides with a second plastic ball of mass 0.100 kg that is moving along the same line at a velocity of 0.10 m/s. After the collision, the velocity of the 0.100-kg ball is 0.26 m/s. What is the velocity of the second ball?

8. 6.67 m/s in its original direction

9. 1.0×10^3 m/s

10. -2.0 m/s

11. 0.22 m/s in its original direction

9:4 Internal and External Forces

The law of conservation of momentum tells us that an external force, one originating outside the system, is needed to change the momentum of the system. An internal force, one that originates within the system, can never change the momentum of the system.

Consider the two skaters shown in Figure 9-6 as an isolated system. Skater A has a mass of 60.0 kg and Skater B has a mass of 30.0 kg. The skaters are standing still on smooth ice, so the force of friction is negligible. The initial momentum of the system is zero. Skater A

An internal force cannot change the total momentum of a system.

$v_1 = -0.20$ m/s $\qquad$ $v_2 = 0.40$ m/s

FIGURE 9-6. The internal forces exerted by these skaters cannot change the total momentum of the system.

pushes Skater B away. The equation for the conservation of momentum for this situation is

$$p_A + p_B = p_A' + p_B'$$
$$0 = p_A' + p_B'$$
$$p_A' = -p_B'$$
$$m_A v_A' = -m_B v_B'$$
$$v_A' = -\frac{m_B}{m_A} v_B'$$
$$v_A' = -\frac{30.0 \text{ kg}}{60.0 \text{ kg}} v_B'$$
$$v_A' = -\frac{1}{2} v_B'$$

Note that although the magnitude of the velocity of the larger skater is half that of the smaller skater, the magnitudes of their momenta are equal. The larger skater also moves in the opposite direction of the smaller one. The vector sum of the momenta of A and B after the interaction is zero.

Note also that the momentum of each skater is changed. But, the total momentum of the system does not change. The force between the two skaters was an internal force in the two-skater system. On the other hand, if we consider the system to be only one of the skaters, the force would be an external force. Classifying a force as internal or external depends on how we define the boundaries of the system.

Define the system carefully! A force can be either internal or external depending on the definition of the system.

To better understand the law of conservation of momentum, consider a system consisting of many particles, such as the molecules in a small container of gas. The gas particles are constantly colliding and changing one another's momentum. However, each particle can gain only the momentum lost by another particle during a collision. Therefore, the total momentum of the system does not change. The total momentum of an isolated system is constant.

Suppose we consider all the particles in the universe as one large system. Then all forces would be internal forces and there could never be a change in the total momentum of the universe. This reasoning follows the law of conservation of momentum in its broadest sense—the total momentum of the universe is constant.

EXAMPLE

Conservation of Momentum—2

What is the recoil velocity of a 1.20×10^3-kg launcher if it projects a 20.0-kg mass at a velocity of 6.00×10^2 m/s?

Given: $m_1 = 2.00 \times 10^1$ kg

$m_2 = 1.20 \times 10^3$ kg

$v_1' = 6.00 \times 10^2$ m/s

$v_1 = v_2 = 0$ m/s

Unknown: v_2'

Basic equation: $p_1 + p_2 = p_1' + p_2'$

Solution: $p_1 + p_2 = p'_1 + p'_2$

$$m_1v_1 + m_2v_2 = m_1v'_1 + m_2v'_2$$

$$m_2v'_2 = m_1v_1 + m_2v_2 - m_1v'_1$$

$$v'_2 = \frac{m_1v_1 + m_2v_2 - m_1v'_1}{m_2}$$

Because v_1 and $v_2 = 0$

$$v'_2 = \frac{-(2.00 \times 10^1 \text{ kg})(6.00 \times 10^2 \text{ m/s})}{1.20 \times 10^3 \text{ kg}}$$

$$= \frac{-1.2 \times 10^4 \text{ kg} \cdot \text{m/s}}{1.2 \times 10^3 \text{ kg}}$$

$$v'_2 = -1.0 \times 10^1 \text{ m/s}$$

The negative sign indicates the launcher moves in a direction opposite the moving projectile.

Problems

12. A 40.0-kg projectile leaves a 2.00×10^3-kg launcher with a velocity of $+8.00 \times 10^2$ m/s. What is the recoil velocity of the launcher?

12. 16.0 m/s in the opposite direction

13. Upon launching, a 4.0-kg model rocket expels 50.0 g of oxidized fuel from its exhaust at an average velocity of 6.00×10^2 m/s. What is the vertical velocity of the model rocket after the launch? (Disregard gravitational effects.)

13. 7.5 m/s upward

14. Two campers dock a canoe. One camper steps onto the dock. This camper has a mass of 80.0 kg and moves forward at 4.0 m/s. With what speed and direction will the canoe and the other camper move if their combined mass is 110 kg?

14. 2.9 m/s in the opposite direction

15. A thread holds two carts together on a frictionless surface as in Figure 9-7. A compressed spring acts upon the carts. After the thread is burned, the 1.5-kg cart moves with a velocity of 27 cm/s to the left. What is the velocity of the 4.5-kg cart?

15. 9.1 cm/s to the right

1.5 kg   4.5 kg

F

FIGURE 9-7. Use for Problem 15.

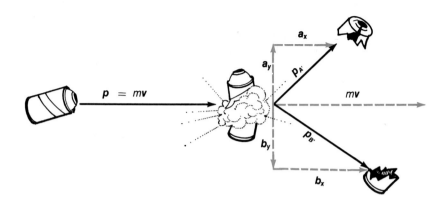

FIGURE 9-8. The momentum of the can before it explodes is the same as the sum of the momenta of the pieces of the can after it explodes.

16. 5.0 m/s backwards

Momentum is conserved even if motion occurs in two or three dimensions.

16. A 5.00 -g projectile is launched with a horizontal velocity of 647 m/s from a 4.65-kg launcher moving at 2.00 m/s. What is the velocity of the launcher after the projectile is launched?

9:5 Conservation of Momentum in General

Thus far, our treatment of the law of conservation of momentum has covered only interactions that take place along the same line. But the law of conservation of momentum holds for all interactions. Momentum, a vector quantity, is conserved regardless of the directions of the particles before and after they collide.

Figure 9-8 shows a spray can exploding after being thrown from a spacecraft into the near-vacuum conditions of space. We will assume that the can breaks into only two pieces. Before the explosion, the momentum of the can is represented by the vector p. After the explosion, the momenta of the two pieces are represented by p_A' and p_B'. The vertical components of p_A' and p_B' are equal and opposite and have a vector sum of zero, because the can had no vertical momentum initially. The vector sum of the horizontal components of p_A' and p_B' is equal to the original momentum of the can.

FIGURE 9-9. The vector sum of the momenta is constant.

As shown in Figure 9-9, the vectors representing the momenta of the two pieces can be added. The resultant is the original momentum of the can. Even if the can breaks into many pieces, the vector sum of the momenta of all the pieces will still be equal to the initial momentum of the can.

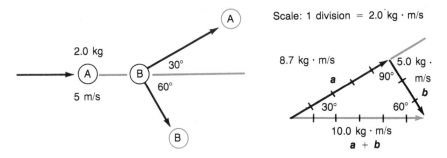

Scale: 1 division = 2.0 kg · m/s

FIGURE 9-10. The vector sum of a and b equals the initial momentum of A.

The total momentum is the vector sum of the momenta of all the pieces of a system.

Teaching suggestion: Have students use tracing paper to copy the momentum vectors of Figure 9–9. Then have them demonstrate that momentum is conserved.

EXAMPLE

Conservation of Momentum in Two Dimensions

A 2.0-kg ball is moving at a velocity of 5.0 m/s. It collides with a stationary ball also of mass 2.0 kg (Figure 9-10). After the collision, the first ball moves off in a direction 30.0° to the left of its original direction. The second ball moves off in a direction 90.0° to the right of ball A's final direction. **a.** Draw a vector diagram to find the momentum of the first ball and of the second ball after the collision. **b.** What is the speed of each ball after collision?

Given: $m_A = 2.00$ kg   **Unknowns:** $p_A, p_A', p_B', v_A', v_B'$

   $v_A = 5.0$ m/s   **Basic equation:** $p_A + p_B = p_A' + p_B'$

   $m_B = 2.00$ kg

   $v_B = 0.0$ m/s

Solution:
The initial momentum of the system is $p_A + p_B$. Substituting the values m_A, v_A, m_B, and v_B into the equations yields 1.0×10^1 kg m/s, the value of p_A. The magnitude of p_A is the hypotenuse of a right triangle. With respect to the 30° angle, p_B' is the opposite side, and p_A' the adjacent side. Solving for p_B' and p_A' gives the magnitudes of the momenta of ball B and ball A after interaction has taken place.

ball A | ball B

$$\cos 30° = \frac{p_A'}{p_A}$$ $$\sin 30° = \frac{p_B'}{p_A}$$

$$p_A' = p_A (\cos 30°)$$ $$p_B' = p_A (\sin 30°)$$

$$= (1.0 \times 10^1 \text{ kg} \cdot \text{m/s})(0.866)$$ $$= (1.0 \times 10^1 \text{ kg m/s})(0.500)$$

$$p_A' = 8.7 \text{ kg} \cdot \text{m/s}$$ $$p_B' = 5.0 \text{ kg} \cdot \text{m/s}$$

To find the magnitude of the velocities of A and B after the collision, use the momentum equation $p = mv$.

$$p_A' = m_A v_A'$$

$$v_A' = \frac{p_A'}{m_A}$$

$$= \frac{8.7 \text{ kg} \cdot \text{m/s}}{2.0 \text{ kg}}$$

$$v_A' = 4.4 \text{ m/s}$$

$$p_B' = m_B v_B'$$

$$v_B' = \frac{p_B'}{m_B}$$

$$= \frac{5.0 \text{ kg} \cdot \text{m/s}}{2.0 \text{ kg}}$$

$$v_B' = 2.5 \text{ m/s}$$

Problems

17. Ball A of mass 5.0 kg moves at a speed of 4.0 m/s and collides with a second stationary ball B, also of mass 5.0 kg. After the collision, ball A moves off in the direction 45° to the left of its original direction. Ball B moves off in the direction 45° to the right of ball A's original direction.

a. Draw a vector diagram and determine the momentum of ball A and of ball B after the collision.

b. What is the velocity of each ball after the collision?

18. A 6.0-kg object, A, moves at a velocity of 3.0 m/s. It collides with a second 6.0-kg object, B, at rest. After the collision, A moves off in the direction 50.0° to the left of its original direction and B moves off in the direction 40.0° to the right of A's original direction.

a. Draw a vector diagram and determine the momentum of object A and of object B.

b. What is the velocity of each object after the collision?

19. A stationary billiard ball of mass 0.17 kg is struck by a second, identical billiard ball moving at 10.0 m/s. After the collision, the second ball moves off in a direction 60.0° to the left of its original direction. The stationary ball moves off in a direction 30.0° to the right of the second ball's original direction. What is the velocity of each ball after the collision?

17. a. 14 kg · m/s for both balls
    b. For ball A:
       v = 2.8 m/s, 45° to the left
          of its original direction
       For ball B:
       v = 2.8 m/s, 45° to the
          right of its original direc-
          tion

18. a. a = 12 kg · m/s
       b = 14 kg · m/s
    b. For A: v = 2.0 m/s
       For B: v = 2.3 m/s

19. For first ball:
    v = 8.8 m/s, 30° to the right of
       second ball's original
       direction
    For second ball:
    v = 5.0 m/s, 60° to the left of its
       original direction

FIGURE 9-11. Use with Problem 19.

Summary

1. Momentum is the product of the mass of an object and its velocity.   9:1
2. The change of momentum of an object is equal to the impulse that acts on it.   9:1
3. Newton's third law of motion is a statement of the law of conservation of momentum.   9:2
4. The law of conservation of momentum states that in an isolated system whenever two objects interact, the total momentum is the same before and after the interaction.   9:3
5. Only an external unbalanced force can change the total momentum of a system.   9:4
6. The sum of the momenta of any closed system cannot change.   9:4

Detailed answers to all Questions and Problems are given in the Teacher's Guide at the front of this book.

Questions

1. A spacecraft in outer space accelerates by firing rockets. How can the hot gases escaping from the rocket propel the craft if there is nothing in space for these gases to push against?

2. If only an external force can change the momentum of an object, how can the internal force of a car's brakes bring the car to a stop?

3. During a "space walk" the rope connecting an astronaut to the space capsule has broken. Using a pistol, the astronaut manages to get back to the capsule. Explain.

4. Billiard ball A travels across a pool table and collides with a stationary billiard ball B. The mass of ball B is equal to the mass of ball A. After the collision, ball A is at rest. What must be true of ball B?

5. Is it possible for a bullet to have the same momentum as a truck? Explain.

6. Newton's third law of motion states that for every action force there is an equal and opposite reaction force. The gravitational force acting on a falling object is its weight. If we recognize the pull of the earth on the object as one force, what is the reaction force?

7. Carlos constructed a sail in the center of a skateboard. He then mounted a small battery-powered fan near the end of the board and directed the flow of air toward the sail. Describe the motion of the board when the fan is in operation.

FIGURE 9-12. Use with Question 7.

Problems–A	

1. A force of 30.0 N is applied to a hockey puck for 0.80 s. Calculate the magnitude of the impulse.

2. Assume the puck in Problem 1 has a mass of 0.20 kg and is at rest before the impulse acts upon it. With what speed does it move across the ice after the 0.80-s period?

3. A 1.50×10^3-kg car leaves a parking lot. Thirty seconds later it is moving along a highway at 72 km/h.
   a.   What is the car's change in momentum?
   b.   What average force does the motor produce to bring about this change in momentum?

4. A force of 8.0 N acts on a 2.0-kg mass for 5.0 s.
   a.   What is the change in momentum of the mass?
   b.   What is the change in the velocity of the mass?

5. The mass of a car is 1.60×10^3 kg. The car's velocity is 2.0 m/s.
   a.   What is its momentum?
   b.   How long must a force of 8.00×10^2 N act on the car to give it this momentum? (Assume the direction of the force and the direction of the motion are the same.)

6. A plastic ball of mass 1.00×10^2 g moves with a speed of 20.0 cm/s. A second plastic ball of mass 40.0 g is moving along the same path at 10.0 cm/s. The two balls collide. After the collision, the 1.00×10^2-g mass has a velocity of 15.0 cm/s in its original direction. What is the velocity (speed and direction) of the 40.0-g ball after the collision?

Problems–B	

1. A space probe of mass 7600 kg is traveling through space at 120 m/s. Mission Control determines that a change in course of 30.0° is necessary and by electronic communication instructs the probe to fire rockets perpendicular to its direction of motion. If the escaping gas leaves the craft's rockets at an average speed of 3200 m/s, what is the mass of the gas mission Control should allow to be expelled?

2. A brick that weighs 24.5 N is released from rest on a 1.00-m, frictionless plane inclined at an angle of 30.0°. The brick slides down the incline and strikes a second brick that weighs 36.8 N.
   a.   If the two bricks stick together, with what initial speed will they move along the table?
   b.   If the force of friction acting on the two bricks is 5.0 N, what time will elapse before the bricks come to rest?
   c.   How far will the two bricks slide before coming to rest?

FIGURE 9-13. Use with Problem B-2.

3. A glass ball of mass 5.0 g moves at a velocity of 20.0 m/s. The ball collides with a second glass ball of mass 10.0 g, which is moving along the same line with a velocity of 10.0 m/s. After the collision, the 5.0-g ball is still moving at a velocity of 8.0 m/s.

  a. What is the change of momentum of the 5.0-g ball?
  b. What is the change of momentum of the 10.0-g ball?

3. a. $-6.0 \times 10^1 \text{g} \cdot \text{m/s}$
   b. $6.0 \times 10^1 \text{g} \cdot \text{m/s}$

Readings

Angier, Natalie, "To Build a Better Bridge." *Discover*, July, 1983.

Bernardo, Stephanie, "The Physics of the Sweet Spot." *Science Digest*, May, 1984.

Carter, W. E., "Variations in the Rotation of the Earth." *Science*, June 1, 1984.

Mark, Robert, "Gothic Structural Experimentation." *Scientific American*, November, 1984.

Stroink, G., "Superball Problem." *The Physics Teacher*, October, 1983.

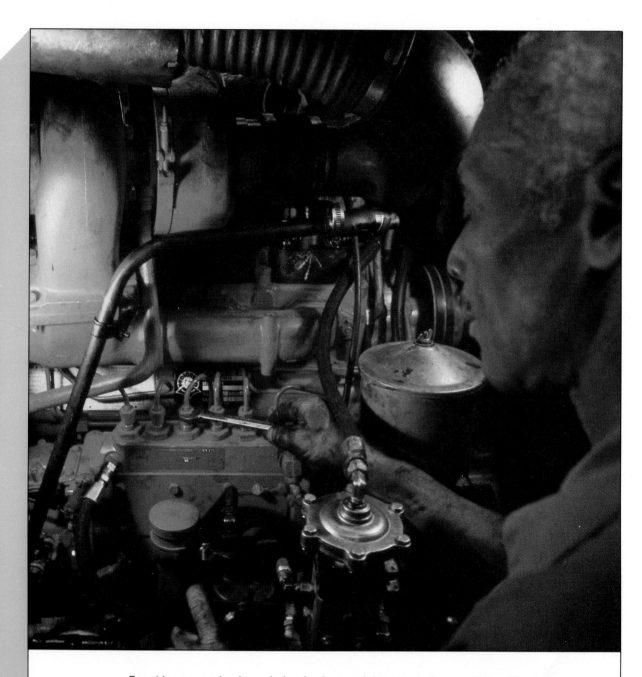

Repairing an engine is work. In physics, work is not merely an activity where one exerts strength. Work is a physical quantity. The amount of work done in tightening the bolt can be calculated. Power is also a physical quantity. It is not merely a measure of one's strength, but the rate at which work is done. What factors affect the amount of work required to tighten the bolt? How does this master mechanic use machines to help him in his job?

Work, Power, and Simple Machines

Chapter 10 introduces the concepts of work, simple machines, and efficiency. Work is treated as the product of the component of the force in the direction of motion and the distance through which the object moves.

In everyday conversation, the words work and power have very general meanings. However, these terms have specific meanings in physics. Work and power are measurable quantities.

Work is performed every time you exert force and move an object. You are doing work when you lift the pull-tab of a can of soda, push a plate across a table, or climb stairs. Sometimes devices, called machines, are used to make work easier to perform. These machines can be as simple as a screwdriver or as complex as a tractor. By measuring how quickly work is done, we can determine power—your power or that of a machine.

Goal: You will gain understanding of the concepts of work and power.

10:1 Work

When a person lifts a chair, pushes a lawnmower, or shovels snow work is done. All examples of work have one thing in common—a force acts through a distance. Work is done only when an object moves some distance due to an applied force. Work is the product of the applied force and the distance through which an object moves in the direction of the force. Work is expressed as

Work is the product of the force and the displacement of the object in the direction of the force.

$$W = Fd$$

165

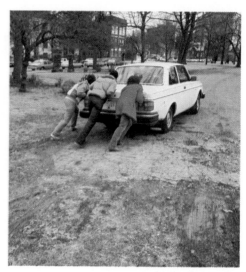

FIGURE 10-1. In order to do work on the car, the car must move. Work is done only when an object moves some distance due to an applied force.

Work is done only if an object is moved in the direction of the force.

One joule, the unit of work, is one newton-meter.

W is the work, F is the net force, and d is the displacement. Work is a scalar quantity even though force and displacement are vectors. Note that this definition includes a force and a displacement. If you push against a car for hours and do not move it, you may become very tired. However, you have done no work on the car. The force must cause motion if work is to be done.

The SI unit of work is the **joule** (jool). A joule is equivalent to a force of one newton applied through a displacement of one meter. That is

$$1 \text{ joule (J)} = 1 \text{ newton-meter (N} \cdot \text{m)}$$

Figure 10-2 shows the force-displacement graph of a box being pushed across the floor. A constant force of 20 N was required to move the box 4.0 m. The work done on the box is 80 J. The shaded area under the curve of Figure 10-2 is equal to 20 N × 4.0 m, or 80 J. The area under the curve of a force-displacement graph is equivalent to the work done by the force.

Force versus Displacement

FIGURE 10-2. A force-displacement graph of a box being pushed across a floor.

EXAMPLE

Work

A student pushes on a desk with a horizontal force of 120 N and moves the desk 2.0 m directly across the floor. How much work is done?

Given: F = 120 N **Unknown:** Work (W)

d = 2.0 m **Basic equation:** $W = Fd$

Solution: $W = Fd$

$$= (120 \text{ N})(2.0 \text{ m})$$
$$= 240 \text{ N} \cdot \text{m}$$
$$W = 240 \text{ J}$$

Problems

1. A force of 8.00×10^2 N is needed to push a car across a lot. Two students push the car 40.0 m. How much work is done?

2. How much work is done in lifting a 60.0-kg crate a vertical distance of 10.0 m?

3. A person carries a 34-N package from the ground floor to the fifth floor of an office building, or 15 m upward. How much work does the person do to move the package?

4. What work is done to lift a 49-kg crate a distance of 10.0 m?

5. A worker carries cement blocks, weighing 1.50×10^2 N each, up a ladder onto a scaffold 8.00 m high. The worker carries them at a rate of 2 blocks per minute. How much work is done by the worker in
   a. 10.0 min?
   b. 1.00 h?

6. The hammer of a pile driver has a mass of 1.00×10^2 kg. The machine's engine lifts it to a height of 5.00 m every 10.0 s.
   a. How much work must the machine do to lift the hammer?
   b. How much work does the machine do in 1.00 min?

1. 3.20×10^4 J

2. 5890 J

3. 510 J

4. 4.8×10^3 J

5. a. 2.40×10^4 J
   b. 1.44×10^5 J

6. a. 4.90×10^3 J
   b. 2.94×10^4 J

10:2 Work and the Direction of Force

If a net force is applied to an object at an angle with the direction of motion, the component of the net force that acts in the direction of motion is the force that does the work. For example, if you pull a bobsled across the snow, the force that is doing the work on the sled is the horizontal component (F_x) of the force in the rope. In Figure 10-3, a 125-N force (F) is applied to the handle of a lawn mower. The vertical component of the force (F_y) is balanced by the upward push of the ground. The force causing the motion is F_x.

Only the component of the force in the direction of the motion does work.

a

$F_x = F \cos 25.0°$
    $= (125 \text{ N}) (0.906)$
$F = 113 \text{ N}$

FIGURE 10-3. If a force is applied to the mower at an angle, the net force doing the work is the component that acts in the direction of the motion.

b

The value of the component of the force **F** acting in the direction of motion is found by multiplying the force **F** by the cosine of the angle between **F** and the direction of motion.

$$W = (F)(\cos \theta)(d)$$
$$= Fd \cos \theta$$

EXAMPLE

Work—Force and Displacement at an Angle

A sailor pulls a boat along a dock by a rope held at an angle of 60.0° with the horizontal. How much work is done if the sailor exerts a force of 2.50×10^2 N on the rope and pulls the boat 30.0 m?

Given: $\theta = 60.0°$ **Unknown:** W

$F = 2.50 \times 10^2$ N   **Basic equation:** $W = Fd \cos \theta$

$d = 30.0$ m

Solution: $W = Fd \cos \theta$

$= (2.50 \times 10^2 \text{ N})(3.0 \times 10^1 \text{ m})(\cos 60.0°)$

$= (2.50 \times 10^2 \text{ N})(3.0 \times 10^1 \text{ m})(0.500)$

$= 3.75 \times 10^3 \text{ N} \cdot \text{m}$

$W = 3.75 \times 10^3 \text{ J}$

Problems

7. 6.3×10^3 J

7. A force of 6.00×10^2 N is applied to a metal box to pull it 15.0 m across a floor. The rope used to pull the box is held at an angle of 46° with the floor. How much work is done?

8. A person uses a rope to pull a 1.00×10^3 kg boat 50.0 m along a wharf. The rope makes an angle of 45° with the horizontal. If a force of 40.0 N is used to move the boat, how much work is done?

8. 1.4×10^3 J

9. It takes 1.20×10^4 J of work to pull a loaded sled weighing 8.00×10^2 N a distance of 2.00×10^2 m. To do this, a force of 1.20×10^2 N is exerted on a rope, which makes an angle with the horizontal. At what angle is the rope held?

9. 60.0°

10. A cable attached to a small tractor pulls a barge through a canal lock. The cable makes an angle of 30.0° with the direction in which the barge is moving and has a tension of 2.50×10^3 N.

   a. What force moves the barge along the lock?
   b. If the lock is 2.00×10^2 m long, how much work is done to get the barge through the lock?

10. a. 2.17×10^3 N
    b. 4.34×10^5 J

11. Due to friction, a force of 4.00×10^2 N is needed to drag a wooden crate across a floor. The rope tied to the crate is held at an angle of 56.0° with the horizontal.

   a. How much tension is needed in the rope to move the crate?
   b. What work is done if the crate is dragged 25.0 m?

11. a. 7.15×10^2 N
    b. 1.00×10^4 J

12. A student librarian picks up a .95 N book from the floor to a height of 1.25 m. She carries the book 8.0 m to the shelves and places the book on a shelf that is 2.0 m high. How much work has been done on the book?

12. 1.9 J

10:3 Power

The concept of power is important in physics because it allows us to measure the rate at which work is done. Power is the rate of doing work—that is, power is the work done in a unit time interval. Mathematically, power can be found by the following equation.

Power is the rate at which work is done.

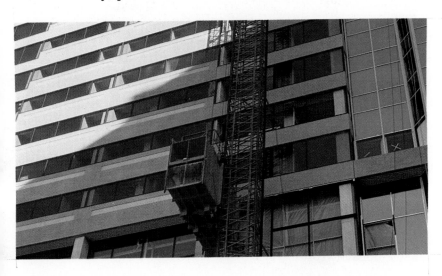

FIGURE 10-4. The power of the electric motor that moves this elevator can be calculated.

$$P = \frac{W}{t}$$

Power is measured in **watts** (W). A watt is one joule per second. A machine that does work at a rate of one joule per second has a power of one watt. Since a joule is a newton-meter, a watt is a newton-meter per second. A watt is a relatively small unit of power. For example, the power needed to lift a glass of water in a normal way is about one watt. Thus, power is often measured in kilowatts (kW). A kilowatt is 1000 watts.

Justify this estimate. What force, distance, and time is used to obtain the value of 1 W?

A 12-oz glass weighs 3.3 N. It is lifted about 0.30 m in about 1.0 s.

EXAMPLE
Power

An electric motor hoists an elevator (weighing 1.20×10^4 N) 9.00 m in 15.0 s.   **a.** What is the power of the motor in watts?   **b.** in kilowatts?

Given: $F = 1.20 \times 10^4$ N   **Unknown:** Power (P)

$d = 9.00$ m

$t = 15.0$ s   **Basic equation:** $P = \dfrac{W}{t}$

Solution:

a. $P = \dfrac{W}{t}$ **b.** $P = 7.20 \times 10^3 \, W \times \dfrac{(kW)}{(10^3 \, W)}$

$\quad = \dfrac{Fd}{t}$ $P = 7.20$ kW

$\quad = \dfrac{(1.20 \times 10^4 \text{ N})(9.00 \text{ m})}{(1.5 \times 10^1 \text{ s})}$

$\quad = 7.20 \times 10^3 \dfrac{\text{N} \cdot \text{m}}{\text{s}}$

$\quad = 7.20 \times 10^3 \dfrac{\text{J}}{\text{s}}$

$\quad P = 7.20 \times 10^3$ W

Problems

13. 2.00×10^3 W, 2.00 kW

13. A box that weighs 1.00×10^3 N is lifted a distance of 20.0 m straight up by a rope and pulley system. The work is done in 10.0 s. What is the power developed in watts and in kilowatts?

14. 9.00 kW

14. A diesel engine lifts a 2.25×10^3-N hammer of a pile driver 20.0 m in 5.00 s. What is the power of the engine in kilowatts?

15. a. 960 J
    b. 5.9×10^3 J

15. A rock climber wears a 12.0-kg knapsack while scaling a cliff. After 30.0 minutes, the climber is 8.2 m above the starting point.
   a. How much work in joules is done on the knapsack?
   b. If the climber weighs 6.00×10^2 N, how much total work is done?

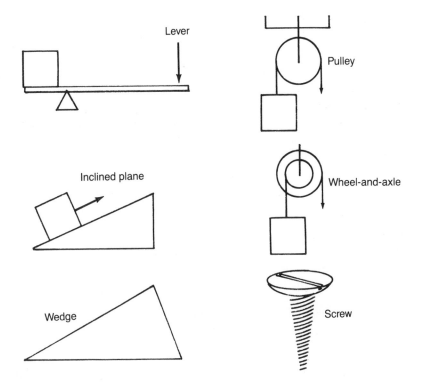

FIGURE 10-5. The six simple machines.

Lever

Pulley

Inclined plane

Wheel-and-axle

Wedge

Screw

All machines are combinations of the simple machines: the lever, pulley, wheel-and-axle, inclined plane, wedge, and screw.

  c. During the 30.0 min., what is the climber's average power in kilowatts?

16. An electric motor develops 65 kW of power as it lifts a loaded elevator 18.0 m in 40.0 s. How much force does the motor deliver?

17. A gardener applies a force of 150 N to push a wheelbarrow 60.0 m at a constant speed for 2.0×10^1 s.
  a. What is the gardener's power in watts?
  b. What is the gardener's power if the speed is doubled?

15. c. 3.3×10^{-3} kW

16. 1.4 $\times 10^5$ N

17. a. 450 W
   b. 9.0×10^2 W

10:4 Simple Machines

You use machines every day. Typewriters, needles, bicycles, and doorknobs are machines. Obviously, some machines are more complex than others. We can study the characteristics of machines by analyzing simple machines, because all machines are modifications or combinations of six simple machines. The six simple machines are the lever, the pulley, the wheel-and-axle, the inclined plane, the wedge, and the screw. Figure 10-5 shows the six simple machines. Consider the bottle opener shown in Figure 10-6. In using the opener, you do work on the opener by lifting one end of it. The opener does work by lifting the cap. The work you do is the input work. The work the machine does is the output work.

FIGURE 10-6. A bottle opener is a simple machine.

F_r

F_e

FIGURE 10-7. The output work of a real machine is always less than the input work.

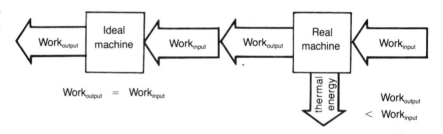

10:5 Mechanical Advantage

Machines make work easier to do even though they deliver less work than is supplied to them. One can understand how work is made easier by considering an ideal machine, that is a machine with 100% efficiency. In this machine,

$$W_i = W_o$$

The input work is the product of the force that was exerted on the machine, called the **effort force,** F_e, and the displacement of this force, d_e. Likewise, the output work is the product of the force that the machine exerted, called the **resistance force,** F_r, and the displacement of this force, d_r. Thus,

The mechanical advantage of a machine is the ratio of the force exerted by the machine to the force applied to the machine.

$$F_e d_e = F_r d_r$$

By rearranging the equation,

$$\frac{F_r}{F_e} = \frac{d_e}{d_r}$$

The ratio of F_r to F_e indicates the magnitude of the resistance force compared to the effort force. This ratio depends upon the ratio of d_e to d_r. By increasing the ratio of d_e to d_r, the effect of the effort force can be multiplied. The left member of the equation is called the **mechanical advantage** (MA). The ratio of F_r to F_e indicates the amount that the machine has increased the effect of the effort force. The right side of the equation is the ratio of d_e to d_r and is called the **ideal mechanical advantage** (IMA). By designing a machine to have a given ratio of d_e to d_r, one can choose the ratio of F_r to F_e. In an ideal machine, the MA and the IMA are equal. In real machines, the MA is less than the IMA due to work in overcoming friction.

Efficiency is the ratio of the work done by the machine to the work put into the machine.

The efficiency of any machine is the ratio of the output work to input work. Mathematically, the efficiency can be expressed as

$$\text{eff} = \frac{W_o}{W_i} \times 100\%$$

in which eff is the efficiency, W_o is the output work, and W_i is the input work.

Real machines are less than 100% efficient. The output work is less than the input work.

For an ideal machine, the efficiency is 100%; the output work equals the input work. In reality, the efficiency of a machine is less than 100%; the output work is less than the input work.

The efficiency of a machine can be expressed in terms of the MA and the IMA. The efficiency of a machine is given by

$$eff = \frac{W_o}{W_i} \times 100\%$$

$$eff = \frac{F_r d_r}{F_e d_e} \times 100\%$$

$$eff = \frac{F_r}{F_e} \times \frac{d_r}{d_e} \times 100\%$$

However, multiplying by d_r/d_e is the same as dividing by d_e/d_r. Therefore,

$$= \frac{F_r}{F_e} \div \frac{d_e}{d_r} \times 100\%$$

$$= \frac{F_r/F_e}{d_e/d_r} \times 100\%$$

$$= \frac{MA}{IMA} \times 100\%$$

$$\boxed{eff = \frac{MA}{IMA} \times 100\%}$$

EXAMPLE

Simple Machines

The bottle opener shown in Figure 10-6 requires that a force of 35 N must be applied to the handle in order to lift the bottle cap 0.90 cm. The opener has an *IMA* of 8.0 and an efficiency of 75%.   **a.**   What is the MA of the opener?   **b.** What force is applied to the bottle cap?   **c.** How far does the handle of the opener move?

Given: effort force (F_e) = 35 N

Ideal Mechanical Advantage (IMA) = 8.0

Efficiency (eff) = 75%

resistance distance (d_r) = 0.90 cm

Unknowns: **a.** Mechanical Advantage (MA)

b. resistance force (F_r)

c. effort distance (d_e)

Solution: **a.** $eff = \frac{MA}{IMA} \times 100\%$

$$MA = \frac{(eff)(IMA)}{100\%}$$

$$= \frac{(75\%)(8.0)}{100\%}$$

$$MA = 6.0$$

b. $MA = \frac{F_r}{F_e}$

$$F_r = (MA)(F_e)$$

$$= (6.0)(35 \text{ N})$$

$$F_r = 210 \text{ N}$$

$$\textbf{c.} \quad IMA = \frac{d_e}{d_r}$$

$$d_e = (IMA)(d_r)$$
$$= (8.0)(0.90 \text{ cm})$$
$$d_e = 7.2 \text{ cm}$$

Problems

18. a. 1.51
    b. 90.6%

18. A pulley system is used to raise a 225 N carton. To move the carton 1.65 m, a force of 149 N must travel 2.75 m.

    a. What is the mechanical advantage of the pulley system?
    b. What is the efficiency of the pulley system?

19. 1.20 m

19. A force of 2.25×10^3 N is exerted on a lever to raise a 1.20×10^3 N rock 1.32 m. If the efficiency of the lever is 58.7%, how far did the effort force move?

20. 1.91 m

20. A wheel and axle is a machine made so the wheel (larger diameter) and axle will rotate at the same speed. A resistance of 85.0 N, attached to the wheel, is displaced by an effort of 275 N. The machine has an efficiency of 78.5%. If the axle has a diameter of 8.00×10^{-2} m and makes 3 revolutions, what is the displacement of the resistance?

Physics Focus

Robotics

    The Robot Institute of America says that a robot is a "programmable, multifunctional manipulator designed to move material, parts, or specialized devices through variable programmed motions for the performance of a variety of tasks." The mid-1970's development of microprocessors has made industrial robots practical.

    Robots are used mainly in metal-working industries, such as automaking. They perform many repetitious, boring jobs with consistently high quality. They work 24 hours a day and do not get sick. This greatly increases productivity and reduces cost.

    A human must put a robot through its task step-by-step and put each step into the memory of the robot's microprocessor. Then robots use a variety of sensing devices such as television cameras and pressure- and weight-sensing instruments to make comparisons with the stored data. For example, a robot that spray paints car bodies must "recognize" the body type of the car before it paints it.

    A new Saturn division of GM will use many robots, as the Japanese auto industry already does. Saturn cars will compete in quality and cost with many Japanese imports.

Summary

1. Work is the product of a net force and the distance through which an object moves in the direction of the force. Work is measured in Joules.   10:1
2. The net force that does work acts parallel to the direction of motion.   10:2
3. The rate of doing work is power and is measured in watts.   10:3
4. Work output in real machines is always less than work input.   10:4
5. Mechanical advantage (MA) is the ratio of resistance force to effort force.   10:5
6. Ideal mechanical advantage (IMA) is a ratio of the displacement of the effort to the displacement of the resistance. In real machines the MA is less than the IMA.   10:5

Detailed answers to all Questions and Problems are given in the Teacher's Guide at the front of this book.

Questions

1. Define work and power.
2. Two people of the same mass climb the same flight of stairs. The first person climbs the stairs in 25 seconds and the second person takes 35 seconds. Which person does the most work? Explain your answer.
3. In the preceding question, which person expends the most power? Explain your answer.
4. How much work is performed on an object to keep it moving on a frictionless surface? Explain your answer.
5. How are the pedals of a bicycle a simple machine?
6. A hammer is used to pull a nail from a piece of wood. How could you modify the hammer to make the task easier?
7. How can one increase the ideal mechanical advantage of a machine?

Problems—A

1. The third floor of a house is 8.0 m above street level. How much work is required to move a 150 kg refrigerator up to the third floor?

    1. 1.2×10^4 J

2. A crane lifts a 2.25×10^3 N bucket containing 1.15 m³ of dirt (density = 2.00×10^3 kg/m³) to a height of 7.5 m. Calculate the work performed in
    a. newton · meters.
    b. joules.

    2. a. 1.9×10^5 N · m
    b. 1.9×10^5 J

3. How much work does a 420-watt motor do in 5.0 min.?

    3. 1.3×10^5 J

4. 450 W

5. 630 W

6. a. 1800 N
   b. 1.8×10^4 J
   c. 2.3×10^3 W

7. 9.0×10 kW

8. a. 3.0×10^5 J
   b. 39 kW

9. 54.7 m

10. 1.96 m

11. 1.53×10^4 J

12. a. 5.96
    b. 7.54
    c. 79.0%

13. a. 64.0 J
    b. 89.5%

4. Calculate the wattage of a motor that does 11 250 J of work in 25 s.

5. A pump raises 35 liters of water per minute from a depth of 110 m. What is the wattage expended? (A liter of water has a mass of 1.00 kg.)

6. A horizontal force of 8.0×10^2 N is needed to drag a crate across a horizontal floor. A worker drags the crate by means of a rope held at an angle of 63°.
   a. What force is applied to the rope?
   b. How much work is performed in dragging the crate 22 m?
   c. If the worker completes the job in 8.0 s, what is the power in watts?

7. A boat's engine propels it through water at a steady rate of 15 m/s. The force of friction that the boat must overcome to maintain this speed is 6.0×10^3 N. What is the power of the engine in kilowatts?

8. a. Neglecting frictional effects, how much work is done to accelerate a 1.0×10^3 kg car from an initial speed of 25 m/s to 35 m/s, if the acceleration given to it by its engine is 1.25 m/s²?
   b. What is the power of the car's engine in kilowatts?

9. A lawnroller is rolled across a lawn by a force of 115 N along the direction of the handle. The handle makes an angle of 22.5° with respect to the horizontal. If the person exerts 64.6 watts of power for 90.0 seconds, what is the distance the lawnroller travels?

10. A resistance of 475 N is displaced 6.23×10^{-1} m by an effort of 178 N. The efficiency of the machine is 85.0%. What is the displacement of the effort?

11. The efficiency of a lift is 72.5%. What is the work needed to raise a 2.00×10^2-kg mass 5.65 m?

12. A force of 225 N is displaced 7.35 m while moving a weight of 1340 N to a height of 0.975 m.
   a. What is the mechanical advantage?
   b. What is the ideal mechanical advantage?
   c. What is the efficiency of the machine?

13. A dockhand rolls a barrel up a plank 6.40 m long. The barrel weighs 425 N and is displaced a height of 1.28 m. The dockhand exerts a constant force of 95.0 N parallel to the plank.
   a. What work is needed to overcome friction?
   b. What is the efficiency of the machine?

Problems–B

1. a. See Teacher's Guide.
   b. 0.50 J
   c. See Teacher's Guide.

1. In Figure 10-8 the magnitude of the force necessary to stretch a spring is plotted against the distance the spring is stretched.
   a. Calculate the slope of the graph and show that
   $$F = kd$$
   where $k = 25$ N/m

b. Find the amount of work done in stretching the spring from 0.00 m to 0.20 m by calculating the area under the curve from 0.00 m to 0.20 m in Figure 10-8.

c. Show that the answer to Part b can be calculated using the formula

$$W = \tfrac{1}{2}kd^2$$

where W is the work, $k = 25$ N/m (the slope of the graph), and d is the distance the spring is stretched (0.20 m).

2. A complex machine is a combination of two or more simple machines arranged so that the output work of one machine becomes the input work of another. For example, a lever can be attached to a pulley system in such a way that the resistance force of the lever becomes the effort force applied to the pulley system. By attaching the lever to the pulley system, the distance the resistance moves in the lever is equal to the distance the effort moves in the pulley system. Consider an ideal complex machine consisting of a lever with an *IMA* of 3.0 and a pulley system with an *IMA* of 2.0.

a. Show that the *IMA* of this complex machine is 6.0.

b. If the complex machine is 60.0 % efficient, how much effort must be applied to the lever to lift a 540-N box?

c. If the effort moves 12.0 cm when applied to the lever, how far will the box be lifted.

2. a. See Teacher's Guide.
   b. 150 N
   c. 2.0 cm

FIGURE 10-8. Use with Problem B-1.

Readings

Britton, Peter, "How Canada is Tapping the Tides for Power." *Popular Science,* January, 1985.

Kyle, Chester, "The Aerodynamics of Human Powered Land Vehicles." *Scientific American,* December, 1983.

All forms of energy are interchangeable. When energy changes form, the total energy of a system remains the same. The potential energy of the roller coaster at the top of the loop is converted to kinetic energy as it plunges toward the ground. What is energy? What are other examples of energy changing form? How do energy changes help you?

Energy

Chapter 11 introduces the quantitative nature of the law of conservation of energy and the relationship between energy and work.

Energy, like work, is a term that we use freely. However, to scientists, energy, like work (Chapter 10), is a defined, measurable quantity. In this chapter, we will define energy as the capacity to do work. This statement defines what energy does, not what it is. Even though this definition may be limited, it will allow us to investigate various types of energy and its conservation.

Goal: You will gain understanding of energy and its conservation and the relationship between energy and work.

11:1 A More Meaningful View of Work

Work is a quantity that can be used as a measure of energy transfer. Work has about the same relationship to energy as a meter stick has to length. It is a measuring tool.

Work is the measure of energy transferred.

For example, if you push a wooden block across the surface of a table, you do work. What this statement really means is that your body loses energy while the surface of the table and the wooden block gain energy. The act of pushing the block causes your body to use a small amount of the energy you obtain from the food you eat. On the other hand, the rubbing of the block on the table causes the particles that compose the table and the block to move faster. The block-table system becomes a bit warmer. Thus, energy has been transferred from you to the system.

It would be impossible to measure the energy obtained by the particles in the table and the block. The particles are too small, there are too many of them, and they quickly pass along some of the energy to other particles. Still, we know how much energy, in joules, the block-table system gained. All we need to do is measure the work done on the block—that is, the force applied to the block times the distance it is moved. This quantity, work, is the energy transferred. All measurements of work are actually measurements of energy transfer.

Energy is the capacity to do work.

Since work and energy transferred are equivalent in ideal systems, energy is defined as the capacity to do work. This definition states what energy can do, not what it is. As you learn the basic concepts of energy, this definition will become more obvious.

Since only a few basic forces exist to do work, there are ultimately only a few forms of energy. These are gravitational, electromagnetic, and nuclear energy. Yet in science books you read of other different forms of energy. Terms such as thermal energy, mechanical energy, and light energy often appear. These are general terms used to avoid lengthy discussions of the true nature of energy. For example, thermal energy concerns the motions of particles.* The faster particles move, the more thermal energy we say they have. This energy is transferred when the particles strike each other. When two particles collide, it is the electric force between the electrons that does work and transfers energy. The transfer of thermal energy is basically electromagnetic in nature. Perhaps you can understand why the scientist prefers to use the term thermal energy rather than make a lengthy statement about the nature of electromagnetic transfer of energy that occurs when particles collide.

Potential energy is energy that is due to the position of an object.

An object at rest will have a quantity of energy with respect to some reference or zero position. The energy with respect to a reference position is called **potential energy**. When an object is in motion, the mass has **kinetic energy**.

Kinetic energy is due to motion of an object.

Energy is measured in terms of the amount of work done on an object. Both work and energy are scalar quantities and have the same units, joules.

1. Energy is measured in terms of the work it does or can do.
   a. Energy has the same units as work.
   b. Like work, energy is a scalar quantity.
2. Regardless of its form, energy is always either potential or kinetic.
   a. Potential energy is energy of position.
   b. Kinetic energy is the energy of motion.

11:2 Potential Energy and Base Levels

Potential energy is the energy an object has because of its position. Since there are four basic forces, there are four forms of potential energy. An object has gravitational potential energy because of its position in a gravitational field. Likewise, a charged particle has electromagnetic potential energy because of its position in an electric field. A subatomic particle has nuclear potential energy because of its location in the nucleus of an atom.

There are as many kinds of potential energy as there are types of force.

---

*The general term particles can mean atoms, ions, or molecules.

FIGURE 11-1. A pile driver does work as it falls from a higher to lower position.

A change in potential energy is always measured with reference to some arbitrary position where the potential energy is defined to be zero. For example, an object can do work if it falls from a higher to a lower position. Since the object in the higher position has the capacity to do work, it has stored energy. This stored energy is **gravitational potential energy**. As the object falls, there is a transfer of energy. The energy transferred is equal to the change in gravitational potential energy of the object. A change in gravitational potential energy is measured with reference to a **base level** where the gravitational potential energy is arbitrarily chosen to be zero. In most cases the base level is the floor or the surface of the earth.

Gravitational potential energy depends on the position of the body above the earth's surface.

A base level is a position where the potential energy is chosen to be zero.

FIGURE 11-2. Gravitational potential energy is arbitrarily chosen to be zero at a base level.

11:3 Work and Change in Potential Energy

Consider the following situation. Two hundred joules of work are needed to lift a 20-newton building block from the ground to the top of a 10-meter wall. If the block falls back to the ground, it should be able to do 200 joules of work. The capacity of the block to do work is equal to its increase in gravitational potential energy. The increase in potential energy of any system is equal to the work done on the system. The mathematical expressions of this statement are

The increase in the potential energy of a system which starts and ends at rest is equal to the work done on the system.

$$\Delta PE = W$$

$$\Delta PE = Fd$$

The increase in gravitational potential energy of an object is equal to the work done in placing the object in its final position. The work done is the product of the force needed to place the object in its final position and the vertical displacement of the object. This force has the same magnitude as the weight of the object (mg) but acts in the opposite direction. The displacement of the object above the surface of the earth is expressed as h. Therefore,

Gravitational potential energy depends on mass and height.

$$PE_f - PE_i = \Delta PE = mgh$$

If the initial potential energy PE_i is equal to zero when the object is on the earth's surface, the gravitational potential energy of an object is

$$\boxed{PE = mgh.}$$

EXAMPLE

Gravitational Potential Energy

A 5.00-kg bowling ball is lifted from the floor to a height of 1.50 m. What is its increase in gravitational potential energy?

Given: $m = 5.00$ kg
      vertical displacement
      $(h) = 1.50$ m

Unknown: Change in potential
      energy (ΔPE)

Basic equation: $\Delta PE = mgh$

Solution: $\Delta PE = Fd$
      $= mgh$
      $= (5.00 \text{ kg})(9.81 \text{ m/s}^2)(1.50 \text{ m}) = 73.6$ J

Problems

1. The 200.0-kg hammer of a pile driver is lifted 10.0 m. Find the gravitational potential energy of the system when the hammer is at this height.

1. 1.96×10^4 J

2. A 60.0-kg shell is shot from a cannon to a height of 4.0×10^2 m.
  a. What is the gravitational potential energy of the earth-shell system when the shell is at this height?
  b. What is the change in potential energy of the system when the shell falls to a height of 2.00×10^2 m?

2. a. 2.4×10^5 J
   b. 1.2×10^5 J

3. A person weighing 630 N climbs up a ladder to a height of 5.0 m.
  a. What work does the person do?
  b. What is the increase in the gravitational potential energy of the person at this height?
  c. Where does the energy come from to cause this increase in the gravitational potential energy?

3. a. 3200 J
   b. The work done is the increase in gravitational potential energy.
   c. The energy came from food eaten by the person.

11:4   Kinetic Energy

Kinetic energy is the energy an object possesses by virtue of its motion. In deriving an equation for kinetic energy, let us consider an object of mass m resting on a frictionless surface. A constant force F acts on it through a displacement d. The force will accelerate the object in accordance with Newton's second law of motion,

Kinetic energy is energy of motion.

Kinetic energy depends on mass and velocity.

$$F = ma$$

If we multiply both sides of this equation by d, the left side of the equation represents work done on the mass.

$$Fd = mad$$

$$Fd = \Delta KE$$

FIGURE 11-4. The increase in kinetic energy of an object is equal to the work done on it.

The product ad is related to the final and initial velocities by the equation

$$v_f^2 = v_i^2 + 2ad$$

or

$$ad = \frac{v_f^2 - v_i^2}{2}$$

Therefore,

$$Fd = \frac{m(v_f^2 - v_i^2)}{2}$$

Simplifying

$$W = \tfrac{1}{2}mv_f^2 - \tfrac{1}{2}mv_i^2$$

The kinetic energy of an object is defined as $\boxed{KE = \tfrac{1}{2}mv^2.}$ The equation then becomes

$$W = KE_f - KE_i = \Delta KE$$

This equation shows mathematically that the increase in kinetic energy of an object is equal to the work done on it.

EXAMPLE

Kinetic Energy

An 8.0-kg mass moves at 30.0 m/s. **a.** What is its kinetic energy? **b.** If the object was initially at rest, how much work was done on the object to give it this KE?

Given: $m = 8.0$ kg **Unknowns:** **a.** kinetic energy (KE)

$v_f = 30.0$ m/s **b.** W

$v_i = 0.0$ m/s **Basic equations:** **a.** $KE = \tfrac{1}{2}mv^2$

b. $W = \Delta KE$

Solution: a. $KE = \tfrac{1}{2}mv^2$ **b.** $W = \Delta KE$
$= \tfrac{1}{2}(8.0 \text{ kg})(30.0 \text{ m/s})^2$ $= KE_f - KE_i$
$= 3.6 \times 10^3 \text{ kg} \cdot \text{m}^2/\text{s}^2$ $= 3.6 \times 10^3 \text{ J} - 0 \text{ J}$
$KE = 3.6 \times 10^3 \text{ J}$ $W = 3.6 \times 10^3 \text{ J}$

Problems

4: a. 2.3×10^3 J
 b. 5.6×10^2 J
 c. $4/1$; KE varies as the square of the velocity.

4. a. A person has a mass of 45 kg and is moving with a velocity of 10.0 m/s. Find the person's kinetic energy.
b. The person's velocity becomes 5.0 m/s. What is the kinetic energy of the person?
c. What is the ratio of the kinetic energy in Part a to b? Why?

5. 2.0×10^2 J

5. A child and bicycle have a mass of 45 kg together. The child rides the bicycle 1.80 km in 10.0 minutes at a constant velocity. What is the kinetic energy of the system?

6. 34.5 m

6. A 15.0-kg object is moving with a velocity of $+7.50$ m/s. A force of -10.0 N acts on the object and its velocity becomes 3.20 m/s. What is the displacement of the object while the force acts?

7. A baseball that weighs 1.6 N leaves a bat with a speed of 40.0 m/s.

   a. Calculate the kinetic energy of the ball.

   b. If the ball struck the bat at 30.0 m/s, what is the change in the kinetic energy of the ball?

7. a. 130 J

   b. 58 J

11:5 Conservation of Energy

If an isolated system does work, or as work is done on an isolated system, energy changes form. You can store energy in a bow by pulling back on the bowstring and doing work on the bow. That energy can be transferred to the arrow and appears as the kinetic energy of the moving arrow.

The law of conservation of energy states that the total energy of an isolated system cannot change unless work is done on it by an outside force or the system does work on something outside the system. Within an isolated system energy can change from one form to another, but the total amount of energy always remains the same.

As an example of the law of conservation of energy, consider a rock weighing 1.00×10^2 newtons located 2.0×10^1 meters above the earth.

At this height above the earth's surface, the potential energy of the rock is

$$Fd = (1.00 \times 10^2 \text{ N})(2.0 \times 10^1 \text{ m}) = 2.0 \times 10^3 \text{ J}$$

If the rock is allowed to fall freely for a distance of 10.0 meters, its potential energy will be

$$Fd = (1.00 \times 10^2 \text{ N})(1.0 \times 10^1 \text{ m}) = 1.0 \times 10^3 \text{ J}$$

The rock loses half of its potential energy in falling 10.0 meters.

The velocity of the rock after it has fallen 10.0 meters can be calculated by the equation

$$v_f^2 = 2gd + v_i^2$$
$$v_f^2 = 2(9.80 \text{ m/s}^2)(10.0 \text{ m}) + 0$$
$$v_f = \sqrt{196 \text{ m}^2/\text{s}^2}$$
$$v_f = 14 \text{ m/s}$$

When the rock has fallen 10.0 meters, its vertical velocity will be 14 m/s. Its kinetic energy will be

$$KE = \frac{mv^2}{2}$$
$$= \left(\frac{W}{g}\right)\left(\frac{v^2}{2}\right)$$
$$= \frac{(1.00 \times 10^2 \text{ N})(14 \text{ m/s})^2}{(9.80 \text{ m/s}^2)(2)} = 1.0 \times 10^3 \text{ J}$$

For a freely falling object, the decrease in its gravitational potential energy is always equivalent to its gain in kinetic energy. The transfer of potential energy to kinetic energy occurs as the object falls. By the time

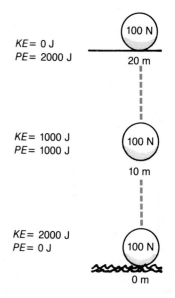

$KE = 0$ J
$PE = 2000$ J

  100 N

20 m

$KE = 1000$ J
$PE = 1000$ J

  100 N

10 m

$KE = 2000$ J
$PE = 0$ J

  100 N

0 m

FIGURE 11-5. The decrease in potential energy is equal to the increase in kinetic energy.

The law of conservation of energy states that energy can neither be created nor destroyed.

A decrease in potential energy is accompanied by an increase in kinetic energy.

FIGURE 11-6. The path an object follows in reaching the ground does not affect its final kinetic energy.

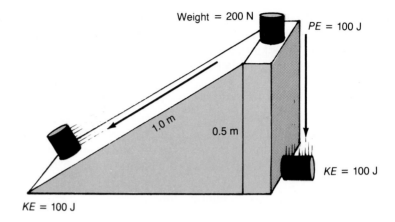

Weight = 200 N

PE = 100 J

1.0 m

0.5 m

KE = 100 J

KE = 100 J

the object reaches the earth's surface, all of its potential energy has been changed to kinetic energy. The equation showing that potential or kinetic energies are conserved is

$$KE_i + PE_i = KE_f + PE_f$$

Upon impact with the earth, the kinetic energy is changed to thermal energy, and sometimes, to sound energy and energy to compress the particles.

The path an object follows as it is raised does not affect the potential energy of the object. A 200-N barrel positioned 0.5 meters above the ground has 100 joules of potential energy whether it is raised straight up to that height or pushed up an incline. This same principle also applies to kinetic energy. The barrel's kinetic energy, neglecting friction, is 100 joules when it reaches ground level, whether it falls straight down or slides down the incline.

The simple harmonic motion of a pendulum or an object oscillating on a spring clearly demonstrates the conservation of energy. The initial gravitational potential energy of the raised pendulum bob is

FIGURE 11-7. For the simple harmonic motion of a pendulum bob (a), the sum of the potential and kinetic energies is a constant (b).

b   *PE, KE* versus Position

a

A   B   C

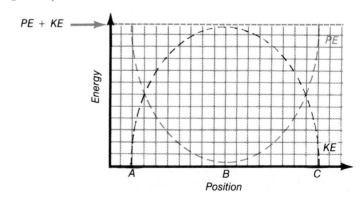

PE + KE

Energy

PE

KE

A   B   C

Position

transferred to kinetic energy of the bob as it moves along its path. At the lowest point along the path, its gravitational potential energy is a minimum (arbitrarily chosen to be zero) and its kinetic energy is a maximum. Figure 11-7 shows the graph of the gravitational potential energy and the kinetic energy of a pendulum bob for one period of its oscillation. As can be seen, the total energy remains constant.

In simple harmonic motion, energy is continually converted between kinetic and potential energy.

EXAMPLE

Conservation of Energy

A large chunk of ice with a mass of 15.0 kg falls from a roof 8.00 meters above the ground. **a.** What is the kinetic energy of the ice as it reaches the ground? **b.** What is its speed as it reaches the ground?

Given: $m = 15.0$ kg   **Unknown: a.** KE_f **b.** v_f

$g = 9.80$ m/s²   **Basic equation:**

$h = 8.00$ m $PE_i + KE_i = PE_f + KE_f$

$KE_i = 0$

$PE_f = 0$

Solution:

a. $PE_i + KE_i = PE_f + KE_f$

$mgh + \frac{1}{2}mv^2 = PE_f + KE_f$

$(15.0 \text{ kg})(9.80 \text{ m/s}^2)(8.00 \text{ m}) + 0 = 0 + KE_f$

$1180 \text{ J} = KE_f$

b. $KE_f = \frac{1}{2}mv_f^2$

$v_f^2 = \dfrac{2KE}{m} = \dfrac{(2)(1180 \text{ J})}{15.0 \text{ kg}}$

$v_f = \sqrt{157 \text{ m}^2/\text{s}^2}$

$v_f = 12.5$ m/s

Problems

8. An 8.0-kg flower pot falls from a window ledge 12.0 m above a sidewalk.

   a. What is the kinetic energy of the pot just as it reaches the sidewalk?

   b. Using energy considerations only, determine the speed of the pot just before it strikes the walk.

8. a. 940 J
   b. 15 m/s

9. A 15.0-kg model plane flies horizontally at 12.5 m/s.

   a. Calculate its kinetic energy.

   b. The plane goes into a dive and levels off 20.4 m closer to the earth. How much potential energy did it lose during the dive?

9. a. 1170 J
   b. 3.00×10^3 J

9. c. 3.00×10^3 J
   d. 4170 J
   e. 23.6 m/s

10. a. 6270 J
    b. 28.0 m/s

11. a. 6270 J
    b. 35.4 m/s

12. 1.0×10^1 m

13. 20.0 m

14. 15 m/s

15. a. 12.5 m/s
    b. 781 J

c. How much kinetic energy did the plane gain during the dive?

d. What is its new kinetic energy?

e. Neglecting frictional effects, what is its new horizontal velocity?

10. A partially filled bag of cement having a mass of 16.0 kg falls 40.0 m into a river from a bridge.

a. What is the kinetic energy of the bag as it hits the water?

b. Using energy considerations only, what vertical speed does it have on impact?

11. A block weighing 98.0 N falls 64.0 m.

a. What is the potential energy of the block at 64.0 m?

b. What speed does the block have as it strikes the ground?

12. During the hammer throw at a track meet, an 8.0-kg hammer is accidentally thrown straight up. If 784.0 J of work were done on the hammer to give it its vertical velocity, how high will it rise?

13. A 10.0-kg test rocket is fired vertically from Cape Canaveral. Its fuel gives it a kinetic energy of 1960 J before it leaves the pad. How high will the rocket rise?

14. A skater on a frozen pond pushes a 5.0-kg log to clear a skating area. If the skater does 560 J of work on the log in pushing it across the nearly frictionless ice, what speed is given to the log?

15. In an electronics factory, small cabinets slide down a 30.0° incline a distance of 16.0 m to reach the next assembly stage. The cabinets have a mass of 10.0 kg each.

a. Calculate the speed each cabinet would acquire if the incline were frictionless.

b. What kinetic energy would a cabinet have under such circumstances?

FIGURE 11-8. In an elastic collision, the total kinetic energy is constant.

FIGURE 11-9. Momentum is conserved in the collision between the bowling ball and pins. However, the total kinetic energy of the system decreases.

16. A 5.0-kg mass is projected straight up with a speed of 15 m/s.
   a. What is the initial kinetic energy of the mass?
   b. To what height does the mass rise?

16. a. 560 J
    b. 11 m

11:6 Elastic and Inelastic Collisions

   An elastic collision is a collision in which the total kinetic energy of the objects involved is exactly the same before and after the collision. A collision between two billiard balls or two glass marbles moving across a smooth surface may be considered an elastic collision.

   The behavior of two objects involved in an elastic collision can be predicted. This is done by considering the laws of conservation of energy and conservation of momentum. For example, suppose a billiard ball of mass m moves with a speed v. This ball collides head-on with a billiard ball of equal mass that is at rest. After the collision, the first ball comes to a complete stop. The second ball moves off at exactly the speed of the first ball before the collision. Momentum and kinetic

In an elastic collision, the total kinetic energy of the objects is the same before and after the collision.

energy are both conserved. If the first ball had a final speed other than zero or the second ball had a speed less than the original speed of the first ball, kinetic energy would not have been conserved.

When the total kinetic energy decreases during the collision, the velocity of the objects involved in the collision also decreases. The decrease in kinetic energy is accounted for by an increase in the thermal energy content of the colliding objects, by the generation of sound during the collision, or by both.

Momentum is conserved in all collisions when no external forces act.

The law of conservation of momentum holds for all collisions. Although kinetic energy decreases during an inelastic collision, there is no change in momentum. For example, consider a 1-kg block of putty sliding across a frictionless surface at + 20 m/s. This block of putty collides head-on with a 1-kg block of putty which is at rest. In this completely inelastic collision, the two blocks of putty stick together and move off as one object. According to the law of conservation of momentum, the total momentum of the two blocks sticking together is equal to the momentum of the original block of putty. The momentum of the original block is

$$p = mv$$
$$= + 20 \text{ kg} \cdot \text{m/s}$$
$$= (1 \text{ kg})(+ 20 \text{ m/s})$$

Since the momentum is conserved, the two blocks moving together have a momentum of 20 kg · m/s. Thus, after the collision, the two blocks move with a velocity of 10 m/s in the direction of the original velocity. However, the kinetic energies of the blocks of putty before and after the collision are not the same.

$$KE_i = \frac{1}{2}mv^2$$
$$= \frac{(1 \text{ kg})(20 \text{ m/s})^2}{2}$$
$$= 200 \text{ J}$$

and
$$KE_f = \frac{1}{2}mv^2$$
$$= \frac{(2 \text{ kg})(10 \text{ m/s})^2}{2}$$
$$= 100 \text{ J}$$

Many collisions are neither elastic nor completely inelastic. In such cases, it becomes difficult to calculate what will happen during a collision.

Summary	
1. All energy depends upon forces. Since there are four basic forces, there are four basic types of energies.	11:1
2. Energy is defined as the capacity to do work.	11:1
3. Each type of energy can have one of two forms—potential energy or kinetic energy.	11:1
4. Potential energy is the energy an object has because of its position. The change in potential energy of a system is equal to the work done on the system.	11:1, 11:3
5. Kinetic energy is the energy an object has because it is moving.	11:1, 11:4
6. Energy, like work, is measured in joules.	11:1
7. The conservation of energy states that the total energy of an isolated system remains constant unless work is done on or by the system. Within an isolated system, energy can only change form.	11:5
8. In an elastic collision the total kinetic energy of the system remains constant.	11:6
9. In an inelastic collision the total kinetic energy decreases.	11:6

Detailed answers to all Questions and Problems are given in the Teacher's Guide at the front of this book.

Questions

1. Explain how energy and forces are related.

2. What type of energy does a wound watch spring possess? What form of energy does a running watch use? When the watch runs down, what has happened to the energy?

3. Describe the types of energy the earth-sun system possesses.

4. The Northern Hemisphere of the earth is approximately 6.7×10^6 km closer to the sun in winter than in summer. The earth moves along its orbit faster in winter than in summer. Explain these two statements in terms of the earth's potential and kinetic energy.

5. A rubber ball is dropped from a height of 8 m. After striking the floor, it bounces to a height of 5 m.
   a. If the ball had bounced to a height of 8 m, how would you describe the collision between the ball and the floor?
   b. If the ball had not bounced at all, how would you describe the collision between the ball and the floor?
   c. What happened to the energy lost by the ball during the collision?

6. A film was produced that centered around the discovery of a substance called "flubber." This substance could bounce higher than the height from which it was dropped. Explain why "flubber" is not likely to exist.

Problems–A

1. a. How much work is needed to hoist a 98-N sack of grain to a storage room 50 m above the ground floor of a grain elevator?
   b. What is the potential energy of the sack of grain at this height?
   c. The rope being used to lift the sack of grain breaks just as the sack reaches the storage room. What kinetic energy does the sack have just before it strikes the ground floor?

2. A 1600-kg car travels at a speed of 12.5 m/s. What is its kinetic energy?

3. A racing car has a mass of 1500 kg. What is its kinetic energy in joules if it has a speed of 108 km/h?

4. An archer puts a 0.30 kg arrow to the bowstring. An average force of 201 N is exerted to draw the string back 1.3 m.
   a. Assuming no frictional loss, with what speed does the arrow leave the bow?
   b. If the arrow is shot straight up, how high does it rise?

5. A 1200-kg car starts from rest and accelerates to 72 km/h in 20.0 s. The average force needed to overcome the force of friction during this period is 450 N.

   a. What distance does the car move during its period of acceleration?
   b. What force does the engine produce on the car during this time?
   c. How much work does the engine do to accelerate the car?

6. A force of 410 N is applied in a direction straight up to a stone that weighs 32 N. If the force is applied through a distance of 2.0 m, to what height, from the point of release, will the stone rise?

7. a. A 20-kg mass is on the edge of a 100-m high cliff. What potential energy does it possess?
   b. The mass falls from the cliff. What is its kinetic energy just before it strikes the ground?
   c. What speed does it have as it strikes the ground?

8. A steel ball has a mass of 4.0 kg and rolls along a smooth, level surface at 62 m/s.

   a. Find its kinetic energy.
   b. At first, the ball was at rest on the surface. A force acted on it through a distance of 22 m to give it the speed of 62 m/s. What was the magnitude of the force?

9. A railroad car with a mass of 5.0×10^5 kg collides with a stationary railroad car of equal mass. After the collision, the two cars lock together and move off at 4.0 m/s.

    a. Before the collision, the first railroad car moved at 8.0 m/s. What was its momentum?

    b. What is the total momentum of the two cars after the collision?

    c. Find the kinetic energies of the two cars before and after the collision.

    d. Account for the loss of kinetic energy.

9. a. 4.0×10^6 kg · m/s
   b. 4.0×10^6 kg · m/s
   c. Before:
     1.6×10^7 J; 0
     After:
     8.0×10^6 J
   d. *KE* was not conserved; it was turned into heat and sound.

Problems—B

1. A 420-N boy sits in a swing seat that hangs 0.40 m from the ground. A friend pulls the swing back so that the seat is 1.00 m from the ground and releases the swing.

    a. How fast will the boy on the swing be moving when the swing passes through its lowest position?

    b. If the boy moves through the lowest point at 2.0 m/s, how much work was done on the swing by friction?

1. a. 3.4 m/s
   b. 160 J

2. A 10.0-g ball is projected straight down from a height of 1.0 m. It strikes the floor at a speed of 5.5 m/s. What was the initial velocity of the ball?

2. 1.1 m/s

Readings

Ayres, Thomas, "Thermodynamics and Economics." *Physics Today*, November, 1984.

Browne, Malcolm, "Stopping Missles with Energy Beams." *Discover*, June, 1983.

Burns, Jack, "Centaurus A: The Nearest Active Galaxy." *Scientific American*, November, 1983.

Cleveland, C. J., "Energy and the U.S. Economy." *Science*, August 31, 1984.

Scott, David, "Gigantic Dutch Project: Sea Storage for Wind Energy." *Popular Science*, April, 1983.

Heat flows from a warmer object or area to a cooler object or area. Heat loss is a significant problem in these times of energy consciousness. New building materials and advanced housing design are helping to minimize heat loss and conserve energy. Analytical techniques such as this thermograph are used in pinpointing areas of heat loss in houses in an effort to conserve energy. How can heat losses be prevented? How can waste heat be put to good use?

Thermal Energy

Chapter 12 introduces the concepts of thermal energy, heat, and temperature. The laws of thermodynamics are discussed as well as the thermal properties of materials.

Fire has been known since earliest times. In fact, fire, earth, water, and air were considered by ancient Greeks to be the elements out of which the entire world was made. You have had many experiences with hot and cold objects. A piece of metal left in the sunlight becomes too hot to touch. Yet a piece of wood in the sun can be picked up easily. When a nail is rapidly pulled out of a piece of wood with a hammer, the nail becomes too hot to touch. If you put ice in a glass of water, the water is cooled and part of the ice melts. These observations, which are part of our everyday experience, can be explained by the branch of physics called thermodynamics.

Goal: You will learn how heat and work are related to change in the thermal energy of a system and how thermal energy can be used in practical devices.

12:1 Kinetic Theory

Although the effects of fire have been known since ancient times, only in the eighteenth century did scientists begin to understand how a warm body differs from a cold body. Their theory proposed that when a body was warmed, an invisible fluid called "caloric" was added to the body. Hot bodies contained more caloric than cold bodies. Caloric theory could explain observations such as the expansion of objects when heated, but not why two ice cubes rubbed together melted.

In the middle of the nineteenth century, scientists developed a new theory to replace caloric theory. The theory is based on the assumption that matter is made up of many tiny particles. The particles are always in motion. In a hot body, the particles move faster, and thus have a higher energy than the particles in a cold body. This theory is called the kinetic molecular theory.

Kinetic theory assumes that all matter is made up of tiny particles that are always in motion.

195

FIGURE 12-1. A baseball in flight has both internal and external energy. The internal energy is the result of the kinetic and potential energies of its particles. The external energy is the result of the position and motion of the baseball in flight.

The kinetic theory can be difficult to visualize because the motion of particles cannot be seen easily. For example, a thrown baseball has a kinetic energy that depends on its velocity and a potential energy that is proportional to its height above the ground. These external properties can be seen. However, the tiny particles of which the baseball is made are in constant motion within the ball. This internal motion is not readily visible.

Figure 12-2 shows a model of a solid that can help you to understand the kinetic theory. In this model, a solid is made up of tiny spherical particles held together by massless springs. The springs represent the electromagnetic forces that bond the solid together. The particles vibrate back and forth, and thus have kinetic energy. The vibrations compress and extend the springs, so the particles have potential energy as well. The sum of the kinetic and potential energies of the particles that make up an object is called the internal or thermal energy of that object.

Temperature, like density, is an intrinsic property. Thermal energy, like mass, is an extrinsic property.

12:2 Thermal Energy and Temperature

According to the kinetic molecular theory, a hot body has more thermal energy than a cold body. That is, the particles in a hot body have larger kinetic and potential energies than the particles in a cold body. The total amount of thermal energy in a body also varies directly with the number of particles in the body.

In comparing the amount of energy in various objects, we use a quantity that is independent of the size of the objects. The quantity that measures the average kinetic energy of the particles in a body is called **temperature.**

The temperature of an object is proportional to the average kinetic energy of the particles of the object. The temperature is independent of the number of particles in the body. Thus, if a one-kilogram mass of steel is at the same temperature as a two-kilogram mass, the average

FIGURE 12-2. Molecules of a solid behave as if they were held together by springs.

kinetic energy of the particles in both masses is the same, although the total amount of kinetic energy of particles in the two-kilogram mass will be twice that in the one-kilogram mass. Have students list other forms of thermometers, naming the property that changes with temperature.

12:3 Equilibrium and Thermometry

You are familiar with the idea of measuring temperature. If you have a fever, you place a thermometer in your mouth and wait two or three minutes. The thermometer then provides a measure of the temperature of your body.

The microscopic process is less familiar. Your body is hot, which means the particles in your body have high thermal energy. The thermometer is made of a tube of glass. When the cold glass touches your hotter body, the particles in your body hit the particles in the glass. These collisions transfer energy to the glass particles. The thermal energy of the particles that make up the thermometer increases. As the energy of particles in the glass increases, they are able to transfer energy back to the particles in your body. At some point, the transfer of energy between the glass and your body is equal. Your body and the thermometer are in thermal equilibrium. That is, the amount of energy that flows from your body to the glass is equal to that which flows from the glass to your body. The thermometer and your body are at the same temperature. Objects that are in thermal equilibrium are at the same temperature. Note that if the objects are of different masses, they may not have the same thermal energy.

A thermometer is a device placed in contact with an object and allowed to come to thermal equilibrium with that object. The operation of a thermometer depends on some property that changes with temperature. Most household thermometers contain colored alcohol that expands when heated. The hotter the thermometer, the larger the volume of the alcohol in it. Mercury is another liquid commonly used in thermometers.

The useful range of liquid thermometers is limited to temperatures between the freezing and boiling points of the liquids used. If higher or lower temperatures are to be measured, a gas thermometer is often used. The volume of a fixed amount of a gas such as hydrogen or helium depends on temperature and serves as a measure of temperature.

12:4 Temperature Scales

Temperature scales were developed by scientists to allow them to compare their temperature measurements with those of other scientists. A scale based on the properties of water was devised in 1741 by the Swedish astronomer and physicist Anders Celsius (1701-1744). On this scale, now called the Celsius scale, the freezing point of pure water is fixed at 0 degrees (0°C). The boiling point of pure water at sea level is defined as 100 degrees (100°C). On the Celsius scale, the temperature of the human body is 37°C.

5x10⁻³ m³   1x10⁻² m³

FIGURE 12-3. Thermometers use a change in physical properties to measure temperature.

A thermometer measures the temperature of an object with which it is in thermal equilibrium.

FIGURE 12-4. A gas thermometer.

Celsius originally identified the boiling point as 0° and the freezing point as 100°. Discuss how this scale would be better or worse than the present scale.

FIGURE 12-5. Some familiar reference points on the Celsius temperature scale are shown.

No temperature can be colder than absolute zero, −273°C.

FIGURE 12-6. At the temperature of condensing helium, water vapor and gases in the environment condense to form a fog around the container of liquid helium.

12:5   The Kelvin or Absolute Scale

Temperatures do not appear to have an upper limit. The interior temperature of the sun is at least $1.5 \times 10^7°C$. Other stars are even hotter. However, temperatures do have a lower limit. Generally materials contract as they are cooled. As will be discussed in Chapter 13, the contraction of any gas is such that it would have zero volume at −273°C.* At this temperature, all the thermal energy would be removed from the gas. It is impossible to reduce the thermal energy any further. Therefore, there can be no lower temperature than −273°C. This temperature is called **absolute zero.**

Very cold temperatures can be reached by liquifying gases. Helium liquifies at −268.8°C. Even colder temperatures can be reached by using the properties of special substances when they are placed in the fields of large magnets. By these techniques, physicists have reached temperatures of only $3.0 \times 10^{-5}°C$ above absolute zero.

A temperature scale based on absolute zero is named after the British physicist William Thomson (Lord Kelvin) (1824-1907). Absolute zero is also zero on the Kelvin scale. On the Kelvin scale, the freezing point of water (0°C) is 273 K and the boiling point of water is 373 K. Each interval on the Kelvin scale, called a kelvin, is equal to one degree Celsius. Thus, °C + 273 = kelvin.

---

*More precisely, −273.15°C

EXAMPLE
Converting Celsius to Kelvin Temperature
  Convert 25°C to kelvin.
Solution: K = °C + 273
                = 25° + 273 = 298 K

EXAMPLE
Converting Kelvin to Celsius Temperature
  Convert 52 K to degrees Celsius.
Solution: K = °C + 273
                °C = K − 273
                   = 52 − 273 = −221°C

Problems

1. Convert 43°C to kelvins.

2. Convert 43 K to degrees Celsius.

3. Convert 273°C to kelvins.

4. Convert 273 K to degrees Celsius.

5. Convert 27 K to degrees Celsius.

6. Convert these kelvin temperatures to Celsius temperatures.

a.	110 K	**c.**	373 K	**e.**	402 K
b.	22 K	**d.**	323 K		

1. 316 K

2. −230°C

3. 546 K

4. 0°C

5. −246°C

6. a. −163°C
   b. −251°C
   c. 100°C
   d. 50°C
   e. 129°C

12:6 First Law of Thermodynamics

  One way the temperature of a body can be increased is by placing it in contact with a hotter body. The thermal energy of the hotter body is reduced, and the thermal energy of the cooler body is increased. Energy flows from the hotter body to the cooler body. **Heat** is the energy that flows as a result of a difference in temperature.

  You should note that this definition of heat is different from the one in everyday use. We commonly speak of a body containing heat. This description is left over from the caloric theory. In the modern theory, a hot body contains a larger amount of thermal energy than a colder body. Heat is the flow of energy caused by a temperature difference.

  The thermal energy of a body can be increased in other ways. If you rub your hands together, they are warmed, yet they were not brought into contact with a hotter body. Instead, by means of friction, work was done on your hands. The mechanical energy of your moving hands was transformed into thermal energy.

  There are other means of converting mechanical energy into thermal energy. If you use a hand air pump to inflate a bicycle tire, the air and pump become warm. The mechanical energy in the moving piston is

Heat is energy transferred due to a difference in temperature. Heat always spontaneously flows from a warmer to a cooler body.

Work with students to use this definition of heat. Avoid speaking of heat as something contained within a body.

FIGURE 12-7. The heat produced by burning gasoline causes the gases produced to expand and exert force on the cylinder.

A
Intake

B
Compression

C
Ignition

D
Expansion
(power stroke)

E
Exhaust

Energy that flows by means other than a temperature difference is called work.

The first law of thermodynamics states that the increase in thermal energy is the sum of the heat added to and work done on a body.

Have students list various means of warming bodies (microwave cooking, heating over a flame, etc.). Classify each as heat or work.

A heat engine accepts heat from a high temperature source, performs work, and transfers heat out at low temperatures.

converted into thermal energy of the gas. Other forms of energy, light, sound, electrical, as well as mechanical, can be transformed into thermal energy.

Thermal energy can be increased either by adding heat or doing work on a system. Thus, *the total increase in the thermal energy of a system is the sum of the work done on it and the heat added to it.* This fact is called the **first law of thermodynamics.** Thermodynamics is the study of the changes in thermal properties of matter. The first law is merely a restatement of the law of conservation of energy.

All forms of energy are measured in joules, and so is heat. We will use the symbol Q to indicate heat transferred from one body to another. For many years, heat was measured in calories. One calorie is equal to 4.18 joules. The calorie is not used in the SI system.

The conversion of mechanical energy to heat, as in rubbing your hands, is easy. However, the reverse process, conversion of heat to mechanical energy, is more difficult. A device that is able to convert heat to mechanical energy continuously is called a heat engine.

Heat engines require a high temperature source from which heat can be removed, and a low temperature sink into which heat can be delivered. An automobile engine is an example of a heat engine. A mixture of air and gasoline vapor is ignited, producing a very high temperature flame. Heat flows from the flame to the air in the cylinder. The hot air expands and pushes on a piston, changing thermal energy into mechanical energy. In order to obtain mechanical energy continuously, the engine must be returned to its starting condition. The heated air is expelled and replaced by new air, and the piston is returned to the top of the cylinder. The entire cycle is repeated many times each minute. The heat from the burning gasoline and air is converted into mechanical energy that eventually results in the movement of the automobile.

However, not all the heat from the very high temperature flame is transformed into mechanical energy. The exhaust gases and the engine parts become warm. The exhaust comes in contact with outside air, transferring heat to it. The engine warmth is carried to a radiator. Outside air passes through the radiator and its temperature is raised. This heat transferred by the engine is called waste heat. All heat engines generate waste heat. Note that in the automobile engine, the waste heat is at a lower temperature than the heat of the gasoline flame. The overall change in total energy of the car-air system is zero. Thus, according to the first law of thermodynamics, the heat from the flame is equal to the sum of the mechanical energy produced and the waste heat expelled.

Heat spontaneously flows from a warm body to a cold body. It is possible to remove heat from a colder body and add heat to a warmer body. However, an external source of energy, usually mechanical energy, is required to accomplish this feat. A refrigerator is a common example of such a device. Electrical energy runs a motor that does work on a gas called Freon®. Heat is transferred from the contents of the refrigerator to the Freon. Food is cooled, usually to 4.0°C, and the Freon is warmed. Outside the refrigerator, heat is transferred from the Freon to room air, cooling the Freon again. The overall change in the total energy of the Freon is zero. Thus, according to the first law of thermodynamics, the sum of the heat removed from the food at low temperature and the work done by the motor is equal to the heat expelled to the outside at a higher temperature.

A heat pump is a refrigerator that can be run in two directions. In the summer, heat is removed from the house, cooling the house. The heat is expelled to the warmer air outside. In the winter, heat is removed from the cold outside air and transferred into the warmer house. In either case, mechanical energy is required to transfer heat from a cold object to a warmer one.

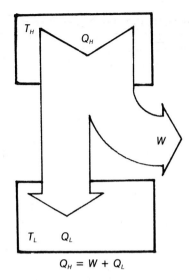

$$Q_H = W + Q_L$$

FIGURE 12-8. Flow chart diagram representing heat at high temperature transformed into mechanical energy and low temperature waste heat.

FIGURE 12-9. A heat pump runs in either direction depending on whether it is used in heating or cooling. In cooling, heat is extracted from the air in the house and pumped outside. In heating, heat is extracted from the outside air and pumped inside.

FIGURE 12-10. Flow chart diagram of heat transfer in a refrigerator.

Entropy is a measure of the randomness or disorder of a body.

All natural processes proceed in the direction that leads to an increase in entropy.

12:7   The Second Law of Thermodynamics

Many processes that do not violate the first law of thermodynamics have never been observed to occur spontaneously. For example, the first law does not prohibit heat flowing from a cold body to a hot body, but when a hot body is placed in contact with a cold body, the hot body has never been observed to become hotter still. Heat flows spontaneously from hot to cold bodies. It would be possible for heat engines to transform heat into mechanical energy with no waste heat and still obey the first law. Yet, waste heat is generated.

In the nineteenth century, the French engineer Sadi Carnot (1796-1832) studied the ability of engines to transform heat into mechanical energy. He proved that even the most ideal engine would generate some waste heat. Carnot's result is best described in terms of a quantity called entropy (EN truh pee). Entropy, like thermal energy, is contained in an object. If heat is added to a body, entropy is increased. If heat flows from a body, entropy is decreased. However, ignoring friction, if an object does work with no change in temperature, the entropy does not change.

On a microscopic level, **entropy** is described as the disorder in a system. When heat is added to an object, the particles move in a random way. Some move quickly, others slowly, many at intermediate speeds. The greater the variety of speeds exhibited by the particles, the greater the disorder. The greater the disorder, the larger the entropy. While it is possible that all the particles could have the same speed, the random collisions and energy exchange of particles makes this extremely unlikely. The following is a statement of the **second law of thermodynamics.** *Natural processes go in the direction that increases the total entropy of the universe.* Entropy and the second law can be thought of as statements of the probability of events happening.

The second law describes the reason heat flows from a hot to a cold body. Consider a hot iron bar and a cold cup of water. The particles in the iron will be moving very fast, the particles in the water more slowly.

Heat cannot be transformed into mechanical energy with 100% efficiency. In Figure 12-11a waste heat is not indicated.

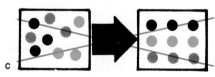

FIGURE 12-11. A representation of three processes forbidden by the second law of thermodynamics.

FIGURE 12-12. An example of the second law of thermodynamics.

The bar is plunged into the water. When equilibrium is reached, the average kinetic energy of the particles in the iron and water will be the same. This final state is less ordered than the first situation. No longer are the fast particles confined to the iron and the slow particles to the water. All speeds are evenly distributed. The entropy of the final state is larger than that of the initial state.

Now, it would be possible that, as a result of collisions, all the particles in the iron would just happen to move slowly. However, the probability of this happening spontaneously is so low as to be effectively impossible.

The second law and entropy also give new meaning to what is commonly called the "energy crisis." When you use an energy resource such as natural gas to heat your home, you do not use up the energy in the gas. The energy contained in the molecules of the gas is converted into thermal energy of the flame, which is transferred to thermal energy of the air in your home. Even if this warm air leaks to the outside, the energy is not lost. Energy has not been used up. However, the entropy has been increased. Natural gas is a very ordered substance. The thermal motion of the warmed air is very disordered. While it is mathematically possible for order to be reestablished, the probability of this occurring is essentially zero. For this reason, entropy is often used as a measure of the unavailability of energy. The energy in the warmed air in a house is not as available to do mechanical work or to transfer heat to other bodies as the original gas flame. The lack of usable energy is really a surplus of entropy.

When a fuel is burned, energy is not lost. Entropy is increased.

12:8 Specific Heat

When the kinetic energy of a body increases, its temperature increases. The amount of increase depends on the size of the body. It also depends on the substance of which the body is made. The **specific heat** of a substance is the amount of energy that must be added to raise the temperature of a unit mass one temperature unit. In SI units, specific heat, C, is measured in J/kg·K. For example, 903 J must be added to one kilogram of aluminum to raise the temperature one kelvin. The specific heat of aluminum is 903 J/kg·K.

Specific heat is the increase in thermal energy required to raise one kilogram of matter one kelvin.

Strictly speaking, what we call specific heat is heat capacity, and specific heat is the ratio of the heat capacity of a substance to the capacity of water, 4.18 J/kg·K.

TABLE 12-1

Specific Heats of Common Substances			
Material	Specific Heat (J/kg · K)	Material	Specific Heat (J/kg · K)
alcohol (ethanol)	2450	ice	2060
aluminum	903	iron	450
brass	376	lead	130
carbon	710	silver	235
copper	385	steam	2020
glass	664	water	4180
gold	129	zinc	388

Note that water has a high specific heat when compared to other substances, even ice and steam. One kilogram of water requires the addition of 4180 J of heat to increase its temperature one kelvin. By comparison, the same mass of copper requires only 385 J. The heat needed to raise the temperature of one kilogram of water one kelvin would increase the temperature of the same mass of copper 11 K. The high specific heat of water is the reason water is used to remove waste heat from automobile engines.

Specific heat can be used to find the amount of heat that must be transferred to change the temperature of a given mass by any amount. The specific heat of water is 4180 J/kg · K. When the temperature of one kilogram of water is increased by one kelvin, the heat absorbed by the water is 4180 J. When 10 kilograms of water are heated 5.0 K, the heat absorbed, Q, is

$$Q = (10 \text{ kg})(4180 \text{ J/kg} \cdot \text{K})(5.0 \text{ K})$$
$$= 2.1 \times 10^5 \text{ J}$$

The heat gained or lost by a given mass as its temperature changes depends on the mass, change in temperature, and specific heat of the substance. The relationship can be written

$$Q = mC\Delta T$$

Heat transferred is the product of specific heat, mass, and temperature change.

where Q is the heat gained or lost, m is the mass of the substance, C is the specific heat, and ΔT is the change in temperature. Note that since one Celsius degree is equal to one kelvin, temperature changes can be measured in either kelvins or degrees Celsius.

EXAMPLE

Heat Transfer

A 4.00 × 10² g block of iron is heated from 22°C to 52°C. How much heat is absorbed by the iron?

Given: mass (m) = 0.400 kg   **Unknown:** Q

T_1 = 22°C

T_2 = 52°C

Specific heat (C) = 450 J/kg · K   **Basic equation:** $Q = mC\Delta T$

Solution: $Q = mC\Delta T$

$= (0.400 \text{ kg})(450 \text{ J/kg} \cdot \text{K})(52°\text{C} - 22°\text{C})$

$= 5.4 \times 10^3$ J

Problems

7. How much heat is absorbed by 2.50×10^2 g of water when it is heated from 10.0°C to 85.0°C?

7. 7.84×10^4 J

8. How much heat is absorbed by 60.0 g of copper when it is heated from 20.0°C to 80.0°C?

8. 1390 J

9. A 38-kg block of lead is heated from -26°C to 180°C. How much heat does it absorb during the heating?

9. 1.0×10^6 J

10. The cooling system of an automobile engine contains 20.0 liters of water. (1 L of water has a mass of 1 kg.)

    a. What is the change in the temperature of the water if the engine operates until 836.0 kJ of heat are added?

    b. Suppose it is winter and the engine is filled with methanol having a specific heat of 2.48 kJ/kg · K. The density of methanol is 0.80 g/cm³. What would be the increase in the temperature of the methanol if it also absorbed 836.0 kJ of heat?

    c. Which is the better coolant, water or methanol? Explain.

10. a. 10.0°C
    b. 21°C
    c. Water is the better coolant; water transfers heat better.

11. A 4.00×10^2 g glass coffee cup at room temperature, 20.0°C, is plunged into hot dishwater, 80.0°C. If the temperature of the cup reaches that of the dishwater, how much heat does the cup absorb?

11. 1.59×10^4 J

12. Five kilograms of ice cubes are moved from the freezing compartment of a refrigerator into a home freezer. The refrigerator's freezing compartment is kept at -4.0°C. The home freezer is kept at -17°C. How much heat does the freezer's cooling system remove from the ice cubes?

12. 1.3×10^5 J

13. A 2.50×10^2 kg cast-iron car engine contains water as a coolant. Suppose the engine's temperature is 35°C when it is shut off. The air temperature is 10.0°C. The heat given off by the engine and water in it as they cool to air temperature is 4.4×10^6 J. What mass of water is used to cool the engine?

13. 15 kg

14. An 8.00×10^2 g block of lead is heated in boiling water, 100.0°C, until its temperature is the same as the water. The lead is then removed from the boiling water and dropped into 2.50×10^2 g of cool water at 12.2°C. After a short time, the temperature of both lead and water is 20.0°C.

a. How much heat is gained by the cool water?

b. On the basis of these measurements, what is the specific heat of lead?

14. a. 8200 J
    b. 130 J/kg · K

12:9 Conservation in Energy Transfer

A system is called isolated if energy can neither be added to it nor removed from it. According to the first law of thermodynamics, then, the total energy of an isolated system is constant. A device designed to isolate a system from its surroundings is called a calorimeter.

The total energy of an isolated system is constant. Energy lost by one part is gained by another.

If the energy of part of an isolated system increases, the energy of another part must decrease. Consider a system composed of two blocks of metal, block A and block B. The total energy of the system is constant.

$$E_A + E_B = \text{constant}$$

Suppose that the two blocks are initially separated, but can be placed in contact. If the thermal energy of block A changed by an amount ΔE_A, then the change in thermal energy of block B, ΔE_B, must be related by the equation

$$\Delta E_A + \Delta E_B = 0$$

The change in energy of one block is positive, the other negative. If the thermal energy change is positive, the temperature of that block rises. If the change is negative, the temperature falls.

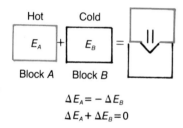

$$\Delta E_A = -\Delta E_B$$
$$\Delta E_A + \Delta E_B = 0$$

FIGURE 12-13. The total energy for this system is constant.

Assume that the initial temperatures of the two blocks were different. When the blocks are brought together, heat will flow from the hotter to the colder block. The flow will continue until the blocks are in thermal equilibrium. The blocks will then have the same temperature.

The change in thermal energy is equal to the heat transferred. That is

$$\Delta E = Q = mC\Delta T$$

The increase in thermal energy of block A is equal to the loss in thermal energy of block B. Thus

$$m_A C_A \Delta T_A + m_B C_B \Delta T_B = 0$$

The change in temperature is the difference between the final and initial temperatures, $\Delta T = T_f - T_i$. If the temperature increases, $T_f > T_i$, and ΔT is positive. If the temperature falls, $T_f < T_i$, and ΔT is negative.

Heat flows as long as one part of a system is at a different temperature than another.

The final temperatures of the two blocks are equal. In most problems, this final, or equilibrium, temperature is to be calculated. The equation for the transfer of energy is

$$m_A C_A (T_f - T_{A,i}) + m_B C_B (T_f - T_{B,i}) = 0$$

To solve this for T_f, expand the equation:

$$m_A C_A T_f - m_A C_A T_{Ai} + m_B C_B T_f - m_B C_B T_{B,i} = 0$$
$$T_f (m_A C_A + m_B C_B) = m_A C_A T_{A,i} + m_B C_B T_{B,i}$$

$$T_f = \frac{m_A C_A T_{A,i} + m_B C_B T_{B,i}}{m_A C_A + m_B C_B}$$

Note that either the Celsius or Kelvin temperature scale may be used with this equation.

Because 1°C = 1 K, either temperature scale may be used in this equation.

EXAMPLE

Conservation in Energy Transfer

A sample of 0.500 kg water is at 15.0°C in a calorimeter. A 0.040-kg mass of zinc at 115°C is placed in the water. What is the final temperature of the system?

Given: zinc

$m_1 = 0.0400$ kg

$T_{1,i} = 115°C$

$C_1 = 388$ J/kg · K

water

$m_2 = 0.500$ kg

$T_{2,i} = 15.0°C$

$C_2 = 4180$ J/kg · K

1 J/kg · K = 1 J/kg · °C

Unknown: T_f

Basic equations:

$$\Delta E_1 + \Delta E_2 = 0$$

$$m_1 C_1 \Delta T_1 + m_2 C_2 \Delta T_2 = 0$$

Solution: $m_1 C_1 (T_f - T_{1,i}) + m_2 C_2 (T_f - T_{2,i}) = 0$

$$T_f = \frac{m_1 C_1 T_{1,i} + m_2 C_2 T_{2,i}}{m_1 C_1 + m_2 C_2}$$

$$\frac{(0.0400 \text{ kg})(388 \text{ J/kg} \cdot \text{C°})(115°C) + (0.500 \text{ kg})(4180 \text{ J/kg} \cdot \text{C°})(15.0°C)}{(0.0400 \text{ kg})(388 \text{ J/kg} \cdot \text{C°}) + (0.500 \text{ kg})(4180 \text{ J/kg} \cdot \text{C°})}$$

$$T_f = \frac{1.78 \times 10^3 \text{ J} + 3.14 \times 10^4 \text{ J}}{15.5 \text{ J/C°} + 2.09 \times 10^3 \text{ J/C°}}$$

$$T_f = \frac{3.32 \times 10^4 \text{ J}}{2.11 \times 10^3 \text{ J/C°}}$$

$$T_f = 15.7°C$$

Problems

15. A 2.00×10^2 g sample of water at 80.0°C is mixed with 2.00×10^2 g of water at 10.0°C. Assume no heat loss to the surroundings. What is the final temperature of the mixture?

15. 45.0°C

16. A 6.0×10^2 g sample of water at 90.0°C is mixed with 4.00×10^2 g of water at 22°C. Assume no heat loss to the surroundings. What is the final temperature of the mixture?

16. 63.°C

17. 59.6°C

18. 23.0°C

19. 840 J/kg · K

20. 12.8°C

17. A 4.00×10^2 g sample of alcohol at 16.0°C is mixed with 4.00×10^2 g of water at 85.0°C. Assume no heat loss to the surroundings. What is the temperature of the mixture?

18. A 1.00×10^2 g mass of brass at 90.0°C is placed in a glass beaker containing 2.00×10^2 g of water at 20.0°C. Assume no heat loss to the glass or surroundings. What is the final temperature of the mixture?

19. A 1.0×10^2 g mass of aluminum at 100.0°C is placed in 1.00×10^2 g of water at 10.0°C. The final temperature of the mixture is 25°C. What is the specific heat of the aluminum?

20. A 10.0-kg piece of zinc at 71°C is placed in a container of water. The water has a mass of 20.0 kg and has a temperature of 10.0°C before the zinc is added. What is the final temperature of the water and zinc?

12:10 Change of State

Our simplified model of a solid consisted of tiny particles bonded together by springs. The springs represented the electromagnetic forces between the particles. If the thermal energy of a solid is increased, both potential and kinetic energy of the particles may increase. The temperature is a measure of the average kinetic energy of the particles.

At sufficiently high temperatures, the forces between the particles are no longer strong enough to hold them in fixed locations. The particles have more freedom of movement. Eventually, the particles become free to slide past each other. The substance has changed from a solid to a liquid. The temperature at which this occurs is called the melting point.

When a substance is in the process of melting, added thermal energy increases the potential energy of particles, breaking the bonds holding them together. The added thermal energy does not increase the kinetic energy of the particles. Thus, the temperature does not increase.

When a substance melts, added energy does not increase temperature.

The amount of energy needed to melt a unit mass of a substance is called the **heat of fusion** of that substance. For example, the heat of fusion of ice is 3.34×10^5 J/kg. If 1 kg of ice at its melting point, 273 K, absorbs 3.34×10^5 J, it will become 1 kg of water at the same temperature, 273 K. The added energy causes a change in state but not in temperature.

The heat of fusion is the thermal energy increase required to melt one kilogram of a substance.

After the substance is totally melted, a further increase in thermal energy once again increases the temperature. Added thermal energy increases both the kinetic and potential energy. As the temperature increases, some particles in the middle of the liquid obtain enough energy to break free from other particles. A tiny bubble of vapor is formed and rises to the surface. At a certain temperature, any added thermal energy is used to increase the potential energy of particles and change them from the liquid to the vapor state. This temperature is known as the boiling point. Water boils at 373 K at a pressure of 1 atm (101 kPa). The amount of thermal energy needed to vaporize a unit mass of liquid is called the **heat of vaporization.** For water, the heat of vaporization is 2.26×10^6 J/kg. Each substance has a characteristic heat of vaporization.

The heat of vaporization is the thermal energy increase needed to boil one kilogram of a substance.

TABLE 12-2

Heats of Fusion and Vaporization of Common Substances			
Material	Heat of Fusion (J/kg)	Material	Heat of Fusion (J/kg)
alcohol	1.09×10^5	lead	2.30×10^4
copper	2.05×10^5	mercury	1.15×10^4
gold	6.30×10^4	silver	1.05×10^5
iron	2.76×10^5	water (ice)	3.34×10^5
	Heat of Vaporization (J/kg)		Heat of Vaporization (J/kg)
alcohol	8.78×10^5	lead	8.64×10^5
copper	4.82×10^6	mercury	3.06×10^5
gold	1.64×10^6	silver	2.36×10^6
iron	6.29×10^6	water	2.26×10^6

The heat, Q_f, required to melt a solid of mass, m, is given by

$$Q_f = mH_f.$$

The value of some heats of fusion, H_f, can be found in Table 12-2.
   Similarly, the heat, Q_v, required to vaporize a mass, m, of liquid is given by

$$Q_v = mH_v.$$

Heats of vaporization, H_v, can also be found in Table 12-2.

EXAMPLE

Heat of Fusion

   If 5.00×10^3 J is added to ice at 273 K, how much ice is melted?

Given: heat added (Q_f)
           $= 5.00 \times 10^3$ J

           heat of fusion (H_f)
           $= 3.34 \times 10^5$ J/kg

Unknown: mass (m)

Basic equation: $Q_f = mH_f$

Solution: $m = \dfrac{Q_f}{H_f}$

$\qquad\quad = (5.00 \times 10^3 \text{ J})/(3.34 \times 10^5 \text{ J/kg})$

$\qquad\quad = 0.0150 \text{ kg}$

Figure 12-14 shows the changes in temperature as thermal energy is added to 1.0 g of H_2O at 173 K. Between points a and b, the ice is warmed to 273 K. Between points b and c, the added thermal energy melts the ice at a constant 273 K. The distance, c to b, represents the heat of fusion. Between c and d, the water temperature rises. The slope is larger here than between a and b, showing that the specific heat of water is higher than that of ice. Between points d and e, the water boils, becoming water vapor. The distance d to e represents the heat of vaporization. Between e and f, the steam is heated to 473 K. The slope is smaller than that from c to d, indicating that the specific heat of steam is less than that of water.

FIGURE 12-14. Graph of the heat absorbed by 1.0 g of ice as its temperature is raised from −100°C to 200°C. Notice that the slope of the graph is steeper from c to d than it is from a to b and from e to f. This is because the specific heats of ice and steam are greater than the specific heat of water. The vertical portions of the graph indicate that heat is being absorbed with no change in temperature.

Heat Absorbed
versus
Temperature

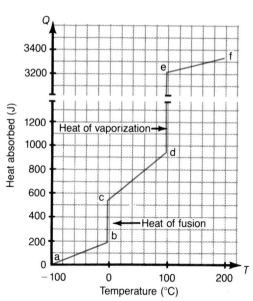

EXAMPLE

Heat of Fusion

Heat is applied to 100.0 g of ice at 0.0°C until the ice melts and the temperature of the resulting water rises to 20.0°C. How much heat is absorbed?

Given: $m = 100.0$ g

$\qquad\quad T_1 = 0.0°$ C

$\qquad\quad T_2 = 20.0°$C

$\qquad\quad H_f = 3.34 \times 10^5$ J/kg

$\qquad\quad C = 4180$ J/kg · C°

Unknown: Q_{total}

Basic equations: $Q_f = mH_f$

$\qquad\qquad\qquad\qquad Q = mC\Delta T$

Solution:

First, find the amount of heat the ice absorbs to cause a change from solid to liquid.

$$Q_f = mH_f$$
$$= (0.100 \text{ kg})(3.34 \times 10^5 \text{ J/kg})$$
$$= 33\ 400 \text{ J}$$

Next, calculate the amount of heat the water absorbs to raise the temperature of the water from 0.0°C to 20.0° C.

$$Q = mC\Delta T$$
$$= (0.100 \text{ kg})(4180 \text{ J/kg} \cdot \text{C}°)(20.0°\text{C} - 0.0°\text{C})$$
$$= 8360 \text{ J}$$

Finally, the two quantities of heat are added.

$$Q_{total} = Q_f + Q$$
$$= 33\ 400 \text{ J} + 8360 \text{ J}$$
$$= 41\ 800 \text{ J}$$

Problems

21. How much heat is needed to change 50.0 g of ice at 0.0°C to water at 0.0°C?

21. 16 700 J

22. How much heat is needed to change 50.0 g of water at 100°C to steam at 100°C?

22. 1.13×10^5 J

23. How much heat is absorbed by 1.00×10^2 g of ice at −20.0°C to become water at 0.0°C? The specific heat of ice is 2.06 J/g · C°.

23. 38 000 J

24. A 2.00×10^2 g sample of water at 60.0°C is heated to steam at 140.0°C. How much heat is absorbed?

24. 5.02×10^5 J

25. How much heat is needed to change 3.00×10^2 g of ice at −30.0°C to steam at 130.0°C?

25. 9.40×10^5 J

26. How much heat is removed from 60.0 g of steam at 100.0°C to change it to 60.0 g of water at 20.0°C?

26. 1.56×10^5 J

27. The specific heat of mercury is 0.14 J/g · C°. Its heat of vaporization is 306 J/g. How much heat is needed to heat 1.0 kg of mercury metal from 10.0°C to its boiling point and vaporize it completely? The boiling point of mercury is 357°C.

27. 3.6×10^5 J

28. Years ago, a block of ice with a mass of about 20.0 kg was used daily in a home icebox. The temperature of the ice was 0.0°C when delivered. As it melted, how much heat in joules did a block of ice of this size absorb?

28. 6.68×10^6 J

Summary

12:1   **1.** Thermal energy of an object is the sum of kinetic and potential energies of the internal motion of the particles.

12:2   **2.** The temperature of an object is proportional to the average kinetic energy of the particles.

12:3   **3.** When two bodies are in thermal equilibrium their temperatures are equal.

12:3   **4.** Thermometers use some property of a substance, such as thermal expansion, that depends on temperature.

12:4-12:5   **5.** The Celsius and Kelvin temperature scales are widely used. One kelvin is equal to one degree Celsius.

12:5   **6.** At absolute zero, 0 K or −273°C, the average kinetic energy of the particles is zero.

12:6   **7.** Heat is thermal energy transferred by means of a difference in temperature.

12:6   **8.** Heat naturally flows from a hot to a cold body.

12:6   **9.** The first law of thermodynamics states that the increase in thermal energy of a body is equal to the sum of the heat and mechanical energy added.

12:6   **10.** A heat engine continuously converts heat to mechanical energy.

12:6   **11.** A heat pump or refrigerator uses mechanical energy to remove heat from something at a low temperature and add heat to something at a higher temperature.

12:7   **12.** Entropy, a measure of disorder, never decreases in natural processes.

12:8   **13.** The specific heat is the quantity of heat required to raise the temperature of one kilogram of a substance one kelvin.

12:9   **14.** In an isolated system, the thermal energy of one part may change but the total thermal energy is constant.

12:10   **15.** The heat of fusion is the quantity of heat required to melt one kilogram of a substance at its melting point.

12:10   **16.** The heat of vaporization is the quantity of heat required to change one kilogram of a substance from the liquid to vapor state at its boiling point.

12:10   **17.** The heat transferred during a change of state does not produce a change in temperature.

Detailed answers to all Questions and Problems are given in the Teacher's Guide at the front of this book.

Questions

1. Explain the difference between an object's external and its thermal energy. Give an example.

2. Distinguish between thermal energy and temperature.

3. How does heat differ from thermal energy?

4. What is the temperature of a typical winter day on the
   a. Celsius scale,
   b. Kelvin scale?

5. What is the temperature of an extremely hot summer day on the
   a. Celsius scale,
   b. Kelvin scale?

6. Ten grams of aluminum and ten grams of lead are heated to the same temperature. The pieces of metal are placed on a block of ice. Which metal melts more ice?

7. An automobile is brought to a stop by applying friction brakes to the wheels. The brakes get hot; their thermal energy is increased. The decrease in kinetic energy of the car is equal to the increase in thermal energy of the brakes. According to the first law of thermodynamics, the brakes could cool and return the thermal energy to the car, causing it to resume its motion. This does not happen. Why?

8. Explain entropy so that a fellow student in your physics course could understand.

9. Which liquid would an ice cube cool faster, water or alcohol? Explain.

Problems–A

1. Convert these Celsius temperatures to Kelvin temperatures.
   a. 51°C   b. 155°C   c. −207°C   d. 302°C

2. Convert these Kelvin temperatures to Celsius temperatures.
   a. 51 K   b. 155 K   c. 273 K   d. 302 K

3. How much heat in joules is needed to raise the temperature of 50.0 g of water from 4.5°C to 83°C?

4. How much heat in joules must be added to 50.0 g of aluminum at 25°C to raise its temperature to 125°C?

5. Suppose the same amount of heat needed to raise the temperature of 50.0 g of water through 1.00×10^2°C is applied to 50.0 g of zinc. What is the temperature change of zinc?

1. a. 324 K
   b. 428 K
   c. 66 K
   d. 575 K

2. a. −222°C
   b. −118°C
   c. 0°C
   d. 29°C

3. 1.6×10^4 J

4. 4.52×10^3 J

5. 1080 C°

6. 1100 J

6. A copper wire has a mass of 165 g. An electric current runs through the wire for a short time and its temperature rises from 21°C to 39°C. What minimum quantity of heat is generated by the electric current?

7. 62°C

7. A 5.00×10^2 g sample of water at 92°C is mixed with 5.0×10^2 g of water at 32°C. Assume no heat loss to surroundings. What is the final temperature of the mixture?

8. 25°C

8. A 2.00×10^2 g sample of brass at 100.0°C is placed in a calorimeter cup that contains 261 g of water at 20.0°C. Disregard the absorption of heat by the cup and calculate the final temperature of the mixture. The specific heat of brass is 0.376 J/g · K.

9. 170 J/kg · K

9. A 1.00×10^2 g sample of tungsten at 100.0°C is placed in 2.00×10^2 g of water at 20.0°C. The mixture reaches equilibrium at 21.6°C. Calculate the specific heat of tungsten.

10. 3.09×10^4 J

10. How much heat is added to 10.0 g of ice at $-20.0°C$ to convert it to steam at 120.0°C?

11. 247 J/g

11. A 40.0-g sample of chloroform is condensed from a vapor at 61.6°C to a liquid at 61.6°C. It liberates 9870 joules of heat. What is the heat of vaporization of chloroform?

12. 35.6°C

12. A 50.0-g sample of ice at 0.00°C is placed in a glass beaker containing 4.00 $\times 10^2$ g of water at 50.0°C. All the ice melts. What is the final temperature of the mixture? Disregard heat loss to the glass.

13. 1.00 J/g · C°

13. A 5.00×10^2 g block of metal absorbs 5016 joules of heat when its temperature changes from 20.0°C to 30.0°C. Calculate the specific heat of the metal.

Problems–B

1. 350 s

1. A 3.00×10^2 watt electric immersion heater is used to heat a cup of water. The cup is made of glass and its mass is 3.00×10^2 g. It contains 250 g of water at 15°C. How much time is needed for the heater to bring the water to the boiling point? The specific heat of glass is 0.664 J/g · K. Assume the temperature of the cup to be the same as the temperature of the water at all times.

2. a. 3.1°C
   b. 12°C

2. A nuclear power plant on the Connecticut River produces 2.00×10^2 megawatts of power but also releases 1.0×10^{11} kJ/day of waste heat into the river. Assume that the average rate of flow of the river is 9.0×10^4 kg/s.

    a. What is the maximum temperature increase in the river water that could be caused by the plant's cooling system?

    b. The construction of four additional nuclear power plants along the river has been proposed. What is the total increase in the temperature of the river that could result if the plants are built? Could this change cause serious damage to the ecological structure of the river?

3. During a game, the metabolism of basketball players often increases by as much as 30.0 watts. How much perspiration will a player vaporize per hour to dissipate this extra thermal energy?

3. 47.8 g

4. Due to the rising cost of oil, a school in Pennsylvania converted its heating system from oil to coal. The school contains 1.70×10^4 kg of air and the heat of combustion of coal is 3.35×10^4 kJ/kg. How many kg of coal must be burned in the school's new furnace to bring the temperature of the unheated air in the school from $-10.0°C$ to $24°C$? The specific heat of air is 1.1 kJ/kg · C°. Assume that 50.0% of the heat produced by the coal actually serves to heat the air in the school.

4. 38 kg

Readings

Brewer, Richard, "Atomic Memory." *Scientific American*, December, 1984.

Lindsley, E. F., "Stirling Auto Engine: A Lot of Progress, but . . . " *Popular Science*, January, 1983.

Nicastro, A. J., "A Dynamical Model of a Carnot Cycle." *The Physics Teacher*, October, 1983.

Smay, Elaine, "Heat-Pipe Furnace." *Popular Science*, February, 1984.

Warren, David, "Solar Systems and Heat Pumps Combine to Cut Energy Bills." *Discover*, January, 1983.

Pressure is defined as the force exerted on a unit area of a surface. Similar forces may produce vastly different pressures—the pressure on the ground under a lady's high heel is far greater than that under an elephant's foot. How does the kinetic theory explain pressure? How does this theory explain everyday events involving gases?

Gas Laws

Chapter 13 introduces the gas laws including Boyle's law, Charles' law, and the combined gas laws.

Since the nineteenth century, the idea has been accepted that all matter is made up of extremely tiny particles. It is the differences in the arrangements of these particles and in the forces acting among them that allows matter to exist in any of four states: solid, liquid, gas, and plasma. In a gas, the particles are widely separated and act independently of one another. A sample of gas will expand to fill any container that encloses it, and the particles will be distributed evenly throughout. In order to describe the physical condition or **state** of a given sample of gas, it is necessary to specify its temperature, pressure, volume, and mass. A change in any one of these quantities will always result in a change in at least one of the others. The relationships between these quantities are called equations of state. They were derived from empirical laws (laws based on experimental results) relating temperature, pressure, and volume that were well established by the eighteenth century. However, knowledge of what a gas was or why it behaved as it did came much later.

Goal: You will gain understanding of how the pressure, temperature, and volume of an ideal gas are related and how these relationships are explained by the kinetic theory.

Four quantities describe the condition, or state, of a gas—temperature, pressure, volume, and mass.

13:1 Assumptions of the Kinetic Theory

The kinetic theory of matter forms the basis of our understanding of how a gas behaves. The three basic assumptions of the kinetic theory are

1. All matter is made of very small particles.
2. These particles are in constant random motion.
3. The particles experience perfectly elastic collisions with each other and with the walls of the container.

Kinetic theory is based on the assumption that all matter is made up of very small particles, in constant random motion, that experience purely elastic collisions.

217

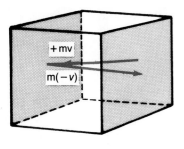

$$Ft = m\triangle v$$

FIGURE 13-1. The force exerted per unit area by many particles of a gas randomly striking the walls of the container is called pressure.

Gas exerts a force on its container as a result of the collisions of particles with the walls.

We will first examine the behavior of an ideal gas. An **ideal gas** is an imaginary gas made up of particles with mass but no volume and with no attraction for each other. Later we will discuss under what conditions the behavior of a real gas is the same as that of an ideal gas. Kinetic theory will be used to find various relationships among volume, pressure, and temperature of an ideal gas.

13:2 Pressure

If a gas is placed in a closed container, the randomly moving particles of the gas will strike the sides of the container. In Figure 13-1, a particle with velocity, v, is shown striking the wall of the container. Since the collision is elastic, the particle rebounds with velocity, $-v$. The particle's change in momentum imparts an impulse (Ft) to the wall of the container. During the brief time the particle is in contact with the wall, it exerts a force on the wall. Because the sample of gas contains a huge number of particles, many collisions take place between the particles and the wall every instant. There are so many collisions that the total force exerted by the gas over a reasonable time interval is constant. The force exerted by the particles on a unit area of surface is defined as **pressure**. Because the particles are moving randomly in all directions, the pressure will be equal on all walls. The SI unit for pressure is the pascal (Pa). A pascal is equal to one newton per square meter.

$$1 \text{ Pa} = 1 \text{ N/m}^2$$

A pressure of one pascal is a very low pressure. For this reason, the kilopascal (kPa) or 1000 pascals is a more useful unit.

$$1000 \text{ N/m}^2 = 1000 \text{ Pa} = 1 \text{ kPa}$$

FIGURE 13-2. An aneroid barometer (a) measures air pressure by means of changes in the size of an evacuated chamber. A mercury barometer (b) measures air pressure by using the height of a column of mercury supported by the atmosphere.

Scientists have long found it convenient to relate pressure to **standard atmospheric pressure**. This value is the average pressure of the atmosphere measured at sea level. Standard atmospheric pressure is 1.013×10^5 pascals, or 101.3 kPa.

Standard atmospheric pressure is 101.3 kPa.

Barometers are instruments used to measure atmospheric pressure. There are two basic types of barometers. Aneroid (AN uh royd) barometers, Figure 13-2a, consist of a metal can or aneroid that contains a near vacuum. A needle is attached to the top of the can. The shape of the aneroid changes slightly when air pressure changes, causing the needle to move along a scale calibrated to read in air pressure units.

Mercury barometers are more accurate and are most frequently used in laboratories. Atmospheric pressure is measured by the height of a column of mercury that the force of the atmosphere will support. Figure 13-2b shows how a mercury barometer is made. A glass tube is sealed at one end and completely filled with mercury. If the filled tube is inverted and placed in a dish of mercury, the mercury drops slightly in the tube, creating a vacuum. Hence, there is no air pressing down on the mercury at the top of the tube. Since the mercury level in the tube remains above the level in the dish, there must be an upward force on the column equal to the weight of the mercury it contains. This force is supplied by the weight of the atmosphere pressing on the mercury in the dish. When the air pressure changes, the height of the column of mercury in the tube will increase or decrease. Therefore, the height of the column of mercury is a direct indication of pressure.

Show small groups of students the detailed construction of the mercury barometer in your laboratory. Have each student individually practice reading the mercury barometer. Compare the mercury barometer to an aneroid barometer.

Atmospheric pressure, under standard atmospheric conditions, will support a column of mercury 760 millimeters (76.0 cm) high. Thus, the standard atmospheric pressure is referred to as 760 millimeters of mercury, or as 760 Torr. The Torr, which replaced the "millimeter of mercury" as a pressure unit, was named in honor of the Italian scientist Evangelista Torricelli (1608-1647), who studied atmospheric pressure and invented the barometer. In meteorology, atmospheric pressure is most commonly expressed in millibars (mb). One millibar equals 0.10 kPa. Thus, standard atmospheric pressure is 1013 mb. One atmosphere (1 atm) of pressure, $1.013 \times 10^5 \, N/m^2$, 101.3 kPa, 1013 mb, and 760 Torr are all equivalent measurements. Meteorologists watch barometric readings carefully because atmospheric pressure changes have a direct relationship to weather conditions.

13:3 Boyle's Law

Robert Boyle (1627-1691), a British chemist and physicist, demonstrated the relationship between the pressure and volume of a gas, now known as **Boyle's law.** *If the temperature remains constant, the volume of a given sample of a gas varies inversely with the pressure of the gas.* Because the pressure-volume relationship is an inverse relationship, the product of the pressure (P) and volume (V) is constant.

Boyle's law states that the product of pressure and volume is constant.

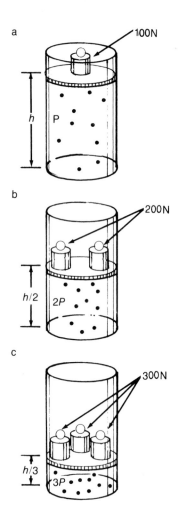

a

100N

h P

b

200N

$h/2$ 2P

c

300N

$h/3$ 3P

FIGURE 13-3. The volume of a gas decreases as the pressure applied to it increases.

$$PV = k$$

If P_1 and V_1 are the initial pressure and volume, and P_2 and V_2 are the final pressure and volume, then

$$P_1V_1 = k = P_2V_2$$

Boyle's law for a given mass of gas at a constant temperature can be expressed mathematically as

$$\boxed{P_1V_1 = P_2V_2}$$

Boyle's law is valid for real gases except at very low temperatures and high pressures.

The kinetic theory predicts an ideal gas should follow Boyle's law. Consider a gas-filled container with a cross-sectional area of 1 m² as shown in Figure 13-3. The container is sealed with a weightless piston that is free to move up and down. A 100-N weight is placed on top of the piston. The piston moves down the container until it comes to rest at some location, h. Here, the piston is in equilibrium. The downward force of the weight on the piston is balanced by the upward force of the gas on the piston. At this volume, the pressure of the gas is 100 Pa (100 N/m²). If the weight is increased to 200 N, the piston will move to a new location where the gas pressure is twice the original pressure. If the average kinetic energy of the particles remains constant (constant temperature), twice the number of collisions will take place if the vertical distance traveled by each particle is halved, or h/2. At this height, the volume is one-half the original volume. If the pressure is increased to 300 Pa, the piston will move to a position where the number of collisions is three times the original number or h/3. The volume is one-third the original. Figure 13-4 shows the pressure-volume graph of an ideal gas. The curve is a hyperbola, indicating an inverse relationship between pressure and volume.

FIGURE 13-4. The curve is a hyperbola indicating an inverse relationship between pressure and volume.

Volume versus Pressure

EXAMPLE

Boyle's Law

Under a pressure of 2.00×10^2 kPa, a confined gas has a volume of 2.6 m³. The pressure acting on the gas is increased to 5.00×10^2 kPa. The temperature of the gas remains unchanged. What is the volume of the gas?

Given: $P_1 = 2.00 \times 10^2$ kPa   **Unknown:** V_2

$V_1 = 2.6$ m³   **Basic equation:** $P_1V_1 = P_2V_2$

$P_2 = 5.00 \times 10^2$ kPa

Solution: $P_1V_1 = P_2V_2$ or $V_2 = \dfrac{P_1V_1}{P_2} = \dfrac{(200 \text{ kPa})(2.6 \text{ m}^3)}{500 \text{ kPa}} = 1.0$ m³

Problems

1. Pressure acting on 60.3 m³ of a gas is raised from 236 kPa to 354 kPa. The temperature is kept constant. What new volume does the gas occupy?

2. A volume of 5.00 m³ of neon gas is expanded until its volume becomes 12.5 m³. The original pressure acting on the gas was 2.00×10^2 kPa. What is the final pressure acting on the gas?

3. A helium-filled balloon occupies a volume of 16 m³ at sea level. The balloon is released and rises to a point in the atmosphere where the pressure is 0.75 atm. What is its volume?

4. An inflated balloon occupies a volume of 2.0 liters. The balloon is tied with a string and weighted with a heavy stone. What is its volume when it reaches the bottom of a pond 20.8 m deep? Note: One atmosphere of pressure supports a column of water 10.4 m high. Assume the pressure acting on the balloon before it submerges is 1.0 atm.

5. A helium-filled balloon occupies a volume of 2.0 m³ at sea level. The balloon then rises to a height in the atmosphere where its volume is 6.0 m³. What is the pressure in kPa at this height?

6. A diver works at a depth of 52 m in fresh water. A bubble of air with a volume of 2.0 cm³ escapes from the diver's mouthpiece. What is the volume of the same bubble as it breaks the surface of the water? (See note in Problem 4.)

1. 40.2 m³

2. 80.0 kPa

3. 21 m³

4. 0.67 L

5. 34 kPa

6. 12 cm³

13:4 Charles' Law

Boyle's law assumes that the temperature of a gas remains constant. We will now consider the relationship that exists between the temperature and volume of a gas where the pressure remains constant.

Jacques Charles (1746-1823) discovered that, at constant pressure, gases expand the same amount for a given temperature change. Charles kept a gas at 0°C under a pressure of 101 kPa. He increased its

An experiment that shows Charles' results should be performed in lab or demonstrated.

Charles found that when the temperature of a gas at constant pressure is changed one kelvin, the volume changed 1/273 of its volume at 0°C.

temperature to 1°C, and the gas expanded 1/273 of its original volume. He increased the temperature to 2°C. Its volume increased 2/273 of the first volume. At 273°C, the volume was twice the volume at 0°C. Charles obtained similar results when he reduced the temperature of the gas below 0°C. For each Celsius degree below 0°C, the volume of the gas was reduced by 1/273 of its original volume. This discovery had startling implications. In theory, it meant that at −273°C a gas would have zero volume. However, substances do not remain a gas as temperatures are lowered. A point is reached when a change of state occurs, and the gas becomes a liquid. Then, a further decrease in temperature causes the liquid to follow a different rate of contraction.

Figure 13-5 plots the volume of a gas against its temperature. The volume of the gas at 0°C is the basic volume. Today, in the laboratory, it is possible to measure most of the data needed to plot such a graph. However, in Charles' day, it was not possible to attain temperatures much below −20°C. Charles extended the line of the graph down to temperatures below −20°C to see what lower limits might be possible. Extending a graph beyond measured points is called **extrapolation**. If extrapolation is based on precise data and used with care, it can provide useful information upon which to draw conclusions.

Through his work with gases, Charles accomplished two things. He postulated the point of absolute zero, and he found the relationship between the temperature and the volume of a gas now known as **Charles' law.** *Under constant pressure, the volume of a given amount of gas varies directly as its kelvin temperature.*

Charles' law states that, at constant pressure, the volume of a fixed amount of gas is directly proportional to its temperature in kelvins.

$$V = k'T$$

$$\frac{V_1}{T_1} = k' = \frac{V_2}{T_2}$$

In calculations using Charles' law, temperature must be expressed in kelvins.

Volume versus Temperature

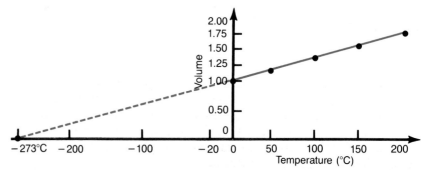

FIGURE 13-5. The straight line curve indicates that the volume varies directly with the temperature. The curve can be extended to show 0 volume at 0 K.

EXAMPLE

Charles' Law

A volume of 22.0 m³ of nitrogen gas at 20.0°C is heated under constant pressure to 167°C. What is the new volume of the nitrogen gas?

Given: $V_1 = 22.0$ m³   **Unknown:** V_2

$T_1 = 20.0$°C   **Basic Equation:** $\dfrac{V_1}{T_1} = \dfrac{V_2}{T_2}$

$T_2 = 167$°C

Solution: $T_1 = 20$°C; 20°C $+ 273$°C $= 293$ K

$T_2 = 167$°C; 167°C $+ 273$°C $= 440$ K

$$\frac{V_1}{T_1} = \frac{V_2}{T_2}$$

$$V_2 = \frac{V_1 T_2}{T_1} = \frac{(22.0 \text{ m}^3)(440 \text{ K})}{293 \text{ K}} = 33.0 \text{ m}^3$$

Problems

7. A volume of 30.0 m³ of argon gas is kept under constant pressure. The gas is heated from 20.0°C to 293°C. What is the new volume of the gas?

8. Thirty liters of oxygen gas are kept under constant pressure. The gas is cooled from 20.0°C to −146.5°C. What is the new volume of the gas?

9. A gas at 60.0°C has a volume of 0.021 m³. Under constant pressure, it is heated to twice its original volume. What is the temperature of the gas?

10. A volume of 4.0 m³ of a gas is kept under constant pressure. Its temperature is increased from 40.0°C to 140.0°C. What is the new volume of the gas?

7. 58.0 m³

8. 13 L

9. 670 K

10. 5.3 m³

13:5 Combined Gas Law

By combining Boyle's law and Charles' law, an equation can be derived that relates pressure, temperature, and volume of a constant amount of gas.

$$\boxed{\frac{P_1 V_1}{T_1} = \frac{P_2 V_2}{T_2}}$$

This equation is called the combined gas law. It applies to gases at moderate pressures. However, under high pressures or low temperatures, the law is modified. The combined gas law reduces to Boyle's law if the temperature is constant. If the pressure is kept constant, it reduces to Charles' law. If the volume is kept constant, the pressure varies directly with the temperature.

The combined gas law relates temperature, pressure, and volume of a gas.

Point out that the combined gas law reduces to Boyle's law if *T* is held constant. If *P* is held constant, the combined gas law reduces to Charles' law.

a

b

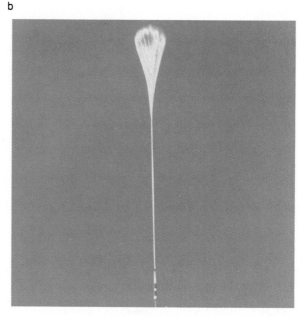

FIGURE 13-6. The volume of a balloon is controlled by the temperature, mass of gas and air pressure. As the balloon rises, changes in air pressure and temperature occur.

EXAMPLE

Combined Gas Law

A 20.0 L sample of gas is kept under a pressure of 1.00×10^2 kPa at a temperature of 273 K. The gas temperature is lowered to 91 K. The pressure is increased to 1.50×10^2 kPa. What is the new volume of the gas?

Given: $V_1 = 20.0$ L

$P_1 = 1.00 \times 10^2$ kPa

$T_1 = 273$ K

$T_2 = 91$ K

$P_2 = 1.50 \times 10^2$ kPa

Unknown: V_2

Basic Equation: $\dfrac{P_1V_1}{T_1} = \dfrac{P_2V_2}{T_2}$

Solution: $\dfrac{P_1V_1}{T_1} = \dfrac{P_2V_2}{T_2}$

$$V_2 = \frac{P_1V_1T_2}{P_2T_1}$$

$$= \frac{(1.00 \times 10^2 \text{ kPa})(20.0 \text{ L})(91 \text{ K})}{(1.50 \times 10^2 \text{ kPa})(273 \text{ K})}$$

$$= 4.4 \text{ L}$$

Problems

11. 410 kPa

11. Ten cubic meters of hydrogen gas are confined in a cylinder under a pressure of 205 kPa at a temperature of 91 K. The volume is kept constant, but the temperature is increased to 182 K. What pressure does the gas exert on the walls of the container?

12. Two hundred liters of gas at 0°C are kept under a pressure of 150 kPa. The temperature of the gas is raised to 273°C. The pressure is increased to 350 kPa. What is the final volume?

12. 170 L

13. Fifty liters of gas are kept at a temperature of 200 K and under pressure of 15 atm. The temperature of the gas is increased to 400 K. The pressure is decreased to 7.5 atm. What is the volume of the gas?

13. 200 L

13:6   Ideal Gas Law

Consider a sample of ideal gas at constant temperature and constant volume. If we increase the number of particles, n, we will increase the number of collisions with the container wall, thereby increasing the pressure. If we remove particles, the reverse will take place. However, to maintain constant temperature and pressure, an increase or decrease in the number of particles must be accompanied by a respective increase or decrease in volume. Both volume and pressure vary directly with the number of particles.

$$PV = kn$$

Consider a sample of gas in a rigid container at constant pressure. If we increase the number of particles of gas, we increase the number of collisions with the walls of the container. In order to maintain a constant pressure, the impulse imparted to the wall by each collision must be reduced. This can be done by reducing the velocity, and therefore the average kinetic energy of the particles. Because temperature is a measure of the average kinetic energy of the particles, the temperature must be decreased. If the number of particles decreases, the temperature must rise to keep the pressure constant. Thus, at constant volume and pressure, the number of particles and the absolute temperature are inversely proportional.

$$nT = k'$$

We are now able to combine our knowledge of the behavior of a gas into one equation that describes the interrelationship among the four variables. Combining all of the equations in this chapter, we can write

$$PV = k''nT.$$

This equation is called the ideal gas law.

The proportionality constant k'' is often written as R, the universal constant, or k, the Boltzmann constant, depending on whether n is expressed in number of moles or number of particles. The value of the constant is determined by the units used for the variables.

The ideal gas law relates changes in the number of particles to changes in pressure, volume, and temperature.

13:7 Real Gases

Boyle's and Charles' laws were developed experimentally, using real gases. In Section 13:6, we combined these empirical laws into the equation $PV = nRT$. This equation is called the ideal gas law because only an ideal gas obeys it for all values of P and V. However, many gases at moderate temperatures and pressures approach the behavior of an ideal gas. Deviations become more significant as temperatures decrease and pressures increase.

Consider a gas such as oxygen. At laboratory temperatures and pressures, the volume of the particles is small compared to the total volume of the gas. Any effects due to particle volume or attractive forces are slight.

Now consider the same gas at $-80°C$ and pressures starting at 10 atm. At this temperature, the gas particles have reduced kinetic energy. As the pressure increases and the particles approach each other, the forces of attraction between the particles draw the particles together. The volume shrinks faster than the equation $PV = k$ predicts. As the pressure continues to increase, the actual volume of real gas particles begins to make up a larger part of the total gas volume. It is more and more difficult to compress the gas. Therefore, increases in pressure do not cause proportional volume decreases. Volume shrinks more slowly than predicted for an ideal gas.

The differences between real gas particles and ideal gas particles are very important in changing gases to liquids. The electromagnetic forces between real gas particles are relatively weak. However, as the thermal energy and the distance between the particles decrease, these forces begin to predominate. At some combination of temperature and pressure, determined by the structure of the particle, every real gas changes to a liquid or a solid .

Gases at normal pressures and temperatures are almost ideal gases.

Real gases have particles that take up space and weakly attract each other over short distances.

FIGURE 13-7. A pressure-temperature graph shows the fusion and vaporization curves of water (a). The three phases of water are present in the chamber (b).

a

b

| Summary |

1. The kinetic theory assumes that a gas is made up of tiny, perfectly elastic particles in constant random motion.   13:1

2. An ideal gas is made up of particles that have mass but no volume and no attraction for each other.   13:1

3. Pressure is force per unit area and is expressed as pascals (newtons per square meter). The kilopascal (kPa) is 1000 Pa.   13:2

4. An important standard for pressure is the average pressure of the atmosphere at sea level. This value is 101 kPa.   13:2

5. Boyle's law states that the volume of a gas varies inversely with the applied pressure, provided the temperature remains constant.   13:3

6. Charles' law states that the volume of a gas varies directly with its kelvin (absolute) temperature provided the pressure remains constant.   13:4

7. The ideal gas law describes the physical state of an ideal gas in terms of its temperature, pressure, volume, and number of particles.   13:6

8. Real gases differ from ideal gases in that real gas particles do have volume and attraction for one another. However, at moderate temperatures and pressures, real gases follow the ideal gas laws.   13:7

Detailed answers to all Questions and Problems are given in the Teacher's Guide at the front of this book.

| Questions |

1. State the assumptions of the kinetic theory.

2. State standard atmospheric pressure in four different terms.

3. Explain why the liquid rises in the straw when you drink a soda.

4. What happens when the pressure acting on a gas is held constant but the temperature of the gas changes?

5. What happens when the temperature of a gas remains constant and pressure is changed?

6. If you made a barometer that was filled with a liquid one-third as dense as mercury, how high would the level of the liquid be on a day of normal atmospheric pressure?

7. Explain how Charles' experiments with gases indicated the possible location of absolute zero.

8. Describe how a real gas differs from an ideal gas. What are some of the consequences of these differences?

Problems–A

1. 2.0 × 10² cm³

1. The pressure acting on 50.0 cm³ of a gas is reduced from 1.2 atm to 0.30 atm. What is the new volume of the gas if there is no temperature change?

2. −5.40°C

2. The pressure acting on a volume of 50.0 m³ of air is 1.01×10^5 N/m². The air is at a temperature of −50.0°C. The pressure acting on the gas is increased to 2.02×10^5 N/m². Then the gas occupies a volume of 30.0 m³. What is the temperature of the air at this new volume?

3. 606 K

3. Two cubic meters of a gas at 30.0°C are heated at constant pressure until the volume is doubled. What is the final temperature of the gas?

4. 0.33 m³

4. A cubic meter of gas at standard temperature and pressure is cooled to 91 K. The pressure is not changed. What volume does the gas occupy?

5. 2.33 m³

5. A cubic meter of gas at standard temperature and pressure is heated to 364°C. The pressure acting on the gas is kept constant. What volume does the gas occupy?

6. 200 K

6. At 40.0 K, 10.0 m³ of nitrogen is under 4.0×10^2 kPa pressure. The pressure acting on the nitrogen is increased to 2000 kPa. Its volume remains constant. What is the temperature of the nitrogen?

7. 2.3 × 10² m³

7. A balloon contains 2.0×10^2 m³ of helium while on the surface of the earth. Atmospheric pressure is 1.0 atm. Temperature is 20.0°C. The balloon expands freely and rises to a height where the pressure is only 0.67 atm and the temperature is −50.0°C. What is the new volume of the balloon?

8. 0.50 cm³

8. A bubble of air with a volume of 0.050 cm³ escapes from a pressure hose at the bottom of a tank. The tank is filled with mercury to a height of 6.84 m. What is the volume of the air bubble as it reaches the surface of the mercury? Assume the pressure at the surface that acts on the bubble is 1.0 atm. The pressure at the bottom of the tank is the pressure due to the mercury plus the pressure at the surface.

Problems–B

1. 10.3 m

1. Mercury has a specific gravity of 13.6, which means that mercury is 13.6 times more dense than water. If a barometer were constructed using water rather than mercury, how high (in meters) would the water rise under normal atmospheric pressure?

2. 12 L

2. Suppose that a scuba diver filled her lungs to a capacity of 6.0 liters while at a depth of 10.3 m below the surface of a pond. To what volume would her lungs (attempt to) expand if she suddenly rose to the surface?

3. $P\Delta V$: N · m
   $W = Fd$: N · m

3. The volume of a confined gas is changed by applying a force F to a piston and moving the piston a displacement d. Thus, work must be done on a gas to change its volume V and pressure P an amount $P\Delta V$. Ideally, if the gas is allowed to expand it should be able to do an equal amount of work. Therefore, $P\Delta V$ and Fd must be equivalent and have the same units. Recalling that pressure is force per unit area and that volume can be expressed as m^3 show that the work done on the piston must have the same units as does $P\Delta V$.

4. The pressure acting on 20.0 liters of a gas is 120.0 kPa. If the temperature is 23.0 °C, how many molecules are present?
($k = 1.38 \times 10^{-23}$ L · kPa/mol · K)

4. 5.88×10^{23} molecules

Readings

Allen, Philip, "Conduction of Heat." *The Physics Teacher*, December, 1983.

Giedd, Ronald, "Real Otto and Diesel Engine Cycles." *The Physics Teacher*, January, 1983.

Hollister, Charles, "The Dynamic Abyss." *Scientific American*, March, 1984.

Overbye, Dennis, "Mapping the Heat of Heaven." *Discover*, April, 1983.

Tierney, John, "Perpetual Commotion." *Science 83*, May, 1983.

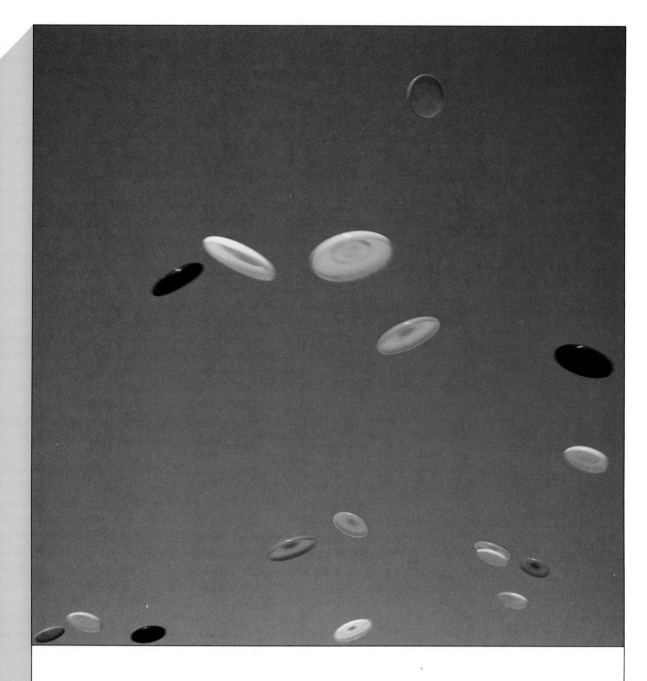

The motion of these Frisbees™ is determined by their construction as well as by the material through which they are moving. All materials can be classified into four broad categories: gases and liquids, called fluids, solids, and plasmas. Materials in each classification have common properties. What are these properties? How do changes in these properties affect materials?

States of Matter

Chapter 14 introduces fluids, solids, and plasmas. Physical properties of these materials are discussed.

In Chapter 13, we discussed some laws that apply only to the gaseous phase of matter. In this chapter, we will be considering another aspect of gases as well as some of the characteristics and behaviors of liquids, solids, and plasmas.

We will find out how airplanes fly, how ocean liners float, and how submarines can either float or submerge. We will learn why paper towels absorb spilled milk, how certain insects walk on the surface of water, and what causes the northern lights. All of these phenomena demonstrate specific principles that govern the behavior of matter.

Goal: You will gain understanding of the basic properties of liquids and solids and how microscopic properties cause observable phenomena.

14:1 Fluids at Rest—Hydrostatics

A **fluid** is any material that flows and offers little resistance to a change in its shape when under pressure. Both liquids and gases can be classified as fluids. To simplify our study, we will examine the behavior of an ideal fluid: one that is incompressible and in which there is no internal friction among the particles.

If you have ever dived down deep into a swimming pool or lake, you know that fluids exert pressure. Your body is sensitive to water pressure. You probably noticed that the pressure you feel on your ears does not depend on whether your head is upright or tilted; the pressure is the same on all parts of your body. *Pressure applied to a fluid at any point is transmitted undiminished throughout the fluid.* Blaise Pascal, (1623–1662), a French physician, was the first to discover this principle, which is now called **Pascal's principle.**

Fluids transmit pressure equally to all parts of the fluid.

Pascal's principle is applied in the operation of machines that use fluids to multiply forces, for example, hydraulic lifts.

231

FIGURE 14-1. Increased pressure is transmitted equally throughout a confined fluid.

Force exerted is proportional to the ratio of areas of the two pistons.

A fluid is confined in two connecting chambers. Each chamber has a piston that is free to move. A force F_1 is exerted on the piston with surface area A_1. The pressure exerted on the fluid is

$$P_1 = F_1/A_1$$

This pressure is transmitted undiminished throughout the fluid. The pressure exerted on the piston with surface area A_2 is given by

$$P_2 = F_2/A_2$$

However, this pressure, P_2, is the same as P_1. Therefore,

$$\boxed{\frac{F_1}{A_1} = \frac{F_2}{A_2}}$$

The force that the second piston can exert is given by

$$F_2 = F_1 \frac{A_2}{A_1}$$

EXAMPLE

Hydraulic System

A 20.0 N force is exerted on the small piston of the hydraulic system shown in Figure 14-2. The cross-sectional area of the small piston is $5.00 \times 10^{-2} \text{ m}^2$. What is the magnitude of the weight that can be lifted by the large piston, which has a surface area of $1.00 \times 10^{-1} \text{ m}^2$?

Given: $F_1 = 20.0 \text{ N}$ **Unknown:** F_2

$A_1 = 5.00 \times 10^{-2} \text{ m}^2$

$A_2 = 1.00 \times 10^{-1} \text{ m}^2$

Basic equation: $\dfrac{F_1}{A_1} = \dfrac{F_2}{A_2}$

Solution: $\dfrac{F_1}{A_1} = \dfrac{F_2}{A_2}$

$$F_2 = \frac{F_1 A_2}{A_1}$$

$$= \frac{(20.0 \text{ N})(1.00 \times 10^{-1} \text{ m}^2)}{5.00 \times 10^{-2} \text{ m}^2}$$

$$F_2 = 40.0 \text{ N}$$

FIGURE 14-2. An example of a hydraulic system.

20.0 N

5.00 × 10⁻² m²

1.00 × 10⁻¹ m²

Another characteristic of fluids can also be observed while swimming. The deeper you swim, the greater the pressure you feel on your eardrums. The pressure of a fluid is the weight per unit area (A) of the fluid above you. The weight (W) of the water above you is

$$W = mg.$$

Recall that ρ (density) $= m/V$ and $V = Ah$,

therefore $W = \rho V g = \rho A h g$. Substituting this value for W will give

$$P = W/A = \frac{\rho A h g}{A} = \rho h g$$

FIGURE 14-3. Breathing compressed air at a normal rate prevents the diver's lungs from collapsing at increased pressure.

FIGURE 14-4. Pascal's vases show that the container shape has no effect on pressure.

Therefore, the pressure is proportional only to the depth of the fluid and its density. The shape of the container has no effect, Figure 14-4.

When a body is placed in a fluid, pressure is exerted on all sides. However, as demonstrated above, the pressure on the bottom is larger than the pressure on the top surface.

As a result, the water exerts a net upward force on every body in it. The force is called the **buoyant force.** It is possible to calculate the magnitude of the buoyant force on an object. From Figure 14-5, you can see that

$$F_{top} = P_{top}A = \rho ghA$$

$$F_{bottom} = P_{bottom}A = \rho g(h + l) A$$

Therefore the net upward, or buoyant, force is

$$F_{bottom} - F_{top} = Ag\rho(h + l) - Ahg\rho$$

$$= Ag\rho\, l = V\rho g$$

Do you also see that the volume of the immersed object is the same as the volume of the fluid displaced? Therefore, the buoyant force, $Ag\rho l$, also represents the weight of the volume of fluid displaced by the immersed object. This relationship was discovered by the Greek scientist Archimedes in 212 B.C. and is called **Archimedes' principle.** *An object immersed in a fluid is buoyed up by a force equal to the weight of the fluid displaced by the object.* It is important to note that the buoyant force *does not* depend on the weight of the submerged object, only the weight of the displaced fluid. A solid cube of aluminum, a solid cube of iron, and a hollow cube of iron, all of the same volume, would experience the same buoyant force.

The buoyant force is equal to the weight of the fluid displaced.

FIGURE 14-5. Archimedes' principle can be derived from considering a volume of fluid as shown.

Archimedes' principle applies to objects of all densities. If the density of the object is greater than that of the fluid, the buoyant force will be less than W_{object} and the object will sink. If the density of the object is equal to the density of the fluid, the buoyant force and W_{object} will be equal. The object will neither sink nor float. If the density of the object is less than the fluid, the object will sink only until it displaces a volume of fluid with a weight equal to the weight of the object. Wearing a life jacket filled with material of very small density has the effect of decreasing the body's density.

Shipbuilders can build ships of steel (density 9.0×10^3 kg/m³) by designing them with large hollow hulls so that the overall density of the ship is less than that of water. You will notice that a ship loaded with cargo rides much lower in the water than a ship with an empty hold. Submarines take advantage of Archimedes' principle by pumping water into or out of special chambers to regulate the depth at which they operate. Fish have air sacs that allow them to swim level at any depth.

EXAMPLE

Archimedes' Principle

A cubic decimeter of steel is submerged in water. **a.** What is the magnitude of the buoyant force acting on the steel? **b.** What is the net weight of the body? (The density of steel is 9.0×10^3 kg/m³.)

Given: $V = 1.00$ dm³

$\rho_{steel} = 9.0 \times 10^3$ kg/m³

$\rho_{water} = 1.00 \times 10^3$ kg/m³

Unknowns: **a.** $F_{buoyant}$

b. W_{net}

Basic equations:

a. $F_{buoyant} = V\rho_{water}g$

b. $W_{net} = mg - F_{buoyant}$

Solution:

a. $F_{buoyant} = V\rho_{water}g = (1.00 \times 10^{-3} \text{ m}^3)(1.00 \times 10^3 \text{ kg/m}^3)(9.8 \text{ m/s}^2)$
$= 9.8 \text{ N}$

b. $W_{net} = mg - F_{buoyant}$
$= [(1.00 \times 10^{-1} \text{ m})^3(9.0 \times 10^3 \text{ kg/m}^3)(9.8 \text{ m/s}^2)] - 9.8 \text{ N}$
$= 88.2 \text{ N} - 9.8 \text{ N}$
$W_{net} = 78.4 \text{ N}$

Problems

FIGURE 14-7. Blowing across the surface of a sheet of paper demonstrates Bernoulli's principle.

1. If the diameter of the larger piston shown in Figure 14-2 were doubled, what force would be lifted if 20.0 N is applied to the smaller piston?

1. 160 N

2. Dentist's chairs are examples of hydraulic lift systems. If the chair weighs 1600 N and rests on a piston with a cross-sectional area of 1440 cm², what force must be applied to the small piston with a cross-sectional area of 72 cm² in order to lift the chair?

2. 8.0×10^1 N

3. A teenager is floating in a freshwater lake with her head just above the water. If she weighs 600 N, what is her volume?

3. 6×10^{-2} m³

4. What is the tension in a wire supporting a 1250-N camera submerged in water? The volume of the camera is 8.3×10^{-2} m³.

4. 440 N

14:2 Fluids in Motion—Hydrodynamics

To see the effect of moving fluids, try this experiment. Hold a strip of notebook paper just under your lower lip. Now blow hard across the top surface. The strip will rise. The pressure on the top of the paper where the air is flowing fast is lower than that on the bottom where the air is not in motion. This is an example of Bernoulli's principle, named for the Swiss scientist Daniel Bernoulli (1700-1782).

Picture a horizontal pipe completely filled with a smoothly-flowing ideal fluid. If a certain volume of the fluid enters one end of the pipe, then an equal volume must come out the other end. The kinetic energy of the fluid is dependent on its velocity, and the potential energy is represented by the pressure the fluid exerts on the walls of the pipe. If no energy enters or leaves the system, the sum of the potential and kinetic energies must remain the same. Now consider a section of pipe where the cross section becomes narrower. To move the required volume of fluid through the narrow section, the velocity of the fluid, and hence its kinetic energy, must increase. Since the total energy of the system is conserved, the potential energy, and therefore the pressure exerted by the fluid, will decrease (Figure 14-8) as stated in **Bernoulli's principle.** As the velocity of a fluid increases, the pressure exerted by that fluid decreases.

FIGURE 14-8. The potential energy and the pressure exerted by a fluid decreases as the velocity of the fluid increases.

FIGURE 14-9. The spoiler on a race car is an inverted airfoil.

Bernoulli's principle states that the pressure of a moving fluid decreases as the velocity of the fluid increases.

Most aircraft get their lift by taking advantage of Bernoulli's principle. Airplane wings are airfoils, devices designed to produce lift when moving through a fluid. The curvature of the top surface of a wing is greater than that of the bottom. As the wing travels through the air, the air moving over the top surface travels farther, and therefore must go faster than air moving past the bottom surface. The decreased air pressure created on the top surface results in a net upward pressure producing an upward force on the wings, or lift, that holds the airplane aloft. Racing cars use airfoils with a greater curvature on the bottom surface. The airfoils, called spoilers, produce a net downward pressure that holds the rear wheels of the cars on the road at high speeds.

Did you ever notice that boat docks are designed so that water can flow freely around them? Consider what would happen at a solid-walled pier as a boat approached. As the space between the boat and the pier narrowed, the velocity of the water would increase, and the pressure exerted by the water on the pier-side of the boat would decrease. The boat could be pushed against the pier by the greater pressure of the water against the other side.

FIGURE 14-10. Boat docks are usually open so that a difference in water pressure does not force boats against the docks.

As shown in Figure 14-11, the flow of a fluid can be represented by streamlines. Streamlines can best be illustrated by a simple demonstration. Imagine tiny drops of food coloring carefully dropped into a smoothly-flowing fluid. If the colored lines that form stay thin and well defined, the flow is said to be streamlined. Notice that if the flow narrows, the streamlines move closer together. Closely spaced streamlines indicate greater velocity, and therefore reduced pressure.

If the streamlines swirl and become diffused, the flow is said to be turbulent. Bernoulli's principle does not apply to turbulent flow. Since

FIGURE 14-11. Schlieren photography demonstrates the flow of air around a model in a wind tunnel.

objects require less energy to move through a streamline flow, automobile and aircraft manufacturers spend a great deal of money testing new designs in wind tunnels to ensure a streamlined flow of air around the vehicles.

In a turbulent flow, the streamlines are disrupted.

14:3 Liquids

Although liquids and gases are grouped together as fluids, liquids are different from gases in several ways.

1. A liquid has a definite volume; a gas takes the volume of any container that holds it.

2. A liquid is practically incompressible; a gas is easily compressed.

Liquids have definite volume, are practically incompressible, and the particles take up most of the room in the fluid.

FIGURE 14-12. Molten lava behaves like a fluid.

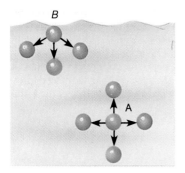

FIGURE 14-13. The net downward force on molecule B draws the surface molecules together.

Surface tension is a result of cohesive forces.

FIGURE 14-14. The water strider (a) can stand on water due to surface tension. The splashing milk drops (b) are spherical due to surface tension.

3. The particles of a liquid are very close together—the volume of the particles make up almost all the volume of the liquid; the particles of a gas take up relatively little space—a volume of gas is mostly empty space.

Furthermore, although the particles of a liquid are free to slide over and around one another, in real liquids the particles do exert electromagnetic forces of attraction on each other. These forces are called **cohesive forces,** and they directly affect the behavior of the liquid.

14:4   Surface Tension

Have you ever noticed that dewdrops on spiderwebs and falling drops of milk or oil are nearly spherical? Perhaps you have observed that a drop of water on a smooth surface forms a rounded shape, while a drop of alcohol tends to flatten out. All of these phenomena are examples of surface tension and are a result of the cohesive forces among the particles of a liquid. **Surface tension** is the tendency of the surface of a liquid to contract.

Beneath the surface of the liquid, Figure 14-13, each particle of the liquid is attracted equally in all directions by neighboring particles. As a result, there is no net force acting on any of the particles beneath the surface. At the surface, however, the particles are attracted to the side and downward, but not upward. Thus, there is a net downward force acting on the top layers. This net force causes the surface layer to be slightly compressed. The layer acts like a tightly stretched rubber sheet or a film. The film is strong enough to support the weight of light

a

b

a

b

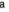

FIGURE 14-15. Water climbs the wall of this capillary tube (a), while mercury is depressed in the tube (b). The force of attraction between mercury atoms is stronger than any adhesive force between the mercury and the glass.

objects. Water bugs can stand on the surface of quiet pools of water because of surface tension. The surface tension of water also supports an object such as a steel sewing needle even though the density of steel is nine times greater than that of water.

Surface tension also accounts for the tendency of unconfined liquids to form drops. The force pulling the surface particles into the liquid causes the surface to become as small as possible. The shape that has the least surface for a given volume is a sphere. Liquid mercury has a much stronger cohesive force between its particles than water. Thus, small amounts of mercury form spherical drops even when placed on a smooth surface. On the other hand, liquids such as alcohol or ether have weak cohesive forces between their molecules. A drop of either of these liquids flattens when placed on a smooth surface.

A force similar to cohesion is adhesion. **Adhesion** is the attractive force that acts between particles of different substances. Like cohesive forces, adhesive forces are electromagnetic in nature.

If a glass tube open at both ends and with a small inside diameter is placed in water, the water rises inside the tube. The water rises because the adhesive force between glass and water molecules is stronger than the cohesive force between water molecules. This phenomenon is called **capillary action.** The water will continue to rise until the weight of the water lifted balances the adhesive force between the glass and water molecules. As the radius of the tube increases, the volume, and therefore the weight, of the liquid increases proportionally faster than the surface area of the tube. Water will be lifted higher in a narrow tube than in one that is wider.

Note that the surface of the water dips in the center (Figure 14-15a). This is due to the fact that the adhesive force between the glass molecules and water molecules is greater than the cohesive force between the water molecules. If the liquid in the tube had been mercury, it would not have risen in the tube. Furthermore, the center of the surface would have bulged upward (Figure 14-15b). Both of these

Surface tension makes the surface area of a fluid as small as possible.

Adhesion is the attractive force between dissimilar particles.

Capillary action, the result of adhesion, causes some fluids to rise in small tubes.

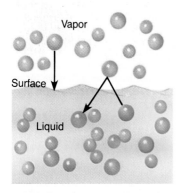

FIGURE 14-16. The vapor pressure above a liquid slows the rate of evaporation.

Evaporation results in the cooling of the remaining liquid.

FIGURE 14-17. A pressure cooker is used to quickly prepare foods by cooking with high internal air pressure and temperature.

observations are due to the fact that the cohesive forces between the mercury molecules are greater than the adhesive forces between the mercury and glass.

Oil rises in the wick of a lamp because of capillary action. Paint moves up through the bristles of a brush for the same reason. It is also capillary action that causes water to move up through the soil to the roots of plants.

14:5 Evaporation and Condensation

The particles in a liquid move at random speeds. Some are moving rapidly while others are moving slowly. The temperature of a liquid is dependent on the average *KE* of its particles. Suppose a fast-moving particle is near the surface of the liquid. If it can break through the surface layers, it will escape from the liquid. Since there is a net downward cohesive force at the surface, only the more energetic particles can escape. This process is called **evaporation.**

Each time a particle escapes from the liquid, the average kinetic energy of the remaining particles decreases. A decrease in kinetic energy is a decrease in temperature. The result is the cooling effect of evaporation.

This effect can be demonstrated by pouring some rubbing alcohol into the palm of your hand. Alcohol molecules have weak cohesive forces (low surface tension). Alcohol molecules, therefore, evaporate easily. The cooling effect is quite noticeable.

Liquids such as alcohol and ether evaporate quickly because the forces between their molecules are weak. A liquid that evaporates quickly is called a **volatile** (VAHL uht uhl) liquid.

The opposite process also exists. Vapor particles moving randomly above the surface of a liquid may strike the surface. If the particle has lost enough energy, the cohesive force will be strong enough to prevent the particle's return to the vapor. This process is called **condensation.** Each time a vapor particle is absorbed by the liquid, the average kinetic energy of the liquid is increased. Thus, the temperature of the liquid is increased. This result is the warming effect of condensation.

An increase in air pressure makes it more likely that an escaping particle will have a collision and return to the liquid. Thus, increased pressure means that the molecules need a higher kinetic energy (temperature) to escape.

14:6 Solid State

When the temperature of a liquid is lowered, the average kinetic energy of the particles is lowered. As the particles slow down, the cohesive forces become more effective, and the particles are no longer able to slide over one another. The particles become frozen into a fixed pattern called a crystal lattice. However, despite the forces that hold

FIGURE 14-18. Minerals exhibit a variety of crystal structures. These structures are dependent upon the chemical composition of the minerals.

the particles in place, the particles do not stop moving completely. Rather they vibrate around their fixed positions in the crystal lattice. Because they have a definite shape and volume, there are certain substances, usually considered to be solids, that are not true crystalline solids. Butter, paraffin, and glass are examples. None of these materials contains a crystal structure and are more correctly classified as very **viscous** (slow-flowing) liquids.

Particles in a solid vibrate about fixed locations.

As a liquid freezes, its particles usually fit more closely together than in the liquid state. Water is an exception. Water molecules in the solid state take up more space than they do as a liquid. Thus, water expands as it freezes, causing ice to have a lower density than liquid water and float on the surface. If water contracted as it froze, ice would have a higher density than water and would sink. Lakes and rivers would freeze from the bottom up.

Solids have a definite shape and volume.

FIGURE 14-19. The expansion and contraction of water as it freezes and melts causes extensive road damage, known as frost heaving.

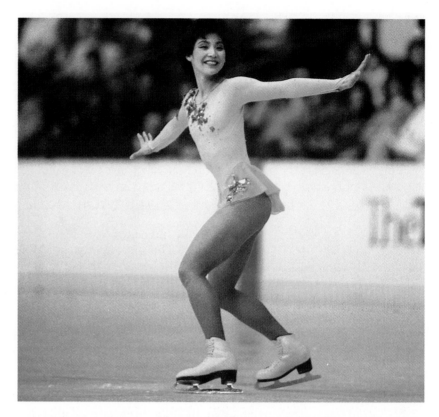

An increase in the pressure on the surface of a liquid forces the particles closer. Then, the cohesive forces become stronger. For most liquids, an increase in surface pressure will raise the freezing point of the liquid. In general, the freezing point of a liquid increases as the pressure on the liquid increases. Again, water is the exception. Since water expands as it freezes, an increase in pressure prevents this expansion. The freezing point of water is lowered as the pressure on its surface is increased. Ice skating is possible because of this fact. Increased pressure from the skate blades cause the ice under the blades to melt forming a lubricant.

14:7 Elasticity

External forces applied to a solid object may twist it or bend it out of shape. The ability of that object to return to its original form when the external forces are removed is called the **elasticity** of the solid. If too much deformation occurs, the object will not return to its original shape—its elastic limit has been exceeded. Elasticity depends on the forces that hold the particles of a substance together. Malleability and ductility, the ability to be rolled into a thin sheet and drawn into a wire, respectively, are two properties that depend on the elasticity of a substance.

14:8 Thermal Expansion of Matter

Most materials expand when heated and contract when cooled. The expansion of solids, liquids, and gases can be understood in terms of the kinetic theory. As a fluid is heated, the particles begin to move about more rapidly, causing more energetic collisions. The particles rebound greater distances after these collisions, increasing interparticle distances. Thus, the fluid expands when heated.

There is a second factor that affects the thermal expansion of fluids. As the fluid is heated, the particles move farther apart. The attractive force between them becomes weaker, and the fluid tends to expand. On the other hand, as the fluid cools, the particles move closer together and the attractive force between them becomes stronger. The fluid tends to contract.

A practical application of the expansion and contraction of fluids is found in systems for heating buildings. The air directly around a radiator expands as it is heated. In this way, it becomes less dense than the cool air above it. The warm air rises and the cool air moves in to take its place. This motion results in circulation of air. This kind of movement resulting from density difference and gravity is called a convection current. Through convection currents, all of the air in a room may be warmed quickly.

When a solid is heated, the particles vibrate more violently, moving farther from their centers of vibration. This motion causes expansion and contraction caused by heating and cooling every day. Telephone wires expand in the summer and sag. They contract in the winter and do not sag between poles. Sections of railroad track contract and have more space between them in the winter than in the summer.

FIGURE 14-21. This thermostat (a) is controlled by the expansion of mercury in the glass tubes. When a room becomes too warm, the mercury expands and trips the tubes to the left breaking the electric circuit. A hot air balloon (b) expands and rises as the air inside it is heated.

a

b

a

b

FIGURE 14-22. The motion of molecules in a solid (a) is less than in a liquid (b).

As a result, temperature extremes must be taken into consideration when railroads and bridges are built. The change in length of a solid is proportional to the change in temperature. A solid will expand twice as much if heated by 20C° than if heated by 10C°. The change is also proportional to its length. A two meter bar will expand twice as much as a one meter bar. Thus, the length L of a solid at temperature T is given by

$$L = L_i + \alpha L_i (T - T_i)$$

When L_i is the length at temperature T_o, the proportionality constant, α, is called the coefficient of linear expansion. The equation can also be written

$$L = L_i (1 + \alpha \Delta T)$$

or

$$\boxed{\frac{L - L_o}{L_o} = \frac{\Delta L}{L_i} = \alpha \Delta T}$$

Since

$$\alpha = \frac{\Delta L}{L_i \Delta T}$$

we have

$$\frac{\text{length unit}}{(\text{length unit})(\text{temperature unit})}$$

Therefore, the unit for coefficient of linear expansion is 1/°C or °C^{-1}. Volume expansion is three dimensional. The coefficient of volume expansion is approximately three times the coefficient of linear expansion.

Different materials expand at different rates. The expansion rates of gases and liquids are larger than those of solids. Engineers must consider these different expansion rates in designing structures. Steel bars are often used to reinforce concrete. These bars must expand at the same rate as the concrete. Otherwise, the structure may crack on a hot day. For a similar reason, a dentist must use filling materials that expand and contract at the same rate as a tooth.

Sometimes, different rates of expansion are useful. Engineers have taken advantage of these differences to construct a useful device called a bimetallic strip. A bimetallic strip consists of two strips of different metals. These two metals are either welded or riveted together. Usually, one strip is brass and the other is iron. When heated, brass expands more than iron. Thus, when the bimetallic strip of brass and iron is heated, the brass strip becomes longer than the iron strip. In this case, the bimetallic strip bends with the brass on the outside of the curve. If the bimetallic strip is cooled, it bends in the opposite direction. The brass is on the inside of the curve.

Thermostats that are used in the home usually contain a bimetallic strip. The bimetallic strip is arranged so that it bends toward an electric contact as the room cools. When the room cools below the setting on the thermostat, the bimetallic strip bends enough to make electric

FIGURE 14-23. The change in length is proportional to the original length and the change in temperature.

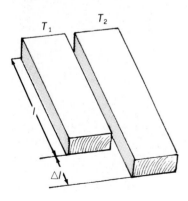

contact with the switch, which turns on the heater. As the room warms, the bimetallic strip bends in the other direction. The electric contact is broken and the heater is switched off.

EXAMPLE
Linear Expansion

A metal bar is 2.60 meters long at 21°C. The bar is uniformly heated to a temperature of 28°C and the change in length was determined to be 7.0×10^{-6} meters. What is the coefficient of linear expansion for the metal bar?

Given: $L_i = 2.60$ m   **Unknown:** α

   $\Delta L = 7.0 \times 10^{-6}$ m

   $T_i = 21°C$ **Basic Equation:** $\dfrac{\Delta L}{L_i} = \alpha \Delta T$

   $T_f = 28°C$

Solution: $\alpha = \dfrac{\Delta L}{L_i \, (T_f - T_i)}$

   $= \dfrac{7.0 \times 10^{-6} \text{ m}}{(2.60 \text{ m})(28°C - 21°C)} = 0.38 \times 10^{-6}°C^{-1}$

Problems

5. A piece of aluminum is 1.65 meters long at 25°C. What is the new length if it is heated to 465°C? $\alpha_{Al} = 25 \times 10^{-6}/°C$

6. A copper rod has a diameter of 0.80 centimeters at 27°C. The rod is heated uniformly to 855°C. What is the new cross-sectional area of the copper rod? $\alpha_{Cu} = 16.6 \times 10^{-6}/°C$ 6. 0.52 cm²

7. A piece of steel ($\alpha = 10.5 \times 10^{-6}/°C$) is 11.5 meters long at 22°C. What is the new length of the steel at 1221°C?

FIGURE 14-24. The properties of a bimetallic strip cause it to bend when heated.

5. 1.67 m   7. 11.6 m

FIGURE 14-25. A sodium vapor lamp (a) contains glowing plasma. The Aurora borealis, also known as the Northern Lights (b), occurs when high energy particles interact with plasma layers that circle the earth.

a

b

14:9   Plasma

We have studied the three common states of matter—solid, liquid, and gas. There is a fourth state of matter called plasma. There is very little plasma on the earth. However, more than 99 percent of the universe is made up of plasma. Stars and much of interstellar space contain plasma.

In the plasma state, the particles have charges. Atoms have lost one or more of their electrons as a result of energetic collisions. An atom that has lost electrons has a net positive charge and is a positive ion. The electrons are negative particles. The main difference between a gas and a plasma is that a plasma can conduct an electric current. A gas cannot conduct an electric current. A fluorescent lamp contains liquid and gaseous mercury. When the lamp is turned on, the electrical forces strip electrons from the atoms, producing plasma. The plasma conducts electricity and gives off energy, causing the chemicals coating the inner surface of the tube to glow. Neon signs and the mercury and sodium vapor lamps used in street lighting also contain glowing plasmas. The aurora borealis and aurora australis (the northern and southern lights) are a result of the interaction of high energy charged particles from the sun and layers of plasma that circle the earth.

Physics Focus   Why Does a Pitched Baseball Curve?

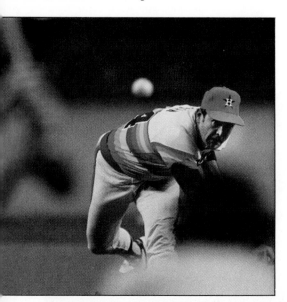

Baseball pitchers have baffled batters for years with the curve ball. When a ball curves downward, it is more difficult for the batter to time the swing of the bat.

Motion of a pitched ball can be "frozen" by strobe-light photography. A curve ball moves in a constant arc. If the earth did not get in the way, the ball would circle back to the pitcher, who could turn around and catch it.

Baseballs curve because of ball spin, aerodynamics, and gravity. A pitcher produces top spin by placing the index and middle fingers along the stitches, then snapping them over the top as the ball is released. Friction between the spinning stitches and the air pulls a thin layer of air around the ball as it spins. Throughout the ball's flight, more air flows around the bottom than around the top of the ball. Therefore, air flows faster around the bottom, and less pressure is exerted there. The ball is pushed downward. Gravity accentuates the downward motion of the ball in the second half of its path. This, along with the batter's perspective, produces the optical illusion of the "break" of a curve ball.

Summary

1. A fluid is any material that flows and offers little resistance to a change in   14:1
   shape when under pressure.

2. Pascal's principle states that pressure is transmitted undiminished   14:1
   throughout a liquid.

3. In a fluid, upward force exerted on an object by the fluid is called the   14:1
   buoyant force.

4. Archimedes' principle states that an object immersed in a fluid is buoyed   14:1
   up by a force equal to the weight of the fluid displaced by the
   object.

5. As the velocity of a fluid increases, the pressure exerted by that fluid   14:2
   decreases.

6. The smooth flow of fluid is called streamlined flow.   14:2

7. The electromagnetic attractive forces that like particles exert on one   14:3
   another are called cohesive forces.

8. The tendency of the particles in a liquid's surface to contract is called   14:4
   surface tension.

9. The attractive forces between particles of different substances are called   14:4
   adhesive forces.

10. Capillary action is explained by adhesive forces of particles.   14:4

11. Evaporation occurs when energetic particles of a liquid break free of the   14:5
    surface.

12. Liquids held together by weak cohesive forces evaporate quickly and are   14:5
    called volatile liquids.

13. As a liquid solidifies, the particles of the liquid become frozen into a   14:6
    regular pattern called a crystal lattice.

14. An increase in pressure generally raises the freezing point of a liquid.   14:6
    Water is an exception.

15. The ability of an object to return to its original form when stressed is   14:7
    elasticity.

16. The thermal expansion of length of a material depends on the type   14:8
    of material, temperature change, and the original length.

17. Plasma is an energetic state of matter made up of a mixture of positive and   14:9
    negative particles.

Detailed answers to all Questions and Problems are given in the Teacher's Guide at the front of this book.

Questions

1. A razor blade, which has a density greater than water, can be made to float on water.
   a. What procedures must you follow for this to happen?
   b. Explain why it happens.

2. A drop of water, a drop of mercury, and a drop of naphtha (lighter fluid) are placed on a smooth, flat surface. The water and the mercury take a definite shape. The naphtha spreads out over the surface. What does this tell you about the cohesive forces between naphtha molecules? Explain why naphtha vaporizes readily.

3. Use your answer to Question 2 to explain why naphtha has a low boiling point.

4. In what way does a plasma differ from a gas? What portion of the universe consists of plasma?

5. The density of carbon tetrachloride is 1.6×10^3 kg/m³. Steel ($\rho = 9.0 \times 10^3$ kg/m³) would sink in both water and carbon tetrachloride. Which liquid would exert a greater buoyant force? Explain.

6. A candle is made by pouring candle wax or paraffin into a mold. Unless care is taken the top surface of the finished candle will be concave or curved inward. Explain.

7. After using a rubber band many times, it will break. Explain what happens to the rubber band to allow it to break.

8. Equal volumes of water were heated in two narrow tubes, identical except that tube A was made of soft glass and tube B was made of Pyrex® glass. As the temperature increased, the water level rose higher in tube B than in tube A to a possible explanation for this observation. Why are many cooking utensils made from Pyrex® glass?

Problems–A

1. a. 9.0×10^2 N
   b. 0.60 cm

1. In a small machine shop, a hydraulic lift is used to raise heavy equipment for repairs and maintenance. The system has a small piston with a cross-sectional area of 7.0×10^{-2} m² and a large piston with a cross-sectional area of 2.1×10^{-1} m². A engine weighing 2.7×10^3 N is resting on the larger piston.
   a. What force must be applied to the small piston in order to lift the engine?
   b. If the engine rose 0.20 m, how far did the smaller piston move?

2. a. 203 N
   b. 197 N

2. During an ecology experiment, an aquarium filled with water is placed on a scale. The scale reading is 195 N.
   a. A rock weighing 8 N is added to the aquarium. If the rock sinks to the bottom of the aquarium, what will be the scale reading?

b. The rock is removed from the aquarium and the amount of water is adjusted until the scale reading is again 195 N. A small fish weighing 2 N is added to the aquarium. What will be the scale reading while the fish is swimming in the aquarium?

3. What is the weight of a rock submerged in water if the rock weighs 54 N in air and has a volume of 2.3 x 10^{-3} m³?

3. 31 N

4. If the rock in Problem 3 is submerged in a liquid with a density exactly twice that of water, what will be its weight reading in the liquid?

4. 8N

5. What is the acceleration of a small metal sphere as it falls through water. The sphere weighs 2.8 x 10^{-1} N in air and has a volume of 13 cm³.

5. 5.3 m/s²

6. What is the maximum weight a helium filled balloon with a volume of 1.00 m³ can lift in air. Assume the density of air is 1.20 kg/m³ and that of helium is 0.177 kg/m³ for this problem.

6. 10.0 N,

7. What will be the change in length of a 2.00 m length of copper pipe if its temperature is raised from 23°C to 978°C. The coefficient of linear expansion for copper is 1.66 x 10^{-5}°C^{-1}.

7. 3.17 × 10^{-2} m

Problems–B

1. An aluminum sphere was heated from 11°C to 580°C. If the volume of the sphere was 1.78cm³ at 10°C, what was the increase in volume of the sphere at 580°C? $\Delta V = V_1 (3\alpha) \Delta T$

1. 7.6 × 10^{-2} cm³

2. The volume of a copper sphere is 2.56 cm³ after having been heated from 12°C to 984°C? What was the volume of the copper sphere at 12°C?

2. 2.44 cm³

Readings

Beasley, Malcolm, "Superconducting Materials." *Physics Today*, October, 1984.

Gosline, John, "Jet-Propelled Swimming in Liquids." *Scientific American*, January, 1985.

Overbye, Dennis, "Spacelab: Doing Science in Orbit." *Discover*, February, 1984.

White, Stuart, "Solar Design—The Last 12 Years." *Mechanix Illustrated*, September, 1984.

William, Peter, *Second Law*, Scientific American Books, New York, N.Y., 1984.

The action of waves is familiar to you. You may have noticed waves at the beach, in a puddle, and even in the bathtub. Much of today's technology involves the use of waves. Television, radio, light bulbs, and microwave ovens are examples. One property of waves is their ability to transfer energy. How do we use the energy of water waves? What are some other properties of waves?

Waves and Energy Transfer

Chapter 15 introduces a general study of wave behavior and emphasizes that energy can be transmitted in only two ways—either by waves or by particle transfer. It also stresses that all waves follow the same general rules.

There are only two methods by which energy can be transported between two points. The first method involves the transfer of matter. For example, falling weight can transfer energy to a stake, driving it into the ground. Electrons moving through a wire carry energy from a generating station to your house.

The second method of energy transport involves wave motion. Waves can carry energy without the transfer of matter. Sound waves bring the energy of a vibrating string of a guitar to your ear. The sun's energy reaches the earth through light waves. Radio waves carry energy from a radio station to your radio. Water waves can do tremendous amounts of damage.

The behavior of all waves follows the same general rules. For example, when a water wave is reflected from a barrier, the angle at which the wave is reflected is the same as the angle at which the wave approaches the barrier. Sound waves, light waves, and all other waves are reflected from barriers in exactly the same way. By learning the general rules of wave behavior, you can understand the behavior of all waves.

15:1 Types of Waves

Mechanical waves need a material medium through which they can travel as they transfer energy. Some examples of mechanical waves are water waves, sound waves, and the waves that travel along a spring or rope. The behavior of most mechanical waves can be readily observed. The material through which the energy of a mechanical wave is transferred from one particle to another is called a **medium**.

Goal: You will gain understanding of the properties that all waves have in common.

Energy can be transferred by particles or by waves.

Demonstrations are helpful in understanding the nature of waves. See Teacher's Guide.

Mechanical waves need a medium.

251

FIGURE 15-1. Electromagnetic waves, such as those producing radar images, need no medium for travel.

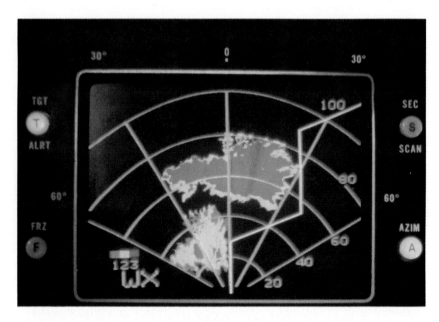

Electromagnetic waves are a large and important family of waves. They need no medium through which to travel. Some examples of electromagnetic waves are light waves, radio waves, and X rays. We cannot observe electromagnetic waves directly. We will use the behavior of mechanical waves in this chapter as a model for the behavior of electromagnetic waves that we will study in later chapters.

Mechanical waves can be classified by the way in which they displace matter. There are three general types of waves—transverse waves, longitudinal waves, and surface waves. A **transverse wave** causes the particles of a medium to vibrate perpendicularly to the direction of the wave itself. Figure 15-2a shows a transverse wave. The wave moves along the spring. However, the spring is displaced perpendicularly to the motion of the wave.

In a transverse wave, particles vibrate at right angles to the direction of the wave.

FIGURE 15-2. Two general types of waves are the transverse wave (a) and the longitudinal wave (b).

a

b

A **longitudinal wave** causes the particles of a medium to move parallel to the direction of the wave. Figure 15-2b shows a longitudinal wave. Note that the motion of the spring is parallel to the direction in which the wave is moving. Thus the difference between transverse and longitudinal waves is apparent. A sound wave is an example of a longitudinal wave.

Surface waves have characteristics of both transverse and longitudinal waves. Surface waves cause particles in the medium to move both horizontally and vertically as the wave moves across the surface. Water waves are examples of surface waves.

Although the particles of a medium move in response to a passing wave, they do not move along with the wave. For example, after a transverse wave has passed through the spring shown in Figure 15-2a, each coil is in the same position it occupied before the wave arrived. In the same way, the coils of the spring shown in Figure 15-2b will return to their original position after the longitudinal wave has passed.

A **pulse** is a single disturbance traveling through a medium. For example, a pulse can be produced by applying a single sideways movement to one end of a spring. Any point in the medium that is at rest before the pulse arrives will be at rest after the pulse passes. A periodic wave is produced by a periodic disturbance. A periodic wave can be produced by applying a smooth back-and-forth movement to one end of the spring. A disturbance that is undergoing simple harmonic motion will produce continuous periodic waves called a wave train. As a wave train passes a given point, the medium at that point will vibrate regularly in response to the waves.

In a longitudinal wave, particles vibrate parallel to the wave direction.

A medium vibrates in response to a wave but does not move with the wave.

A pulse is a single disturbance in a medium.

A wave train is a series of pulses at regular intervals.

FIGURE 15-3. Water waves are examples of surface waves.

15:2 Wave Characteristics

There are several characteristics common to all periodic waves. The **wavelength,** λ, is the horizontal distance between corresponding points on consecutive waves and is measured in meters. In Figure 15-4, all points labeled C are **crests.** Points labeled T are **troughs.** The wavelength of the wave is the distance from one crest to the next crest, or one trough to the next trough. Points A and A' are one wavelength apart. Points A and A'' are two wavelengths apart.

Points along waves that have the same displacement and are moving in the same direction at the same time are said to be in phase. Points C in Figure 15-4 are in phase. Points that have opposite displacements and are moving in opposite directions are said to be 180° out of phase. Points C and T are 180° out of phase.

> Wavelength is the horizontal distance between corresponding points on consecutive waves.

> Points that are in phase move in the same direction at the same time. Two points that are a whole number of wavelengths apart are in phase.

FIGURE 15-4. Points labeled C represent wave crests; points labeled T represent wave troughs.

> Frequency is the number of waves that pass a given point per unit time.

> The basic equation $v = f\lambda$ will also be used for optics and quantum theory calculations.

> The velocity of a wave can be found from the product of its frequency and wavelength.

The **frequency** of a periodic wave is the number of wavelengths that pass a given point per second. Frequency is measured in hertz. One hertz (Hz) is equivalent to 1 "wave" per second or s^{-1}. The frequency of a wave is the same as the frequency of the periodic disturbance that produced it. For example, the frequency of a wave generated in a spring is determined by the person moving the spring.

The velocity of a periodic wave can be found by calculating the product of the frequency and the wavelength.

$$v = f\lambda$$

FIGURE 15-5. The frequency at which the train cars pass the observer is measured as the number of cars that pass per second. The velocity of the train can be calculated by multiplying the frequency by the length of a car.

The product of the frequency unit (Hz) and wavelength unit (m) yields

$$\frac{1}{s} \times m = m/s$$

the velocity unit.

To understand why the velocity of a wave can be found in this way, consider the following analogy. Each car of a train is 20 meters long. The number of cars that pass a given point each second can be counted. If two cars pass per second, the velocity of the train must be 40 m/s. The number of cars passing per second multiplied by the length of each railroad car gives the velocity of the train. In the same way, the velocity of a wave is frequency times wavelength.

EXAMPLE

Velocity of a Periodic Wave

Transverse waves traveling along a rope have a frequency of 12.0 Hz and are 2.40 m long. What is the velocity of the waves?

Given: frequency (f) = 12.0 Hz **Unknown:** v

wavelength (λ) = 2.40 m **Basic equation:** $v = f\lambda$

Solution: $v = f\lambda$

$$= (12.0 \text{ Hz})(2.40 \text{ m}) = 28.8 \text{ m/s}$$

The period of a wave is the time required for one complete wave to pass a given point. The frequency of the wave determines its period. You will recall that the period is the reciprocal of its frequency.

The period of a wave is the reciprocal of its frequency.

$$T = \frac{1}{f}$$

EXAMPLE

Period of a Wave

A sound wave has a frequency of 250 hertz. What is the period of the sound wave?

Given: f = 250 Hz **Unknown:** period (T)

Basic equation: $T = \frac{1}{f}$

Solution: $T = \frac{1}{f}$

$$= \frac{1}{250 \text{ Hz}} = 0.0040 \text{ s}$$

Problems

1. Sound waves have a frequency of 250 hertz. The sound waves are 1.30 m in length. What is the speed of sound?

2. A radio wave has a frequency of 3.0×10^7 Hz. It is 10.0 m long. What is the speed of the radio wave?

1. 330 m/s

2. 3.0×10^8 m/s

3. a. 29 cm/s
   b. 0.21 s

3. Water waves in a small tank are 6.0 cm long. They pass a given point at the rate of 4.8 waves per second.
   a. What is the speed of the water waves?
   b. What is the period of the waves in Problem 3?

4. a. 4.08×10^{-10} s
   b. 0.12 m

4. Microwaves are electromagnetic waves that travel through space at a speed of 3.0×10^8 m/s. Most microwave ovens operate at a frequency of 2450 MHz.
   a. What is the period of these microwaves?
   b. How long is the wavelength of these microwaves?

5. a. 340 m/s
   b. 0.68 m
   c. 2.00×10^{-3} s

5. A sound wave is directed toward a vertical cliff 680 m from the source. A reflected wave is detected 4.0 s after the wave is produced.
   a. What is the speed of sound in air?
   b. The sound wave has a frequency of 5.00×10^2 Hz. What is its wavelength?
   c. What is the period of the wave?

6. a. 0.45 m
   b. 1.3×10^{-3} s

6. The speed of sound waves in air is 340 m/s. A sound wave has a frequency of 750 Hz.
   a. What is its wavelength as it travels through air?
   b. What is its period?

7. a. 5.8×10^{-7} m
   b. 5.2×10^{14} Hz

7. A typical light wave has a wavelength of 580 nm.
   a. What is the wavelength of the light in meters?
   b. The speed of light is 3.0×10^8 m/s. What is the frequency of the wave?

See suggested demonstration in Teacher's Guide.

The energy content of a wave depends on its amplitude.

The amplitude of a wave is its maximum displacement from rest position.

15:3   Amplitude of a Wave

The energy content of a mechnical wave is characterized by the wave's amplitude. The **amplitude** of a wave is its maximum displacement from the rest or equilibrium position. Figure 15-6 shows two waves traveling along identical ropes. The two waves have the same frequency, velocity, and wavelength, but their amplitudes are

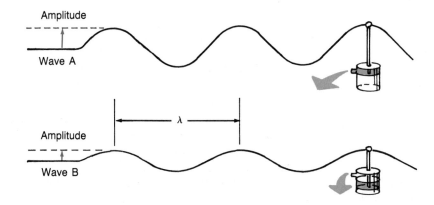

FIGURE 15-6. The relationship of the amplitude of a wave to the work it can perform is shown here. The greater the work done to create the wave, the greater the amplitude of the wave. The greater the amplitude of the wave, the more work it can do. Waves transfer energy.

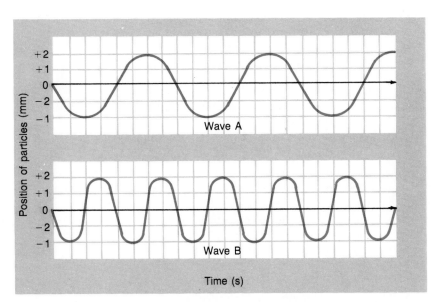

different. The source that generates wave *A* has the same frequency as the source that generates wave *B*. The source generating wave *A* puts more energy into the wave. This increased energy results in a wave of greater amplitude.

Since wave *A* has more energy input and a greater amplitude than wave *B*, wave *A* transfers more energy. Wave *A* can do more work than wave *B*. Suppose that water pumps are attached to each rope. The pumps lift water and transform the wave energy into useful work. Wave *A* can do more work per unit time than wave *B*. It can be shown that the energy transmitted by a mechanical wave is proportional to the square of the wave's amplitude.

15:4   Wave Speed in a Medium

The speed of a mechanical wave is constant in a given medium. The speed depends only on the properties of that medium. If the frequency of a wave in a given medium is changed, then the wavelength is changed. Figure 15-7 shows two waves produced at different times in the same medium. The wavelengths and the frequencies of the waves are different. Wave *B* has a high frequency and a short wavelength. Wave *A* has a low frequency and a long wavelength. In both cases, the product of the frequency and the wavelength gives the same speed. The amplitude of the wave also has no effect on its speed. An increase in amplitude of a wave causes it to transfer more energy. However, an increase in amplitude does not change the speed of the wave. Only the properties of the medium determine the speed of the mechanical waves that pass through.

The speed of a wave depends on the medium.

The amplitude of a wave does not affect its wavelength, frequency, or velocity.

a

b

FIGURE 15-8. A pulse reaching a boundary between two media (a) is partially reflected and partially transmitted (b).

When a wave travels from one medium into another, the wave is both reflected and transmitted.

FIGURE 15-9. A pulse as it approaches a rigid wall (a) and as it is reflected from the wall (b). Notice that the amplitude of the reflected pulse is nearly equal to the amplitude of the incident pulse but that the reflected pulse is inverted.

15:5 Behavior of Waves at Boundaries

Transverse waves are easier to draw and visualize than longitudinal waves. Therefore, transverse waves will be used as examples to discuss wave behavior. However, these rules of wave behavior apply to both transverse and longitudinal waves.

When a wave traveling through a medium reaches the boundary of that medium, a part of the wave will be reflected. The remainder of the wave will be transmitted into the new medium. The fraction that is reflected depends on the difference between the two media. If the difference is slight, the amplitude of the reflected wave is small. The small amplitude of the reflected wave indicates that little of the energy is reflected; most is transmitted.

a

b

FIGURE 15-10. A pulse reflected from an open-ended boundary returns erect.

Consider a spring that is attached to a rigid object, such as a wall. The two media, the spring and the wall, are very different from each other. Thus, when the pulse reaches the spring-wall boundary, most of the pulse is reflected. A small amount of the energy of the pulse does enter the wall. Figure 15-9 shows that the amplitude of the reflected pulse is almost equal to the amplitude of the incident pulse. However, the pulse is inverted upon reflection from the rigid wall. When a wave is reflected at the boundary of a more rigid medium, it undergoes inversion (180° change in phase).

Inverted reflected waves can be shown by attaching a slinky to a rigid clamp.

Now consider a spring that is supported by light threads, Figure 15-10. When a pulse reaches the end of the spring, it passes into a different medium. In this case, the new medium is air. The large difference in the two media causes nearly total reflection of the pulse. Because the pulse is reflected from the boundary of a medium less rigid than the one from which it came, the reflected pulse is erect (no change in phase).

When a wave is reflected from a more rigid medium, the reflected portion is inverted.

In all cases, there is a reflected wave at a boundary. The amount of reflected energy depends on the difference in the properties of the two media. A pulse passing from a less rigid medium into a more rigid medium produces a reflected pulse that is inverted.

Erect reflected waves can be shown by attaching a short length of rubber hose to a clamp and then a slinky to the hose.

Problems

8. A long spring passes along the floor of a room and out a door. A pulse is sent along the spring. After a while, an inverted pulse of almost the same amplitude returns along the spring. Is the spring attached to the wall in the next room or is it lying loose on the floor?

8. attached to the wall

9. To obtain waves of a longer wavelength, is wave frequency along a rope increased or decreased?

9. decreased

10. a. Pulse will be partly
       transmitted and partly
       reflected.
    b. erect
    c. Pulse will be almost
       totally reflected.
    d. inverted

10. A pulse is sent along a spring, Figure 15-11. The spring is attached to a light thread that ends at a wall.
  a. Describe the behavior of the pulse when it reaches *A*.
  b. Is the reflected pulse from *A* erect or inverted?
  c. Describe the behavior of the transmitted pulse when it reaches *B*.
  d. Is the reflected pulse from *B* erect or inverted?

FIGURE 15-11. Use with Problem 10.

11. a. The pulse will be
       partially transmitted
       and partially reflected.
       It will be inverted.
    b. The pulse will be almost
       totally inverted.

11. a. Describe the behavior of the pulse in Figure 15-12 when it reaches boundary *A*.
  b. Describe the behavior of the transmitted pulse when it reaches boundary *B*.

FIGURE 15-12. Use with Problem 11.

12. Boundary *A* is more rigid.
    Boundary *B* is less rigid.
    Boundary *C* is less rigid.
    Boundary *D* is more rigid.

12. The left side of Figure 15-13 shows a pulse. The right side shows the transmitted pulse and reflected pulse. Describe the boundaries *A*, *B*, *C*, and *D*.

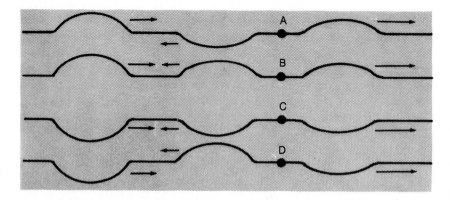

FIGURE 15-13. Use with Problem 12.

15:6 Transmitted Waves

When a wave passes into a new medium, its speed changes.

The speed of a wave is determined by the medium. When a wave passes into a new medium, it has a different speed. The wave in the new medium is generated directly by the wave in the old medium.

Thus, the frequency of the wave in the new medium is the same as the frequency of the wave in the old medium. Because the speed of the transmitted wave changes and the frequency remains the same, the wavelength must change as described by the equation $v = f\lambda$. Figure 15-14 shows a wave passing into a new medium. Since the speed in the new medium is less, the wavelength is shorter. Conversely, if the wave were to pass from the medium on the left to the medium on the right, its speed would be greater in the new medium. Thus, its wavelength would increase.

The wave must have the same frequency in the new medium as in the old medium. Thus, the wavelength adjusts so that $v = f\lambda$.

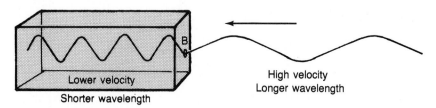

Lower velocity
Shorter wavelength

High velocity
Longer wavelength

FIGURE 15-14. The speed and wavelength of a wave change when the wave enters a new medium.

15:7 Interference

When two or more waves travel through a medium at the same time, each wave affects the medium independently. We can analyze the effects of these waves using the principle of superposition. The **principle of superposition** states that at the point where two or more waves meet, the displacement of the medium is the sum of the displacements of the individual waves. The superposition principle is another example of the independence of vector quantities (Section 6:2).

When two or more waves meet, their displacements add. This process is called superposition.

The effect of two or more waves traveling through a medium is called **interference.** Waves can produce constructive and destructive interference.

Figure 15-15 shows the constructive interference of two equal pulses. When pulse a and pulse b meet, a larger pulse $(a + b)$ is formed. The amplitude of this larger pulse is the vector sum of the amplitudes of the two pulses. Note that once the two pulses have passed through each other, they are completely unaffected and retain their original form and direction.

Constructive interference occurs when two pulses combine to produce a pulse of greater amplitude.

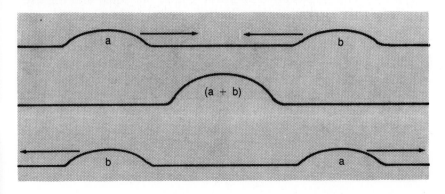

(a + b)

FIGURE 15-15. Constructive interference of two equal pulses.

**FIGURE 15-16. Destructive inter-
ference of two equal pulses.**

**FIGURE 15-17. Interference of
two pulses with the same wavelength but different amplitudes.**

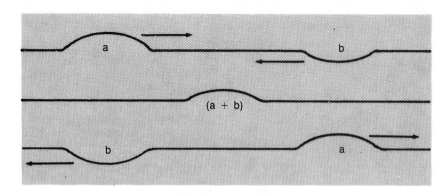

Destructive interference occurs
when two pulses combine to
produce a pulse with smaller
amplitude than either of the
original amplitudes.

After two pulses pass through one
another, they return to their
original shapes.

Point out that the individual waves
are not changed by passing
through one another.

A node is a point in a medium
that never undergoes a
displacement as waves pass
through each other in the
medium.

A wave machine can show nodes.
A slinky or rope can show a
standing wave.

Figure 15-16 shows the destructive interference of two equal but opposite pulses. When pulse a and pulse b meet, the sum of their displacements is zero and the medium is completely undisturbed. The pulses are not affected permanently and move on. An important characteristic of waves is their ability to pass through one another and not change.

If the pulses that meet are of unequal amplitudes, the resulting pulse is the vector sum of the displacements of each pulse, Figure 15-17.

15:8 Nodes, Antinodes, and Standing Waves

Suppose two pulses have identical shapes but equal and opposite amplitudes and move toward each other in a medium. When they meet, there will be a point in the medium that is completely undisturbed at all times. This point is called a **node.** The medium at a node never undergoes a displacement. A node is shown in Figure 15-18. Notice parts b, c, and d of the diagram. The displacement of the part of the pulse above the node is always the same as the displacement of the part below the node. A node is caused by the destructive interference of the two waves.

Consider two pulses with identical shapes and amplitudes traveling in opposite directions in a medium. When the pulses meet, there will be a point in the medium that has a displacement equal to the sum of the two amplitudes, as shown in Figure 15-19. This point of maximum displacement is called an **antinode.** The antinode is produced by constructive interference.

If one end of a string is connected to a vibrating source and the other end is attached to a fixed point, the string will be set into motion causing periodic wave trains. Two wave trains are produced: one by the vibrating source and the other by reflection of the original wave from the fixed end of the string. If there is no energy loss, the two wave trains will have identical amplitudes and wavelengths, but will be traveling in opposite directions. The reflected wave returns to the source and is reflected again. If the second reflection is in phase with the source, constructive and destructive interference will occur producing stationary antinodes and nodes. The string will appear to be vibrating in segments. This is called a **standing wave.** Standing waves are examples of resonance.

An antinode is a point where the displacement caused by interfering waves is largest.

A standing wave is the result of identical waves moving in opposite directions. The frequency and length of medium must be correctly chosen to make the nodes stationary.

FIGURE 15-18. The nodal point is undisturbed during the meeting of two equal and opposite pulses.

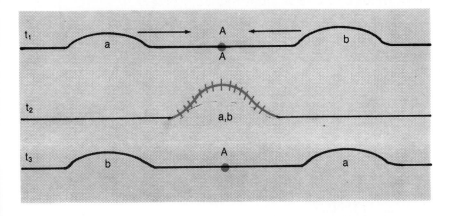

FIGURE 15-19. An antinodal point is formed by the constructive interference of two equal pulses.

FIGURE 15-20. Interference produces standing waves in a string.

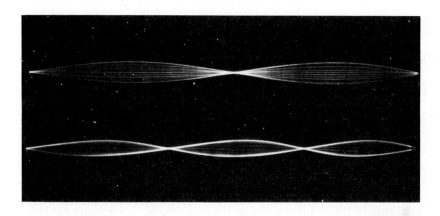

15:9   The Law of Reflection

Figure 15-21 shows an overhead view of parallel waves traveling toward a barrier. The direction of the waves is shown by a line drawn at a right angle to the crests of the waves. This imaginary line is called a ray. Wave behavior is often shown by ray diagrams. Ray diagrams show only the direction of the waves; they do not show the actual waves.

The normal is a line perpendicular to the reflecting surface (the barrier) at the point where the incident ray strikes the surface. The angle of incidence is the angle between the normal and the incident ray. Similarly, the angle of reflection is the angle between the normal and the reflected ray.

Waves are reflected from a barrier at the same angle at which they approach it. The **law of reflection** states that the angle of reflection is equal to the angle of incidence.

The law of reflection states that the angle at which a wave approaches a barrier is equal to the angle at which the wave is reflected.

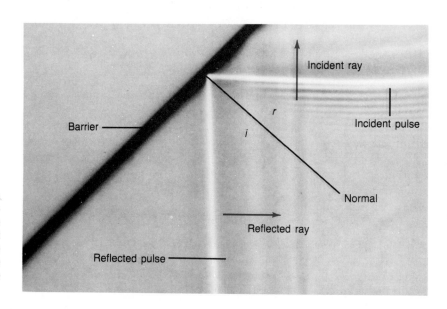

FIGURE 15-21. Reflection of a wave pulse by a barrier. A ray indicates the direction in which the pulse is moving. The angle that the incident ray makes with the normal is equal to the angle the reflected ray makes with the normal.

a

b

Refraction can be shown by placing a glass plate in a ripple tank so that it is at an angle to the oncoming wave.

15:10 Refraction of Waves

The behavior of waves as they move from one medium into another can be observed in a ripple tank, Figure 15-22a. The water above a glass plate placed in the tank is more shallow than the water in the rest of the tank. The shallow water is a different medium.

The velocity of waves is greater in deep water than in shallow water. To demonstrate this fact, the edge of the glass plate is placed parallel to advancing wave fronts. A decrease in the wavelength of the waves is observed as they pass into the shallow water. Since the waves in the shallow water are produced by waves in the deep water, their frequency is the same as the frequency of the waves in the deep water. The decrease in the wavelength of the waves indicates a slower velocity as shown by the following relationship.

$$v = f\lambda$$

When parallel waves approach the boundary of another medium along the normal for that boundary, they continue straight into the new medium. When waves approach the boundary to another medium at an angle to the normal, their direction is changed. This change in the direction of waves at the boundary between two different media is known as **refraction**.

15:11 Diffraction and Interference of Waves

Diffraction is the bending of a wave around obstacles placed in its path. Diffraction may be observed in a ripple tank by placing a small barrier in the path of parallel waves. The waves bend around the edges of the barrier, producing circular waves.

FIGURE 15-22. Straight waves enter a different medium (shallow water) head-on (a). Notice the change in wavelength. When waves enter a new medium at an angle they change direction demonstrating refraction (b).

Refraction is the change of wave direction at the boundary between two media.

FIGURE 15-23. Waves bending around barriers demonstrate diffraction.

a b

FIGURE 15-24. Waves are diffracted at two openings in the barrier (a). At each opening, circular waves are formed. The circular waves interfere with each other. Points of constructive interference are indicated by dashed lines. Two vibrating points can produce an interference pattern (b). Notice the areas of high amplitude and areas where water remains almost undisturbed.

Diffraction is the bending of a wave around an object in its path.

When circular waves from two side-by-side openings interfere, there will be undisturbed points in the medium that lie along definite lines, called nodal lines.

An interference pattern may be created by placing three straight barriers in the path of the waves as shown in Figure 15-24a. The spaces between the barriers are smaller than the wavelength of the approaching waves. The diffraction of the parallel waves around the edges of the openings causes each opening to produce circular waves. The circular waves from the two openings interfere with one another. Along the points marked by lines, wave crests occur at the same places and constructive interference occurs. Troughs also occur together causing constructive interference. These antinodes all lie along the same line. Between these antinodal lines are areas where a crest from one wave and a trough from another meet. Destructive interference occurs and the water remains undisturbed. These undisturbed points lie in definite lines, called nodal lines.

The frequency of waves in the ripple tank can be varied allowing waves of different wavelengths to be sent toward the barriers. Each wavelength produces its own interference pattern. By comparing the interference patterns for several different wavelengths, two facts are learned.

1. Different wavelengths produce similar interference patterns, but the nodal and antinodal lines are in different places.

2. Regardless of the wavelength of the wave, the central ~~nodal~~ *antinodal* line always falls in the center of the pattern.

FIGURE 15-25. Lines of reinforcement (antinodal lines) are shown where crest meets crest.

Summary

1. Waves transfer energy. Different types of waves follow similar behavior patterns making it possible to study waves in general. **15:1**

2. Mechanical waves such as sound waves and the waves in a spring require a medium. Electromagnetic waves do not require a medium. Light and radio waves are electromagnetic. **15:1**

3. Transverse waves cause the particles of a medium to move perpendicularly to the direction of the wave. Longitudinal waves cause a medium to move parallel to the direction of the wave's motion. Surface waves cause the medium to move both perpendicularly and parallel to the direction of the wave's motion. **15:1**

4. Points along a wave train that have the same displacement and are moving in the same direction are said to be in phase. **15:2**

5. The wavelength (λ) of a wave is the linear distance between corresponding points on consecutive waves. **15:2**

6. The frequency of a wave is the number of waves that pass a given point each second. The period of a wave is the reciprocal of the frequency. **15:2**

7. The velocity of a wave is given by its frequency multiplied by its wavelength. **15:2**

8. The energy of a mechanical wave is proportional to the square of its amplitude. **15:3**

9. The speed of a wave depends upon the properties of the medium through which the wave is traveling. **15:4**

10. When waves reach the boundary of a medium, they are always partially transmitted and partially reflected. The fraction of reflection depends upon the difference in the media involved. **15:5**

11. When a wave reaches the boundary of a more rigid medium, the reflected wave is inverted. When a wave reaches the boundary of a less rigid medium, the reflected wave is erect. **15:5**

12. When a mechanical wave passes into a new medium, it will have a new velocity. **15:6**

13. When waves meet, their displacements add as vectors. This is called the principle of superposition. **15:7**

14. The effect of two or more waves moving simultaneously through a medium is called interference. Interference does not affect the individual waves. **15:7**

15:8   **15.** In an interference pattern, maximum destructive interference produces a node and maximum constructive interference produces an anti-node.

15:8   **16.** In a standing wave, the nodes and antinodes are stationary.

15:9   **17.** The law of reflection states that when waves reach a boundary and are reflected, the angle of reflection is equal to the angle of incidence.

15:10   **18.** The change in direction of a wave as it enters a new medium at some angle is known as refraction.

15:11   **19.** Diffraction is the bending of a wave around obstacles in its path.

Detailed answers to all Questions and Problems are given in the Teacher's Guide at the front of this book.

Questions

1. How many general methods of energy transfer are there? Give two examples of each.

2. Distinguish between a mechanical wave and an electromagnetic wave.

3. How do a transverse wave, a longitudinal wave, and a surface wave differ?

4. If a pulse is sent along a rope, how does the rope behave at any given point after the pulse has passed?

5. A pulse differs from a wave. How?

6. Distinguish among the wavelength, frequency, and period of a wave.

7. What is the equation used to find the velocity of a wave?

8. What is the amplitude of a wave and what does it measure?

9. Waves are sent along a spring of fixed length. Can the speed of the waves in the spring be changed? How can the frequency of a wave in the spring be changed?

10. When a wave reaches the boundary of a new medium, part of the wave is reflected and part is transmitted. What determines the amount of reflection?

11. A pulse reaches the boundary of a medium more rigid than the one from which it came. Is the reflected pulse erect or inverted?

12. A pulse reaches the boundary of a medium less rigid than the one from which it came. Is the reflected pulse erect or inverted?

13. When a wave passes into a new medium, what remains the same? What changes?

14. List three different means of changing the direction of a wave.

15. State the law of reflection.

16. What is diffraction?

17. Name two facts about the diffraction patterns produced by waves of different wavelengths as they pass through the same pair of openings.

Problems–A

1. An ocean wave has a wavelength of 10.0 m. A wave passes by every 2.0 s. What is the speed of the wave?

1. 5.0 m/s

2. A sonar signal of frequency 1.00×10^6 Hz has a wavelength of 1.50 mm in water.
   a. What is the speed of the signal in water?
   b. What is its period in water?
   c. What is its period in air?

2. a. 1.50×10^3 m/s
   b. 1.00×10^{-6} s
   c. 1.00×10^{-6} s

3. Waves of frequency 2.0 Hz are generated along a spring. The waves have a wavelength of 0.45 m.
   a. What is the speed of the waves along the spring?
   b. What is the wavelength of the waves along the spring if their frequency is increased to 6.0 Hz?
   c. If the frequency is decreased to 0.5 Hz, what is their wavelength?

3. a. 0.90 m/s
   b. 0.15 m
   c. 1.8 m

Problems–B

1. The AM radio signals are broadcast at frequencies between 550 kHz and 1600 kHz (kilohertz) and travel at 3.0×10^8 m/s.
   a. What is the range of wavelengths for these signals?
   b. FM frequencies range between 88 MHz and 108 MHz (megahertz) and travel at the same speed. What is the range of FM wavelengths?

1. a. 550 m, 190 m
   b. 3.4 m, 2.8 m

2. The speed of sound in water is 1498 m/s. A sonar signal is sent from a ship at a point just below the water surface and 1.80 s later the reflected signal is detected. How deep is the ocean beneath the ship?

2. 1350 m

Readings

Broad, William, "The Chaos Factor." *Science 83*, January, 1983.

Feldman, Len, "Super Stereo: The Ultimate Sound for Cars." *Popular Science*, January, 1983.

Gilbert, Ray, "Springs: Distorted and Combined." *The Physics Teacher*, October, 1983.

Overbye, Dennis, "The Secret Universe of IRAS." *Discover*, January, 1984.

Snow, John, "The Tornado." *Scientific American*, April, 1984.

The description of sound is partly physical and partly subjective; each listener hears a particular sound differently. Some properties of sound can be described physically; others are perceived. What are these properties of sound? How does the construction of these organ pipes determine the nature of the sounds they produce and the sounds we hear?

Sound

Chapter 16 introduces the concept of sound. How it is measured, produced, and perceived is discussed.

Sound and music are important parts of the human experience. At a first glance music and physics might seem very far apart. However, there are many interesting relationships between the two. Many important discoveries about what makes sounds harmonious were made in the sixth century B.C. by the Greek mathematician Pythagoras. Johannes Kepler discovered one of the laws of the motion of the planets while imagining the celestial music that might be played by the planets. Scientists study acoustics, the science of sound, in order to understand the production of sound by musical instruments as well as to design electronic systems that can record and produce sounds without distortion. In addition, architects study acoustics so they can construct auditoriums in which music and voice can be heard by every member of the audience.

Goal: You will gain understanding of sound and music as applications of wave motion.

16:1 Sound Waves

You have previously studied waves and oscillating motion. Sound is a longitudinal wave in which the pressure of the air oscillates about an average value, the mean air pressure. The frequency of the wave is the number of oscillations in pressure each second.

A sound wave is an oscillation in the pressure in the medium.

Sound waves move through air because the molecules of the air are constantly in motion. The molecules collide, transmitting the pressure oscillations away from the source of the sound. Figure 16-1 shows the relationships between the motion of molecules and the air pressure in a sound wave. Sound is a longitudinal wave because the motion of the air molecules is parallel to the direction of motion of the wave.

Sound is a longitudinal wave.

271

FIGURE 16-1. Kepler's *Harmony of the Worlds* contained celestial music.

The speed of sound in air at room temperature is 343 m/s.

Sound cannot travel through a vacuum.

Sound waves can be reflected, diffracted, and can interfere.

In any wave, frequency, wavelength, and velocity are related by the equation $v = f\lambda$.

The velocity of the sound wave depends on the mean pressure and the temperature of the air. Sound waves move through air at a velocity of 343 m/s at standard pressure and room temperature. Sound can also travel through liquids and solids. In general, the velocity of sound is greater in solids and liquids than in gases. Sound cannot travel through a vacuum because there are no particles to move and to collide.

Sound waves share the properties of other waves. They can be reflected off hard objects, such as the walls of a room. Reflected sound waves are called echoes. Sound waves can also be diffracted, spreading outward after passing through narrow openings. Two sound waves can interfere. Destructive interference of sound waves in auditoriums can cause "dead spots" at nodes where little sound can be heard.

The wavelength of a sound wave is the distance between regions of maximum pressure. The frequency and wavelength of a wave are related to the velocity of the wave by the equation $v = f\lambda$.

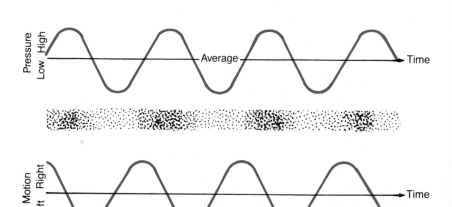

FIGURE 16-2. Graphic representation of the relationships between the motion of molecules and the air pressure in a sound wave.

EXAMPLE

A sound wave has a frequency of 261.6 Hz. What is the wavelength of this sound traveling in air at 343 m/s?

Given: $f = 261.6$ Hz   **Unknown:** λ

$v = 343$ m/s   **Basic equation:** $v = f\lambda$

Solution: $v = f\lambda$

$$\lambda = \frac{v}{f}$$

$$\lambda = \frac{(343 \text{ m/s})}{(261.6 \text{ Hz})} = 1.31 \text{ m}$$

Problems

1. The speed of sound in water is 1435 m/s. Find the wavelength of sound with a frequency of 261.6 Hz traveling through water.

2. Find the frequency of a wave moving in air at room temperature with a wavelength of 0.667 m.

3. When a frequency 440-Hz sound is sent through steel, a wavelength of 11.66 m is measured. Find the velocity of sound in steel.

The frequency of sound depends on the oscillation frequency of the source. If sound is emitted by a moving source the wavelength of the sound wave is changed. This change is called the **Doppler shift.** If the source is moving toward the sound detector, more waves will be

1. 5.485 m

2. 514 Hz

3. 5100 m/s

The Doppler shift is the change in the wavelength of sound emitted by a moving source.

FIGURE 16-3. A point source moving across a ripple tank (a) can be used to show the Doppler effect (b).

a

b

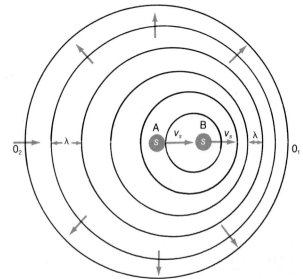

FIGURE 16-4. The loudness heard at a concert depends on the response of our ears to sound in different frequency ranges.

FIGURE 16-5. The decibel scale measures relative loudness of sounds.

120	Threshold of pain	
	Ship engine room	
110	Low-flying jet aircraft	
	Loud rock band	
100	Riveter at 10 m	
90	Noisy factory	fff
	Heavy traffic	
80	Factory	ff
70		
	Normal conversation	f
60	Busy office	mf
	Department store	
50	Average office	p
40	Library	pp
30	Quiet day in	ppp
	the country	
20	Whisper	
	Gentle breeze	
10	Rustle of leaves	
0	Threshold of hearing	

decibels

crowded into the same space, decreasing the wavelength of the sound. Since the velocity remains constant, the detector will register an increase in frequency.

If the source is moving away from the detector, the wavelength will be increased and the frequency will appear to decrease. The Doppler effect also occurs if the detector is moving and the source is stationary.

The Doppler shift is often heard as a car with a siren approaches, passes, and then moves away. The siren frequency (pitch) is high as it approaches, then suddenly drops as the car passes.

The Doppler effect is observed in all wave motion, both mechanical and electromagnetic.

16:2 Pitch and Loudness

The characteristics of a sound wave, such as frequency, wavelength, and amplitude can be detected by the human ear. These characteristics of sound are then described by a different set of names. **Pitch** is equivalent to frequency. **Loudness** indicates the amplitude of the wave.

While the pitch of a sound can be expressed in terms of its frequency, pitch can also be given the name of a note on a musical scale. Musical scales are based on the work of Pythagorus. Two notes whose frequencies are related by the ratio 2/1 are said to differ by an **octave.** For example, if one note has a frequency of 440 Hz, a note one octave higher has a frequency of 880 Hz. It is important to recognize that the interval between notes is not the difference in their frequencies, but the ratio of their frequencies.

The human ear is sensitive to an enormous variation in the loudness of sound. The amplitude of a sound that causes pain is one trillion times (10^{12}) larger than the smallest sound that can be detected by the ear. To the ear, loudness approximately doubles if the amplitude of the sound waves increases by a factor of twenty. For that reason, the scale by which sound intensity or loudness is measured is based on the ratio of amplitudes. All intensities are measured in terms of the amplitude of a sound that can just be heard. Sound at the threshold of hearing is said to have an intensity level of zero decibels (0 dB). The intensity of sound 10 times larger is 10 dB. A sound intensity 10 times larger than this is 20 dB. Table 16-5 shows the intensity in decibels for a variety of sounds.

16:3 Sources of Sound

Sound is produced by a vibrating object. The vibrations of the object create molecular motions and pressure oscillations in the air. A loudspeaker has a diaphragm, or cone, that is made to vibrate by electrical currents. The cone creates the sound waves. Musical instruments such as gongs or cymbals are other examples of vibrating sources of sound. The membrane on a drum is yet another example.

The human voice is the result of vibrations of the vocal cords, two membranes located in the throat. Air from the lungs rushing through the throat starts the vocal cards vibrating. The frequency of vibration is controlled by the muscular tension placed on the cords.

Brass instruments, such as the trumpet, trombone, and tuba, produce their sounds as the result of vibrations of the lips of the performer. In this sense, the source of sound in a brass instrument is very similar to that of the voice. Reed instruments, like the clarinet, saxophone, and oboe, have a thin wooden strip, or reed, that vibrates as a result of air

FIGURE 16-6. The vibrations of our vocal cords create sound waves in the air.

The intensity of sound waves is measured in decibels (dB).

Sound waves are produced by vibrating objects.

The sound of a wind instrument is the result of a vibrating column of air.

Brass instrument

Mouthpiece

Woodwind instrument

Mouthpiece

Reed

FIGURE 16-7. The shapes of the mouthpieces of a brass instrument (a) and a woodwind (b) determine the characteristics of the sound each instrument produces.

blown across it. In a flute, recorder, organ pipe, or whistle, air is blown across an opening in a pipe. Air moves in and out of the pipe at the frequency of the note. The vibration of the column of air in the instrument causes the sound.

In stringed instruments, such as the piano, guitar, and violin, a wire or string is set into vibration. In the piano the wire is struck; in the guitar, it is plucked. In the violin, the friction of the bow pulls the string aside. The string is attached to a sounding board that vibrates with the string. The vibrations of the sounding board cause the pressure oscillations in the air that we hear as sound. Electric guitars use electronic devices to detect and amplify the vibrations of the strings.

16:4   Resonance

If you have ever blown through the mouthpiece of a brass or reed instrument, you know that the vibration of your lips or the reed alone does not make a sound with any particular pitch. The long tube that makes up the instrument must be attached if music is ever to result. When the instrument is played, the air within this tube vibrates at the same frequency, or in **resonance,** with a particular vibration of the lips or reed. The pitch of the instrument is varied by changing the length of the resonating column of vibrating air. The length of the air column controls the resonant frequency of the vibrating air. The mouthpiece creates a mixture of different frequencies. The resonating air column acting on the vibrating lips or reed amplifies a single note.

To understand resonance in the air column, consider a tuning fork above a hollow tube. The tube is placed in water so that the bottom end of the tube is below the water surface. The length of the air column is adjusted by raising or lowering the height of the tube. The tuning fork is struck with a rubber hammer. When the length of the air column is varied the sound of the fork will alternately become louder and softer. The sound is loud when the air column is in resonance with the tuning fork. The air column has intensified the sound of the tuning fork.

Consider the effect of the vibrating tuning fork on the molecules in the air. The molecules are struck by the fork and produce a sound wave that moves down the air column. When the wave hits the water surface it is reflected back up to the tuning fork. If the reflected wave is at the same point in its oscillation as the wave leaving the tuning fork, the motion of the leaving and returning waves will reinforce each other. A **standing wave** will be produced.

In a standing wave the motion of air molecules has nodes and antinodes. Nodes in the motion occur where the molecules are moving normally. Antinodes occur where the motions have their maximum forward or backward values. Two antinodes (or two nodes) are separated by one-half wavelength. There is an antinode in the molecular motion at the tuning fork. The surface of the water stops the motion of the molecules, producing a **node** at that location.

The sound of a stringed instrument is the result of the vibration of a sounding board.

The shape of sound waves can be demonstrated by attaching a microphone to an oscilloscope.

Hammer

Tuning fork

Air column

Water

FIGURE 16-8. An example showing resonance of an air column.

In a standing wave, the separation between two nodes (or antinodes) is one-half wavelength.

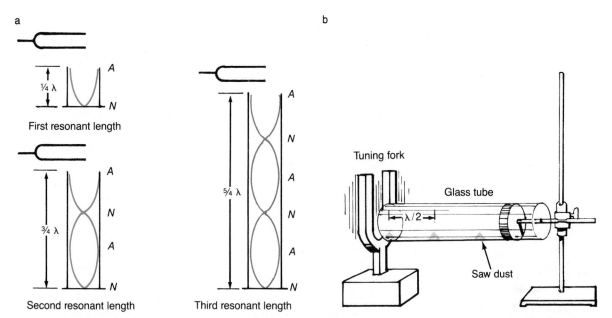

a

b

First resonant length

Second resonant length

Third resonant length

Tuning fork

Glass tube

Saw dust

Pieces of plastic water pipe can be used to demonstrate closed and open pipes.

FIGURE 16-9. Standing waves are produced in closed pipes (a). Standing waves deposit tiny mounds of saw dust at half-wavelength intervals in a closed pipe or tube (b).

A closed pipe resonates when its length is λ/4, 3λ/4, 5λ/4, . . .

The shortest column of air that can have a node at the bottom and an anti-node at the top is one-fourth wavelength long. As the air column is lengthened, additional resonances are found. Thus columns λ/4, 3λ/4, 5λ/4, 7λ/4, etc. will all be in resonance with the tuning fork.

In practice the first resonance length is slightly longer than one-fourth wavelength. This is caused by the gap between the tuning fork and the tube. However, each additional resonance is spaced by exactly one-half wavelength. Measurement of the spacings between resonances can be used to find the velocity of sound in air.

EXAMPLE

A tuning fork with a frequency of 392 Hz is found to cause resonances in an air column spaced by 44.3 cm. The air temperature is 27°C. Find the velocity of sound in air at that temperature.

Given: $f = 392$ Hz

$l = 44.3$ cm

Unknown: v

Basic equation: $v = f\lambda$

Solution: Resonances are spaced by one-half wavelength.

$$l = \frac{\lambda}{2} \quad \text{or} \quad \lambda = 2l$$

Thus,

$$v = f\lambda = (392 \text{ Hz})(0.886 \text{ m})$$

$$= 347 \text{ m/s}$$

4. 0.39 m

5. 970 m/s

6. 443 Hz

An open pipe resonates if its length is λ/2, 2λ/2, 3λ/2, ...

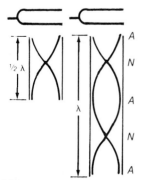

FIGURE 16-10. The normal modes of oscillation of an open tube showing the fundamental and the second harmonic.

7. 64.7 Hz

8. 260 Hz

A sound detector converts the energy of a sound wave into a different form of energy.

Problems

4. A 440 Hz tuning fork is used at 27°C. Find the spacings between resonances.

5. The 440 Hz tuning fork is used with a resonating column to determine the velocity of sound in helium gas. If the spacings between resonances are 110 cm, what is the velocity of sound in He?

6. The frequency of a tuning fork is unknown. A student uses an air column at 27°C and finds resonances spaced by 39.2 cm. What is the frequency of the tuning fork?

An open pipe will resonate with a source of sound. In a closed pipe there is a node in molecular motion at the closed end. In an open pipe there is an antinode at both ends. Thus the minimum length of a resonating open pipe is one-half wavelength. If open and closed pipes of the same length are used as resonators, the wavelength of the sound resonant with the open pipe will be half as long. Therefore the frequency will be twice as high for the open pipe as for the closed pipe. The resonances in the open pipe are spaced by half wavelengths just as in closed pipes. You have probably experienced an open-pipe resonator if you have shouted into a long tunnel or underpass. Many musical instruments are also open-pipe resonators.

Problems

7. A bugle can be treated as an open pipe. If a bugle were straightened out, it would be 2.65 m long. If the speed of sound is 343 m/s, find the lowest frequency that is resonant in a bugle.

8. A soprano saxophone is an open pipe. If all keys are closed, it is approximately 65 cm long. Using 343 m/s as the speed of sound, find the lowest frequency that can be played on this instrument.

16:5   Detection of Sound

Sound detectors convert sound energy, kinetic energy of the air molecules, into another form of energy. In a sound detector, a diaphragm vibrates at the frequency of the sound wave. The vibration of the diaphragm then is converted into another form of energy. A microphone is an electronic device which converts sound energy into electrical energy. It will be discussed in Chapter 26.

The ear is an amazing sound detector. Not only can it detect sound waves over a very wide range of frequencies, it is also sensitive to an enormous range of sound intensities. In addition, human hearing can distinguish many different qualities of sound. The ear is a complex detector that requires knowledge of both physics and biology to understand. The interpretation of sounds by the brain is even more complex, and not totally understood.

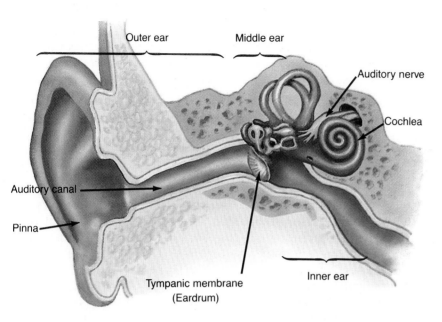

Outer ear

Middle ear

Auditory nerve

Cochlea

Auditory canal

Pinna

Tympanic membrane
(Eardrum)

Inner ear

FIGURE 16-11. The human ear is a complex sense organ which translates sound vibrations into nerve impulses that are then sent to the brain for interpretation.

The ear (Figure 16-11) is divided into three parts: the outer, middle, and inner ear. The outer ear consists of the fleshy, visible part of the ear called the pinna, the auditory canal, and the eardrum. The pinna collects sound waves which then travel through the air-filled auditory canal to the eardrum. The waves cause vibrations in the eardrum. The middle ear consists of three tiny bones in an air-filled space in the skull. The bones transmit the vibrations of the eardrum to the oval window on the inner ear. The inner ear is filled with a watery liquid. Sound vibrations are transmitted through the liquid into sensitive portions of the spiral-shaped cochlea. In the cochlea tiny hair cells are vibrated by the waves. Vibrations of these cells stimulate nerve fibers that lead to the brain, producing the sensation of sound.

The ear is not equally sensitive to all frequencies. Most people cannot hear sounds with frequencies below 20 Hz or above 16 000 Hz. Most people are most sensitive to sounds with frequencies between 1000 and 5000 Hz. Older people are less sensitive to frequencies above 10 000 Hz than are young people. Exposure to loud sounds, either noise or music, has been shown to cause the ear to lose its sensitivity, especially to high pitched sounds.

The ear consists of the outer, middle, and inner ear. In the inner ear, sound waves stimulate nerves.

Try to borrow a model or a poster showing parts of the ear.

16:6 The Quality of Sound

Musical instruments sound very different, even when playing the same note, because most sounds are made up of a number of frequencies. The quality of a sound depends on the relative intensities of these frequencies. In music, sound quality is **timbre** (TIM bur).

The quality of sound is called timbre.

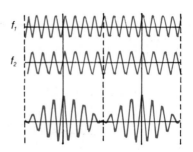

FIGURE 16-12. Beats occur as a result of the superposition of two sound waves of slightly different frequencies.

Two waves of slightly different frequencies produce beat notes.

Two penny whistles or adjustable toy whistles can be blown at the same time. Adjust one to produce various beats and dissonant or consonant mixtures.

When two waves of the same frequency arrive at the ear or another sound detector, the detector senses the sum of the amplitudes of the waves. If the waves are of slightly different frequencies, the sum of the two waves has an amplitude that oscillates in intensity. A listener hears a pulsing variation in loudness. This oscillation of wave amplitude is called a **beat** (Figure 16-12). The frequency of the beat is the difference in frequency of the two waves. Measurement of the beat frequency is often used to adjust, or tune, two waves so that they have the same frequency. This technique is used by piano tuners.

EXAMPLE

Beats

A 442-Hz tuning fork and a 444-Hz tuning fork are struck simultaneously. What beat frequency will be produced?

Solution: The beat frequency is 444 Hz − 442 Hz, or 2 Hz.

The human ear can detect beat frequencies as high as seven hertz. When two waves differ by more than 7 Hz, the ear detects a complex

FIGURE 16-13. Time graphs showing the superposition of two waves having the ratios of 1:2, 2:3, 3:4, and 4:5.

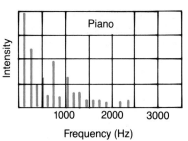

FIGURE 16-14. A violin, clarinet, and piano produce characteristic sound spectra.

wave. If the resulting sound is unpleasant, the result is said to be a **dissonance.** If the sound is pleasant the result is a **consonance** or a chord. As discovered by Pythagoras, consonances occur when the wave frequencies have ratios that are small whole numbers. The waves that result when sound waves with frequencies in ratios of 2:1 (octave), 3:2 (fifth), 4:3 (fourth), and 5:4 (major third) are shown in Figure 16-13.

As discussed earlier, open and closed pipes resonate at more than one frequency. As a result, musical instruments using pipe resonators produce sounds that contain more than one frequency. The lowest frequency produced by an instrument is called the **fundamental.** Waves of higher frequency are called **overtones.** Usually the intensity of the overtones will be less than the intensity of the fundamental. An open pipe resonates when the length is an integral number of half wavelengths, $\lambda/2, 2\lambda/2, 3\lambda/2, \ldots$. Thus the frequencies produced by an instrument with an open pipe with fundamental frequency f are $f, 2f, 3f, \ldots$. The first overtone ($2f$) is one octave above the fundamental. The second overtone ($3f$) is an octave and a fifth above the fundamental. Brass instruments, flutes, oboes, and saxophones are examples of open-pipe instruments.

Sound can be transmitted through the air or changed into electrical energy and back into sound by a public address system. The air transmits different frequencies with varying efficiencies that could lead to a distortion of the original sound. An electrical system can also distort the sound quality. A high-fidelity system is carefully designed to transmit all frequencies with equal efficiency. A system that has a response within 3 dB between 20 and 20 000 Hz is considered to be very good.

On the other hand, it is sometimes useful to transmit only certain frequencies. Telephone systems transmit only frequencies between 300 and 3000 Hz, where most of the information in spoken language exists. Words can be understood even when the high and low frequencies are missing. The distortion of musical sounds can also produce effects that are interesting and even desired by musical groups.

Noise consists of a large number of frequencies with no particular relationship. If all frequencies are present in equal amplitudes the

Unpleasant mixtures of tones are called dissonances.

When the frequencies of sounds have ratios that are the ratios of small numbers, the resulting sound is pleasant, or a consonance.

The frequency of an overtone is a multiple of the frequency of the fundamental.

FIGURE 16-15. This machine generates "white" sound.

FIGURE 16-16. The shape of the vocal tract determines the resonant wave forms for a as in sat (a) and u as in suit (b).

a

b

Vocal tract

Sound waves

a

u

Noise is a mixture of a large number of unrelated frequencies.

The throat and mouth change the quality of the human voice.

result is white noise. White noise has been found to have a relaxing effect, and as a result has been used by dentists to help their patients relax.

The human voice uses the throat and mouth cavity as a resonator. The number of overtones present, and thus the quality of the tone, depends on the shape of the resonator. Closing the throat, moving the tongue, and closing the teeth change the shape of the resonant cavity. Even the nasal cavities, or sinuses, can affect the sound quality. The complex sound waves produced when the vowels a (as in sat), and u (as in suit) are shown in Figure 16-16.

Physics Focus   Ultrasound Surgery

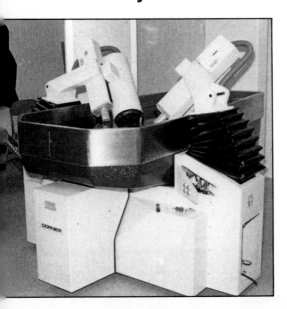

Ultrasound, inaudible to the human ear, has frequencies between 16 000 and 10 000 000 000 Hz. It is used, usually at low intensity, for many medical purposes. Ultrasonic vibrations travel at different speeds through tissues of different densities and elasticities, allowing tissues and organs to be outlined by ultrasonography.

Ultrasonography is used during surgery to locate kidney calculi ("stones"). This surgery, done through a long incision, requires a 10- to 12-week convalescence.

Recently, ultrasonics have been used to disintegrate the calculi, making extraction easier or allowing the pieces to be passed naturally from the body. Several techniques have been developed to accomplish this. In one technique, a catheter is threaded up the ureter to "catch" a calculus in a basket. An ultrasound transducer placed directly on the calculus literally shakes it apart. The pieces are pulled out in the basket or flushed out with water. Another technique involves inserting a catheter directly through the skin to the calculus, and the transducer operates as before. Neither technique requires an incision. After a three- to four-day hospital stay, the patient may return to normal activities.

Summary

1. Sound is a longitudinal wave.   16:1

2. A sound wave is an oscillation in air pressure. It is also an oscillation in   16:1
the motion of air molecules.

3. The velocity of sound in air is 343 m/s at standard atmospheric pressure   16:1
and room temperature.

4. The Doppler effect describes the change in wavelength of sound caused   16:1
by motion of either the source or the detector.

5. The frequency of a sound wave is called its pitch.   16:2

6. Two notes that differ by one octave have pitches in the ratio of two to   16:2
one.

7. The amplitude of a sound wave is described by its loudness, measured in   16:2
decibels.

8. Sound is produced by vibrating objects.   16:3

9. An air column vibrating at the same frequency as a sound source is in   16:4
resonance with the source.

10. A resonant air column increases the intensity of the sound.   16:4

11. A closed pipe resonates when its length is $\frac{1}{4}$, $\frac{3}{4}$, $\frac{5}{4}$, . . . wave-   16:4
lengths.

12. An open pipe resonates when it is $\frac{1}{2}$, $\frac{2}{2}$ $\frac{3}{2}$,, . . . wavelengths long.   16:4

13. Sound detectors convert sound energy into a different form of   16:5
energy.

14. Two waves with almost the same frequency produce a beat note.   16:6

15. Most sound waves consist of more than one frequency. The quality of the   16:6
sound wave is called its timbre.

16. The timbre of a musical instrument depends on the number and intensity   16:6
of the overtones it produces.

17. The shape of the throat and mouth cavity determines the vowel sounds   16:6
produced by the human voice.

Detailed answers to all Questions and Problems are given in the Teacher's Guide at the front of this book.

Questions

1. In many science-fiction movies, when a spaceship explodes a loud sound
is heard by occupants of a nearby spaceship. Is this realistic? Why?

2. In the last century, people put their ears to a railroad track to get an early
warning of an approaching train. Why did this work?

3. A loud sound wave causes vibration of a set of hanging ribbons. Do they vibrate back and forth in the direction of the source or perpendicular to that direction?

4. If the pitch of sound is increased, what are the changes in
   a. the frequency?
   b. the wavelength?
   c. the wave velocity?
   d. the amplitude of the wave?

5. Suppose the horns of all cars emitted sound of the same pitch.
   a. What would be the change in the pitch of the horn of a car moving toward you?
   b. Away from you?

6. Is a sound of 20 dB a factor of 100 (10^2) times more intense than the threshold of hearing, or a factor of 20 times more intense?

7. A closed organ pipe plays a certain note. If the cover is removed to make it an open pipe, is the pitch increased or decreased?

8. The speed of sound increases with temperature. Would the pitch of a closed pipe increase or decrease when the temperature rises? Assume the length of the pipe does not change.

9. What property distinguishes notes played on both a trumpet and a clarinet if they have the same pitch and loudness?

| Problems–A |

Use 343 m/s as the speed of sound.

1. 686 m

1. If you shout across a canyon and hear an echo 4.00 seconds later, how wide is the canyon?

2. 0.0175 s

2. A certain instant camera determines the exact distance to the subject of the picture by sending out a sound wave and measuring the time needed for the echo to return to the camera. How long would it take if the subject were 3.00 m away?

3. 1450 m/s

3. If the wavelength of a 4.40×10^2 Hz sound in fresh water is 3.30 m, what is the speed of sound?

4. a. 10 times as intense
   b. 100 times

4. A rock band plays with a 90 dB loudness. How much more intense is the sound from another rock band playing at
   a.   100 dB?   b.   110 dB?

5. a. 10.5 m
   b. 8.20 Hz

5. The lowest note on an organ is 16.4 Hz.
   a. What is the shortest open organ pipe that will resonate at this frequency?
   b. What would be the pitch if the same organ pipe were closed?

6. One tuning fork has a 445 Hz pitch. When a second fork is struck beat notes occur with a frequency of 3 Hz. What are the two possible frequencies of the second fork?

7. A flute sounds a note with 370 Hz pitch. What are the frequencies of the first, second, and third overtones of this pitch?

7. 740 Hz, 1110 Hz, 1480 Hz

8. A clarinet also sounds the same note, 370 Hz. However, it only produces overtones that are odd multiples of the fundamental frequency. What are the frequencies of the lowest three overtones produced by this clarinet?

8. 1110 Hz, 1850 Hz, 2590 Hz

Problems–B

1. One closed organ pipe has a length of 2.40 m. Assume 343 m/s as the speed of sound.
   a. What is the frequency of the note played by this pipe?
   b. When a second pipe is played at the same time, a 1.40 Hz beat note is heard. By how much is the second pipe too long?

1. a. 35.7 Hz
   b. 0.10 m

2. The equation for the Doppler shift of a sound of speed v, reaching a moving detector, is $f' = f(v - v_d)/(v - v_s)$, where v_d is the speed of the detector and v_s is the speed of the source. If the detector moves toward the source, v_d is negative. A train moving toward a detector at 31 m/s blows a 305 Hz horn. What pitch is detected by a
   a. stationary train?
   b. train moving toward the first at 21 m/s?

2. a. 340 Hz
   b. 360 Hz

Readings

Engel, Kenneth, "They Can See What You Can Hear." *Technology Illustrated*, August, 1983.

Fletcher, Neville, "The Physics of Organ Pipes." *Scientific American*, January, 1983.

Mims, Forrest, "The Electronics Scientist—Ultrasonic Sound." *Computers and Electronics*, June, 1983.

Oster, Gerald, "Muscle Sounds." *Scientific American*, March, 1984.

Ruby, Daniel, "Visible Wind." *Popular Science*, August, 1984.

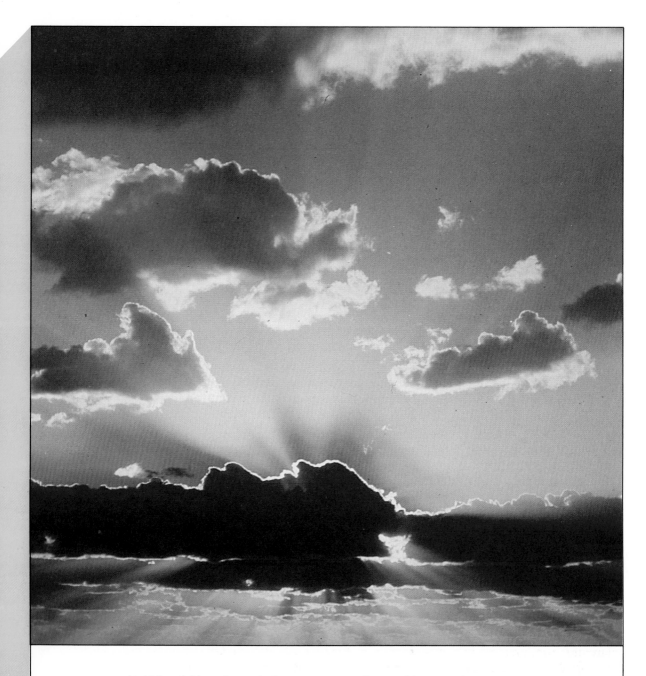

Light has intrigued people for many years. Some objects such as our sun produce their own light. Other objects such as the moon only reflect light from some other source. What is the source of the moon's light? Light travels in straight lines. How does this photograph show this fact? What are other properties of light?

Nature of Light

Chapter 17 introduces optics. Methods of measuring the speed of light and the inverse-square law governing illumination are discussed.

The sun is a source of huge quantities of electromagnetic energy. Electromagnetic energy is also emitted from incandescent lamps, fluorescent lamps, and flames. Some of this energy can stimulate the retina of the human eye and is called **light.**

Light waves have wavelengths that range from about 380 nm (3.80×10^{-7} m) to 760 nm (7.60×10^{-7} m). Although visible light is only a small portion of the entire range of electromagnetic waves, there are many good reasons for us to study optical effects. A study of visible light is, in many ways, a study of all electromagnetic radiation. Light is perhaps our most important means of learning about the physical nature of our world. Microscopes, telescopes, and the human eye all are important scientific tools.

Goal: You will gain understanding of the wave properties of light, the illumination of a surface by a point source, and the methods used to measure the speed of light.

Light is electromagnetic radiation capable of stimulating the retina of the eye.

17:1 Light Travels in a Straight Line

Light travels in a straight line. For example, when the air contains many dust particles, the path of light coming from a flashlight can be seen. The light forms a "beam" of light. Also, an opaque object casts a sharp shadow when light falls on the object. Shadows are further evidence that light travels in straight lines.

A small beam of light consists of a very large number of individual waves traveling together in a straight line. Lines representing the direction of the light waves are called **rays.** A beam of light is composed of rays traveling in the same direction. Using ray diagrams in studying light is called **ray optics.**

Point out that the ray optics method of studying light is based on the fact that light travels in a straight line.

Since light travels in straight lines, the direction of light waves can be represented by rays.

287

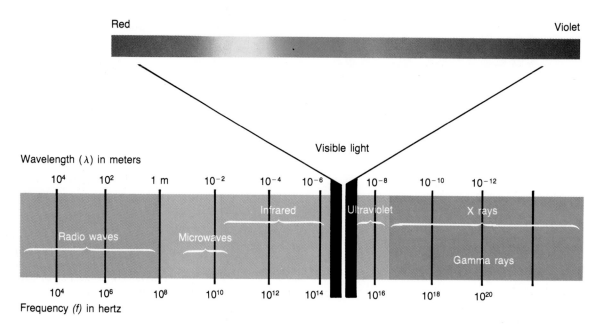

Visible light

Wavelength (λ) in meters

| 10^4 | 10^2 | 1 m | 10^{-2} | 10^{-4} | 10^{-6} | | 10^{-8} | 10^{-10} | 10^{-12} |

Infrared

Ultraviolet

X rays

Radio waves

Microwaves

Gamma rays

| 10^4 | 10^6 | 10^8 | 10^{10} | 10^{12} | 10^{14} | 10^{16} | 10^{18} | 10^{20} |

Frequency (f) in hertz

FIGURE 17-1. The visible spectrum is only a very small portion of the whole electromagnetic spectrum.

Point out that it is no longer possible to measure the speed of light because *c* has been *defined* to be 299 792 458 m/s. What appears to be a measurement of *c* is now a measurement of the length of the meter.

Roemer made the first calculation of the speed of light using data from astronomical observations.

Michelson made an accurate measurement of the speed of light.

17:2 The Speed of Light

Before the seventeenth century, most people believed that light traveled instantaneously. Galileo unsuccessfully tried to measure the speed of light. He was forced to conclude that the speed of light was too fast to be measured accurately. About 1676, Olaf Roemer (1644-1710), an astronomer, was studying one of the moons of Jupiter. While the earth was in position E_1, he observed a moon move behind Jupiter, Figure 17-2, and emerge from the other side. Roemer carefully timed several of these eclipses. From this data, he made a table that predicted the occurrence of moon eclipses during the next few months. At first, Roemer's table was fairly accurate. However, as time passed, an error of increasing size gradually appeared. The eclipses occurred later than predicted. But after six months, the error began to decrease. At the end of twelve months the table was once again accurate. Roemer immediately understood the source of error. He had made the table while the earth was at position E_1. As the earth followed its orbit around the sun, it moved away from Jupiter. Jupiter, however, moved only a short distance along its orbit. The error occurred because the light from Jupiter's moon had to travel a greater distance to reach the observer on the earth as the months went by. He concluded that light must travel at some fixed speed.

Albert A. Michelson (1852-1931) modified a method used to measure the speed of light that was designed originally by the Frenchman Jean Foucault. In 1879, Michelson used Foucault's method of a rotating mirror and accurately measured the speed of light. Almost fifty years later, Michelson, the first American to win a Nobel Prize,

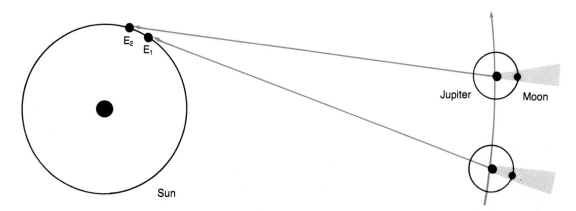

FIGURE 17-2. Roemer's method of determining the speed of light involved measuring the time differences of an eclipse of one of Jupiter's moons.

improved the rotating mirror method and measured the speed of light in air to be 2.99729 ± 0.00004 × 10⁸ m/s.

Michelson measured the time for light to complete a round trip between two California mountains 35 km apart. To do this, he used a rotating octagonal mirror, Figure 17-3. Light was sent from the source S to the mirror A. The light then traveled the path shown. For the observer O to see the light through the telescope, mirror B had to move into the exact position of mirror C in the time it took the light to travel the path. The time required for B to move into position C was just one-eighth of the time needed for one revolution of the mirror. During these experiments, the octagonal mirror was turned by an electric motor. Starting from rest, the speed of the motor was adjusted until the light reflected from C was clearly observed through the telescope. Then, with the rate of rotation of the mirror known, the speed of light was calculated.

Problems

1. The octagonal mirror in Figure 17-3 makes 625 rev/s. What time is required for one revolution?

1. 1.60 × 10⁻³ s

FIGURE 17-3. Michelson's method of determining the speed of light involved measuring the time for light to be reflected from one mountain to another.

2. a. 2.00×10^{-4} s
   b. 60 km

3. a. 3×10^5 km/s
   b. 3×10^8 m/s

4. Yes, the eight-sided mirror, revolving twice as fast, would always have a face in the proper position to reflect the beam of light.

5. The observer can start to rotate the mirror from rest and increase its rate of revolution to the first rate that gives the brightest reflected spots.

FIGURE 17-4. The transparent and translucent glass window ornament contrasts with the opaque window frame.

FIGURE 17-5. The standard light source contains glowing thoria. The brightness of all other light sources is defined in terms of light emitted by this standard.

2. **a.** For the octagonal mirror of Problem 1, what time is needed for B to move into position C?
   b. Using Figure 17-3, find the total distance the light travels in this time.

3. Use the solutions to Problem 2 to find the speed of light in
   a. km/s.　　**b.** m/s.

4. The speed of the motor is increased until the mirror is rotating at the speed of 1250 rev/s. Will an observer see the pulse of light? Explain.

5. What steps can an observer take to be sure that the octagonal mirror does not rotate at some multiple of the proper number of rev/s?

17:3　Transmission and Absorption of Light

Many materials transmit light. Objects can be seen clearly through glass, quartz, air, and some other materials. These materials are called **transparent** materials. Other matter, such as frosted glass, transmits light, but objects cannot be seen clearly through them. These materials are called **translucent.** Lampshades and most light bulbs are translucent. Materials such as brick transmit no light. They absorb or reflect all light that falls on them. These materials are called **opaque.**

17:4　Illumination by a Point Source

A **luminous** body emits light waves; an **illuminated** body reflects light waves. The sun is a luminous body and the moon is an illuminated body. The word luminous refers only to bodies that emit light waves.

The amount of light that a source gives out, its luminous intensity, depends on the amount of energy being put into the source. It also depends on how efficiently the source converts the energy input to light energy. Incandescent lamps are very inefficient sources of light. For the same amount of electric energy, a fluorescent lamp produces about four times more light than an equivalent incandescent light bulb. It is clear that a homeowner can reduce electric costs by using fluorescent lamps rather than incandescent lamps.

The **luminous intensity,** I, is measured by comparing it with the international unit, the candela, cd. At first, the unit for luminous intensity was called a candle. An actual candle made to meet certain specifications was used as a standard. However, even carefully made candles have an unsteady light intensity. Thus, a candle was not a good reference device.

The **candela,** the current unit, is one sixtieth of the luminous intensity of a square centimeter of fused thoria maintained at 2046 K (Figure 17-5).* At this temperature, thoria is incandescent and steadily emits light energy.

---

*Thoria is a powdery white oxide of the element thorium.

The rate at which light energy is emitted from a source is named the **luminous flux.** The unit of luminous flux is called the **lumen** (lm). Since the lumen measures the rate of energy emitted, transmitted, or received, it is a power unit.

In order to define the lumen, standards must be made for the area that light passes through and the intensity of the light. Imagine a hollow sphere with a radius of one meter. At the center of the sphere is a point light source of one candela intensity. A point light source is a very small light source that sends out light uniformly in all directions. Now, imagine four radii leaving the point source, each forming a corner of one square meter on the surface of the hollow sphere. The light energy flowing through that area would be one lumen.

The surface area of a sphere is $4\pi r^2$. The sphere of one meter radius has a total surface area of $4\pi(1 \text{ m})^2$ or 4π m². Accordingly, the rate at which light crosses the entire surface is 4π lumens. A two-candela source would emit 8π lumens, a three-candela source, 12π lumens, and so on. The energy flux in lumens from a light source is directly proportional to the intensity of the source.

The rate at which light energy falls on a unit area some distance from a light source is **illuminance,** E. Illuminance is measured in lumens per square meter, lm/m² or lux (lx). One lumen per square meter (1 lux) is the illuminance of a surface located one meter from a one-candela source. A surface one meter from a 10-candela source receives illuminance of 10 lux or 10 lumens per square meter.

Light from a point source radiates in all directions. Therefore, it spreads out with distance. Surfaces far from a light source receive less illumination than surfaces closer to the source. Figure 17-7 shows that the amount of illumination received by a surface varies inversely with the square of its distance from the source. A given amount of light energy falls on one square meter of a surface one meter away from a source. This same amount of energy spreads to cover an area of four square meters on a surface two meters from the source. Hence, the illumination of the surface two meters from the source is only one fourth that of the surface one meter from the source. In the same way, the source provides one ninth the illumination to a surface three meters away.

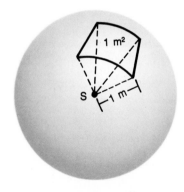

FIGURE 17-6. The lumen is the unit of luminous flux and is a measure of the rate of flow of light energy from a source.

The lumen is the unit for luminous flux. It is a power unit.

Illuminance is the rate at which light falls on a surface of unit area.

The SI unit for illuminance is lux (lx).

One lux equals one lumen per square meter.

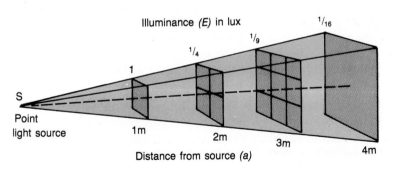

Illuminance (E) in lux

S
Point light source

Distance from source (a)

FIGURE 17-7. The illuminance of a surface varies inversely as the square of its distance from a light source.

There are two ways to increase the illuminance of a surface. The luminous intensity of a light source can be increased, or the distance between the source and the surface can be decreased. Thus, the illuminance of a surface varies directly with the intensity of the light source and inversely with the square of its distance from the source. Let I represent the luminous intensity of the source in candelas. Let E represent the illuminance of the surface in lum/m² or lx. Then, the illuminance of any surface can be expressed as

$$E = \frac{I}{d^2}$$

EXAMPLE

Illumination

A student's desk top is 2.5 m below a 150-cd incandescent lamp. What is the illumination of the desk top?

Given: Luminous intensity   **Unknown:**   Illuminance (E)
$(I) = 1.50 \times 10^2$ cd
Basic equation: $E = \dfrac{I}{d^2}$
Distance $(d) = 2.5$ m

Solution: $E = \dfrac{I}{d^2}$

$$= \frac{1.50 \times 10^2 \text{ cd}}{(2.5 \text{ m})^2} \times 1\frac{\text{lum}}{\text{cd}}$$

$$= 24 \text{ lum/m}^2 = 24 \text{ lx}$$

Problems

6. Find the illumination 4.0 m below a 32-cd source of light.

7. A lamp is moved from 30 cm to 90 cm above the pages of a book. Compare the illumination of the book before and after the lamp is moved.

8. The intensity of illumination on a surface 3.0 m below a 150-watt incandescent lamp is 10 lx. What is the intensity of the lamp in candelas?

9. A light produces an illumination of 18.0 lx on a road. The light is suspended 5.0 m above the road. What is the intensity of the light source in candelas?

10. A public school law requires a minimum illumination of 160 lx on the surface of each student's desk. An architect's specifications call for classroom lights to be located 2.0 m above the desks. What must be the minimum intensity of the lights?

11. A screen is placed between two lamps so that they illuminate the screen equally. The first lamp has an intensity of 125 cd and is 2.5 m from the screen. What is the distance of the second lamp from the screen if the lamp has an intensity of 190 cd?

11. 3.1 m

17:5 Light—An Electromagnetic Wave

Visible light is an electromagnetic wave. Like other waves, the product of the frequency and wavelength of a light wave is equal to is velocity, c. For light and other electromagnetic waves moving in a vacuum

Light waves, like all electromagnetic waves, do not need a medium.

$$c = f\lambda$$

The velocity of light in a vacuum is 2.99792×10^8 m/s.

17:6 Light and Color Vision

Sir Isaac Newton made some of the first studies of the relationship between light and color. Newton observed that light was dispersed into an orderly arrangement of colors after passing through a glass prism. This arrangement of colors is called a **spectrum.** Early scientists thought that the colors were produced somehow inside the glass. Newton disproved this assumption. He allowed a beam of sunlight to fall on a prism. Then he allowed the emerging spectrum to fall on a second, inverted prism. White light was produced once again. Newton was the first to demonstrate that white light is made of many colors.

White light is composed of many colors.

Suggested demonstration: Produce a continuous spectrum using a prism and white light.

If correct amounts of red light, green light, and blue light are projected onto a white screen, the screen will appear white. Red light, green light, and blue light are the **primary colors** of light. **Secondary colors** are produced by combining two primary colors. If red light and green light are mixed, the screen will appear yellow. Yellow is a secondary color. The other secondary colors are cyan (blue light and green light) and magenta (red light and blue light). The production of secondary colors from two primary colors reflecting from a surface demonstrates the additive process of color formation.

Red, blue, and green are the primary colors of light. The correct mixture of red, blue, and green light will produce white light.

FIGURE 17-8. White light, when passed through a prism, is separated into a band of colors.

FIGURE 17-9. The additive mixture of blue, green, and red light produce white light.

White light can also be produced by mixing one primary color with its complementary secondary color.

The color of an object depends on which wavelengths of light the object reflects.

FIGURE 17-10. An apple absorbs the colors of white light and reflects red light (a). In red light the apple still appears red (b). In blue light, the apple appears black (c) since the blue light is absorbed.

Each primary color has a **complementary** secondary color made up of the two remaining primary colors. Light of a primary color added to its complement will produce white light. For example, a white surface is illuminated by red light and cyan light at the same time. The surface will appear white because red light, plus green light and blue light from the cyan light are reflected. The primary light colors and their complementary colors, respectively, are red and cyan, green and magenta, and blue and yellow.

An object appears a particular color because it reflects light of that color. A shirt appears red because it reflects red light. When white light falls on the shirt, the pigments in the dye absorb most of the light. Only wavelengths in the red region are not absorbed. These wavelengths are reflected into the eye and the shirt appears red. Suppose that only blue light falls on the shirt. The pigments in the dye would absorb all the blue light. No light would be reflected from the shirt. The shirt would appear black. Black is the absence of reflected light.

a

b

c

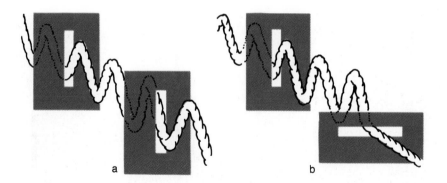

The absorption of light demonstrates the subtractive process of color formation. Pigments absorb certain colors from white light. **Primary pigments** absorb only one color each from white light. Yellow is a primary pigment. A yellow pigment absorbs blue light from white light and reflects red light and green light. The primary pigments are yellow, cyan, and magenta. A **secondary pigment** is a pigment that absorbs two primary colors from white light. The secondary pigments are red (absorbs green light and blue light), green (absorbs red light and blue light), and blue (absorbs red light and green light). Note the primary pigment colors are the same as the secondary light colors. Likewise, the secondary pigment colors are the same as the primary light colors.

The primary pigments are yellow, cyan, and magenta.

If white light shines on a primary pigment and its complementary pigment, the surface will appear black. A primary pigment and its complementary pigment absorb all light. The primary pigments and their respective complementary pigments are yellow and blue, cyan and red, and magenta and green.

A primary pigment and its complementary secondary pigment absorb all light, producing black.

17:7 Polarization of Light

In Figure 17-11, waves sent along a rope pass through a slot. Under these circumstances, waves can be sent along the rope only if the waves are generated parallel to the plane of the slot. Each slot permits only those waves with the proper orientation to pass through. The waves are said to be **polarized** in a particular plane, or plane polarized.

Waves oriented to a particular plane are plane polarized.

A beam of light contains a huge number of waves vibrating in every possible plane. All of the waves can be resolved into vertical and horizontal components. Thus, it averages out as if half of the waves vibrate vertically and half vibrate horizontally. If a filter (polarizer), such as in Polaroid® sunglasses, is placed in front of the beam light, only those waves that vibrate parallel to the permitted plane pass through. Thus, half of the light rays are eliminated. Suppose a second sheet of polarizing material (analyzer) is placed in the path of the polarized light. If its permitted plane is perpendicular to the light that passed through the polarizer, almost no light will pass through.

Light can be polarized by passing it through a Polaroid® filter.

Two Polaroid® sheets can be used to demonstrate the polarization of light.

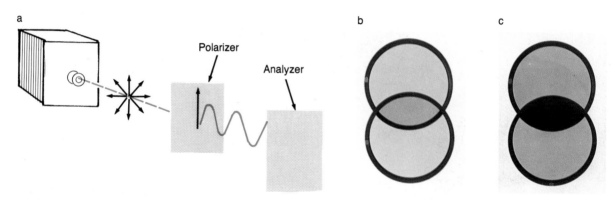

a

b

c

FIGURE 17-12. The arrows show that unpolarized light vibrates in many planes (a). Plane polarized light vibrates in only one plane. Polarized light from the first polarizer (b) is absorbed by the analyzer (c).

Light can also be polarized by reflection.

The colorful patterns of thin films and soap bubbles can be displayed by using a soap and glycerine solution.

Colors in thin films are caused by the interference of light reflected from the front surface with that reflected from the rear surface.

FIGURE 17-13. Light becomes polarized when it is reflected from a smooth surface such as glass or water.

Light can also be polarized by reflection. If you look through a piece of polarizing material at the light reflected by a sheet of glass and rotate the filter, you will notice that the light brightens and dims. Reflected light has been polarized upon its reflection. There will be one angle at which maximum polarization occurs and no light is able to pass through the filter. That is, the light reflected from the glass is completely polarized. The fact that light reflected off roads and pavements is polarized is the reason polarizing sunglasses reduce glare.

17:8   Interference in Thin Films

If a soap film is held vertically, its weight makes it thicker at the bottom than at the top. In fact, the thickness of the film varies gradually from top to bottom. When a light wave strikes the film, part of it is reflected, as shown by R_1 in Figure 17-14. Part of the wave is transmitted, as shown by the ray T. The transmitted wave travels through the film to the inner surface. Again, part of the wave is reflected, R_2. If the thickness of the film is one quarter of the wavelength ($\lambda/4$), the "round trip" path length in the film is $\lambda/2$. It would appear

a

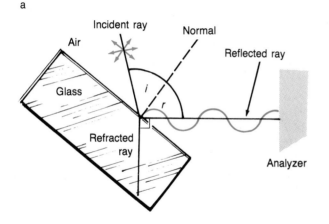

Incident ray

Normal

Air

Reflected ray

Glass

i

r

Refracted ray

Analyzer

b

a

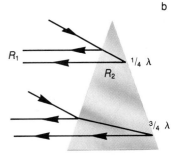

b

FIGURE 17-14. Each color is reinforced where the soap film is ¼, ¾, ⁵⁄₄, . . ., of the wavelength for that color. Since each color has a different wavelength, a series of color bands are seen reflected from the soap films.

that the wave returning from the inner surface would arrive back at the outer surface just one-half wavelength (180°) out of phase with the first reflected wave and that the two waves would cancel. However, remember from Chapter 15 that when a wave is reflected from a more dense medium, it undergoes inversion. Thus, the first reflected wave, R_1, is inverted upon reflection. The second reflected wave, R_2, returning from the boundary of a less dense medium, is not inverted. The wave reflected from the inner surface arrives back at the first surface in phase with the first reflected wave. Thus, reinforcement occurs. Wavelengths that do not meet the λ/4 wavelength requirement for this region of the film arrive back at the outer surface out of phase. They cancel or at least weaken the first reflected wave. The strongest light from any given region of the film is the wavelength that satisfies the λ/4 requirement.

A film will have a particular color when the thickness of the film is λ/4, 3λ/4, 5λ/4, . . .

The individual colors of light have different wavelengths. Since the thickness of the film changes, the λ/4 requirement for different colors is met at intervals down the film. If the region of the film has a thickness of one quarter the wavelength of red light, it appears to be red. Thus, white light falling on the film results in a rainbow of color. A soap bubble can be thought of as a continuous thin film that is constantly changing in thickness. As white light falls on the bubbles, various colors appear to move across the surface of the bubbles.

Point out that thin film interference is often seen when oil or gasoline lies on the surface of water.

When a point is reached where the thickness is 3λ/4 for the first color, the first color reappears. This point again gives a λ/2 path difference. Any odd multiple of quarter wavelengths, such as λ/4, 3λ/4, or 5λ/4, satisfies the conditions for reinforcement for a given color. If the film is λ/2 thick, or any multiple thereof, the returning wave cancels the wave reflected from the outer surface. There is no reflected wave for the wavelength at that point.

The film looks black if it is so thin that no color satisfies the λ/4 thickness criterion.

Summary

17:1   **1.** Electromagnetic radiation capable of stimulating the retina of the eye is called light.

17:2   **2.** The speed of light is 3.00×10^8 m/s in a vacuum. Light travels in a straight line.

17:4   **3.** The standard of luminous intensity is the candela.

17:4   **4.** The flow of light energy from a source is called luminous flux. The unit of luminous flux is the lumen.

17:4   **5.** Illuminance is the rate at which light energy falls on a unit area. The unit of illuminance is the lux.

17:4   **6.** The illumination received by a surface varies directly with the intensity of the source and inversely with the square of its distance from the source.

17:6   **7.** White light is a combination of many colors of light. Each color has a different wavelength.

17:7   **8.** Waves are said to be plane polarized if only waves oriented to a particular plane are present.

17:8   **9.** Light can cause interference effects by reflection from the outer and inner surfaces of thin films.

Detailed answers to all Questions and Problems are given in the Teacher's Guide at the front of this book.

Questions

1. Distinguish among transparent, translucent, and opaque objects.

2. Distinguish between a luminous body and an illuminated body.

3. In what unit is the intensity of a light source measured?

4. In what unit is the illumination of a surface measured?

5. To what is the illumination of a surface by a light source directly proportional? To what is it inversely proportional?

6. Of what colors does white light consist?

7. Why does grass appear green?

8. Is black a color? Why does an object appear to be black?

Problems—A

1. 3.00×10^8 m/s   **1.** An observer uses a 20-sided mirror to measure the speed of light. A clear image occurs when the mirror is rotating at 5.00×10^2 rev/s. The total path of the light pulse is 30.00 km. What is the speed of light?

2. A 64-cd point source of light is 3.0 m above the surface of a desk. What is the illumination of the desk's surface in lux?

2. 7.1 lx

3. A 1.00×10^2-cd point source of light is 2.0 m from screen A and 4.0 m from screen B. How does the illumination of screen B compare with the illumination of screen A?

3. ¼

4. The illumination of a tabletop is 2.0×10^1 lx. The lamp providing the illumination is 4.0 m above the table. What is the intensity of the lamp?

4. 320 cd

5. Two lamps illuminate a screen equally. The first lamp has an intensity of 101 cd and is 5.0 m from the screen. The second lamp is 3.0 m from the screen. What is the intensity of the second lamp?

5. 36 cd

Problems–B

1. a. Calculate the illumination of a screen when it is located at the following distances from a 4.0×10^2-cd source: 5.0 m, 10.0 m, 15.0 m, 20.0 m, 25.0 m.

1. See Teacher's Guide.

    b. Make a table to show the distances in the first column and the corresponding illuminations in the second column.

    c. Use graph paper to plot illumination versus distance. Plot the distance on the x-axis.

    d. Draw the curve that best fits these points. What is the resulting curve called? What does it indicate?

2. It takes light 1.188 s to reach the earth from the moon when the two are closest. It takes 1.356 s when they are farthest.

2. a. 3.8×10^8 m
   b. 390/1

    a. On an average, how far is the moon from the earth?

    b. If it takes 8.312 minutes for light to reach the earth from the sun, compare the distance the earth is from the sun to the distance the earth is from the moon.

Readings

Baird, Ken, "Frequency Measurements of Optical Radiation." *Physics Today*, January, 1983.

Edelson, Edward, "Faster Than Light." *Popular Science*, April, 1984.

Shapiro, Alan, "Experiment and Mathematics in Newton's Theory of Color." *Physics Today*, September, 1984.

Townes, Charles, "Harnessing Light." *Science 84*, November, 1984.

Tsang, W. T., "The C³ LASER." *Scientific American*, November, 1984.

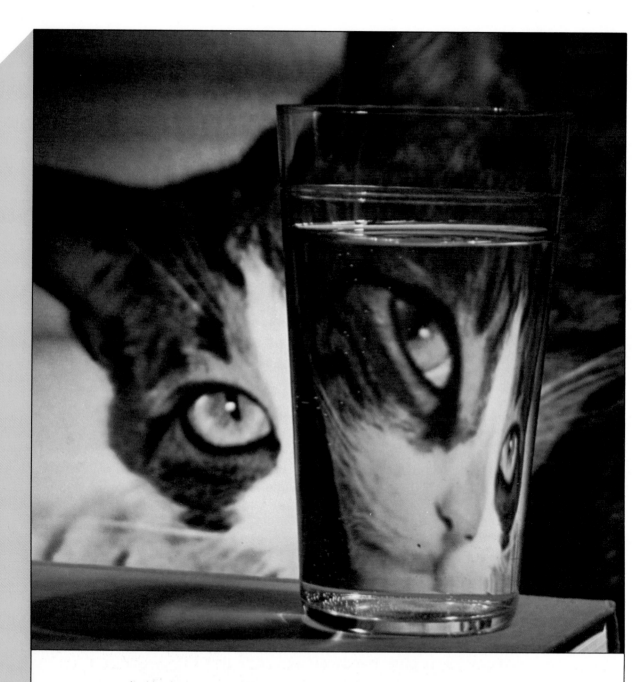

In this chapter you will look closely at the way light behaves as it passes from one medium to another. Using your knowledge of how water waves behave, you should be able to explain some of the interesting effects of reflection and refraction. How does refraction determine the way we see the cat through the glass of water? What are other effects of refraction?

Reflection and Refraction

Chapter 18 introduces the laws of reflection and refraction and presents the ray-optics method of treating these laws. The relationship between the index of refraction and speed of light in a medium is examined. A discussion of total internal reflection is also included.

In our study of the nature of light, we found that light travels in straight lines and at a very high speed. Let us now study some specific behaviors of light. What happens when light is bounced off a barrier? How does light behave when it passes from one medium into another medium?

Goal: You will gain understanding of reflection and refraction of light.

An optical disk or ray box is useful in demonstrating ray optics.

18:1 The Law of Reflection

When a light ray is incident upon a reflecting surface, the angle of reflection is equal to the angle of incidence. Both of these angles are measured from a normal (perpendicular) to the surface at the point of incidence. The incident ray, the reflected ray, and the normal all lie in the same plane.

18:2 Diffuse and Regular Reflection

When a beam of light strikes most surfaces, it reflects in many directions. Most surfaces do not reflect light in a regular manner because they are not smooth. A painted wall or a page of a book may appear to be smooth. Actually, their surfaces are rough and have many small projections. Rays of light strike different parts of these projections. Each ray reflects according to the law of reflection. The rays are reflected in many different directions producing a **diffuse reflection** (Figure 18-2).

FIGURE 18-1. A light ray reflecting from a mirror shows the angle of incidence equals the angle of reflection.

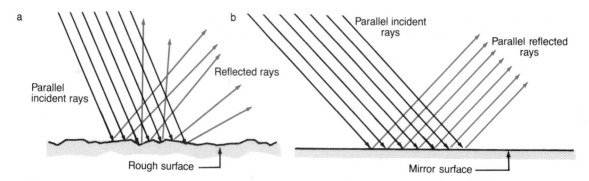

Parallel incident rays

Reflected rays

Parallel incident rays

Parallel reflected rays

b

Rough surface

Mirror surface

FIGURE 18-2. When parallel light rays strike a rough surface, they are randomly reflected. When parallel light rays strike a mirror surface, they are reflected as parallel rays.

It is important to emphasize that refraction is a boundary phenomenon.

Refraction is the bending of light as it enters a new medium.

FIGURE 18-3. Comparison of the refraction of light at a boundary to the deflection of a car at the boundary of mud and pavement. Light is refracted toward the normal as it enters a more dense medium.

If a beam of light falls on a very smooth surface, the rays undergo **regular reflection.** Figure 18-2 shows a beam of parallel rays reflecting from a smooth, flat surface. Since each ray follows the law of reflection, the reflected rays are also parallel. The rays are arranged in the same order after they leave a smooth surface as they were before they approached the surface.

18:3 Refraction of Light

Light travels at different speeds in different media. Light also changes direction, or bends, as it moves from one medium to another if the angle of incidence is not zero degree. The change in direction or bending of light at the boundary between two media is called **refraction.**

Consider an incident ray that falls on the boundary between two media. Once the ray enters a new medium, it is a refracted ray. The angle between the incident ray and a normal to the surface at the point of incidence is the angle of incidence, i. The angle between the

c

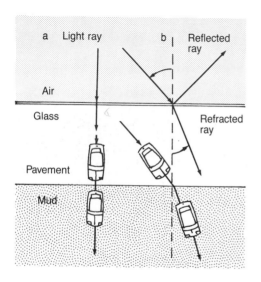

a Light ray

b Reflected ray

Air

Glass

Refracted ray

Pavement

Mud

refracted ray and the same normal is the angle of refraction, r. The incident ray, the refracted ray, and the normal lie in the same plane. Refraction occurs only when the incident ray strikes the boundary between the two media at an angle. When the angle of incidence is zero (the ray is perpendicular to the surface), there is no refraction. The ray passes straight into the new medium.

An angle of incidence is measured from the normal to the incident ray. The angle of refraction is measured from the normal to the refracted ray.

Figure 18-3 shows a ray of light as it passes from air into glass at different angles of incidence. Part of the ray is reflected and part is transmitted. Notice that as the ray enters a medium in which it travels more slowly, the refracted ray bends toward the normal. The angle of refraction is smaller than the angle of incidence.

Light is refracted only when it hits a boundary at an angle.

In Figure 18-4, a light ray passes from glass into air. Rays that strike the surface at an angle are refracted away from the normal. When a light ray passes into a medium in which it travels faster, the light ray refracts away from the normal. In other words, the angle of refraction is larger than the angle of incidence.

Light bends toward the normal if its speed is reduced as it enters the new medium; light bends away from the normal if its speed increases as it enters the new medium.

Optical density is the property of a medium that determines the speed of light in that medium. If a medium is optically dense, it slows light more than a medium which is less optically dense.

Optical density of a medium determines the speed of light in that medium.

Figures 18-3 and 18-4 compare the refraction of light to a car entering or leaving a patch of mud. When the car enters the mud at an angle, Figure 18-3b, its right wheel enters the mud before the left wheel. The right wheel slows. As a result, the car swings to the right or toward the normal. In Figure 18-4c, the car leaves the mud at an angle. The right wheel leaves the mud first and speeds up. The left wheel is still held back. Therefore, the car swings to the left or away from the normal. Keep this car analogy in mind until the behavior of light at various surfaces becomes more familiar to you.

This analogy is often quite helpful to the student in understanding the concept of refraction.

FIGURE 18-4. Light is refracted away from the normal as it enters a less dense medium.

a

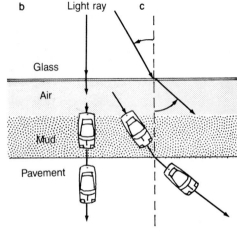

18:4   Snell's Law

Rays of light that travel from air into glass, or any other medium more optically dense than air, are refracted toward the normal. As the angle of incidence increases, the angle of refraction increases, Figure 18-5. However, the angle of refraction does not vary directly with the angle of incidence. Still, the increase in the angle of refraction as the angle of incidence increases suggests that a definite relationship exists.

The relationship between the angle of incidence and the angle of refraction was discovered by the Dutch scientist Willebrord Snell (1591-1626) and is called **Snell's law**. A ray of light bends in such a way that the ratio of the sine of the angle of incidence to the sine of the angle of refraction is a constant. For a light ray passing from a vacuum into a given medium, this constant (the ratio of the sines) is called the **index of refraction**, n, for that medium. Snell's law can be written

Snell's law states that the ratio of the sine of the incident angle to the sine of the refracted angle is a constant.

$$n = \frac{\sin i}{\sin r}$$

In this equation, i is the angle of incidence, r is the angle of refraction, and n is the index of refraction of the medium. Note that this equation applies only to a ray traveling from a vacuum to another medium.

In general, for a ray traveling from one medium to another medium, Snell's law can be written

$$n_1 \sin \theta_1 = n_2 \sin \theta_2$$

In this equation, n_1 is the index of refraction of the incident medium and n_2 is the index of refraction of the second medium. Angles θ_1 and θ_2 are the angles of incidence and refraction, respectively.

FIGURE 18-5. Pencils of light entering a glass prism are refracted at different angles depending upon their angle of incidence.

a

b

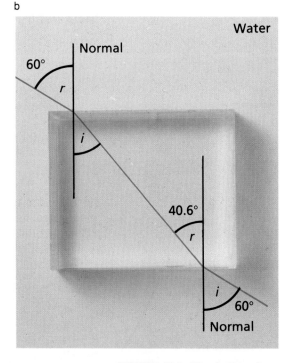

FIGURE 18-6. The index of refraction for glass is greater than that for water. If light enters both media at the same angle, the angle of refraction is greater for water. This result agrees with Snell's law.

TABLE 18-1

Indices of Refraction			
Medium	n	Medium	n
vacuum	1.00	crown glass	1.52
air	1.00*	quartz	1.54
water	1.33	flint glass	1.61
ethanol	1.36	diamond	2.42

EXAMPLE

Snell's Law

A ray of light traveling through air is incident upon a sheet of crown glass at an angle of 30.0°. What is the angle of refraction?

Given: incident medium (air)   **Unknown:**

second medium (crown glass)   Refracted angle (θ_2)

incident angle (θ_1) = 30.0°   **Basic equation:**

$$n_1 \sin \theta_1 = n_2 \sin \theta_2$$

---

*Index of refraction of air is 1.0003, which is higher than that of vacuum, which is 1.0000. However, for practical purposes, they are the same.

Solution:

From Table 18-1, the index of refraction of crown glass is 1.52

$$n_1 \sin \theta_1 = n_2 \sin \theta_2$$

$$\sin \theta_2 = \frac{n_1 \sin \theta_1}{n_2}$$

$$= \frac{(1.00)(\sin 30.0°)}{1.52}$$

$$= \frac{0.500}{1.52} = 0.329$$

$$\theta_2 = 19.2°$$

Problems

1. 27.7°

1. Light is incident upon a piece of crown glass at an angle of 45.0°. What is the angle of refraction?

2. 22.1°

2. A ray of light passes from air into water at an angle of 30.0°. Find the angle of refraction.

3. 27.3°

3. Light is incident upon a piece of quartz at an angle of 45.0°. What is the angle of refraction to the nearest degree?

4. a. 17.0°
   b. diamond

4. A ray of light is incident upon a diamond at 45.0°.
   a. What is the angle of refraction?
   b. Compare your answer to that for Problem 1. Does glass or diamond bend light more?

5. a. 1.33
   b. water

5. A ray of light travels from air into a liquid. The ray is incident upon the liquid at an angle of 30.0°. The angle of refraction is 22.0°.
   a. What is the index of refraction of the liquid?
   b. Look at Table 18-1. What might the liquid be?

6. a. 19.2°
   b. 30.0°
   c. away from

6. In the Example on Snell's law, a ray of light is incident upon crown glass at 30.0°. The angle of refraction is 19.2°. Assume the glass is rectangular in shape. Construct a diagram to show the incident ray, the refracted ray, and the normal. Continue the ray through the glass until it reaches the opposite edge.
   a. Construct a normal at this point. What is the angle at which the refracted ray is incident upon the opposite edge of the glass?
   b. Assume the material outside the opposite edge is air. What is the angle at which the ray leaves the glass?
   c. As the ray leaves the glass, is it refracted away from the normal or toward the normal?

18:5   Index of Refraction and the Speed of Light

Refraction occurs because the speed of light depends on the medium in which the light is traveling. The index of refraction is a measure of

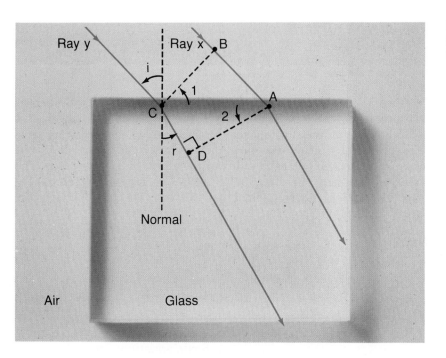

the amount of bending (refraction). In this section, the relationship between the index of refraction and the speed of light in a medium will be derived.

Figure 18-7 shows the behavior of two parallel rays of light that are incident upon a glass plate from air. The rays are refracted toward the normal. Consider the wave front CB as it approaches the glass plate. After a time interval, the wave front reaches position DA. Since the speed of the wave is slower in the glass, point C on ray y travels only distance CD. Point B on ray x travels distance BA. This difference causes the wave front to turn.

During a time interval t, point B on ray x travels to A and point C on ray y travels to D. Therefore, the ratio of BA to CD is the same as the ratio of the speed of light in vacuum, c, to the speed of light in glass, v_g.

$$\frac{\dfrac{BA}{t}}{\dfrac{CD}{t}} = \frac{BA}{CD} = \frac{c}{v_g}$$

Angle θ_1 in Figure 18-7 is equal to the angle of incidence of the ray. Angle θ_2 is equal to the angle of refraction of the ray (corresponding sides mutually perpendicular). The sine of angle θ_1 is BA/CA. The sine of angle 2 is CD/CA. Using Snell's law, the index of refraction is

$$n_{glass} = \frac{\sin i}{\sin r} = \frac{\sin \theta_1}{\sin \theta_2} = \frac{BA/CA}{CD/CA} = \frac{BA}{CD} = \frac{c}{v_{glass}}$$

The index of refraction of a medium is the ratio of the speed of light in a vacuum to the speed of light in the medium.

The index of refraction for any substance is

$$n_s = \frac{c}{v_s}$$

where v_s represents the speed of light in the substance.

The index of refraction of many transparent substances, such as water or glass, can be found by measurement. A small ray of light is caused to fall on the substance and the resulting angle of refraction is measured. The sine of the angle of incidence divided by the sine of the angle of refraction gives the index of refraction of the substance. The speed of light in a vacuum, 3.00×10^8 m/s, is known. Therefore, it is possible to calculate the speed of light in many substances by using the equation $v_s = c/n_s$.

EXAMPLE

Speed of Light in a Medium

The index of refraction of water is 1.33. Calculate the speed of light in water.

Given: $n_{water} = 1.33$ **Unknown:** v_{water}

$c = 3.00 \times 10^8$ m/s

Basic equation: $n_s = \frac{c}{v_s}$

Solution: $n_{water} = \frac{c}{v_{water}}$

$$v_{water} = \frac{c}{n_{water}} = \frac{3.00 \times 10^8 \text{ m/s}}{1.33} = 2.26 \times 10^8 \text{ m/s}$$

Problems

7. a. 2.20×10^8 m/s
   b. 1.95×10^8 m/s
   c. 1.86×10^8 m/s

8. 1.50

9. 1.52

7. Use Table 18-1 to find the speed of light in
   a. ethanol   **b.** quartz   **c.** flint glass

8. The speed of light in a plastic is 2.00×10^8 m/s. What is the index of refraction of the plastic?

9. The speed of light in a glass plate is 196 890 km/s. Find the index of refraction of this material.

FIGURE 18-8. Ray 1 is refracted. Ray 2 is refracted along the boundary of the medium showing the critical angle. An angle of refraction greater than the critical angle results in the total internal reflection of Ray 3.

a

b

c

18:6   Total Internal Reflection

When a ray of light passes from a more optically dense medium into air, it is bent away from the normal. In other words, the angle of refraction is larger than the angle of incidence. The fact that the angle of refraction is larger than the angle of incidence leads to an interesting phenomenon known as total internal reflection. **Total internal reflection** occurs when light falls on the surface of a less optically dense medium at an angle so great that there is no refracted ray. Figure 18-8 shows such an occurrence. Ray 1 is incident upon the surface of the water at angle i_1. Ray 1 produces the angle of refraction, r_1. Ray 2 is incident at such a large angle, i_c, that the refracted ray lies along the surface of the water. The angle of refraction is 90°.

Applying Snell's law for light traveling from one medium into another, the equation is

$$(n_{water})(\sin \theta_1) = (n_{air})(\sin \theta_2)$$
$$(1.33)(\sin \theta_1) = (1.00)(\sin 90°)$$

FIGURE 18-9. While a meter stick is visible in an empty aquarium (a), as the aquarium is filled with water (b) the meter stick will seem to disappear because of refraction of light from the meter stick (c).

In total internal reflection, no light rays are transmitted into the new medium.

FIGURE 18-10. When the submerged legs of a person sitting at the edge of a pool are observed by an underwater swimmer close to the surface of a pool (a) the swimmer will not see the upper torso of the person but will see the submerged legs and an inverted image of the legs above the surface of the water in place of the person's torso (b).

a

b

a

b

c

Eyepiece lens

Reversing prisms

Objective lens

Light path

FIGURE 18-11. The passage of light through the reflecting prisms in a pair of binoculars shows total internal reflection (a). The angle of the prisms changes the path of the reflected rays (b) and (c).

FIGURE 18-12. Optical fibers exhibit total internal reflection along the inner surface of the fiber.

Solving the equation for sin θ_1

$$\sin \theta_1 = \frac{(1.00)(\sin 90°)}{(1.33)}$$

$$= 0.750$$

$$\theta_1 = 48.6°$$

When an incident ray of light passing from water to air makes an angle of 48.6°, the angle of refraction is 90°.

The incident angle that causes the refracted ray to lie right along the boundary of the substance, angle i_c is unique to the substance. It is known as the **critical angle** of the substance.

The critical angle, i_c, of any substance may be calculated as follows.

$$n_1 \sin \theta_1 = n_2 \sin \theta_2$$

In this situation, $\theta_1 = i_c$; $n_2 = 1.000$ (vacuum); and $\theta_2 = 90°$

$$\sin i_c = \frac{(1.00)(\sin 90°)}{n_1}$$

$$\sin i_c = \frac{1}{n_1}$$

For crown glass, the critical angle can be calculated as follows.

$$\sin i_c = \frac{1}{1.52} = 0.658$$

$$i_c = 41°$$

Any ray that falls on the surface of water at an angle greater than the critical angle (ray 3) cannot be refracted. All of the light is reflected. Total internal reflection has occurred.

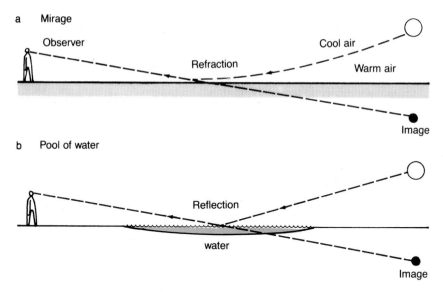

a   Mirage

b   Pool of water

FIGURE 18-13. Refraction of light in air of different densities (a) produces an effect similar to the reflection of light off a pool of water (b).

Total internal reflection causes some curious effects. Suppose an underwater swimmer looks at the surface of the water. The legs of a second swimmer, seated on the edge of the pool, may appear to be inverted. Likewise, if a swimmer is near the surface of a quiet pool, the swimmer may not be visible to an observer standing near the side of the pool. Total internal reflection is important in the design of binoculars. It has also given rise to a field of optics known as fiber optics.

Fiber optics is an example of the practical application of total internal reflection.

18:7 Effects of Refraction

Many interesting effects are caused by the refraction of light. Mirages, the apparent shift in the position of objects immersed in liquids, and the lengthening of the day are examples.

Mirages can be observed along highways in summer. A driver looking down the road sees what looks like a puddle of water. However, the puddle disappears as the car approaches. The mirage occurs because the air next to the surface of the road is heated sooner than the air above it. This heated air expands. As the distance above the road increases, the air gradually becomes cooler. As a result, the density of the air gradually increases. The index of refraction of the air also increases with distance above the road because of the greater optical density of the air. As a ray of light moves toward the road, it passes through air of increasingly lower index of refraction. The ray bends in the manner shown in Figure 18-13. To an observer, the refracted light looks like light reflected from a puddle.

An object viewed in a liquid is not where it appears to be. As a result of the refraction of light, an object may appear to be much closer to the surface of the liquid than it really is. This same effect makes a spoon placed in a glass of water appear broken.

FIGURE 18-14. After the sun has actually set, it is still visible due to refraction of light over the horizon through the atmosphere.

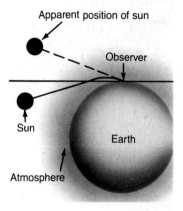

FIGURE 18-15. Newton showed that white light can be dispersed into a spectrum of colors and that the white light can be reconstituted by sending the dispersed light through a second prism.

FIGURE 18-15. Newton showed that white light can be dispersed into a spectrum of colors and that the white light can be reconstituted by sending the dispersed light through a second prism.

Light travels at a slightly slower speed in the earth's atmosphere than it does in the conditions of outer space. As a result, sunlight is refracted by the atmosphere. In the morning, this refraction causes sunlight to reach the earth before the sun actually is above the horizon. In the evening, the sunlight is bent above the horizon after the sun has actually set. Thus, daylight is extended in the morning and evening because of the refraction of light.

18:8 Dispersion of Light

All wavelengths of light travel through space at 3.00×10^8 m/s. However, in all other media, these waves travel more slowly, and waves of different frequency travel at different speeds. Therefore, the index of refraction is slightly different for each wavelength of light.

When white light falls on a prism, the waves of each frequency refract by different amounts, and the colors are separated. Red light is refracted the least by the prism because light in the red frequency range has the fastest speed in the glass. Violet light is always refracted the

White light is dispersed into an array of colored light when it passes through a prism.

Red light has the longest wavelength and the highest speed for visible light in a medium. Violet light has the shortest wavelength and the lowest speed.

FIGURE 18-16. White light directed through a prism is dispersed into a band of different colors.

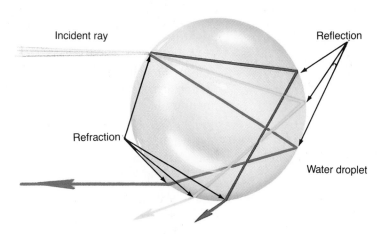

most because light in this frequency range has the slowest speed in glass. Therefore, the light emerging from the prism has been dispersed to produce a spectrum.

Different light sources produce different spectra. Light from an incandescent light bulb contains all visible wavelengths of light. When this light passes through a prism, a continuous spectrum is seen. A solar spectrum is a continuous spectrum produced when sunlight passes through a prism.

The dispersion of sunlight by water droplets in the atmosphere produces a solar spectrum commonly called a rainbow. Sunlight incident on a water droplet refracts, and the light disperses. The dispersed light will undergo internal reflection at the interior surface of the droplet and emerge in Figure 18-17. Although each droplet produces a complete spectrum, an observer will see only certain wavelengths of light from each droplet, depending on the positions of the droplet and observer. However, the observation of thousands of droplets at every instant results in seeing a complete solar spectrum or rainbow.

FIGURE 18-17. This rainbow is the result of dispersion of white light by water droplets in the air (a). Refraction occurs at the outside of a water drop. Reflection occurs at the inside surface (b).

A visible spectrum is a display of color formed when a light beam of multiple wavelengths is bent and spread by passing through a prism.

A rainbow shows the various components of white light.

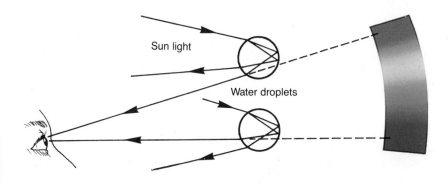

FIGURE 18-18. The formation of a rainbow by the dispersion of light from water droplets.

| Summary |

18:1 **1.** Light rays follow the law of reflection. This law states that the angle of reflection is equal to the angle of incidence.

18:3 **2.** Refraction is the bending of light rays at the boundary between two media. Refraction occurs only when the incident ray strikes the boundary of a new medium at an angle.

18:4 **3.** Snell's law states that when a light ray passes from air into a more optically dense medium at an angle, the ratio of the sine of the angle of incidence to the sine of the angle of refraction is a constant. This ratio is given the symbol n and called the index of refraction.

18:8 **4.** Light waves of different frequencies are refracted by slightly different amounts. Thus, when light falls on a prism, waves of each color bend by different amounts. A spectrum of colored light is produced.

Detailed answers to all Questions and Problems are given in the Teacher's Guide at the front of this book.

| Questions |

1. How does regular reflection differ from diffuse reflection?

2. If a light ray does not undergo refraction at a boundary between two media, what is its angle of incidence?

3. How does the angle of incidence compare with the angle of refraction when a light ray passes from air into glass at an angle?

4. How does the angle of incidence compare with the angle of refraction when a light ray leaves glass and enters air?

5. State Snell's law.

6. Write two equations for finding the index of refraction of a medium.

7. What is the "critical angle" of incidence?

8. Explain mirages.

9. Which travels fastest in glass: red, green, or blue light?

10. What type of spectrum is provided by sunlight?

| Problems—A |

1. a. 53°
   b. 106°

1. A ray of light strikes a mirror at an angle of 53° to the normal.
   a. What is the angle of reflection?
   b. What is the angle between the incident ray and the reflected ray?

2. 108°

2. A ray of light incident upon a mirror makes an angle of 36.0° with the mirror. What is the angle between the incident ray and the reflected ray?

3. A ray of light is incident at an angle of 60.0° upon the surface of a piece of glass (n = 1.5). What is the angle of refraction?

4. A light ray strikes the surface of a pond at an angle of incidence of 36.0°. At what angle, to the nearest degree, is the ray refracted?

5. Light is incident at an angle of 60.0° on the surface of a diamond. Find the angle of refraction.

6. The speed of light in a clear plastic is 1.90 × 10⁸ m/s. A ray of light enters the plastic at an angle of 22°. At what angle is the ray refracted?

3. 35°

4. 26.2°

5. 21.0°

6. 14°

Problems–B

1. A ray of light is incident upon a 60-60-60-degree glass prism (n = 1.5) as shown in Figure 18-19.

  a. Using Snell's law determine the angle r to the nearest degree.
  b. Using elementary geometry determine the value of angles A, B, and C.
  c. Angle C is actually the angle of incidence on the other side of the prism. However, the reversability of light rays tells us that if angle D were the incident angle, angle C would be the angle of refraction. Assume this statement is true and determine angle D.

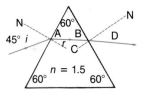

FIGURE 18-19. Use with Problem B-1.

2. A light source, S, is located 2.0 m below the surface of a swimming pool and 1.5 m from one edge of the pool. The pool is filled with water (n = 1.33) to its top.

  a. At what angle does the light reaching the edge of the pool leave the water?
  b. Does this cause the pool to appear to be deeper or less deep than it actually is? (Note: This problem illustrates the reversability of light rays. If angle r were the angle of incidence, then angle i would be the angle of refraction. Solve the problem by reversing the identity of the two angles.)

FIGURE 18-20. Use with Problem B-2.

1. a. 28°
   b. 62°, 58°, 32°
   c. 53°

2. a. 53°
   b. It appears more shallow than it really is.

Readings

Harris, Whitney, "The Corner Reflector." *The Mathematics Teacher,* February, 1983.

Mandolini, Dina, "Fiber Optics in Plants." *Scientific American,* August, 1984.

Millman, Anne, "The Light in the Tomb." *Science Digest,* May, 1983.

Peterson, J. I., "Fiber-Optic Sensors for Biomedical Applications." *Science,* April 13, 1984.

Mirrors reflect light. In contrast, lenses transmit light. Mirrors and lenses may be curved or flat, and both produce images. The type of image produced depends on the shape of the mirror or lens. An image may be larger or smaller than the original object. The image may be upright or inverted. What types of images are formed by this lens? How are mirrors and lenses useful to you?

Mirrors and Lenses

Chapter 19 introduces the ray-optics treatment of mirrors and lenses. Included are discussions of both plane mirrors and converging and diverging mirrors and lenses. Real and virtual images, and optical devices such as microscopes and telescopes are also discussed.

We have studied the behavior of light when it is reflected from a surface. We have also studied light as it moves from one medium into another. These properties of reflection and refraction have many practical uses. Mirrored surfaces demonstrate reflection. Eyeglasses and magnifying glasses are applications of the principle of refraction. Microscopes and cameras use both mirrors and lenses. Let us look at the way in which different mirrors and lenses reflect or transmit light. In this way, we can better understand how they can be put to practical use.

Goal: You will gain an understanding of lenses and mirrors, the images they form, and the instruments that use them.

19:1 Plane Mirrors

The regular reflection of light rays, reflection from a smooth surface, produces images of objects in mirrors. In Figure 19-1a, object A is illuminated by a light source. Many of the light rays that fall on object A are reflected. These reflected rays diverge (spread out) allowing object A to be seen from any direction. If some of the rays reflected from A fall on a plane (flat) mirror, they will be reflected in a regular way from the mirror. The reflected rays from the mirror diverge just as they would have if object A were behind the mirror at location A'. The image of A appears to be behind the mirror.

Suppose an object is located at point P, Figure 19-2a. Light rays extend in every direction from point P. The ray that strikes the mirror at point M is reflected back to the eye of the observer. By extending the reflected ray behind the mirror, point P' is located. The triangles PBM and P'BM are congruent. PB is the distance that the object is from the reflecting surface, d_o. P'B is the distance that the image is from the reflecting surface, d_i. For plane mirrors, d_o and d_i are equivalent. Point

A plane mirror reflects light rays in the same order that they approach it.

The image is the same size as the object and the same distance behind the mirror as the object is in front of the mirror.

317

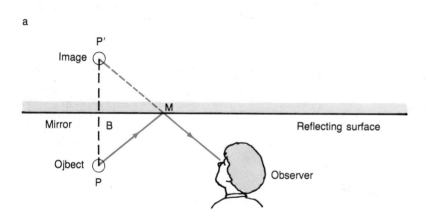

FIGURE 19-1. Formation of an image in a plane mirror. The image is the same size as the object and is the same distance behind the mirror as the object is in front.

P' is as far behind the mirror as point P is in front of the mirror. If the same method is used to locate the image of a second point, that image will also be as far behind the mirror as the point is in front of the mirror. Thus, all points of the image appear to have the same relation to each other as do their corresponding points on the object. The image will be the same size as the object.

Most plane mirrors are made from pieces of plate glass that have been coated on the back with a reflecting material like silver or aluminum. The reflecting surface is against the glass plate and covered by a protective coating. In this type of plane mirror, light entering the glass is refracted before striking the reflecting surface.

In summary, the image observed in a plane mirror is the same size as the object and is as far behind the mirror as the object is in front of the mirror.

FIGURE 19-2. Ray diagram for finding an image in a plane mirror is shown in (a). Two rays from the object are traced to the point behind the mirror at which they intersect. The image appears behind the mirror (b).

b

a

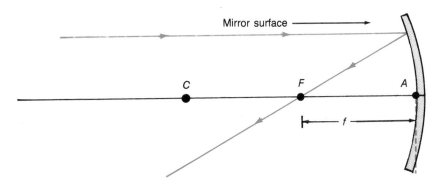

FIGURE 19-3. The focus of a concave spherical mirror is located halfway between the center of curvature and the center of the mirror surface. Rays reflected by this spherical mirror converge at the focal point.

Suggested demonstration: Darken the classroom. Hold a lit candle or a straight filament lamp in one hand and a converging mirror in the other. Project inverted images on a screen.

19:2 Concave Mirrors

Figure 19-3 represents a spherical concave mirror. A **concave mirror** reflects light from its inner curved surface. Remember, an actual spherical mirror is 3-dimensional. The inside of a spoon is a concave mirror. A spherical mirror has a geometric center or vertex, A. A radius perpendicular to a tangent at this point passes back through the center of curvature of the mirror, C. This radius is called the **principal axis**.

A spherical concave mirror can be thought of as an infinite number of plane mirrors arranged in a spherical fashion, Figure 19-4. When parallel rays of light strike the mirror parallel to the principal axis, each

The principal axis is an imaginary line extending from the geometric center of a spherical mirror to its center of curvature C.

FIGURE 19-4. The many plane mirrors of a solar oven reflect light to one small area (a). The surface of a curved mirror reflects light to a given point (b) much like a group of plane mirrors arranged in a curve (c).

a

b

c

ray follows the law of reflection. Rays that are reflected at equal distances from the principal axis are symmetrical because the mirror is symmetrical around the principal axis. The point where these rays converge or meet is the principal focus or the focal point, F, of the mirror. F lies halfway between C and A. A concave mirror is a converging mirror because reflected rays converge at the focal point.

It is important to remember two rules concerning concave mirrors.

A concave mirror is a converging mirror.

1. Any light ray parallel to the principal axis of a mirror is reflected through the focal point.

The focal point F of a converging mirror is the point where parallel rays of light meet after being reflected from the mirror.

2. Any ray that passes through the focal point is reflected parallel to the principal axis.

If the principal axis of a small concave mirror is pointed at the sun, all rays that fall on the mirror are almost parallel to each other and to the principal axis. In fact, the rays from any distant object that fall on the mirror are parallel for all practical purposes. Therefore, to determine the focal point, allow light from a fairly distant source to fall on the concave mirror and reflect on a piece of paper. Move the piece of paper toward and away from the mirror until the smallest and sharpest image is produced. The location of this sharp image is the focal point. The distance from the focal point to the vertex of the mirror is the **focal length**, f, of the mirror.

The difference between F and f is analogous to the difference between first base and the length of the base line between home plate and first.

The focal length f is the distance from F to A.

19:3 Spherical Aberration

In a truly spherical mirror, some rays that approach the mirror parallel to the principal axis are not reflected through F. Those rays that strike the mirror far from its principal axis miss F slightly. This effect is called **spherical aberration** (ab uh RAY shuhn). Spherical aberration can be eliminated by using parabolic mirrors to focus light.

Spherical aberration occurs because rays that strike a spherical mirror along its outer edge are not reflected through F.

Parabolic mirrors are used to produce parallel beams of light in flashlights, car headlights, and searchlights. In these examples, the light source is placed at F and the reflected rays leave the device as a

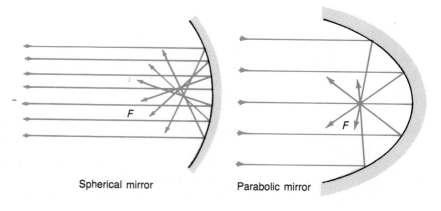

FIGURE 19-5. In a concave spherical mirror, some rays converge at other points than the focus (a). A parabolic mirror focuses all parallel rays at a point (b).

Spherical mirror   Parabolic mirror

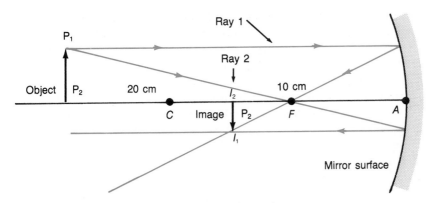

FIGURE 19-6. Finding the real image formed by a concave spherical mirror when the object is located beyond the center of curvature C of the mirror.

parallel beam. A parabolic mirror can also be used in cooking. If a cooking pot is placed at the focal point of a large concave mirror, sunlight can be concentrated upon the point. The intense heat produced can be used to cook food where fuel is scarce. Mirrors used in astronomical telescopes are usually parabolic.

19:4 Real and Virtual Images

When a concave mirror reflects the sun's rays, the reflected rays meet at the principal focus of the mirror, producing an image of the sun at this point. The bright point of light that falls on a piece of paper placed at the principal focus of a concave mirror is a very small image of the sun. The reflected rays actually converge at one location and produce an image that can be projected upon a screen. This type of image is a **real image**.

The image produced by a plane mirror appears behind the mirror. The rays reflected from a plane mirror do not converge to form an image at this point. This type of image is a **virtual image**. A virtual image cannot be projected upon a screen.

An image is real when light rays converge at a point.

An image is virtual when light rays do not converge at any point.

19:5 Real Images Formed by Concave Mirrors

In this section, ray diagrams will be drawn to show how concave mirrors produce real images. They will also aid in locating the image.

Figure 19-6 shows how a concave mirror forms an image. Consider an object that is farther from the mirror than C. This object is said to be "beyond C." When light falls on it, light rays are reflected in all directions. Therefore, rays can be drawn from the object to the mirror in any direction.

To construct a ray diagram, first select a point on the object, P_1. Draw two rays from this point to the mirror. Draw Ray 1 parallel to the principal axis. Ray 1 is called the parallel ray, and therefore reflects

Ray diagrams can be used to locate images graphically.

In a ray diagram, ray 1 is drawn parallel to the principal axis and then is reflected through F; ray 2 is drawn through F and then is reflected parallel to the principal axis.

through F. Draw Ray 2 so that it passes through F on its way to the mirror. Ray 2 is called the principal focus ray. This ray reflects parallel to the principal axis. The two rays from P_1 converge at I_1 beyond F. If two rays are drawn from point P_2 in the same way, they meet at point I_2 on the image. Other points on the object reflect rays that meet at corresponding points forming the image. The object is usually placed with one end on the principal axis. In that case, a ray goes straight to the mirror and straight back. Thus, the bottom of the image is also located on the principal axis.

Figure 19-6 shows an object that is beyond C. The image is between C and F. It is a real image because the rays actually come together to form it at this point. It is also inverted and smaller than the object. Figure 19-6 also shows that the positions of an object and its image are reversible. Thus, if the object is between C and F, its image will be beyond C, inverted, real, and larger.

As the object is moved in toward C from beyond C, the image position also approaches C. The image and the object meet at C. In this case, the image is inverted, real, and the same size as the object. If the object then is moved between C and F, the image moves out beyond C. Object and image positions are interchangeable.

Figure 19-10 summarizes the relationships between the locations of objects and real images produced by concave mirrors.

The mirror equation relates mathematically the locations of the image and object. Suppose the object distance and the focal length of the mirror are given. The position of the image can then be calculated from the mirror equation.

The mirror equation can be used to locate the image.

$$\frac{1}{d_o} + \frac{1}{d_i} = \frac{1}{f}$$

Here, d_o is the distance from the object to the vertex A; d_i is the distance from the image to A; and f is the focal length of the mirror. The ratio of the size of the image and the size of the object equals the ratio of the image distance and the object distance. The ratio of the height of the image h_i to the height of the object h_o is called the **magnification** of the mirror.

When using the magnification equation, only the absolute values of distance are used.

$$\frac{h_i}{h_o} = \frac{d_i}{d_o}$$

EXAMPLE

Real Image From a Concave Mirror

An object 2.0 cm high is 30.0 cm from a concave mirror. The focal length of the mirror is 10.0 cm.   **a.** What is the location of the image?   **b.** What is the size of the image?

Given: object height (h_o) = 2.0 cm

object location (d_o) = 30.0 cm

focal length (f) = 10.0 cm

Unknowns:

a. image location (d_i)

b. image height (h_i)

Basic equations:

$$\frac{1}{d_o} + \frac{1}{d_i} = \frac{1}{f}$$

$$\frac{h_i}{h_o} = \frac{d_i}{d_o}$$

Solution: a. $\dfrac{1}{d_o} + \dfrac{1}{d_i} = \dfrac{1}{f}$

Solving the equation for d_i yields

$$\frac{1}{d_i} = \frac{1}{f} - \frac{1}{d_o} = \frac{d_o - f}{d_o f}$$

$$d_i = \frac{d_o f}{d_o - f}$$

$$d_i = \frac{(30.0 \text{ cm})(10.0 \text{ cm})}{(30.0 \text{ cm} - 10.0 \text{ cm})} = 15.0 \text{ cm}$$

b. $\dfrac{h_i}{h_o} = \dfrac{d_i}{d_o}$

$$h_i = \frac{h_o d_i}{d_o}$$

$$= \frac{(2.0 \text{ cm})(15.0 \text{ cm})}{30.0 \text{ cm}} = 1.0 \text{ cm}$$

Problems

Needed: a compass, a metric ruler, a sharp pencil.

1. An object is 15 cm from a spherical concave mirror having a 20.0-cm radius. Locate the image by means of

   a. a ray diagram.

   b. the mirror equation.

1. a. ray diagram
   b. 3.0 × 10¹ cm

2. Solve the Example in Section 19:5 by constructing a ray diagram. The problem states that the focal length of the mirror is 10.0 cm. Focal length is always half the radius of curvature, so the radius of the mirror is 20.0 cm. Draw to scale if necessary.

2. See Teacher's Guide.

3. An object 3.0 cm high is 10.0 cm in front of a spherical concave mirror having a 12.0-cm radius. Locate the image by means of

   a. a ray diagram.

   b. the mirror equation.

   c. What is the height of the image?

3. a. ray diagram
   b. 15 cm
   c. 4.5 cm

4. An object 1.5 cm in height is 12 cm from a spherical concave mirror having a 12-cm radius. Locate the image by means of
   a. a ray diagram.
   b. the mirror equation.
   c. What is the height of the image?

5. An object 3.0 cm high is 12 cm from a concave mirror having a 6.0-cm radius. Locate the image by means of
   a. a ray diagram.
   b. the mirror equation.
   c. What is the height of the image?

6. An image of an object is 30.0 cm from a spherical concave mirror having a 20.0-cm radius. Locate the object.

7. An image of an object is 30.0 cm from a concave mirror having a 20.0-cm focal length. Locate the object.

19:6   Virtual Images Formed by Concave Mirrors

The object in Figure 19-7 is located between F and the mirror. It is 5.0 cm in front of a mirror of 20.0 cm focal length. To locate the image of the object, construct the same two rays used in previous examples. Ray 1 leaves the object and follows the path it would have followed if it had passed through F. This ray is reflected parallel to the principal axis. Ray 2 approaches the mirror parallel to the principal axis. It is reflected through the focal point. Note that Rays 1 and 2 actually diverge or move apart when reflected. Hence, the rays cannot come together to form a real image. Behind the mirror, the rays are traced back to their apparent origin to form a virtual image.

If an object is located between the focal point and the vertex of a concave mirror, its image will be virtual, erect, and enlarged. This type of image is formed by shaving mirrors and makeup mirrors.

EXAMPLE

Virtual Image From a Concave Mirror

Find the location of the image in Figure 19-7 if the object is 5.0 cm in front of a concave mirror of focal length 10.0 cm.

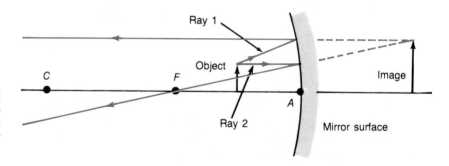

FIGURE 19-7. Finding the virtual image formed by a concave spherical mirror when the object is located between the mirror and F.

Given: $h_o = 2.0$ cm **Unknowns:** a. d_i b. h_i

$d_o = 5.0$ cm **Basic equations:** $\dfrac{1}{d_o} + \dfrac{1}{d_i} = \dfrac{1}{f}$

$f = 10.0$ cm

$$\dfrac{h_i}{h_o} = \dfrac{d_i}{d_o}$$

Solution: a. $\dfrac{1}{d_o} + \dfrac{1}{d_i} = \dfrac{1}{f}$

$$\dfrac{1}{d_i} = \dfrac{1}{f} - \dfrac{1}{d_o}$$

$$d_i = \dfrac{d_o f}{d_o - f} = \dfrac{(5.0 \text{ cm})(10.0 \text{ cm})}{(5.0 \text{ cm} - 10.0 \text{ cm})}$$

$$= \dfrac{5.0 \times 10^1 \text{ cm}^2}{-5.0 \text{ cm}} = -1.0 \times 10^1 \text{ cm}$$

b. $\dfrac{h_i}{h_o} = \dfrac{d_i}{d_o}$

$$h_i = \dfrac{h_o d_i}{d_o}$$

$$= \dfrac{(2.0 \text{ cm})(-10.0 \times 10^1 \text{ cm})}{5.0 \text{ cm}}$$

$$= -4.0 \text{ cm}$$

A negative image distance indicates a virtual image.

The negative sign indicates that the image is a virtual image. When an object is placed between the vertex and the focal point of a concave mirror, the result of the mirror equation is a negative image distance. The negative distance means the image is located behind the mirror and is a virtual image.

Problems

8. An object is 4.0 cm in front of a spherical concave mirror of 12-cm radius. Locate the image.

8. −12 cm

9. An object is 6.0 cm in front of a concave mirror having a focal length of 10.0 cm. Where is the image?

9. −15 cm

10. A 4.0 cm high candle is 10.0 cm from a concave mirror having a focal length of 16 cm.

    a. What is the object distance?

    b. What is the height of the image of the candle?

10. a. −27 cm
    b. 11 cm

19:7 Virtual Images Formed by Convex Mirrors

A **convex mirror** is a spherical mirror that reflects light from its outer surface. The outside of a spoon is a convex mirror. Convex mirrors cause rays to diverge. Thus, convex mirrors never form real images. The focal point, F, of a convex mirror is behind the mirror. The focal length, f, of a convex mirror is negative.

A convex mirror is a diverging mirror.

FIGURE 19-8. Convex spherical mirrors cause reflected light rays to diverge.

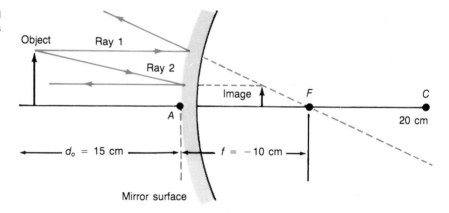

Object   Ray 1

Ray 2

Image

A

$d_o = 15$ cm $f = -10$ cm

F C

20 cm

Mirror surface

Images formed by diverging mirrors are always virtual, erect, and smaller than the object.

The image seen in a convex mirror is always virtual, behind the mirror, erect, and smaller than the object. Figure 19-8 shows how a convex mirror forms a virtual image. Ray 1 approaches the mirror parallel to the principal axis and is reflected. The path of the reflected ray, extended behind the mirror (dotted line), passes through F. Ray 2 approached the mirror on a path that, if extended behind the mirror, would pass through F. The reflected ray of Ray 2 is parallel to the principal axis. The two reflected rays, when traced back to their point of apparent intersection behind the mirror, indicate an erect, smaller, and virtual image.

Convex mirrors are referred to as diverging mirrors because the actual rays reflected from the mirror diverge. Convex mirrors are used when a large field of view is needed. Some rear-view mirrors on vehicles and mirrors used in stores to watch for shoplifters are usually convex mirrors.

FIGURE 19-9. Convex mirrors are used to show a large field of view.

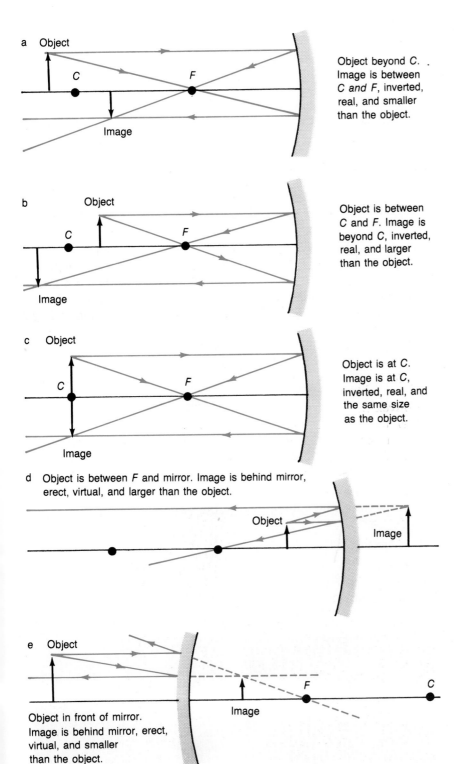

a Object

C   F

Image

Object beyond C. .
Image is between
C and F, inverted,
real, and smaller
than the object.

b   Object

C   F

Image

Object is between
C and F. Image is
beyond C, inverted,
real, and larger
than the object.

c   Object

C   F

Image

Object is at C.
Image is at C,
inverted, real, and
the same size
as the object.

d   Object is between F and mirror. Image is behind mirror,
    erect, virtual, and larger than the object.

Object

Image

e   Object

F   C

Image

Object in front of mirror.
Image is behind mirror, erect,
virtual, and smaller
than the object.

FIGURE 19-10. Formation of images in spherical mirrors.

EXAMPLE

Image From a Convex Mirror

Calculate the position of the image in Figure 19-9. Use the mirror equation.

Given: $d_o = 15$ cm   **Unknown:** d_i

$f = -10.0$ cm   **Basic equation:** $\dfrac{1}{d_o} + \dfrac{1}{d_i} = \dfrac{1}{f}$

Solution: $\dfrac{1}{d_o} + \dfrac{1}{d_i} = \dfrac{1}{f}$

$$d_i = \frac{d_o f}{d_o - f} = \frac{(15 \text{ cm})(-10.0)}{15 \text{ cm} - (-10.0 \text{ cm})}$$

$$= \frac{-150 \text{ cm}^2}{25 \text{ cm}} = -6.0 \text{ cm}$$

Problems

11. −8.6 cm

11. An object is 20.0 cm in front of a convex mirror with a −15-cm focal length. Locate the image.

12. a. −1.0 × 10¹ cm
    b. 1.0 cm

12. A convex mirror has a focal length of −12 cm. A light bulb with a diameter of 6.0 cm is placed 60.0 cm in front of the mirror.
  a. Locate the image of the light bulb.
  b. What is the diameter of the image?

13. −38 cm

13. In a department store a mirror used to watch for shoplifters has a focal length of −40.0 cm. A person stands in an aisle 6.0 m from the mirror. Locate the person's image.

14. −20.4 cm

14. Shiny lawn spheres placed on pedestals are convex mirrors. One such sphere has a focal length of −20.0 cm. A robin sits in a tree 10.0 m from the sphere. Locate the robin's image.

19:8 Lenses

Lenses are an essential part of telescopes, eyeglasses, cameras, microscopes, and other optical instruments. A lens is usually made of glass, although some are made of transparent plastic.

a

b

FIGURE 19-11. Light is refracted as it passes through a lens. In (a) the rays converge while in (b) they diverge.

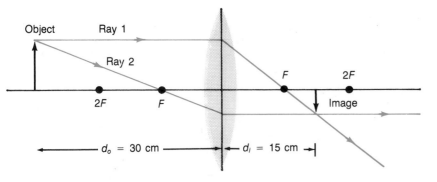

The two main types of lenses are convex lenses and concave lenses. A convex lens is thickest at its middle and becomes thinner at the edge. A concave lens is thinnest at its middle and becomes thicker at the edge, Figure 19-11. Convex lenses are often called converging lenses because the lenses refract parallel light rays so they meet. Likewise, concave lenses are called diverging lenses because they refract light so the rays spread out.

A converging lens is thick in the center and thin at the edges.

A diverging lens is thin in the center and thick at the edges.

19:9   Real Images Formed by Convex Lenses

The principal axis of a lens is a line perpendicular to the plane of the lens through the midpoint. Light rays that approach a convex lens parallel to the principal axis will, upon refraction, converge at a point. This point is called the principal focal point, F, of the convex lens. The distance from the focal point to the lens is the focal length, f. Symmetrical lenses, such as the one in Figure 19-12, have focal points the same distance on each side of the lens. The focal length of a converging lens depends on two factors. These factors are the shape of the lens and the index of refraction of the lens material.

A convex lens is a converging lens. A concave lens is a diverging lens.

The focal point of a converging lens is the point where rays that approach the lens parallel to the principal axis meet after being refracted by the lens.

The focal length of a lens depends on its shape and its index of refraction.

FIGURE 19-13. This camper is using a converging lens to start a fire in this pile of leaves.

FIGURE 19-14. If an object is located at a distance greater than 2F, the image in the lens appears inverted.

An important position along the principal axis of a lens is twice the focal length, *2f*. An object is placed beyond the point *2F* in Figure 19-12. Two rays are drawn to locate the image. Ray 1 is parallel to the principal axis. It refracts and passes through *F* on the other side of the lens. Ray 2 passes through *F* on its way to the lens. It leaves the lens parallel to the principal axis. The two rays converge between *F* and *2F*. The point where the rays converge is the image location. Rays selected from other points on the object would converge at corresponding points on the image. The image is real, inverted, and smaller than the object.

Suppose an object is placed at the image position. The image appears at the original position of the object because light rays are reversible. Thus, if the object is located between *F* and *2F*, the image would appear beyond *2F* on the other side of the lens. The image would be real, inverted, and larger than the object.

The image and object can be reversed.

If an object is placed at *2F*, the image appears at *2F* on the other side of the lens. It is real, inverted, and the same size as the object.

A straight line can be drawn to represent a lens when making ray diagrams for lens problems. To find the size and location of the image mathematically, use these lens equations.

The lens equations are exactly the same as the mirror equations.

$$\frac{1}{d_o} + \frac{1}{d_i} = \frac{1}{f}$$

$$\frac{h_o}{h_i} = \frac{d_o}{d_i}$$

Note that these equations are the same as those used with mirrors. The equations are derived in Section 19:12, page 334.

EXAMPLE

Real Images From a Convex Lens

In Figure 19-12, the object is 30.0 cm from a convex lens of 10.0 cm focal length. Use the lens equation to locate the image.

Given: $d_o = 30.0$ cm   **Unknown:** d_i

$f = 10.0$ cm   **Basic equation:** $\frac{1}{d_o} + \frac{1}{d_i} = \frac{1}{f}$

Solution: $\frac{1}{d_o} + \frac{1}{d_i} = \frac{1}{f}$

$$d_i = \frac{d_o f}{d_o - f}$$

$$= \frac{(30.0 \text{ cm})(10.0 \text{ cm})}{30.0 \text{ cm} - 10.0 \text{ cm}}$$

$$= 15.0 \text{ cm}$$

Problems

15. Use a ray diagram to find the image position of an object 30.0 cm from a convex lens with 10.0-cm focal length. (Let 1.0 cm represent 2.0 cm.)

15. ray diagram

16. An object 1.0 cm high is 15 cm from a convex lens of 10.0-cm focal length. Find the distance and size of the image

   a.   using a ray diagram.
   b.   mathematically.

16. a. See Teacher's Guide.
    b. 3.0×10^1, 2.0 cm

17. An object 3.0 cm high is 10.0 cm in front of a convex lens of 6.0-cm focal length. Find the image distance and height.

17. 15 cm, 4.5 cm

18. An object 1.5 cm high is 12 cm from a convex lens of 6.0-cm focal length. Find the height and position of the image

   a.   using a ray diagram.
   b.   mathematically.

18. a. See Teacher's Guide.
    b. 12 cm, 1.5 cm

19. An object 3.0 cm high is 12 cm from a convex lens of 3.0-cm focal length.

   a.   Locate the image.
   b.   Determine its size.

19. a. 4.0 cm
    b. 1.0 cm

20. An image is 12 cm from a convex lens of 4.0-cm focal length. Locate the object.

20. 6.0 cm

21. A camera lens having a focal length of 8.0 cm is 10.0 cm from the film. What distance from the lens should a flower be placed to obtain a sharp photograph?

21. 4.0×10^1 cm

FIGURE 19-15. Finding the virtual image formed by a converging lens when the object is placed between the lens and the principal focus F.

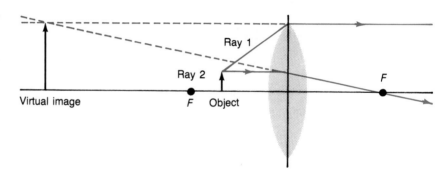

19:10   Virtual Images Formed by Convex Lenses

If an object is placed between a converging lens and its focal point, a virtual, enlarged image is produced.

If an object is placed between a convex lens and the focal point of the lens, the rays do not converge on the opposite side of the lens. Instead, the image appears on the same side of the lens as the object. As Figure 19-15 shows, the image is erect, larger, and virtual.

To understand how a convex lens forms a virtual image, look at Figure 19-15. The object is between F and the lens. Ray 1 is drawn from the tip of the object to the lens. It follows the same path it would have followed if it had started at F. Therefore, Ray 1 is refracted in such a way that it leaves the lens parallel to the principal axis. Ray 2 is drawn parallel to the principal axis. When refracted, Ray 2 travels through the focal point on the other side of the lens. Note that when Rays 1 and 2 leave the other side of the lens they diverge. Therefore, they cannot join to form a real image. However, if the two rays are traced back to their apparent origin, a larger virtual image is seen on the same side of the lens as the object. This image is a virtual image because the rays do not actually converge. A magnifying glass is a convex lens used to produce a large, virtual image.

EXAMPLE

Virtual Image From a Convex Lens

An object is 4.0 cm from a convex lens of 6.0-cm focal length.   **a.** Locate its image.   **b.** What kind of image is formed?

Given: d_o = 4.0 cm   **Unknown:** d_i

f = 6.0 cm   **Basic equation:** $\dfrac{1}{d_o} + \dfrac{1}{d_i} = \dfrac{1}{f}$

Solution:

a. $\dfrac{1}{d_o} + \dfrac{1}{d_i} = \dfrac{1}{f}$

$d_i = \dfrac{1}{f} - \dfrac{1}{d_o}$

$d_i = \dfrac{d_o f}{d_o - f} = \dfrac{(4.0 \text{ cm})(6.0 \text{ cm})}{4.0 \text{ cm} - 6.0 \text{ cm}} = -12 \text{ cm}$

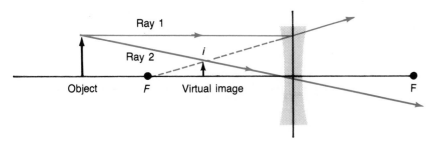

FIGURE 19-16. Formation of a virtual image by a concave lens.

b. Since the image distance is negative, the image is virtual. It is on the same side of the lens as the object.

Problems

22. The focal length of a convex lens is 20.0 cm. A newspaper is 6.0 cm from the lens. Find the image distance.

22. −8.6 cm

23. A magnifying glass has a focal length of 12 cm. A coin, 2.0 cm in diameter, is placed 4.0 cm from the lens.
   a. Locate the image of the coin.
   b. What is the diameter of the image?

23. a. −6.0 cm
    b. 3.0 cm

24. An object is 8.0 cm from a lens. What focal length must the lens have to form a virtual, erect image 16 cm from the lens?

24. 16 cm

19:11   Virtual Images Formed by a Concave Lens

Figure 19-16 shows how a concave lens forms these images. Ray 1 approaches the lens parallel to the principal axis. Upon refraction, ray 1 appears to originate at the focal point. Ray 2 strikes the lens and is refracted toward the normal. As Ray 2 leaves the lens it is refracted. The two refractions produce the same effect to an observer as if Ray 2 passed straight through the lens. The two rays diverge and appear to originate at i. The rays from a concave lens produce the same type of image as a convex mirror because both cause light rays to diverge. The image formed is virtual and erect. A concave lens has a negative focal length. Concave lenses are used in eyeglasses to correct nearsightedness and in combination with convex lenses in cameras and telescopes.

Images formed by concave lenses are always virtual and erect.

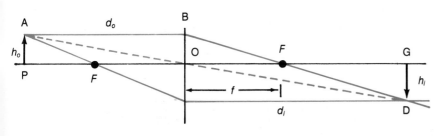

FIGURE 19-17. Diagram for derivation of lens equation.

19:12 Derivation of the Lens Equation

We can mathematically derive the expression for the lens equation using Figure 19-17. Triangles APO and DGO are similar triangles. For similar triangles, the ratios of corresponding sides are equal.

$$\frac{h_o}{h_i} = \frac{AP}{DG} = \frac{OP}{OG} = \frac{d_o}{d_i} \quad and \quad \frac{h_o}{h_i} = \frac{d_o}{d_i}$$

Also, triangles FGB and FOB are similar. Thus,

$$\frac{OF}{GF} = \frac{BO}{DG} = \frac{d_o}{d_i} \quad so, \quad \frac{OF}{GF} = \frac{d_o}{d_i}$$

Since $OF = f$ and $OG = d_i$, the length of GF can be found by

$$GF = d_i - f$$

Substituting f for OF and $d_i - f$ for GF yields

$$\frac{OF}{GF} = \frac{f}{d_i - f} = \frac{d_o}{d_i} \quad fd_i + fd_o = d_i d_o$$

Dividing both sides of the equation by $fd_i d_o$ gives the lens equation.

$$\frac{1}{d_o} + \frac{1}{d_i} = \frac{1}{f}$$

19:13 Chromatic Aberration

Chromatic aberration limits the sharpness of an image.

Newton invented the reflecting telescope because of this lens defect.

Light is refracted when it falls on a lens. Upon passing through a medium, such as glass, different wavelengths of light refract at slightly different angles. Thus, the light that passes through a lens is slightly dispersed. Any object observed through a lens appears ringed with color. This effect is called chromatic aberration. Chromatic aberration is one factor that limits the sharpness of an image on the film of a camera.

Chromatic aberration will always be present when a single lens is used. However, by joining a converging lens to a diverging lens with a different index of refraction, chromatic aberration can be eliminated.

a

b

FIGURE 19-18. Chromatic aberration occurs when light passing through a lens is dispersed causing an object to appear ringed with color (a). An achromatic lens reduces chromatic aberration (b).

Lens

Achromatic lens

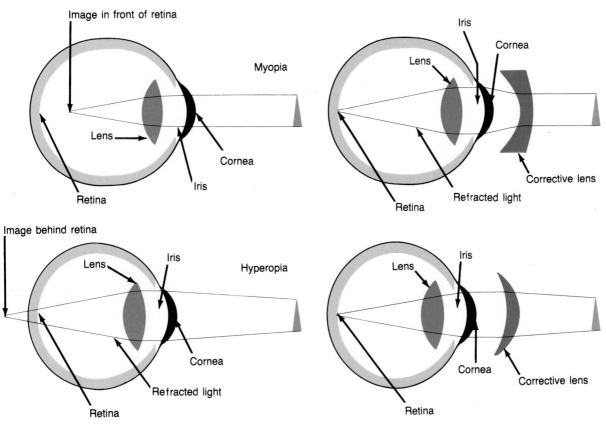

Both lenses disperse light. However, the effect (of dispersion) caused by the converging lens is the opposite of that produced by the diverging lens. The dispersion caused by the two lenses cancel each other. A lens prepared by combining a diverging and converging lens is called an achromatic lens.

19:14 Optical Devices

For normal vision, the lens of the eye must focus the image of an object on the retina. If the shape of the lens of the eye or the eye itself is distorted, external lenses (eyeglasses) or contact lenses are needed to adjust the image distance. The adjustment focuses the image on the retina. The cause of nearsightedness usually is a bulging cornea or an elongated eyeball. Thus, images are formed in front of the retina. Concave lenses correct this defect by diverging the light rays so that the image distance is greater. The image will focus on the retina. Farsightedness is usually caused by the lens' inability to change shape or by a shortened eyeball. The image in this case is formed behind the retina. Convex lenses correct this defect by converging the light rays. The image distance is shorter and the image will focus on the retina.

FIGURE 19-19. A person with far-sightedness (hyperopia) cannot see close objects. The image is focused behind the retina. A convex lens will correct the problem by refracting light to focus the image on the retina. A person with nearsightedness (myopia) cannot see distant objects. The image is focused in front of the retina. A concave lens will correct this defect.

Corrective glasses, microscopes, and telescopes are important uses of lenses.

FIGURE 19-20. The lens system of an astonomical telescope has two converging lenses.

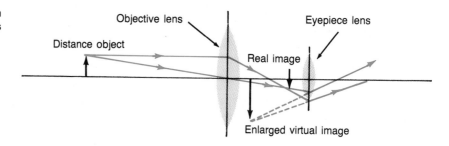

Microscopes use at least two convex lenses. An object is placed close to the lower lens, called the objective lens. This lens produces a real image located between the second lens, called the eyepiece, and its focal point. The eyepiece produces a greatly magnified virtual image of the real image.

A simple refracting telescope also uses two convex lenses. However, the objective lens of a telescope has a longer focal length. The objective lens of a telescope forms a real, inverted image of a star or other distant object. As in the microscope, the image is located at the focal point of the eyepiece. The viewer sees an enlarged, virtual, and inverted image.

Physics Focus

Gravity Lenses

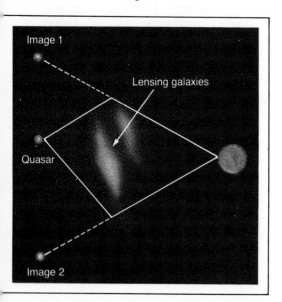

Albert Einstein stated that the gravity field of an object can be thought of as a series of surfaces curving toward the object. He predicted that light rays would be bent by the gravitational field of the object. In other words, a large gravitational mass can act as a gravity lens, bending light much like a lens made of glass.

When a radiation-producing object, a mass acting as a gravity lens, and the observer are lined up, light from the distant object is bent by the large gravitational mass in the middle. The lensing mass is either a galaxy or a group of galaxies; the radiation-producing object is a quasar. A quasar is an object producing incredible amounts of radiation, including light, X rays, and radio waves.

When radiation is bent, double or possibly multiple images form. If a quasar is variable, its output of radiation varies over time. The variation should be the same in both images, confirming that the two images are not separate quasars, but are in fact a single quasar. In one case, there was a 19-month difference in the sequence of variation, making it possible to calculate the distance between the earth and the quasar. This is the first direct method of measuring such distances.

========================= **Summary** =========================

1. The image in a plane mirror is the same size as the object. It is as far behind   19:1
the mirror as the object is in front of the mirror. The image is virtual and
erect.

2. The focal point of a spherical mirror is halfway between the center of   19:2
curvature of the mirror and the center of the mirror.

3. The distance from the focal point to the center of the mirror is the focal   19:2
length of the mirror.

4. An imaginary radius that passes from the center of the mirror through the   19:2
center of curvature and beyond is called the principal axis of the
mirror.

5. All spherical mirrors have an inherent defect known as spherical   19:3
aberration. Light rays that fall on the outer edges of the mirror do not pass
through the focal point of the mirror.

6. Light rays do not converge to form a virtual image. A virtual image cannot   19:4
be cast upon a screen. A real image is located where light rays converge
and can be cast upon a screen.

7. Concave mirrors produce real, inverted images if the object is farther from   19:5, 19:6
the mirror than the focal point. If the object is between the focal point and
the mirror, an enlarged, virtual image is formed behind the mirror.

8. Convex mirrors always produce virtual images.   19:7

9. Lenses that are thinner at their outer edges than at their centers are called   19:8
converging or convex lenses. Lenses that are thicker at their outer edges
are diverging or concave lenses.

10. The location of an image can be determined by using the lens or mirror   19:9
equation, as the case may be. The equation is the same in either
case.

11. Chromatic aberration is a lens defect caused by the dispersion of the   19:13
different wavelengths of light as they pass through the lens.

Detailed answers to all Questions and Problems are given in the Teacher's Guide at the front of this book.

========================= **Questions** =========================

1. Describe the image of a person seen in a plane mirror.

2. An object is located beyond the center of curvature of a spherical concave
mirror. Locate and describe the image of the object.

3. Locate and describe the image produced by a concave mirror when the
object is located at the center of curvature.

4. An object is located between the center of curvature and the principal focus of a concave mirror. Locate and describe the image of the object.

5. How does a virtual image differ from a real image?

6. An object produces a virtual image in a concave mirror. Where is the object located?

7. Describe the image seen in a convex mirror.

8. Describe the properties of a virtual image.

9. What factor, other than the curvature of a lens, determines the location of its focal point?

10. Locate and describe the image produced by a convex lens if an object is placed some distance beyond 2F.

11. What causes an inherent defect of all lenses?

12. What causes an inherent defect of a concave spherical mirror?

13. To project an image from a movie camera onto a screen, the film is placed between F and 2F of a converging lens. This arrangement produces an inverted image. Why do the actors appear to be erect when the film is viewed?

14. Convex mirrors are used as rearview mirrors on school buses. Why are these mirrors used?

Problems–A

1. a. ray diagram
   b. 13 cm

1. An object is 20.0 cm from a spherical concave mirror of 8.0 cm focal length (16 cm radius). Locate the image
  a. using a ray diagram.
  b. mathematically.

2. a. See Teacher's Guide.
   b. 38 cm, 4.6 cm

2. An object 3.0 cm high is placed 25 cm from a concave mirror of 15- cm focal length. Find the location and height of the image
  a. using a ray diagram.
  b. mathematically.

3. a. 3.0 × 10¹ cm
   b. 1.8 cm

3. An object is 30.0 cm from a concave mirror of 15-cm focal length. The object is 1.8 cm high.
  a. Locate the image.
  b. How high is the image?

4. a. −24 cm
   b. 9.0 cm

4. A jeweler inspects a watch with a diameter of 3.0 cm by placing it 8.0 cm in front of a concave mirror of 12.0-cm focal length.
  a. Where will the image of the watch appear?
  b. What will be the diameter of the image?

5. −15 cm

5. A convex mirror has a focal length of − 16 cm. How far behind the mirror does the image of a person 3.0 m away appear?

6. An object is 8.0 cm in front of a concave mirror having a focal length of 30.0 cm. Locate the image.

7. How far behind the surface of a convex mirror of −6.0 cm focal length does an object 10.0 m from the mirror appear?

8. The convex lens of a copy machine has a focal length of 25.0 cm. A letter to be copied is placed 40.0 cm from the lens.

a. How far from the lens is the copy paper located?

b. The machine was adjusted to give an enlarged copy of the letter. How much larger will the copy be?

Problems–B

1. A microscope slide of an onion cell is placed 12 mm from the objective lens of a microscope. The focal length of the objective lens is 10.0 mm.

a. How far from the lens is the image formed?

b. What is the magnification of this image?

c. The real image thus formed is located 10.0 mm beneath the eyepiece lens of the microscope. If the focal length of the eyepiece is 20.0 mm, where does the final image appear?

d. What is the final magnification of this compound system?

2. A dentist uses a small mirror of radius 40 mm to locate a cavity in a patient's tooth. If the mirror is concave and is held 16 mm from the tooth, what is the magnification of the resulting image?

3. Camera lenses are described in terms of their focal length. A 50.0 mm lens has a focal length of 50.0 mm.

a. A camera is focused on an object 3.0 m away using a 50.0 mm lens. Locate the position of the image.

b. A 1.00×10^3 mm lens is focused on an object 125 m away. Locate the position of the image.

4. The 50.0 mm lens in Problem 3 is focused on a dog 0.50 m high. What is the size of the image?

Readings

Coffey, Timothy, "New Sources of High-Power Coherent Radiation." *Physics Today*, March, 1984.

Conery, Christopher, "The Reality of a Real Image." *The Physics Teacher*, December, 1984.

Moran, Paul, "The Physics of Medical Imaging." *Physics Today*, July, 1983.

Tierney, John, "Here Comes The Sun." *Science 83*, January, 1983.

Worrell, Francis, "Where's the Virtual Image?" *The Physics Teacher*, November, 1983.

Light has the same property as water waves in that it bends around the edges of a barrier. This photograph was taken with a special diffraction filter. Its surface contains many cross-hatched lines. Light passing through the filter bends around the edges of these lines to produce the star effects shown. Diffracted and re-fracted light can be separated to form spectra. How does diffraction differ from refraction?

Diffraction and Interference of Light

Chapter 20 contains a discussion of the diffraction and interference of light waves. Methods for measuring the wavelengths of light are introduced and treated quantitatively.

We have learned that light travels in straight lines. In most cases, this appears to be so. When light passes through a large opening, the shadow that is cast looks quite sharp. However, when light passes through a small opening, the edges of the shadow cast look blurred. This blurring effect can be understood if we think of light as bending around barriers. The bending of light as it passes the edge of a barrier is called diffraction. Diffraction can be explained in terms of the wave nature of light.

Goal: You will gain an understanding of the diffraction and interference of light and the methods of measuring the wavelength of light.

Diffraction is the bending of light around the edges of barriers.

20:1 Diffraction and Interference Patterns

The Italian physicist Francesco Grimaldi (1618-1663) first demonstrated that the edges of a shadow appear to be slightly blurred when examined closely. This observation could be explained by assuming light bends around obstacles just as waves diffract around barriers placed in their path. Grimaldi suggested that the diffraction was hardly noticeable because the light waves were very small. If the light rays had short wavelengths, then observable diffraction would take place only when the waves passed through very small openings.

During the 19th century, Thomas Young tested Grimaldi's hypothesis. Young postulated that if light is diffracted as it passes through narrow openings, it should form an interference pattern. Figure 20-1a shows the arrangement used by Young to demonstrate the interference pattern of light waves due to diffraction. Young placed a barrier with a single slit in front of a **monochromatic** (mahn uh kroh MAT ik) light source. Monochromatic light is light of only one wavelength. Any wave

341

FIGURE 20-1. The diffraction of a monochromatic light source produces an interference pattern on the screen (a) resulting in a pattern, such as the one shown for blue light (b). The diffraction of white light produces bands of colors (c).

a

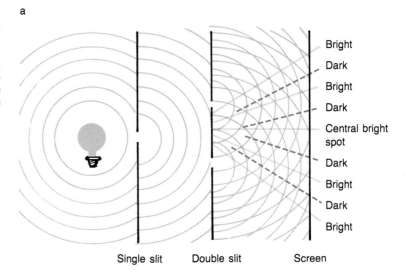

Bright
Dark
Bright
Dark
Central bright spot
Dark
Bright
Dark
Bright

Single slit   Double slit   Screen

b

c

that falls on a narrow slit is diffracted. Another barrier with two narrow slits was placed between the first barrier and a screen. The single slit acts as a source of new uniform circular waves that strike the double slit at the same time. The double slit acts as two sources of new circular waves. In Figure 20-1a, the semicircles represent wave crests moving outward from the sources. Midway between the crests are the troughs. The two waves interfere constructively at points where crests overlap. They interfere destructively where a crest and a trough meet. The interference pattern can be interpreted similarly to the interference pattern discussed in Section 15:7.

The solid lines in the diagram represent antinodal lines because they pass through points of constructive interference. At points where the antinodal lines fall on the screen, bright bars of light appear. Note that a bright bar of light appears on the screen directly opposite the midpoint between the two slits. On both sides of this central bright bar are other bars of light that correspond to the other antinodal lines.

Antinodal lines pass through points where waves interfere constructively.

The dotted lines in Figure 20-1a represent nodal lines because they pass through points of destructive interference. The nodal lines trace paths where the light waves cancel each other and light is, in effect, absent. Black bars appear at the points where nodal lines fall on the screen. Figure 20-1b shows an interference pattern produced by the diffraction of blue light.

Nodal lines pass through points where waves interfere destructively.

When white light is used as the source for a double-slit diffraction pattern, the light is dispersed into a continuous spectrum, Figure 20-1c. Each wavelength in white light produces a bright line at the center of the pattern. The addition of all wavelengths at the central bright line produces a line of white light. On both sides of the central bright line, the bright lines for each color do not fall in exactly the same place. Each wavelength produces a pattern that is slightly different from that of the other wavelengths. Thus, white light is separated into a continuous spectrum of colors on each side of the central bright line.

When white light passes through a double slit, a continuous spectrum is formed.

Each wavelength of light produces an interference pattern that is not dependent on other wavelengths.

20:2   Measuring the Wavelength of a Light Wave

An interference pattern can be used to measure the wavelength of light waves. In Figure 20-1a, the interference pattern produced by a monochromatic light source is shown. Choose an antinodal line other than the central line. Select any point along one of these lines where two crests meet. Count the wavelengths back to S_1. Then from the same point, count the wavelengths back to S_2. The difference is always a whole number of wavelengths. For the first antinodal line to both the right and the left of the central line, the path difference is one wavelength. For the second antinodal line, the path difference is two wavelengths. For the third line, the difference is three wavelengths, and so on. Any point on an antinodal line is always a whole number of wavelengths farther from one slit than the other because the waves must arrive at that point in phase to reinforce each other.

The wavelength of light can be determined by using interference patterns.

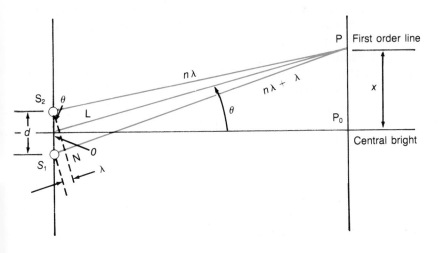

FIGURE 20-2. Schematic diagram for analysis of double-slit interference.

Each antinodal line is a whole
number of wavelengths farther
from one slit than the other.

Lines appear on each side of the
central bright line. The first lines,
which are one wavelength farther
from one slit than the other, are
called first order lines.

Along the first antinodal line, the path difference is always one wavelength. Thus, the distance to the first bright line where this wavelength falls on the screen, P, is just one wavelength farther from S_1 than from S_2. This situation is shown in Figure 20-2. Here, P_o is a point of the central bright line on the screen. P is the point where the first bright line of light appears on the screen. L is the distance from the center of the two slits to P, and x is the distance from the central bright line to P.

During an actual trial, a bright line will appear on either side of the central bright line. These lines are called **first-order lines.** Some distance away, a second line can be found on either side of the central line. These lines are called **second-order lines.**

The distance between the two slits is marked d in Figure 20-2. The distance from the central line to any first-order line on the screen is x. The distance from S_1 to P is one wavelength longer than the distance from S_2 to P. Thus, in right triangle $S_1 N S_2$, the side $S_1 N$ equals the wavelength, λ. This triangle is similar to triangle PP_oO if θ is very small. Therefore, the ratio of corresponding sides of these similar triangles are the same.

$$\frac{x}{L} = \frac{\lambda}{d}$$

Solving this equation for λ, we obtain the equation

$$\lambda = \frac{xd}{L}$$

By using interference patterns, the wavelengths of light waves can be measured with considerable precision. It is not unusual for wavelength measurements to be precise to four digits.

EXAMPLE

Wavelength of Light

Red light falls on two small slits 1.90×10^{-6} m apart. A first-order line appears 0.221 m to the left of the central bright line on a screen opposite the slits. The distance from the center of the slits to the first-order line is 0.600 m. What is the wavelength of the red light in meters? (Figure 20-1 is used to assign the values given in the problem.)

Given: $d = 1.90 \times 10^{-6}$ m   **Unknown:** λ

$x = 2.21 \times 10^{-1}$ m   **Basic equation:** $\lambda = \frac{xd}{L}$

$L = 6.00 \times 10^{-1}$ m

Solution: $\lambda = \frac{xd}{L}$

$= \frac{(2.21 \times 10^{-1} \text{ m})(1.90 \times 10^{-6} \text{ m})}{(6.00 \times 10^{-1} \text{ m})}$

$\lambda = 7.00 \times 10^{-7}$ m

Problems

1. Violet light falls on two small slits 1.90×10^{-6} m apart. A first-order line appears 1.32×10^{-1} m from the central bright spot on a screen opposite the slits. The distance from the center of the slits to the first-order violet line is 6.00×10^{-1} m. What is the wavelength of the violet light?

1. 4.18×10^{-7} m

2. Yellow light of wavelength is 6.0×10^{-7} m is used instead of the violet light of Problem 1. The distance from the center of the slits to the first-order line for the yellow light is measured and found to be 58.0 cm. How far from the central bright spot on the screen is the first-order yellow line?

2. 18 cm

3. Green light falls on a pair of slits 1.90×10^{-4} cm apart. A first-order line appears 0.284 m to the left of the central bright line. The distance between the center of the slits and the first-order is 1.00 m.

a. What is the wavelength of the light in meters?
b. What is the wavelength in nanometers?

3. a. 5.40×10^{-7} m
   b. 5.40×10^{2} nm

4. A first-order line appears 0.184 cm from the central bright line on a screen opposite slits that are 2.00×10^{-4} m apart. The distance from the midpoint between the slits to the first-order line is 80.0 cm. What is the frequency of the light?

4. 6.52×10^{14} Hz

20:3 Single-Slit Diffraction

When a light passes through one narrow slit, an interference pattern appears on a distant screen. This single-slit pattern differs from the double-slit pattern. The spacing between the bright lines lacks the regularity found in a double-slit diffraction pattern. Also, the central bright band is much larger and brighter than when two slits are used.

A diffraction pattern is the result of light passing through a single narrow slit.

To observe single-slit diffraction, fold a small piece of paper and make a cut along its folded edge with a pair of scissors. Unfold the paper and peer through the slit at a light source. You will see an interference pattern. You can vary the width of the slit by pulling on the opposite edges of the paper. Observe the effect the change in slit width has on the pattern.

Figure 20-3 shows how a single slit can cause an interference pattern. Here, monochromatic light falls on a slit. Because the slit is very narrow, all points of the wave along the slit are in phase. The pattern falls on a screen placed some distance from the slit. P_o is the wide central bright band on the screen. P is a dark band. L is the distance from the center of the slit to P_o and w is the slit width. L is so much larger than w that all rays falling on w are, in effect, the same distance from P_o. Therefore, BP and L are equal. It follows that the band at point P_o is very bright because all waves arriving at that point from w are in phase. Point P, however, is exactly one wavelength farther from point $7'$ on the slit than it is from point 1 on the slit. Therefore, point P is one-half wavelength farther from point $1'$ than it is from point 1. Hence, waves

FIGURE 20-3. Schematic diagram for analysis of single-slit diffraction.

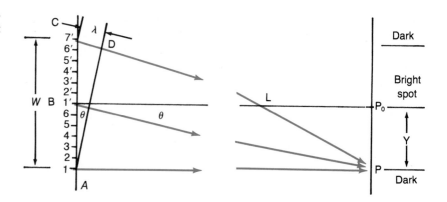

from points 1 and 1' arrive 180° out of phase at point P and cancel. The same is true for points 2 and 2', points 3 and 3', and so on down the slit. Therefore, no light is observed at point P. In our example, we used only six points along the slit. In reality, there are an infinite number of points acting in this way.

If θ is very small, triangles CDA and PP_oB are similar. From triangle CDA

$$\sin \theta = \lambda/w$$

Likewise, from triangles PP_oB

$$\sin \theta = y/BP = y/L$$

since BP and L are equal. Therefore

$$\frac{\lambda}{w} = \frac{y}{L}$$

$$\lambda = \frac{yw}{L}$$

a

b

c

FIGURE 20-4. These diffraction patterns for red light (a), blue light (b), and white light (c) were produced with a slit of width 0.02 cm.

If w is very small, the bright central band will be large. If w is one wavelength, then $\lambda/w = 1$. In the language of trigonometry, $\sin \theta = 1$, and θ is 90°. The bright band will then spread over 180° and no dark lines will be observed on the screen.

With other slit widths, second-order dark bands will appear on the screen beyond the point P. In keeping with our explanation of the first-order dark bands, second-order bands appear where angle θ is large enough to cause CD to equal 2λ. When CD is equal to 3λ or some other multiple of λ, another dark band will appear.

Diffraction is a maximum when the width of the opening is equal to the wavelength of light.

EXAMPLE

Single-Slit Diffraction

Monochromatic orange light falls upon a single slit of width 1.00×10^{-4} m. The slit is located 1.00 m from a screen. If a first-order dark band is observed 6.00×10^{-3} m from the center of the central bright band, what is the wavelength of the orange light?

Given: $w = 1.00 \times 10^{-4}$ m   **Unknown:** λ

$L = 1.00$ m

$y = 6.00 \times 10^{-3}$ m

Basic equation: $\lambda = \dfrac{yw}{L}$

Solution: $\lambda = \dfrac{yw}{L}$

$$= \frac{(6.00 \times 10^{-3} \text{ m})(1.00 \times 10^{-4} \text{ m})}{1.00 \text{ m}}$$

$$\lambda = 6.00 \times 10^{-7} \text{ m}$$

Problems

5. Monochromatic green light falls on a slit 1.00×10^{-4} m wide and produces a first-order dark band 5.50×10^{-3} m from the center of the central bright band on a screen 1.00 m away. Find the wavelength of the green light.

5. 5.50×10^{-7} m

6. Violet light of wavelength 4.00×10^{-7} m falls on a slit 1.5×10^{-4} m wide. The screen is located 80.0 cm from the slit. How far from the central band will the first-order dark band appear?

6. 0.21 cm

7. Yellow light from a sodium vapor lamp falls upon a single slit 0.0295 cm wide. A screen 60.0 cm away reveals a first-order dark band located 0.120 cm from the center of the bright central band. What is the wavelength of the yellow light?

7. 5.90×10^{-5} cm

8. Light of wavelength 4.80×10^{-7} m passes through a single slit and falls on a screen 1.20 m away. What is the width of the slit if the center of the first-order dark band is 5.00×10^{-3} m away from the center of the bright central band?

8. 1.15×10^{-4} m

Keep fingerprints off film

Transmission Diffraction Grating Replica

13,400 Grooves per inch

Best Results Observe Sunlight, Moon, Fluorescent Light

FIGURE 20-5. This diffraction grating can be used to create an interference pattern.

20:4 Diffraction Gratings

In practice, double- and single-slit diffraction is not used as a method of analyzing light. Instead, diffraction gratings are used. **Diffraction gratings** are made by making very fine lines with a diamond point on glass. The spaces between the lines where the glass is undisturbed serve as slits. Gratings that have as many as 12 000 lines per centimeter are commonly used today.

Essentially, diffraction gratings serve the same purpose as double slits with the added advantage of permitting much more light to pass through. This produces stronger images of the spectral lines. Many lines, which may be too faint to be visible by means of a double slit, are clearly visible when a grating is used.

In Section 20:2, the expression used for the calculation of the wavelengths of light using a double slit was given as

$$\lambda = \frac{xd}{L}$$

In most laboratory work, it is easier to calculate or measure the angle between the central bright line and each of the first-order, second-order, or higher-order lines. As can be seen in Figure 20-2, for first-order interference the value of x/L is sin θ. Therefore,

$$\boxed{\lambda = \frac{xd}{L} = d \sin \theta}$$

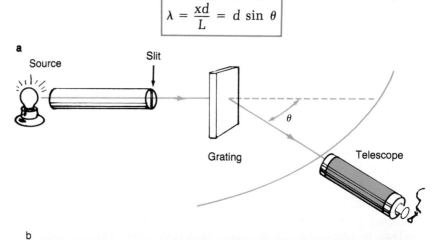

a

Source

Slit

Grating

θ

Telescope

b

FIGURE 20-6. A spectrometer is used to measure the wavelengths of light emitted by a light source (a). A grating was used to produce interference patterns for white light and red light (b).

FIGURE 20-7. The resolving power of a lens is increased if the diameter of the lens is increased.

The wavelengths of light from any source are measured quickly and efficiently by the use of a device known as a spectrometer, Figure 20-6. The source emits light that falls on a slit and then passes through a grating. To the left and right of the central bright line, O, a cluster of lines appears representing the various first-order wavelengths from the source. The position of a movable telescope is then adjusted until a spectral line is in strong focus. The angle θ is then read directly from the calibrated base of the spectrometer. Since d is known, λ can be quickly calculated.

Spectrometers are used to measure the wavelength of light.

20:5 Resolving Power of Lenses

When the light from two points that are close together falls on a lens, the light is diffracted. The lens acts in the same way as a slit. It causes the diffracted light from the two points to interfere. As a result, the width of a lens limits its ability to distinguish between images of the two points. To reduce the effects of diffraction, a wide lens must be used. However, in the case of the objective lens of a microscope, it is not possible to use a wide lens. In a microscope, diffraction is reduced by using a light of a shorter wavelength. Since diffraction is most apparent when the opening is the same order of magnitude as the wavelength, reducing the wavelength will decrease diffraction. As a result, the same effect as using a wider lens can be achieved. For this reason, biology classes often use blue or violet lamps when working with microscopes.

Resolving power indicates a lens' ability to distinguish between the images of two points.

Summary

20:1   **1.** When light falls on two close, narrow slits, it is diffracted as it passes through the slits. The resulting circular waves interfere with each other both constructively and destructively.

20:1   **2.** The interference due to a double slit causes alternating dark and bright lines to appear on a screen some distance from the slits.

20:2   **3.** The interference pattern obtained by using double slits can be analyzed geometrically to obtain the wavelengths of the light passing through the slits.

20:3   **4.** Narrow single slits will also cause interference patterns to appear on a screen some distance from the slit.

20:4   **5.** In practice, gratings with large numbers of evenly spaced slits are used to obtain interference patterns.

Detailed answers to all Questions and Problems are given in the Teacher's Guide at the front of this book.

Questions

1. Explain why the central bright line resulting from the diffraction of light by a double slit cannot be used to measure the wavelength of light waves.

2. Using a compass and a ruler, construct a diagram of the interference pattern that results when waves 1 cm in length fall on two slits that are 2 cm apart. The slits may be represented by two dots spaced 2 cm apart and kept to one side of the paper. Draw a line through the central line of reinforcement and through all other lines of reinforcement. Draw dotted lines where crests meet troughs and produce nodal lines.

3. If you are using light of a known wavelength in a double-slit experiment, how can you find the distance between the slits?

4. More accurate measurements of light waves can be made if the lines obtained for each wavelength are as far apart as possible. We know that $\lambda = xd/L$. How can the value of x be increased?

5. How does a single-slit interference pattern differ from the pattern obtained by using two slits?

6. What happens to a single-slit interference pattern when the width of the slit approaches the wavelength of the light falling on it?

7. How does the size of the lens limit the ability to distinguish between two objects that are very close together?

Problems–A

1. Light falls on a pair of slits 1.90×10^{-4} cm apart. The slits are 80.0 cm from a first-order bright line. The first-order line is 19.0 cm from the central bright line. What is the wavelength of the light?

2. Light of wavelength 4.00×10^{-5} cm falls on a pair of slits. First-order bright lines appear 4.00 cm from the central bright line. The first-order lines are 2.00 m from the center of the slits. How far apart are the slits?

3. A good diffraction grating has 2.50×10^3 lines per centimeter. What is the distance between two lines in the grating?

4. Using the grating of Problem 3, a red line appears 0.165 m from the central bright spot on a screen opposite the grating. The distance from the center of the grating to the red line is 1.00 m. What is the wavelength of the red light?

5. Light of frequency 6.0×10^{14} Hz falls on a pair of slits that are 2.00×10^{-4} cm apart. The center of the slits is 50.0 cm from the screen. How far from the central bright line will the first-order bright lines appear?

6. Light falls on a single slit 1.00×10^{-4} m wide and develops a first-order dark band 5.90×10^{-3} m from the center of the central bright band on a screen 1.00 m away. Calculate the wavelength of the light.

1. 4.51×10^{-5} cm

2. 2.00×10^{-5} m

3. 4.00×10^{-4} cm/line

4. 6.60×10^{-5} cm

5. 13 cm

6. 5.90×10^{-7} m

Problems–B

1. Sound waves of frequency 550 Hz enter a window 1.2 m wide. The window is in the exact center of one wall of a theater 24 m × 12 m. The window is 12 m from the opposite wall along which is a row of seats filled with people. The theater is acoustically prepared to prevent the reflection of sound waves, and the speed of sound is 330 m/s. Two people in a row along the wall hear no sound. Where are they sitting?

2. A radio station uses two antennas and broadcasts at 600 kHz.
   a. What is the wavelength of the signals emitted by the station?
   b. The occupants of a home that is located 17 500 m from one antenna and 19 500 m from the other antenna have their receiver tuned to the station. Is their reception good or poor?

1. 6.0 m on either side of the center.

2. a. 500 m
   b. Reception should be good.

Readings

Edelson, Ed., "Holography—Out of the Lab at Last." *Popular Science*, March, 1984.

Hecht, Jeff, "Store It With Light." *Computers and Electronics*, July, 1984.

Ronada, David, "Compact Disc Digital Audio Systems." *Computers and Electronics*, August, 1983.

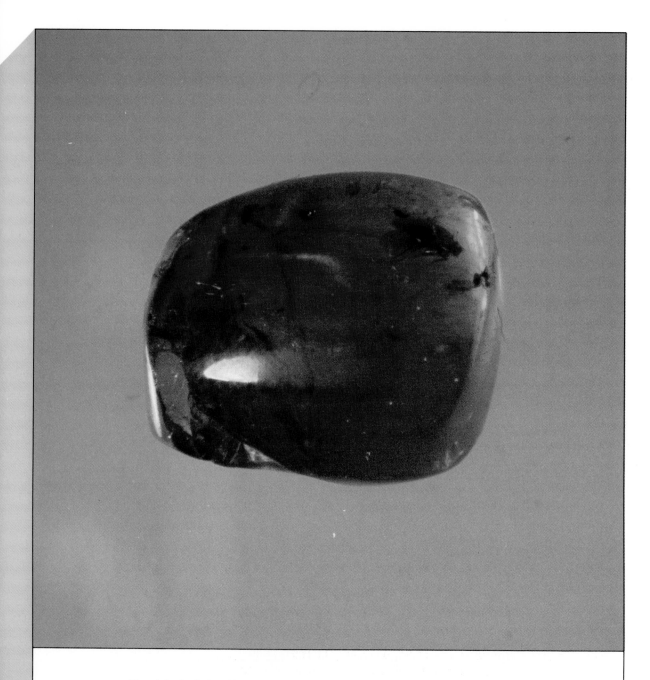

Electricity is derived from the Greek word for amber, a form of petrified tree sap. The fossilized remains of insects and plants are often clearly visible in amber. The ancient Greeks discovered that amber attracted small objects and even produced tiny sparks when rubbed. How are these effects related to static electricity? In what ways have you experienced static electricity?

Static Electricity

Chapter 21 introduces the concept of electric charge and discusses the properties of charged bodies. The inverse-square law for electric force is presented.

You probably have created sparks by touching a doorknob after rubbing your shoes on the carpet. The rubbing action caused two kinds of electric charges to separate. The sparks occurred when the separated electric charges were combined again. Benjamin Franklin named these two kinds of charges "positive" and "negative." He showed that lightning was the recombination of electric charges. Electricity is the name given to electric charges and the effects they cause. Static electricity describes the effects of charges that can be collected and held in one place. The existence of electric charges is the result of the structure of the atom.

Goal: You will gain understanding of static charges and the forces between them.

21:1   The Electrical Atom

Between 1909 and 1911, Ernest Rutherford, a New Zealander, discovered that atoms have a massive, positively-charged nucleus, or center. The nucleus is surrounded by less massive, negatively-charged electrons. The positive charge of the nucleus is exactly balanced by the negative charge of the electrons.

The nucleus is made up of protons and neutrons. Protons have a charge equal in size to that of the electron, but positive rather than negative. Neutrons have no net charge. The proton and the neutron have nearly the same mass, which is about 1830 times as massive as the electron.

The nucleus of an atom contains protons (positively charged) and neutrons (no charge).

About the nucleus is a "cloud" of electrons (negatively charged).

353

Electron movements cause electric phenomena.

A neutral object has the same number of electrons as protons.

When a neutral object gains electrons, it gains a net negative charge.

When a neutral object loses electrons, it has a net positive charge.

An electrically-charged object has a static charge.

By adding energy to an atom it is possible to remove one or more electrons. Rubbing the atoms in your shoes against the atoms in a carpet is one way of adding energy. Removal of electrons results in an atom with a net positive charge, called a positive ion. Adding electrons will create a negative ion, an atom with a net negative charge. It is not possible, by ordinary means, to remove protons from the atom. The protons and neutrons are held together in the nucleus by the strong nuclear force, and can be separated only by supplying very large amounts of energy.

21:2 Transferring Electrons

Positive and negative charges can be separated by transferring electrons. If a glass rod is rubbed with a piece of silk, electrons will move from the glass rod to the silk. The glass rod is left with some positive ions, atoms with fewer electrons than protons. The glass rod has a positive charge. Rubbing a hard rubber rod with fur also separates charges. However, in this case, electrons move from the fur to the rubber rod. The rubber rod gains electrons and becomes negatively charged. The glass rod and the rubber rod became charged when electrons were transferred from one body to another. The energy necessary to transfer the electrons was supplied by rubbing two bodies together. Individual charges are never created or destroyed. The separation of positive and negative charges always means that electrons have been transferred.

21:3 Conductors, Insulators, and Semiconductors

Electrons added to one part of a rubber rod will remain on that part of the rod. Materials through which electrons will not move are called

FIGURE 21-1. A rubber object can be charged when rubbed with fur.

Hard rubber rod

Fur

insulators. Electrons removed from one area on an insulator are not replaced by electrons from another area. Glass, dry wood, most plastics, cloth, and dry air are good insulators.

Materials which do not conduct electricity well are insulators.

Extra electrons added to one end of a piece of metal will spread very quickly throughout the entire piece. Materials such as metals that allow electrons to move about easily are called electrical **conductors.** Electrons carry, or conduct, electric charges through the material. Metals are good conductors because at least one electron on each atom can be removed easily. These electrons act as if they no longer belong to any atom, but to the metal as a whole. They are free to move throughout the metal in the same way atoms in a gas move about a container. Thus, they are said to form a "gas" of electrons. Copper and aluminum are both excellent conductors and are used commercially to carry electricity. Graphite, the form of carbon used in pencils, also is a good conductor.

Metals are good electric conductors.

Semiconductors are materials, such as silicon and germanium, with a conductivity capacity between conductors and insulators. Within these materials, only a few electrons are free to move. The number of free electrons in a semiconductor can be greatly increased by adding small amounts of other elements. By adding the correct element, a scientist can create a semiconductor with a specific conductivity. Transistors and the integrated circuits used in computers are made

a

b

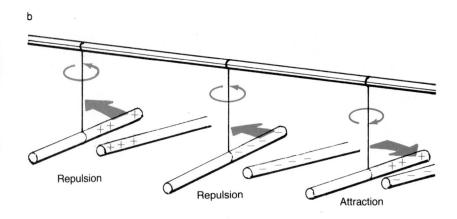

Repulsion

Repulsion

Attraction

FIGURE 21-3. A charged rod, when brought close to another suspended rod, will attract or repel the suspended rod.

from silicon treated by this method. Light can also produce free electrons in semiconductors, increasing their conductivity. "Electric eyes," solar cells that generate electricity directly from sunlight, and photocopy machines use semiconductors that are sensitive to light.

21:4 Forces on Charged Bodies

A negatively-charged rubber rod, suspended so that it turns easily, can be used to demonstrate the forces due to electrical charges (Figure 21-3). If one brings a similarly-charged rod near the suspended rod, it will turn away. The negative charges on the rods repel each other. It is not necessary to bring the rods very close; the force, called the electric force, acts over a distance. If a positively-charged glass rod is suspended, and a similarly-charged glass rod is brought close, the two positively-charged objects will also repel. However, if a negatively-charged rod is brought near the positively-charged rod, the two will attract each other, and the suspended rod will turn toward the opposite charge. These observations can be summarized as follows.

1. There are two kinds of electrical charges, positive and negative.
2. Charges exert force on other charges over a distance.
3. Like charges repel; opposite charges attract.

Electroscopes are used to detect the presence of static charges.

A large rod hanging in open air is not a very sensitive or convenient way of determining charge. Instead, a device called an **electroscope** is used. An electroscope consists of a metal knob connected by a metal stem to two thin, lightweight pieces of metal called *leaves* as shown in Figure 21-4. Note that the leaves are enclosed to eliminate stray air currents.

Neutral conductors can be charged by conduction if they come in contact with charged objects.

When a negatively-charged rod is touched to the knob, negative charges (electrons) are added to the knob. The charges spread over all metal surfaces. The two leaves are charged negatively and repel each other, causing them to spread apart. This process of charging a neutral body by touching it with a charged body is called **charging by conduction.**

The leaves will also spread if the electroscope is charged positively. The type of charge on the electroscope can be determined by observing what happens to the spread leaves if a rod of known charge is brought close to the knob. The leaves will spread farther apart if the electroscope has the same charge as the rod. The leaves will fall slightly if the electroscope has a charge opposite to that of the rod.

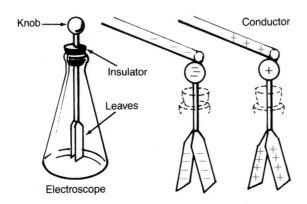

Knob
Conductor
Insulator
Leaves
Electroscope

FIGURE 21-4. Electroscope with accompanying diagrams of possible charge distributions.

21:5 Charging by Induction

If a charged rod is brought close to, but does not touch, the knob of an uncharged electroscope, the leaves will spread apart. The spreading indicates the leaves have been charged. Since air is an insulator, electrons could not have been transferred from the rod to the knob. The electroscope must still be neutral. To understand what happened, assume the rod was charged negatively. When the rod was brought near the knob, it repelled the negative charges from the knob down the stem to the leaves. The knob was positively charged. The leaves became negatively charged and spread apart. The separation of charges in the electroscope caused, or induced, simply by the proximity of the charged rod is called **charging by induction**. Note: When the charged rod is removed, the separation of charge ends and the leaves fall.

Separation of charge can be induced in other bodies as well. If a negatively-charged rod is brought close to one of two identical metal spheres that are touching, electrons from the first sphere will be pushed onto the sphere farther from the rod. The closer sphere remains positively charged. If the spheres are separated while the rod is nearby, the two spheres will have equal but opposite charges. This process is also called charging by induction.

Charges can be separated on a neutral conductor by induction.

FIGURE 21-5. A negatively charged rod repels electrons from the electroscope down to the leaves; a positively charged rod attracts electrons from the leaves to the top of the electroscope.

a   b

21:6 Coulomb's Law

In 1785, a French physicist named Charles Coulomb (1736-1806) used a torsion balance to measure the force between two charged spheres (Figure 21-7). An insulating rod with small conducting spheres

FIGURE 21-6. The negative rod is brought near the touching spheres and the electrons are repelled to the right-hand sphere. The spheres are separated to show that they are charged.

at each end was suspended by a thin wire. A third sphere, B, was placed in contact with sphere A. Both were then charged. Because they received the same charge, they repelled each other and sphere A moved away from B.

To determine how the distance between sphere A and sphere B affected the force, Coulomb carefully measured the amount of force needed to twist the suspending wire through a given angle. He placed equal but opposite charges on spheres A and B and varied the distance, d, between them. By measuring the deflection of A from its rest position, he could calculate the force of repulsion. Coulomb made many measurements with spheres charged both positively and negatively. He showed that the force, F, varied inversely with the square of the distance between the spheres.

The electric force varies inversely with the square of distance between two charged objects.

$$F \propto \frac{1}{d^2}$$

The electric force between two charged objects varies directly with the product of their charges.

To investigate the relationship between the force and the amount of charge, Coulomb first charged spheres A and B as before. Then he selected an extra uncharged sphere, C, the same size as sphere B. When C was placed in contact with B, the spheres shared the charge that once was on B alone. Because the two were the same size, B now had only half the charge it once had. Therefore, the charge on B was only one half of the charge on A. The extra sphere was then removed. After

FIGURE 21-7. Coulomb used this type of apparatus to measure the force between two spheres. He observed the deflection of A while varying the distance between A and B.

Coulomb adjusted the position of B so that the distance, d, between A and B was the same as before, he found that the force between A and B was half of its former value. That is, he found that the electric force varied directly with the charge of one of the bodies. After many similar measurements, Coulomb summarized the results in a law known as **Coulomb's law.** *The magnitude of the force that a sphere with charge q exerts on a second sphere with charge q', separated a distance d, is*

Coulomb's law describes the force between two charged objects.

$$F = \frac{Kqq'}{d^2}$$

This equation yields the force that the charge q exerts on q' and also the force that q' exerts on q. These two forces are equal in magnitude, but opposite in direction. They are examples of action-reaction forces described by Newton's third law of motion. In this equation, K is a constant that depends on the units used to measure charge. Coulomb's law has been found to be true for individual electrons separated by less than 10^{-18} m. This is a separation one one-thousandth as large as the size of the nucleus.

It might prove helpful to point out the similarity between Coulomb's law and the law of universal gravitation.

21:7 The Unit of Charge: The Coulomb

The unit of charge is called the coulomb (C). The charge of an electron, called the elementary unit of charge, is 1.60×10^{-19} C. Therefore, one coulomb is the charge on 6.25×10^{18} electrons.

Using the coulomb as the unit of charge and measuring d in meters and F in newtons, the force on a body with charge q caused by a body with charge q' can be written.

$$F = \frac{Kqq'}{d^2},$$

where the constant K is 9.0×10^9 N $\cdot$ m²/C².

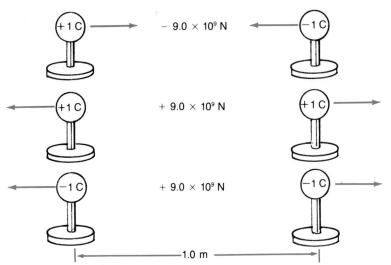

FIGURE 21-8. A positive force indicates repulsion of like charges. A negative force indicates attraction of unlike charges.

FIGURE 21-9. The force of repulsion.

A negative force indicates attraction.

A positive force between charges indicates repulsion.

The electric force, like all other forces, is a vector quantity. Coulomb's law in this form given above does not indicate the direction of the force. However, it does tell us that a positive force indicates a force of repulsion and a negative force indicates attraction.

EXAMPLE

Coulomb's Law--Two Charges

A positive charge of 6.0×10^{-6} C is 0.030 m from a second positive charge of 3.0×10^{-6} C.   **a.** Calculate the force between the charges. **b.** What would be the force if the second charge were negative?

Given: $q = +6.0 \times 10^{-6}$ C   **Unknown:** F

$\quad\quad\quad\quad d = 0.030$ m

$\quad\quad\quad\quad q' = +3.0 \times 10^{-6}$ C   **Basic equation:** $F = K\dfrac{qq'}{d^2}$

Solution:

   a. $F = K\dfrac{qq'}{d^2}$

$\quad\quad = \dfrac{(9.0 \times 10^9 \text{ N·m}^2/\text{C}^2)(+6.0 \times 10^{-6} \text{ C})(+3.0 \times 10^{-6} \text{ C})}{(0.030 \text{ m})^2}$

$\quad\quad = \dfrac{(9.0 \times 10^9 \text{ N·m}^2/\text{C}^2)(18 \times 10^{-12} \text{ C}^2)}{(9.0 \times 10^{-4} \text{ m}^2)}$

$\quad\quad = +1.8 \times 10^2$ N

The positive sign of the force between the charges indicates repulsion.

   b. If the second charge were negative, the sign of the force would be negative, which indicates attraction.

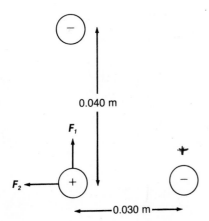

FIGURE 21-10. Use with Example problem below.

EXAMPLE

Coulomb's Law—Three Charges

A positive charge of 6.0×10^{-6} C has two other charges nearby. One, -3.0×10^{-6} C, is 0.040 m to the north. The other, $+1.5 \times 10^{-6}$ C, is 0.030 m to the east. What is the total force on the 6.0×10^{-6} C charge?

Solution:

A sketch of the problem is shown in Figure 21-10. Force F_1, due to the charge to the north, is attractive. That is, its direction is north (0°). Force F_2, due to the charge to the east, is repulsive or toward the west (270°).

First, the magnitudes of the two forces are calculated.

$$F_1 = K \frac{qq'}{d^2}$$

$$= \frac{(9.0 \times 10^9 \text{ N·m}^2/\text{C}^2)(6.0 \times 10^{-6} \text{ C})(-3.0 \times 10^{-6} \text{ C})}{(4.0 \times 10^{-2} \text{ m})^2}$$

$$F_1 = -1.0 \times 10^2 \text{ N at } 0°$$

$$F_2 = \frac{(9.0 \times 10^9 \text{ N·m}^2/\text{C}^2)(6.0 \times 10^{-6} \text{ C})(1.5 \times 10^{-6} \text{ C})}{(3.0 \times 10^{-2} \text{ m})^2}$$

$$F_2 = 9.0 \times 10^1 \text{ N at } 270°$$

Next the forces are added vectorially to find the resultant force.

$$F^2 = F_1^2 + F_2^2$$
$$= 1.8 \times 10^4 \text{ N}^2$$
$$F = 1.3 \times 10^2 \text{ N}$$

The angle can be found by $\tan \theta = 1.0 \times 10^2 \text{ N}/9.0 \times 10^1 \text{ N} = 1.1$; $\theta = 48°$. $F = 1.3 \times 10^2$ N at 318°.

Problems

1. Two positive charges of 6.0×10^{-6} C are separated by 0.50 m. What force exists between the charges?

FIGURE 21-11. Photocopier drums utilize electric forces.

FIGURE 21-11. Photocopier drums utilize electric forces.

2. -1.6×10^4 N, attractive

3. 1.0×10^{-8} N, repulsive

4. 3.0×10^{-6} C

2. A negative charge of -2.0×10^{-4} C and a positive charge of 8.0×10^{-4} C are separated by 0.30 m. What is the force between the two charges?

3. Two electrons in an atom, each with charge -1.6×10^{-19} C, are separated by 1.5×10^{-10} m. What is the force between them?

4. A negative charge of -6.0×10^{-6} C exerts an attractive force of 65 N on a second charge 0.050 m away. What is the magnitude of the second charge?

21:8   Forces on Neutral Bodies

A charged body may either attract or repel another charged body. However, a charged body always attracts a neutral (uncharged) body. A charged rod brought near a neutral body separates the charges in the neutral body. The charge separation occurs in conductors and to some extent in insulators. The opposite charges are pulled closer to the rod; the like charges are pushed away. According to Coulomb's law, the force on the closer charges will be stronger than the force on the charges that are farther away. Therefore, the neutral body will have a net force of attraction to the rod. The force of attraction on neutral bodies explains how a small piece of paper is attracted to a charged body. Forces on both charged and uncharged bodies are important in the operation of photocopiers like those made by the Xerox Corporation. The copier has a drum made of a conductor, aluminum, coated with a thin layer of the semiconductor selenium. The selenium layer is first charged by a spray of charged air molecules. In the dark, selenium is a poor conductor, and the charges stay where they are put. Light is reflected from the page to be copied, passed through a lens, and is focused on the drum. In the places where light hits the selenium, the semiconductor becomes a conductor, letting the charges flow away from the surface to the aluminum drum. However, where there was a black area on the subject, there will be a dark area on the drum, and the charge will remain on the selenium layer. The drum is then rotated through a container of *toner*. Toner consists of tiny charged plastic beads coated with carbon grains. The coated beads are attracted to the charged areas of the selenium layer on the drum, but not to the areas where the charge has flowed away. Paper is pressed against the drum and the coated beads are transferred to the paper. The paper is heated and the beads melt, attaching the carbon to the paper. The carbon makes a copy of the material on the original page. Thus, electrostatics and semiconductors allow everyone to have inexpensive and quick copies of important documents.

In other applications, electric forces on neutral particles can be used to collect soot in smokestacks, reducing air pollution. Tiny paint droplets with induced charges can be used to paint automobiles and other objects very uniformly.

Mapping the Ocean Floor

Physics Focus

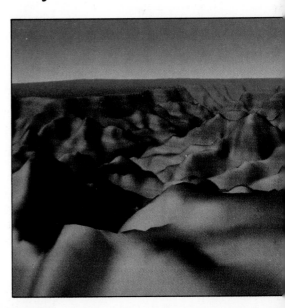

A radar altimeter uses microwave radiation to very accurately measure distances between objects. Thin beams of microwaves are transmitted to the ocean surface from a SEASAT satellite and are reflected back to the satellite. From beam travel time transmission speed, the distance to the ocean surface can be calculated to within 5 cm.

Water attracted to the greater gravitational pull of ridges and seamounts on the ocean floor creates "bumps" on the ocean surface. Trenches, with their lack of gravitational mass, create "valleys" on the sea surface.

Data have been transformed by a computer graphics program into maps that reveal incredible features in the ocean basins. Long mid-ocean ridges and trenches six times deeper than the Grand Canyon have been mapped. The program can vary the color shading on maps of ocean floor features. The program can also rotate the viewpoint of the observer to highlight certain features.

The information on these computer-generated maps confirms data collected by terrestrial techniques such as depth sounding. The major advantage of satellite imagery is its complete coverage of the earth's surface in a relatively short period of time.

Summary

21:1   **1.** The atom consists of negatively-charged electrons in a cloud around a positively-charged, tiny, massive nucleus. The net charge is zero.

21:2   **2.** Bodies can be charged negatively or positively because electrons can be transferred easily. An object is charged negatively by adding electrons to it. Removing electrons leaves behind positive ions and thus a net positive charge.

21:3   **3.** Charges added to or removed from one part of an insulator will remain in that part.

21:3   **4.** Charges added to a conductor will immediately spread throughout the body.

21:3   **5.** Semiconductors have a conductivity between conductors and insulators. The amount of conduction can be changed by exposing them to light or by adding other elements.

21:4   **6.** Like charges repel; unlike charges attract.

21:4   **7.** Charges are determined by an electroscope. Charges cause thin metal leaves to spread.

21:5   **8.** A charged body can induce separation of charge in a neutral body.

21:8   **9.** A charged body of either sign will attract a neutral body in which a charge separation is induced.

21:6   **10.** Coulomb's law states that the force between two charged objects varies directly with the product of the two charges and inversely with the square of the distance between them.

21:7   **11.** The unit of charge is the coulomb. One coulomb (C) is the charge on 6.25×10^{18} electrons or protons. The elementary unit of charge, the charge on the proton or electron, is 1.60×10^{-19} C.

Detailed answers to all Questions and Problems are given in the Teacher's Guide at the front of this book.

Questions

1. List the three major particles in the atom. State the electric charge of each.

2. Using a charged rod and an electroscope, how could you find out if an object is a conductor?

3. List some insulators, some conductors, and some semiconductors.

4. Explain what will happen to the leaves of a positively-charged electroscope when a charged rod is nearby but not touching.

     a. when the rod is positive.
     b. when the rod is negative.

5. Explain how Coulomb made sure that the pair of spheres (A and B in Figure 21-7) had equal charges.

6. State Coulomb's law.

Problems–A

1. A positive charge of 1.8×10^{-6} C and a negative charge of -1.0×10^{-6} C are 0.014 m apart. What is the force between the two particles?

2. Two negative charges of -5.0×10^{-5} C are 0.20 m from each other. What force acts on each particle?

3. The hydrogen atom contains a proton and an electron separated by 5.0×10^{-11} m. Find the force of attraction between the two particles.

4. Charges of 4.5×10^{-6} C exist on the three spheres shown in Figure 21-10, page 361. Find the magnitude of the total force on the top sphere.

1. -83 N

2. 5.6×10^2 N

3. -9.2×10^{-8} N

4. 280 N

Problems–B

1. Two pith balls shown in Figure 21-12 have a mass of 1.0 g each and have equal charges. One pith ball is suspended by an insulating thread. The other is brought to 3.0 cm from the suspended ball. The suspended ball is now hanging with the thread forming an angle of 30.0° with the vertical. The ball is in equilibrium with F_E, $m\mathbf{g}$, and $\mathbf{T}$ adding vectorially to yield zero. Calculate
   a. $m\mathbf{g}$.   b. F_E.   c. the charge on the balls.

2. Benjamin Franklin once wrote that he had "erected an iron rod to draw the lightning down into my house, in order to make some experiment on it, with two bells to give notice when the rod should be electrify'd. . ." The chime had two small bells mounted side by side. One bell was connected to the iron rod (source of charge), the other was attached to the earth. Between the two, a small metal ball was suspended on a silk thread so it could swing back and forth, striking the two bells. Explain why, when the one bell was charged, the ball would keep swinging, hitting first one bell then the other.

3. Water drips slowly from a narrow dropper inside a negatively-charged metal ring (Figure 21-13).
   a. Will the drops be charged?
   b. If they are charged, are they positive or negative?
   The drops fall into a can that is on an insulating platform.
   c. Will the can be charged?
   d. What will be the sign of the charge on the can?

FIGURE 21-12. Use with Problem B-1.

1. a. 9.8×10^{-3} N
   b. 5.7×10^{-3} N
   c. 2.4×10^{-8} C
2. See Teacher's Guide.
3. a. yes
   b. positive by induction
   c. yes
   d. positive by conduction

FIGURE 21-13. Use with Problem B-3.

Readings

Bardeen, John, "To A Solid State." *Science*, November, 1983.

Bier, M., "Electrophoresis: Mathematical Modeling and Computer Simulation." *Science*, March, 1983.

Eskow, Dennis, "Striking Back at Lightning." *Popular Mechanics*, August, 1983.

Lightning is an impressive display of the energy released when static charges are brought together. How is electric potential energy related to the work done in separating static charges? As you will see, the concept of an electric field will help to answer this question. What other effects can be explained by electric fields?

The Electric Field

Chapter 22 introduces the concept of the electric field. The relationship between the electric potential and work is discussed. Capacitance is described.

The electric force, like the gravitational force, varies inversely as the square of the distance between the bodies. Both forces can act at great distance. How, then, can a force be exerted across what seems to be empty space? Our usual idea of a force is something that acts when two bodies touch each other. In trying to understand the electric force, Michael Faraday (1791–1867) invented the concept of an electric field. His concept of the electric field introduced the idea of a force acting between a charge and the electric field at the location of the charge. The idea that a force must act between particles separated by some distance is no longer required. In this chapter, we will describe the electric field concept and discuss its uses.

Goal: You will gain an understanding of electric fields, how they help us understand static electricity, and how they are used in various devices.

22:1 Electric Fields

Consider an electric charge, q, at some fixed position in space. A positive test charge of unit magnitude is placed near the charge. The force that q exerts on the test charge at this location is measured. The test charge is then moved to another location and the force on the test charge is measured again. This process is repeated again and again until every location in space has a measurement of the electric force on the test charge associated with it. The measured forces are vector quantities.

The collection of these vector quantities is called an **electric field.** A charge placed in this electric field experiences a force on it due to the electric field at that location. The magnitude of the field indicates the strength of the force. The direction of the field determines the direction of the force on the charge. A picture of an electric field can be made by using arrows to represent the force vectors at various locations, Figure 22-1. The length of the arrow shows the magnitude of the force and the direction of the arrow shows the direction of the force.

An electric field exists around charged objects. The electric field exerts a force on charged objects.

367

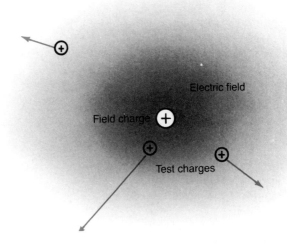

The collection of arrows is not a very useful picture. A better picture of an electric field is shown in Figure 22-2. The lines are called **electric field lines.** Each line shows the path that would be followed by a positive test charge placed in the field. Each field line shows the direction of the force, but not its magnitude. If a large number of field lines are drawn, the strength of the electric force is indicated by the spacing between the lines. The force is strong where the lines are close together. It is weaker where the lines are spaced farther apart.

The direction of the force on the test charge near a positive charge is away from the charge. The field lines extend radially outward like the spokes of a wheel (Figure 22-2a). Remember the test charge is always positive. Near a negative charge the direction of the force on the test charge is toward the charge and so the field lines point radially inward (Figure 22-2b).

When there are two or more charges, the force on a test charge is the vector sum of the forces due to the individual charges. The field lines become bent and the pattern complex, as shown in Figure 22-2c. Note

Electric field lines produce a picture of the electric field.

If electric field lines are close together, the field is strong.

The direction of an electric field is away from positive charges and toward negative charges.

a   b

FIGURE 22-2. Lines of force are drawn perpendicularly away from the positive object and perpendicularly into the negative object (a). Electric field lines between oppositely charged objects are shown in (b).

a

b

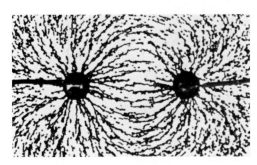

FIGURE 22-3. Lines of force between unlike charges (a) and between like charges (b) describe the behavior of a positively charged object in a field. The top photographs are computer tracings of electric field lines.

that field lines always start on a positive charge and end on a negative charge.

Another method of visualizing field lines is to use grass seed in an insulating liquid such as mineral oil. The electric forces cause a separation of charge in the long, thin grass seed. The seeds turn so they line up along the direction of the electric force. Therefore, the seeds form a pattern of the electric field lines. The patterns in Figure 22-3 were made this way.

Field lines do not really exist, but are just a means of providing a picture of an electric field. Electric fields, on the other hand, do exist. An electric field is produced by one or more charges and is independent of the existence of the test charge that is used to measure it. The field provides a method of calculating the force on a charged body. However, it does not explain why charged bodies exert forces on each other. That question is still unanswered.

Electric fields are real. Field lines are imaginary, but useful in making a picture of a field.

22:2 Electric Field Intensity

According to Coulomb's law, the electric force acting on a charge is proportional to the magnitude of that charge. If the magnitude of the charge is doubled, the force is doubled. Therefore, the value of the ratio of force to charge is independent of the size of the charge. The ratio is called the **electric field intensity.** That is,

$$E = \frac{F \text{ on test charge } q'}{q'}$$

Electric field intensity is force per unit charge.

The magnitude of the electric field intensity is measured in newtons per coulomb, N/C. The direction of the electric field intensity is indicated by the field lines, away from positive charges, toward negative charges.

The force on a charge q' due to a single charge q, a distance d away, is given by the equation

$$F = \frac{Kqq'}{d^2}$$

Therefore, the electric field due to a single charge is given by the equation

The electric field caused by a single charge is proportional to the magnitude of the charge and inversely proportional to the distance from the charge.

$$E = \frac{F}{q'} = \frac{\frac{Kqq'}{d^2}}{q'} = \frac{Kq}{d^2}$$

Note that this equation indicates that **E**, the electric field intensity, is independent of the test charge.

The test charge also produces an electric field that exerts a force on other charges. For this reason, a small test charge should be used. The field of the test charge should be so small that the field it produces is very weak in comparison to the field of the charge being measured.

EXAMPLE

Electric Field Intensity

A positive test charge of 4.0×10^{-5} C is placed in an electric field. The force acting on it is 0.60 N at 10°. What is the electric field intensity at the location of the test charge?

Given: charge $(q') = 4.0 \times 10^{-5}$ C **Unknown:**
$$F = 0.60 \text{ N at } 10°$$
electric field intensity (**E**)

Basic equation: $E = \frac{F}{q'}$

Solution: $E = \frac{F}{q'}$

$$E = \frac{0.60 \text{ N}}{4.0 \times 10^{-5} \text{ C}}$$

$$= 1.5 \times 10^4 \text{ N/C at } 10°$$

Note: If the field were negative, the force on the test charge would be in the opposite direction, that is, 1.5×10^4 N/C at 190°.

Problems

1. 3.0 × 10⁶ N/C

1. A negative charge of 2.0×10^{-8} C experiences a force of 0.060 N when in an electric field. What is the magnitude of the field intensity?

2. 0.50 N/C

2. A positive test charge of 5.0×10^{-4} C is in an electric field, which exerts a force of 2.5×10^{-4} N on it. What is the magnitude of the electric field intensity at the location of the test charge?

3. A positive test charge of 8.0×10^{-5} C is placed in an electric field. It experiences a force of 4.0×10^{-3} N. What is the magnitude of the electric field intensity at this point?   3. 5.0×10^{1} N/C

4. Suppose the electric field in Problem 3 were caused by a point charge. The test charge is moved to a distance twice as far from the charge. What force does the field now exert on the test charge?

4. 1.0×10^{-3} N

22:3 Work and the Electric Potential

If a unit positive charge at point A is moved to point B, which is farther away from a negative charge, the attractive force between the two charges will oppose the motion; therefore, work will be done. The work done is proportional to the magnitude of the charge moved. The **difference in electric potential** between points A and B, $V_B - V_A$, is defined to be the work done per unit charge.

$$V_B - V_A = W/q$$

The work done moving the charge from A to B is positive, so the potential of point B, V_B, is larger than the potential at point A, V_A. The potential difference, like field intensity, does not depend on the size of the charge moved. The unit of electric potential is joule per coulomb. One joule per coulomb is called a volt (J/C = V).

As the positive charge mentioned above returns to point A, it will be able to do work. This means that the work done on it is negative. Therefore, the change in potential between B and A will be negative. The work done by the charge moving from B to A will equal the work done on the charge when it was moved from A to B. Thus the potential of point A depends only on its location, not on the path taken to get there.

Only changes or *differences* in potential are related to work done. Thus only differences in potential are important. Potential differences are measured with a voltmeter.

Defining the potential of any point, for example, point A, to be zero will not affect potential differences. If $V_A = 0$, then the potential of B will equal W/q. W is the work done in moving the charge to point B from the reference point A.

Electric potential increases when two unlike charges are separated. Between two like charges, however, the force is repulsive. Work is done pushing the two charges closer together. Therefore, the potential is larger when two like charges are close together, as shown in Figure 22-5. Electric potential, V, is increased when work is done in moving a charge. The change in potential is also related to the intensity of the electric field in which the charges are moved.

22:4 The Electric Field Between Two Parallel Plates

It is possible to create an electric field that is uniform in intensity. Such fields are found in oscilloscopes and particle accelerators. To

FIGURE 22-4. Gravitational potential difference (a) and electric potential difference (b) are both found by multiplying field intensity by distance moved.

FIGURE 22-5. Electric potential is larger when two like charges are closer together (a) and smaller when two unlike charges are closer together (b).

FIGURE 22-6. An electric field between parallel plates.

FIGURE 22-6. An electric field between parallel plates.

A uniform electric field exists between two parallel metal plates that have opposite charges.

Note that when we are concerned only about the magnitude of a vector quantity, the bold face notation is not used.

make a uniform field, two flat conducting plates are placed parallel to each other. One is charged positively and the other negatively. The electric field between the plates is uniform, except at the edges of the plates. Figure 22-6 shows a grass seed representation of the field between parallel plates.

In a uniform gravitational field, the work needed to raise a body of mass m a distance h is given by $W = mgh$ (Chapter 11). Remember that g, the gravitational field intensity near the earth, is given by $g = F/m = 9.8$ (N/kg). The gravitational potential, work per unit mass, is equal to $mgh/m = gh$.

In a uniform electric field, the work done in moving a charge a distance, d, is given by $W = Fd$. Thus, the potential, work per charge, is given by the equation $V = Fd/q = (F/q)d$. However, force per charge is the electric field intensity, $E = F/q$. Therefore,

$$\boxed{V = Ed}$$

A uniform electric field can be created by charging two parallel plates. If the plates are a distance, d, apart and the field intensity between them is E, then the potential difference between the two plates is given by $V = Ed$.

EXAMPLE

Potential Difference Between Parallel Plates

Two parallel plates are 0.500 m apart. The electric field intensity between them is 6.00×10^3 N/C.   **a.** What is the potential difference between the plates?   **b.** What work is done moving a charge equal to that on one electron from one plate to the other?

Note that by unit analysis the product of the units of E and d is N/C · m. This is equivalent to a J/C, the definition of a volt.

Given: $d = 0.500$ m   **Unknowns:** V, W

$E = 6.00 \times 10^3$ N/C   **Basic equation:** $V = Ed$

Solution: **a.** $V = Ed$

$= (6.00 \times 10^3 \text{ N/C})(0.500 \text{ m})$

$= 3.00 \times 10^3 \text{ N} \cdot \text{m/C}$

$= 3.00 \times 10^3 \text{ J/C}$

$= 3.00 \times 10^3 \text{ V}$

b. $W = qV$

$= (1.6 \times 10^{-19} \text{ C})(3.00 \times 10^3 \text{ V})$

$= 4.8 \times 10^{-16} \text{ CV}$

$= 4.8 \times 10^{-16} \text{ J}$

EXAMPLE

Electric Field Intensity Between Two Parallel Plates

A voltmeter measures the potential difference between two parallel plates to be 60.0 V. The plates are 0.030 m apart. What is the magnitude of the electric field intensity?

Given: $V = 60.0$ V   **Unknown:** E

$d = 0.030$ m   **Basic equation:** $V = Ed$

Solution: $V = Ed$, so $E = V/d$

$= (60.0 \text{ V})/(0.030 \text{ m})$

$= (60.0 \text{ J/C})/(0.030 \text{ m})$

$= 2.0 \times 10^3 \text{ N/C}$

Problems

5. The electric field intensity between two charged metal plates is 8000 N/C. The plates are 0.05 m apart. What is the potential difference between them?

5. 400 V

6. A voltmeter reads 500 V when placed across two parallel plates. The plates are 0.020 m apart. What is the field intensity between them?

6. 3×10^4 N/C

7. What voltage is applied to two metal plates 0.500 m apart if the field intensity between them is 2.50×10^3 N/C?

7. 1250 V

8. A spark will jump across dry air when the electric field is larger than 1×10^6 N/C. If two parallel plates have a potential difference of 5×10^3 V, how far apart must they be kept to prevent a spark from jumping across them?

8. 5 mm

9. 7.5 J

10. a. 6000 J
    b. 1.2 kW

9. What work is done when 5.0 C is raised in potential by 1.5 V?

10. A charge of 50 C is raised in potential by 110 V.

    a. What work is done in raising the potential of this charge?

    b. What power is required if the work is done in 5.0 s?

22:5 Millikan's Oil Drop Experiment

One important application of the uniform electric field between two parallel plates was the measurement of the charge of an electron made by the American physicist Robert A. Millikan (1868-1953) in 1909.

The charge of an electron was found by Millikan in his oil drop experiment.

Figure 22-7 shows the method used by Millikan to measure the charge carried by a single electron. Fine oil drops were sprayed from an atomizer into the air. These drops were often charged by friction with the atomizer. Gravity acting on the drops caused them to fall. A few entered the hole in the top plate of the apparatus. A potential difference was placed across the two plates. The resulting electric field between the plates exerted a force on the charged drops. When the top plate was positive, the electric force caused negatively-charged drops to rise. The potential difference between the plates was adjusted to suspend a charged drop between the plates. Then the downward force of the weight and the upward force of the electric field were equal in magnitude.

When the electric force balances the gravitational force, the drop is suspended.

$$Eq = mg$$

The intensity of the electric field, E, was found from the voltage across the plates. A second measurement had to be made to find the weight of the drop, mg, which was too tiny to measure by ordinary methods. To make this measurement, a drop was first suspended. Then the electric

b

FIGURE 22-7. This apparatus, (a) and (b), can be used to determine the charge on an oil drop.

a

field was turned off and the rate of the fall of the drop measured. Because of friction with the air molecules, the oil drop quickly reached terminal velocity. This velocity is related to the drop mass by a complex equation. Using the measured terminal velocity to calculate mg and knowing E, the charge q can be calculated. When Millikan used X rays to add or remove electrons from the drops, he found the drops had a large variety of charges. However, he found that the *changes* in the charge were always a multiple of 1.6×10^{-19} C. The changes were caused by electrons being added to or removed from the drops. As a result, the smallest change in charge that could occur was the amount of charge of one electron. Therefore, Millikan said that each electron always carried the same charge, -1.6×10^{-19} C. As a result of Millikan's experiment, we say that charges are quantized. This means that an object can have only a charge with a magnitude that is some integral multiple of the charge of the electron.

The mass of the oil drop was found from measurements of the terminal velocity.

The charge on the electron is -1.6×10^{-19} C.

In recent years, physicists have used updated Millikan balances to look for the proposed fundamental particles called quarks. The charge on a quark is either $+\frac{1}{3}$ or $-\frac{2}{3}$ the charge on an electron. William Fairbank (1917-) of Stanford University has reported finding such a charge on tiny metal spheres. However, no other experimenters have been able to duplicate his work. The discovery of a single quark with a fraction of the electron's charge has not been confirmed.

EXAMPLE

Finding the Charge of an Oil Drop

An oil drop weighs 1.9×10^{-14} N. It is suspended in an electric field of intensity 4.0×10^4 N/C.   **a.**   What is the charge on the oil drop?   **b.**   If the drop is attracted toward the positive plate, how many excess electrons does it have?

Given: $W = mg = 1.9 \times 10^{-14}$ N   **Unknown:** excess charge (q)

$E = 4.0 \times 10^4$ N/C   **Basic equation:** $Eq = mg$

Solution: a. $Eq = mg$

$$\text{Thus } q = mg/E = \frac{1.9 \times 10^{-14} \text{ N}}{4.0 \times 10^4 \text{ N/C}}$$

$$= 4.8 \times 10^{-19} \text{ C}$$

b.   number of electrons $= \dfrac{\text{total charge on drop}}{\text{charge per electron}}$

$$= \frac{4.8 \times 10^{-19} \text{ C}}{1.6 \times 10^{-19} \text{ C/e}^-}$$

$$= 3 \text{ e}^-$$

There are three extra electrons because a negatively-charged drop is attracted toward a positively-charged plate.

Problems

11. An oil drop weighs 1.9×10^{-15} N. It is suspended in an electric field intensity of 6.0×10^3 N/C.

    a. What is the charge on the drop?

    b. How many excess electrons does it carry?

12. A positively-charged oil drop weighs 6.4×10^{-13} N. An electric field intensity of 4.0×10^6 N/C suspends the drop.

    a. What is the charge on the drop?

    b. How many electrons is the drop missing?

13. If three electrons were removed from the drop in Problem 12, what field would be needed to balance the drop?

14. During a Millikan experiment, a student recorded the weight of four different oil drops. A record was also made of the field intensity needed to suspend each drop.

W (N)	E (N/C)
1.7×10^{-14}	1.1×10^5
5.6×10^{-14}	3.5×10^5
9.3×10^{-14}	5.8×10^5
2.9×10^{-14}	1.8×10^5

    a. Plot the readings on a graph of W vs E. Plot W vertically.

    b. Find the slope of the line. What does the slope represent?

22:6   Sharing of Charge

Charges are shared in a way that gives a system the minimum amount of energy.

All systems, both mechanical and electrical, come to equilibrium when the energy of the system is at a minimum. For example, if a ball is put on a hilly surface, it will finally come to rest in a valley where its potential energy is least. This principle explains what happens when an insulated, negatively-charged metal sphere (Figure 22-8) touches a second, uncharged sphere.

The excess electrons on the charged sphere, A, repel each other. The potential on sphere A is high. The potential of the neutral sphere B is zero. When one electron is transferred from sphere A to sphere B, the

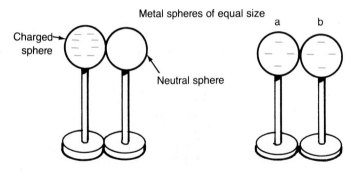

FIGURE 22-8. A charged sphere shares charges equally with a neutral sphere of equal size.

Metal spheres of unequal size

FIGURE 22-9. A charged sphere gives much of its charge to a larger sphere.

potential of sphere *A* is reduced. The potential of sphere *A* is reduced because it has fewer excess electrons. The potential of sphere *B* does not change because no work is done adding the first excess electron to this neutral sphere. As more electrons are transferred, however, work must be done to overcome the growing repulsive force between the electrons on sphere *B*. Therefore, the potential of sphere *B* increases. Electrons continue to flow from sphere *A* to sphere *B* until the work done adding an electron to sphere *B* is equal to the work gained in removing the electron from sphere *A*. The potential of sphere *A* now equals the potential of sphere *B*.

Consider a large sphere and a small sphere. The two spheres have the same charge. The larger sphere has a larger surface area, so electrons can spread farther apart than they can on the smaller sphere. With the electrons farther apart, the repulsive force between them is reduced. Therefore, the potential on the larger sphere is lower than the potential on the smaller sphere.

If the two spheres are now touched together, electrons will move to the sphere with the lower potential. Electrons will move from the smaller to the larger sphere. For this reason, a larger sphere has a greater

If a large and a small sphere have the same charge, the large sphere will have a lower potential.

If a large and small sphere have the same potential, the large sphere will have a greater charge.

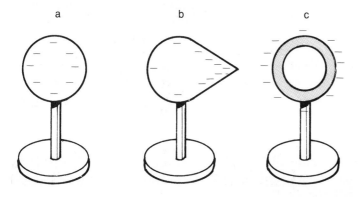

FIGURE 22-10. Electric field around a conducting body depends on the structure and shape of the body.

FIGURE 22-11. Ground wire on a fuel truck.

FIGURE 22-11. Ground wire on a fuel truck.

charge than a smaller sphere when the two spheres are at equal potentials.

The earth is a very large sphere. If a charged body is touched to the earth, almost any amount of charge can flow to the earth without increasing the earth's potential. When all the excess charge on the body flows to the earth, the body becomes neutral. Touching an object to the earth in order to eliminate excess charge is called **grounding.** If a computer or other sensitive instrument were not grounded, static charges could accumulate, raising the potential of the computer. A person touching the computer could suddenly lower the potential of the computer. The charges flowing through the computer to the person could damage it.

An object is grounded if it is touching or connected to the earth.

Grounding removes excess charges from an object.

22:7 Electric Fields Near Conductors

The charges on a conductor are spread as far apart as they can be to make the potential as low as possible. The result is that all charges are on the surface of a solid body. If the conductor is hollow, excess charges will move to the outer surface because it is larger than the inner surface. If a closed tin can is charged, there will be no charges on the inside surfaces of the can.

All charges are on the outside of a closed conductor.

The electric field around a conducting body depends on the shape of the body as well as the charge on it. The field is strongest near sharp points on the body. The field there can become so strong that nearby air molecules are separated into electrons and positive ions. The electrons and ions are accelerated by the field. They hit other molecules, producing more ions and electrons. The stream of ions and electrons that results is a conductor. As the electrons and ions recombine, energy is released and light is produced. The result is a spark. Conductors that are highly charged or put at high potentials are carefully rounded to reduce the electric fields and prevent sparking. On the other hand, lightning rods are pointed so that the electric field will be strong near the rod and cause a conducting path from the rod to the clouds. This shape allows the static charges in the clouds to spark to the rod rather than to a chimney or other high point on a house. From the rod, a conductor takes the charges safely to ground.

Electric fields are largest in the region around sharp edges.

22:8   Storing Charges: The Capacitor

Work is needed to add more than one excess charge to a body. The work varies directly with the electric potential of the charged body. The potential depends on the magnitude of the total charge as well as the distances between the individual charges. The distance depends on the shape of the body as well as the location of nearby charged objects. For any body in a given location, the ratio of charge to potential, q/V, is a constant. The constant is called the capacitance, C, of the body. A device designed to have capacitance is called a capacitor. Capacitors are used in electrical circuits to store charge. Benjamin Franklin stored the charge from lightning in a Leyden Jar, one form of a capacitor.

A capacitor is a device that stores charge.

Capacitance is the ratio of charge stored to increase in potential.

FIGURE 22-12. A lightning rod allows charges from the clouds to be grounded, rather than conducted into a house.

FIGURE 22-13. Various types of capacitors.

The capacitance of a body is independent of the charge on it. Capacitance can be measured by placing a specific charge on a body and measuring the potential that results. The capacitance is then found by using the equation

$$C = \frac{q}{V}$$

Capacitance is measured in farads, F, named after Michael Faraday. One farad is one coulomb per volt. Just as one coulomb is a large amount of charge, one farad is an enormous capacitance. Commercial capacitors are usually between 10 picofarads and 500 microfarads.

$$1pF \text{ (picofarad)} = 10^{-12}F$$

Capacitors often are made of parallel plates. Commercial capacitors contain strips of aluminum foil separated by thin plastic and are tightly rolled up to save room.

EXAMPLE

Finding the Capacitance from Charge and Potential

A sphere has a potential of 60.0 V when charged with 3.0×10^{-6} C. What is its capacitance?

Given: $V = 60.0$ V 　　　　**Unknown:** capacitance (C)

　　　　　$q = 3.0 \times 10^{-6}$ C 　**Basic equation:** $C = \frac{q}{V}$

Solution:　$C = \frac{q}{V}$

　　　　$= \frac{3.0 \times 10^{-6} \text{ C}}{60.0 \text{ V}}$

　　　　$= 5.0 \times 10^{-8}$ C/V

　　　　$= 5.0 \times 10^{-8} \cancel{F} \times 1 \ \mu F/10^{-6} \cancel{F}$

　　　　$= 5.0 \times 10^{-2} \ \mu F$

EXAMPLE

Finding the Charge on a Capacitor

A commercial $5.0 \times 10^1 \ \mu F$ capacitor has a potential difference of 25 V across it. What is the charge on this capacitor?

Given: $C = 5.0 \times 10^1 \ \mu F$ 　**Unknown:** q

　　　　$V = 25$ V 　　　　**Basic equation:** $C = \frac{q}{V}$

Solution: $C = \frac{q}{V}$

　　　　　$q = CV$

　　　　　$= (5.0 \times 10^1 \ \cancel{\mu F} \times 10^{-6} \ F/\cancel{\mu F})(25 \text{ V})$

　　　　　$= (5.0 \times 10^{-5} \ F)(25 \text{ V})$

　　　　$q = 1.3 \times 10^{-3}$ C

Summary

1. An electric field exists around any charged object. The field produces forces on other charged bodies.   22:1

2. The electric field intensity is the force per unit charge. The direction of the electric field is the direction of the force on a tiny positive test charge.   22:2

3. Electric field lines, also called lines of force, provide a picture of the electric field. They are directed away from positive charges and toward negative charges.   22:2

4. Electric potential is the work done moving a unit charge in an electric field. Potential differences are measured in volts.   22:3

5. The electric field intensity between two parallel plates is uniform between the plates except near the edges.   22:4

6. The elementary unit of charge, the charge on the proton or electron, is 1.6×10^{-19} C. This was first measured by Robert A. Millikan.   22:5

7. Electrons flow in conductors until the electric potential is the same everywhere on the conductor.   22:6

8. A charged object can have its charge removed by touching it to the earth or to an object touching the earth. This is called grounding.   22:6

9. Electric fields are strongest near sharply-pointed conductors.   22:7

10. A capacitor can store charge. The capacitance of a body is independent of the charge on the body.   22:8

11. The potential difference across a capacitor is proportional to the charge stored.   22:8

Detailed answers to all Questions and Problems are given in the Teacher's Guide at the front of this book.

Questions

1. Draw the electric field lines between
   a. two like charges.
   b. two unlike charges.
   c. two parallel plates of opposite charge.

2. How is the direction of the electric field defined?

3. Define a volt in terms of work done against an electric field.

4. If 120 joules of work is done to move 1 coulomb of charge from a positive plate to a negative plate, what voltage difference exists between the plates?

5. Why does a charged object lose its charge when it is touched to the ground?

6. A charged rubber rod placed on a table maintains its charge for some time. Why does the charge not "ground" immediately?

7. Describe in your own words what a capacitor is.

8. Which has a larger capacitance, a 1-cm diameter sphere or a 10-cm diameter sphere made of the same material?

Problems–A

1. a. 4.0 N/C
   b. toward

1. A charge of 2.0×10^{-4} C is placed in the electric field produced by a negative charge. The force acting on the positive charge is 8.0×10^{-4} N.
   a. What is the electric field intensity at the test charge?
   b. Is the field direction toward or away from the negative charge?

2. 7.0×10^{-5} C

2. What charge exists on a test charge that experiences a force of 1.4×10^{-8} N at a point where the electric field intensity is 2.0×10^{-4} N/C?

3. 120 V

3. The electric field intensity between two charged plates is 1.5×10^3 N/C. The plates are 0.080 m apart. What is the potential difference between the plates in volts?

4. 2.5×10^3 N/C

4. A voltmeter indicates that the difference in potential between two plates is 50.0 V. The plates are 0.020 m apart. What field intensity exists between them?

5. 1.4 J

5. How much work is done to transfer 0.15 C of charge through a potential difference of 9.0 V?

6. 1.0×10^2 C

6. A 12-V battery does 1200 J of work transferring charge. How much charge was transferred?

7. a. 1.6×10^{-18} C
   b. 10 electrons

7. A negatively-charged oil drop weighs 8.5×10^{-15} N. The drop is suspended in an electric field intensity of 5.3×10^3 N/C.
   a. What is the charge of the drop?
   b. How many electrons does it carry?

8. 1.0×10^{-4} C

8. A 6.8-μF capacitor has a 15-V potential difference across it. What charge does it hold?

Problems–B

1. 0.450 J

1. The work required to charge a capacitor until it has a potential difference V is given by $W = \frac{1}{2}CV^2$. This work is then available as stored electric energy. One application is in the electronic photoflash or strobe light. In this unit, a capacitor of 10.0 μF is charged to 3.00×10^2 V. Find the energy stored.

2. **a.** Suppose it took 30 s to charge the capacitor in the problem above. Find the power that is required to charge it in this time.

   b. When this capacitor is discharged through the strobe lamp, it transfers all its energy in 1.0×10^{-4} s. Find the power delivered to the lamp.

2. a. 2×10^{-2} W
   b. 4.5 kW

Readings

Conway, John, "Personal Robots." *Computers and Electronics*, December, 1984.

Forsyth, E. B., "The Brookhaven Superconducting Power Transmission System." *The Physics Teacher*, May, 1983.

Hilbert, Richard, "Automobile Idiot Lights." *Computers and Electronics*, March, 1983.

Parrott, Mary, "Electrography: A Metal Detective Story." *Science Teacher*, May, 1983.

Patterson, David A. "Microprogramming." *Scientific American*, March, 1984.

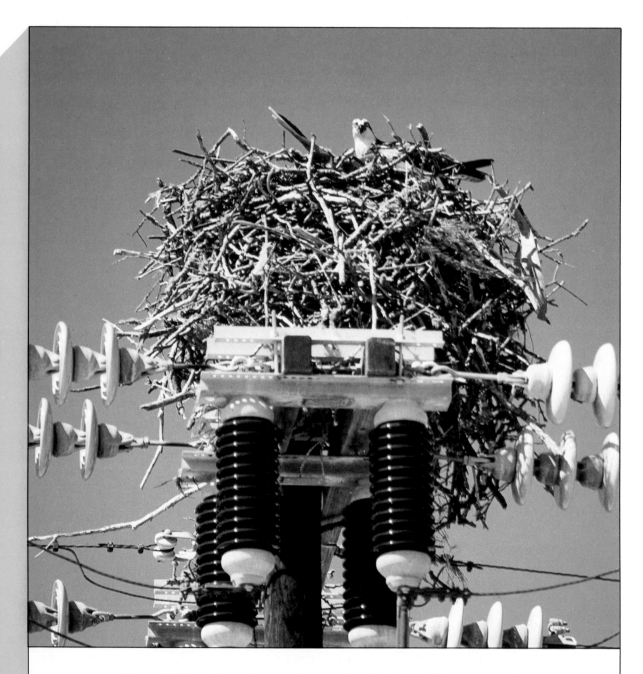

The availability of large, inexpensive supplies of electricity is important to the development of a nation. Without electricity, industry would grind to a halt, communications would cease, and our food supply would be seriously affected. The utilization of electric current allows us to enjoy our present standard of living. How is electric current controlled? What is involved in the design of high voltage transmission lines that allow current to flow with a minimum of energy loss?

Electric Currents

Chapter 23 introduces the concept of electric current as a means of transferring energy. Circuits, Ohm's law, and the units for electric current and resistance are presented and lead to a discussion of the heating effect of electric current.

The most important aspect of electricity is its ability to transfer energy. The large amounts of natural potential and kinetic energy possessed by resources such as Niagara Falls are of little use to an industrial complex one hundred kilometers away unless that energy can be transferred efficiently. Electricity provides the means to transfer large quantities of energy great distances with little loss.

At the industrial site, electric energy can be converted into other forms of energy, such as kinetic, sound, light, and thermal energy. Devices that make these conversions are very important in our everyday lives. Motors, loudspeakers, lamps, television sets, heaters, and air conditioners are examples of common devices that convert electric energy into another form of energy.

23:1 Producing Electric Current

Two conductors, A and B, in Figure 23-1, are at different potentials and connected by a third conductor, C. A flow of electrons occurs from the higher potential, B, to the lower potential, A. This electron flow is an **electric current**. The flow will stop as soon as the potentials become equal. The only way to maintain the electric current is to pump electrons from conductor A back to conductor B. The pumping will increase the potential energy of the electrons. Therefore, the electron pump requires energy. There are several devices available that can convert some other form of energy into electric energy. A voltaic or galvanic cell (a common dry cell) converts chemical energy to electric energy. Several cells connected together are called a **battery**. A **photovoltaic cell**, or solar cell, changes light energy into electric energy. A generator converts kinetic energy into electric energy.

Goal: You will gain an understanding of electric current, circuits, and the transfer of energy by means of current electricity.

Current soon ceases

Electron pump

Current maintained

FIGURE 23-1. Electrons flow from the negative to positive plate (a). A generator (b) pumps electrons back to the negative plate allowing current to continue to flow.

385

FIGURE 23-2. Sources of electric energy include chemical, solar, hydrodynamic, wind, and nuclear energies.

Electrons flow around a closed loop called a circuit.

Current is produced by an electron pump that increases the potential of electrons. Batteries, generators, and photovoltaic cells are electron pumps.

23:2   Current in Electric Circuits

An electric circuit is a closed loop. A circuit consists of an electron pump, which increases the potential of the electrons, connected to a device that reduces the potential of the electrons. As the potential of the electron is reduced, the work done by the electric charge (qV) can be converted into another form of energy. A motor can convert electric energy to kinetic energy. A lamp can change electric energy into light. A heater can convert electric energy into thermal energy.

Electrons are able to flow through all of these energy conversion devices. As they flow, the electrons lose electric potential. Any device that reduces the potential of electrons flowing through it is said to have resistance.

The electron pump creates the flow of electrons or current. Consider a generator driven by a water wheel (Figure 23-3). The potential energy of the water is converted to kinetic energy as the water falls. This energy is converted to kinetic energy within the generator. This energy is used by the generator to remove electrons from wire B and add them to wire A, increasing the electric potential difference between B and A. Work is done raising the potential of the electrons ($W = qV$). This work came from the change in potential energy of the water. However, no generator is 100 percent efficient. Two percent of the kinetic energy put into most generators is converted into thermal energy rather than electric energy.

If the wires A and B are connected to a motor, the excess electrons in wire A flow through the wires in the motor. The electron flow continues through wire B back to the generator. A motor converts electric energy to kinetic energy. Like generators, motors are not 100 percent efficient. Perhaps 10 percent of the electric energy is changed into thermal energy instead of kinetic energy.

> The drop in potential energy of electrons in a motor creates kinetic energy.

The net change in potential of the electrons going completely around the circuit is zero. The potential increase produced by the generator equals the potential loss in the motor. The total amount of charge (number of electrons) in the circuit does not change. If one coulomb flows through the generator in one second, one coulomb will also flow through the motor in one second.

> The net change in potential around a circuit is zero. Current is the same everywhere in a circuit.

If the difference in potential between the two wires is 120 V, the generator must do 120 J of work on each coulomb of charge that it transfers from the positive wire to the negative wire. Thus, every coulomb of charge that moves from the negative wire through the motor and then back to the positive wire delivers 120 J of energy to the motor. Note that electric energy serves as a way to transfer the initial potential energy of falling water to the kinetic energy of a turning motor.

23:3 The Ampere and Electric Power

The unit used for quantity of electric charge is the **coulomb**. Thus, the rate of flow of electric charge, or electric current (I), is measured in coulombs per second. A flow of one coulomb per second is called an **ampere**, A.

> One ampere of current is the flow of one coulomb of charge each second.

$$1 \text{ C/s} = 1 \text{ A}$$

The ampere is named for the French scientist Andre Marie Ampere (1775-1836). An ammeter is a device that measures current.

> Electric current is measured in amperes.

Energy in

Potential difference = 90 V
Each coulomb of charge transfers 90 J of energy to the motor.

A

Energy out

Falling water turns a water wheel

Generator

Electron flow

Motor

B

FIGURE 23-3. This diagram shows the production and use of electric current. Electric potential energy is converted to kinetic energy of the turning motor.

Suppose that the current through the motor of Figure 23-3 is 3.0 C/s (3.0 A). The potential difference of 120 V means that each coulomb of charge supplies the motor with 120 J of energy. The energy delivered to the motor per second is

$$(120 \text{ J/C})(3.0 \text{ C/s}) = 360 \text{ J/s} = 360 \text{ watts.}$$

Power consumed (P) is equal to potential difference (V) times current (I). $P = VI$

The power rating of an electric device is found by multiplying the voltage V by the current I.

$$\boxed{P = VI}$$

EXAMPLE

Electric Power

A 6-V battery delivers 0.5 A of current to an electric motor connected across its terminals. **a.** What is the power rating of the motor? **b.** How much energy does the motor use in 5.0 min?

Given: $V = 6$ V

Current $(I) = 0.5$ A

$t = 5.0$ min (300 s)

Unknowns: a. P **b.** W

Basic equation: a. $P = VI$

b. $P = \dfrac{W}{t}$

Solution: a. $P = VI$

$= (6 \text{ V})(0.5 \text{ A}) = (6 \text{ J/\!\!\!C})(0.5 \text{ \!\!\!C/s}) = 3 \text{ J/s} = 3 \text{ W}$

b. $P = \dfrac{W}{t}$

$W = Pt$

Energy is power times the time.

$= (3 \text{ W})(300 \text{ s})$

$= 900 \text{ J}$

Problems

1. 60 W

1. The current through a light bulb connected across the terminals of a 120-V outlet is 0.5 A. At what rate does the bulb use electric energy?

2. 24 W

2. A 12-V automobile battery causes a current of 2.0 A to flow through a lamp. What is the power rating of the lamp?

3. 960 W

3. The current through a toaster connected to a 120-V source is 8.0 A. What is the power rating of the toaster?

4. 140 W

4. A light bulb uses 1.2 A when connected across a 120-V source. What is the wattage of the bulb?

5. 0.63A

5. What current flows through a 75-W light bulb connected to a 120-V outlet?

6. 2.5 × 10⁴ J

6. The current through the starter motor of a car connected to a 12-V battery is 210 A. What electric energy is delivered to the starter in 10.0 s?

7. A flashlight bulb is connected across a 3.0-V difference in potential. The current through the lamp is 1.5 A.

  a. What is the power rating of the lamp?
  b. How much electric energy does the lamp convert in 11 min?

8. A lamp draws 0.50 A from a 120-V generator.

  a. How much power does the generator deliver?
  b. How much energy does the lamp convert in 5 minutes?

7. a. 4.5 W
   b. 3.0×10^3 J

8. a. 6.0×10^1 W
   b. 2×10^4 J

23:4   Ohm's Law

Almost every conductor offers **resistance** to an electric current. This resistance causes a potential difference to exist between the ends of a conductor when current passes through it. The German scientist Georg Simon Ohm (1787-1854) found that the ratio of the potential difference between the ends of the conductor and the current through it is constant for many materials.

This ratio is known as the resistance of a conductor. It is constant for any given conductor kept at a constant temperature. This relationship, known as Ohm's law, states that the current through a given conductor varies directly with the applied potential difference and inversely with the resistance.

$$I = \frac{V}{R}$$

The electric current, I, is in amperes. The potential difference, V, is in volts. The resistance of the conductor, R, is given in ohms. One ohm, 1 Ω, is the resistance that permits a current of 1 A to flow through a potential difference of 1 V.

Wires used to connect electric devices have very small resistances. One meter of a typical wire used in physics labs has a resistance of about 0.03 Ω. Wires used in house wiring offer as little as 0.004 Ω resistance for each meter of length. However, a device that is designed to have a specific resistance is called a resistor. Resistors are made of long, thin wires, graphite, or semiconductors.

Ohm's law states that a larger potential difference, or voltage, placed across a resistor causes a larger current through it. Ohm's law also says that if the current through a resistor is doubled, the drop in potential is also doubled. It follows that the voltage applied across the resistor would have to be doubled to obtain the increased current.

$$10\ \Omega$$

Electron flow

3 A

$$I = \frac{V}{R}$$
$$= \frac{30\ V}{10\ \Omega}$$
$$= 3\ A$$

30 V

FIGURE 23-4. Ohm's law is illustrated in calculating the current between a potential difference of 30 volts and a resistance of 10 ohms.

In a conductor, the current flow is $I = V/R$, where V is the potential difference and R the resistance. This is called Ohm's law.

For a device that obeys Ohm's law, the resistance R is independent of the current.

According to Ohm's law, for a given resistance, the potential difference is proportional to the current flow.

EXAMPLE

Ohm's Law

What is the current through a 30-Ω resistance that has a potential difference of 120 V?

Given: $V = 120$ V   **Unknown:** I

Resistance $(R) = 30$ Ω **Basic equation:** $I = \dfrac{V}{R}$

Solution: $I = \dfrac{V}{R}$

$= \dfrac{120 \text{ V}}{30 \text{ } \Omega}$

$= 4$ A

Problems

9. 0.4 A

9. An automobile headlight with a resistance of 30 Ω is placed across a 12-V battery. What is the current through the circuit?

10. 5.0 A

10. A voltage of 75 V is placed across a 15-Ω resistor. What is the current through the resistor?

11. a. 200 Ω
    b. 60 W

11. A lamp draws a current of 0.5 A when it is connected to a 120-V source.
   a. What is the resistance of the lamp?
   b. What is the power rating of the lamp?

12. 120 V

12. A motor with an operating resistance of 32 Ω is connected to a voltage source. The current in the circuit is 3.8 A. What is the voltage of the source?

13. 2 × 10⁴ Ω

13. A transistor radio uses 2×10^{-4} A of current when it is operated by a 3-V battery. What is the resistance of the radio circuit?

14. 20 V

14. A resistance of 60 Ω has a current of 0.4 A throughout it when it is connected to the terminals of a battery. What is the voltage of the battery?

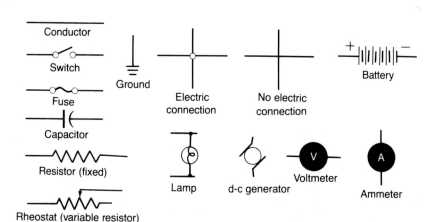

FIGURE 23-5. Electric circuit symbols.

Conductor

Switch

Fuse

Capacitor

Resistor (fixed)

Rheostat (variable resistor)

Ground

Electric connection

No electric connection

Lamp

d-c generator

Voltmeter

Battery

Ammeter

FIGURE 23-6. A simple electric circuit is represented both pictorially (a) and schematically (b).

23:5 Diagramming Electric Circuits

A diagram of an electric circuit often is drawn using symbols for the circuit elements. Such a diagram is called a circuit **schematic.** Some of the symbols are shown in Figure 23-5. Both an artist's drawing and a schematic of the same circuit are shown in Figure 23-6.

An ammeter, which measures current, must be connected so that all of the electrons can flow through the ammeter. Such a connection is called a **series connection.** A voltmeter measures the potential difference across a circuit element. One voltmeter terminal is connected to one side of the element. The other terminal is connected to the other side. This connection is called a **parallel connection.** The potential difference across the element is equal to the potential difference across the voltmeter.

A schematic diagram uses symbols for components rather than pictures.

Problems

15. Draw a schematic to show a circuit that includes a 90-V battery, an ammeter, and a resistance of 45 Ω. What is the ammeter's reading?

16. Draw a circuit diagram to include a 60-V battery, an ammeter, and a resistance of 12.5 Ω. Indicate the ammeter reading.

17. Draw a circuit diagram to include a 16-Ω resistor, a battery, and an ammeter that reads 1.75 A. Indicate the voltage of the battery.

15. 2 A

16. 5 A

17. 28 V

23:6 Controlling Current in a Circuit

There are two ways to control the current in a circuit. Since $I = V/R$, I can be changed by varying either V, R, or both. Figure 23-7a shows a simple circuit. When V is 60 V and R is 30 Ω, the current flow is 2.0 A.

If the current is to be reduced to 1.0 A, the 60-V battery could be replaced with a 30-V battery, Figure 23-7b. The current can also be reduced by increasing the resistance to 60 Ω by adding a 30-Ω resistor to the circuit, 23-7c. Both of these methods will reduce the current to

Current in a circuit can be controlled by changing either the voltage applied or the resistance.

2 A

60 V   30 Ω

a

1 A

30 V   30 Ω

b

1 A

30 Ω

60 V

30 Ω

c

FIGURE 23-7. The current flow through a simple circuit (a) can be regulated by removing some of the dry cells (b) or increasing the resistance of the circuit (c).

A variable resistor is called a rheostat or potentiometer.

1.0 A. Resistors used to control the current in electric circuits are control resistors. Control resistors are used to allow the proper amount of current through circuits or parts of circuits. Radios use such resistors.

Sometimes a smooth, continuous control of the current is desired. A lamp dimmer allows a continuous rather than step-by-step control of light intensity. To achieve this kind of control, a variable resistor, called a rheostat or **potentiometer**, is used (Figure 23-8). A variable resistor consists of a coil of wire and a sliding contact point. By moving the contact point to various positions along the coil, the amount of wire added to the circuit is varied. With more wire placed in the circuit, the resistance of the circuit increases, and thus the current decreases in accordance with Ohm's law. In this way the light output of a lamp can be adjusted. The same type of device controls the speed of electric fans, electric mixers, and other appliances. To save space, the coil of wire is often bent into a circular shape and the slider is replaced by a knob, as shown in Figure 23-9.

Ohm's law is only valid when the resistance of a device is constant. However, in many materials the resistance increases when the

FIGURE 23-8. A variable resistor can be used to regulate current in an electric circuit.

a

Motor

Switch

Variable resistor

+   −

Dry cell

b

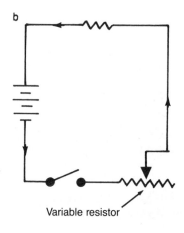

Variable resistor

temperature rises. Light bulb filaments have a much lower resistance when they are cold than when they reach the temperature at which they emit light. As a result of the low resistance when cold, the current through a filament is much higher immediately after the bulb is turned on than the current is only a fraction of a second later. The large current flow causes a rapid increase in temperature. As a result, the filament wire is strained and can break. For this reason, light bulbs often fail as they are switched on, not when they are operating.

Problem

18. The current through a lamp connected across 120 V is 0.5 A when the lamp is on.

    a. What is its resistance when on?

    b. When the lamp is cold, its resistance is one-fifth as large as when the lamp is hot. What is its cold resistance?

    c. What is the current through the lamp as it is turned on, if it is connected to a potential difference of 120 V?

FIGURE 23-9. An inside view of a rheostat.

18. a. 200 Ω
    b. 40 Ω
    c. 3 A

23:7 Heating Effect of Electric Currents

The power (energy per unit time) used by an electric circuit is equal to the voltage multiplied by the current. From Ohm's law, we know that $V = IR$. Substituting this expression into the equation for electric power, we obtain

$$P = VI$$
$$= IR \times I$$
$$\boxed{P = I^2R}$$

The power varies directly with the resistance.

The power used by a resistor is proportional to the square of the current that passes through it and to the resistance.

The energy supplied to a circuit can be used in different ways. A motor converts electric energy into mechanical energy. An electric

The power used by a resistor varies directly with the square of current flowing through the resistor.

FIGURE 23-10. The coils of this space heater are an example of the conversion of electric energy to thermal energy.

lamp changes electric energy into light. However, not all of the electric energy delivered to a motor or an electric light ends up in a useful form of energy. Some energy is always converted into thermal energy. Certain devices, such as curling irons, are designed to convert most of the electric energy to thermal energy. Some electric energy, as in Figure 23-10, is also converted into light.

The electric energy transferred to a resistor in a time interval, t, is equal to I^2Rt. If all the electric energy is converted into thermal energy of the resistor, the increase in thermal energy is

$$Q = I^2Rt$$

The resulting high temperature of the resistor can result in heat flowing to a cold substance. For example, in an immersion heater, a resistor placed in a cup of water can bring the water to the boiling point in a few minutes.

EXAMPLE

Thermal Energy Produced by an Electric Current

A heater has a resistance of 10.0 Ω. It operates on 120.0 V.   **a.**   What is the current through the resistance?   **b.**   What thermal energy in joules is supplied by the heater in 10.0 s?

Given: $R = 10.0 \ \Omega$ **Unknowns:**   **a.** I **b.** Q

$V = 120.0 \text{ V}$ **Basic equations:**   **a.** $I = \dfrac{V}{R}$

$t = 10.0 \text{ s}$

b. $Q = I^2Rt$

Solution: **a.** $I = \dfrac{V}{R} = \dfrac{120.0 \text{ V}}{10.0 \ \Omega} = 12.0 \text{ A}$

b. $Q = I^2Rt$

$= (12.0 \text{ A})^2(10.0 \ \Omega)(10.0 \text{ s}) = 14 \ 400 \text{ J } (14.4 \text{ kJ})$

Problems

19. a. 8.0 A
b. 29 000 J
c. 29 000 J

19. A 15-Ω electric heater operates on a 120-V outlet.
   a.   What is the current through the heater?
   b.   How much energy is used by the heater in 30.0 seconds?
   c.   How much heat is liberated by the heater in this time?

20. a. 2 A
b. 4 × 10⁴ J

20. A 30-Ω resistor is connected to a 60-V battery.
   a.   What is the current in the circuit?
   b.   How much energy is used by the resistor in 5 minutes?

21. a. 1.2 × 10³ J
b. 4.8 × 10³ J

21. A 100.0-W light bulb is 20.0% efficient. That means 20.0% of the electric energy is converted to light energy.
   a.   How many joules does the light bulb convert into light each minute it is in operation?
   b.   How many joules of heat does the light bulb produce each minute?

22. The resistance of an electric stove element at operating temperature is 11 Ω.

   a. 220 V are applied across it. What is the current through the element?

   b. How much energy does the element use in 30.0 s?

   c. The element is being used to heat a kettle containing 1.20 kg of water. Assume that 70% of the heat is absorbed by the water. What is its increase in temperature during the 30.0 s?

22. a. 2.0×10^1 A
 b. 1.3×10^5 J
 c. 18°C

23. An electric heater is rated at 500 W.

   a. How much energy is delivered to the heater in half an hour?

   b. The heater is being used to heat a room containing 50.0 kg of air. If the specific heat of air is 1.10 kJ/kg·C° (1100 J/kg·C°) and 50% of the thermal energy heats the air in the room, what is the change in air temperature?

23. a. 9×10^5 J
 b. 8°C

24. How much energy does a 60.0-W light bulb use in half an hour? If the light bulb is 12% efficient, how much heat does it generate during the half hour?

24. 9.5×10^4 J

23:8 Transmission of Electric Energy

The large sources of available energy found at places such as Niagara Falls and Hoover Dam are not usually near areas where electricity is in greatest demand. Accordingly, electric energy often must be transmitted over long distances. Therefore, it is important to accomplish this transfer with as little energy loss as possible.

All wires have some resistance, even though it is small. For example, one kilometer of the large wire used to carry electric current into a home has a resistance of 0.2 Ω. Suppose a farmhouse were connected directly to a power plant 3.5 km away (Figure 23-11). The resistance in

FIGURE 23-11. All wires possess resistance to carrying an electric current.

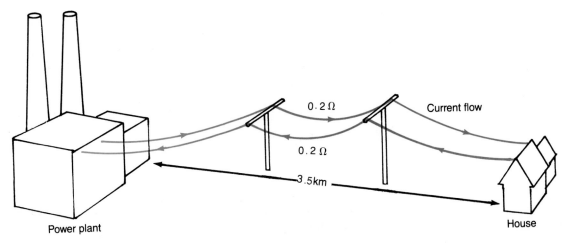

0.2 Ω

Current flow

0.2 Ω

3.5km

Power plant

House

FIGURE 23-12. High voltage transmission lines carry electricity over long distances.

the wires needed to carry current to the home and back to the plant is 3.5 km × 2 × 0.2 Ω/km = 1.4 Ω. An operating electric stove might cause a 41-A current through the wires. The power lost in the wires is given by $P = I^2R = (41 \text{ A})^2 \times 1.4 \text{ Ω} = 2400 \text{ W}$. All this power is wasted. This loss is called "I^2R" loss by electrical engineers.

It is to the advantage of power companies and in the interest of consumers to keep the power loss (I^2R loss) in the transmission lines to a minimum. Reducing the I^2R loss is done in two ways. Obviously, the conductors used to transmit electric energy must have the lowest possible resistance. Cables of high conductivity and large diameter should be used. However, since the loss is also proportional to the square of the current in the conductors, it is of even greater importance to keep the current in the lines at a very low value.

The energy per second (power) transferred over a long-distance transmission line follows the relationship $P = VI$. By keeping the voltage across these lines very high, it is possible to transmit large amounts of energy per second and also keep the current in the lines at a low value. This low current reduces the I^2R loss in the lines by keeping the I^2 factor low. Long-distance transmission lines always operate at high voltages to reduce this loss.

High voltage lines are needed to transmit electric power over long distances with minimum energy loss.

23:9   The Kilowatt Hour

While electric companies often are called "power" companies, it is energy that they provide. When you pay your electric bill, you are paying for electric energy, not power.

The electric energy used by any device is its rate of energy consumption in joules per second (watts) times the number of seconds it is operated. Joules per second times second (J/s × s) equals total joules of energy.

The joule is a relatively small amount of energy. For that reason, electric companies measure their energy sales in a large amount of joules called a kilowatt hour, kWh. A **kilowatt hour** is the energy represented by 1000 watts delivered continuously for 3600 seconds, which is one hour. It is, therefore,

$$1 \text{ kWh} = (1000 \text{ J/s})(3600 \text{ s}) = 3.6 \times 10^6 \text{J}$$

A kilowatt hour is an energy unit. It is the rate of energy use (power) multiplied by a time, one hour.

Not many devices in the home other than stoves, heaters, and hair dryers require more than 1000 watts. Ten 100-watt light bulbs operating all at once would use one kilowatt hour of energy if left on for a full hour.

a   b

EXAMPLE

The Cost of Operating an Electric Device

A new color television set draws 2.0 A when operated on 120 V. **a.** How much power does the set use?   **b.** If the set is operated for an average of 7.0 hours per day, what energy in kWh does it consume per month (30 days)?   **c.** At $0.08 per kWh, what is the cost of operating the set per month?

FIGURE 23-13. Watthour meters (a) measure the amount of electric energy used by a consumer. The more current being used at a given time, the faster the horizontal disk in the center of the meter turns. Meter readings are then used in calculating the cost of energy use (b).

Given: $I = 2.0$ A   **Unknowns:** **a.** P **b.** W

$V = 120$ V   **Basic equation:** $P = VI$

$t = 2.1 \times 10^2$ h $(7.0$ h/d $\times 30$ d)

Solution:

a. $P = VI$

$= (120 \text{ V})(2.0 \text{ A})$

$= 2.4 \times 10^2 \text{ W}$

b. $W = Pt$

$= (2.4 \times 10^2 \text{ W})(2.1 \times 10^2 \text{ h})$

$= 5.0 \times 10^4 \text{ Wh} = 5.0 \times 10^1 \text{ kWh}$

c. Cost $= (5.0 \times 10^1 \text{ kWh})(\$0.08/\text{kWh}) = \$4.00$

Problems

25. a. 1800 W
    b. 270 kWh
    c. $ 21.60

25. An electric space heater draws 15.0 A from a 120-V source. It is operated, on the average, for 5.0 h each day.
   a. How much power does the heater use?
   b. How much energy in kWh does it consume in 30 days?
   c. At $0.08 per kWh, what does it cost to operate the heater in 30 days?

26. a. 9.6 mA
    b. 1.1 W
    c. $.07

26. A digital clock has an operating resistance of 12 000 Ω and is plugged into a 115-V outlet.
   a. How much current does it draw?
   b. How much power does it use?
   c. If the owner of the clock pays $0.09 per kWh, what does it cost to operate the clock for 30 days?

Physics Focus   Career–Physical Therapist

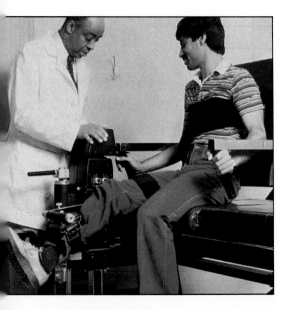

A physical therapist or physiotherapist uses a variety of techniques to treat and rehabilitate patients with dysfunction of soft tissues. Treatment includes application of cold, deep heating, surface heating, exercise with or without weights, and surface radiation with ultraviolet light. A physician prescribes treatment.

Therapists administer many forms of heat treatment. Deep heating by short-wave diathermy uses high-frequency AC current to heat tissue beneath the surface. Electromagnetic diathermy also uses AC current, but induces alternating magnetic fields concentrated deep in the body. Ultrasonic diathermy uses high-frequency sound vibrations to reach deep tissues. Surface heating is usually done by conduction from massage, hot pack, or whirlpool.

Direct application of electrical current through the skin to nerves relieves pain by stimulating production of pain-blocking chemicals. Ultraviolet radiation is used to heat the skin and in the treatment of psoriasis.

To rebuild strength, therapists direct patients in exercise programs with weights or special machines.

Physical therapists are trained usually in a five-year program at universities with health-related colleges.

Summary

1. Electron pumps such as batteries, generators, and solar cells convert   23:1
various forms of energy to electric energy.

2. In an electric circuit, electric energy is transmitted from an electron pump   23:2
to a resistor or other device that uses electric energy.

3. The energy delivered to the resistor is equal to the work done by the   23:2
electron pump.

4. As a charge moves through a circuit, it gives up its potential energy. The   23:3
energy released equals the work done to give the charge potential
energy.

5. One ampere is a current flow of one coulomb per second.   23:3

6. Electric power is found by multiplying voltage by current.   23:3

7. Ohm's law states that the current in a circuit varies directly with the   23:4
applied voltage and inversely with the resistance of the circuit.

8. The current in a circuit can be varied by varying the voltage or by varying   23:6
the resistance of the circuit.

9. The thermal energy produced in a circuit from electric energy varies   23:7
directly with the resistance, the time interval, and the square of the
current.

10. A kilowatt hour, kWh, is an energy unit. It is equal to 3.6×10^6 J.   23:9

Detailed answers to all Questions and Problems are given in the Teacher's Guide at the front of this book.

Questions

1. Describe a number of electric devices used in your everyday life. Indicate
the conversion of energy in each of the devices.

2. Electric space heaters are manufactured in a variety of different designs.
When purchasing such a heater, what information should you look for to
decide if it will adequately heat the area you have in mind?

3. A 12-V battery is connected to a 4-Ω resistor.
   a.   What current flows in the circuit?
   b.   State two ways to reduce the current to 1.5 A.

4. What quantities must be kept small to transmit electric energy over long
distances economically?

Problems—A

1. A 12-V automobile battery is connected to an electric starter motor. The   1. a. 2500 J/s
current through the motor is 210 A.
   a.   How many joules of energy does the battery deliver to the motor each
second?

b. What power does the motor use in watts?
c. How much energy does the motor use in 10 seconds?

2. A 20.0-Ω resistor is connected to a 30.0-V battery. What is the current in the resistor?

3. What voltage is applied to a 4-Ω resistor if the current is 1.5 A?

4. What voltage is placed across a motor of 15 Ω operating resistance to deliver 8.0 A of current?

5. A 6-Ω resistor is connected to a 15-V battery.
   a. What is the current in the circuit?
   b. How much heat is produced in 10 minutes?

6. A lamp consumes 30.0 W when connected to 120 V.
   a. What is the current in the lamp?
   b. What is the resistance of the lamp?

7. A heating coil has a resistance of 4.0 Ω and operates on 120 V.
   a. What is the current in the coil while it is operating?
   b. What energy is supplied to the coil in 5.0 min?
   c. If the coil is immersed in an insulated container holding 20.0 kg of water, what will be the increase in the temperature of the water? Assume that 100% of the heat is absorbed by the water.

Problems–B

1. An electric motor operates a pump that irrigates a farmer's crop by pumping 10 000 L of water a vertical distance of 8.0 m into a field each hour. The motor has an operating resistance of 22.0 Ω and is connected across a 110-V source.

Outlet

Intake

Rotor

FIGURE 23-13. Use with Problem B-1.

   a. What current does it draw?
   b. How efficient is the motor?

2. A transistor radio operates by means of a 9.0-V battery that supplies it with 50 milliamperes (0.050 A) of current.

   a. If the cost of the battery is $0.90 and it lasts for 300 h, what is the cost per kWh to operate the radio in this matter?

   b. The same radio, by means of a converter, is plugged into a household circuit by a homeowner who pays $0.08 per kWh. What does it now cost to operate the radio for 300 hours?

3. The damage caused by electric shock depends on the current flowing through the body. One mA (1×10^{-3} A) can be felt. Five mA is painful. Above 15 mA, a person loses muscle control; 70 mA can be fatal.

   A person with dry skin has a resistance from one arm to the other of about 10^5 Ω. When skin is wet, the resistance drops to about 5×10^3 Ω.

   a. What is the minimum voltage placed across the arms that would produce a current that could be felt by a person with dry skin?

   b. What effect would the same voltage have if the person had wet skin?

   c. What would be the minimum voltage that would produce a current that could be felt when the skin is wet?

2. a. $9
   b. 1 cent

3. a. 100 V
   b. 2×10^{-2} A
   c. 5 V

Readings

Brown, Stuart, "Can Brainy New Cars Outwit Car Thieves?" *Popular Science*, January, 1985.

Fish, Ray, "Electronic Measurements in Medicine." *Radio Electronics*, September, 1984.

Henry, Richard, "Superconducting Microelectronics." *The Physics Teacher*, February, 1984.

Milnes, Harold, "Faster Than Light." *Radio Electronics*, January, 1983.

Trietley, Harry, "All About Thermistors." *Radio Electronics*, January, 1985.

How resistors are connected into an electric circuit determines the total resistance in a circuit. How electronic devices, which are part of the total circuit, are
connected also determines the way the system will function. What components of
this computer circuit do you recognize? What are the advantages of connecting
the resistors in series? In parallel?

Series and Parallel Circuits

Chapter 24 introduces series circuits, parallel circuits, and series-parallel circuits. A discussion of house wiring, fuses, circuit breakers, and ammeter and voltmeter use is also included.

The electric circuits introduced in the last chapter had one source of electric energy and one device that used energy. Often many devices must be connected to one source. In this chapter, you will explore the ways in which devices can be connected in electric circuits.

An electric circuit in which all of the current travels through each device is called a series circuit. A parallel circuit allows the current to split and travel through several devices at once. A closer look will show how these circuits work and how they can be used.

24:1 Series Circuits

When resistors are connected in series, all current travels through each resistor, one after the other. Figure 24-1 shows a series circuit. The electric current in the circuit passes through each lamp (resistance) in succession. The current through each resistance is the same. The current flowing in a series circuit is the same everywhere along the wire. To determine the current in the circuit, the effective resistance of the circuit must be found. The **effective resistance** is the resistance of a single resistor that could replace all the resistors in the circuit. The single resistor would have the same current through it as the resistors it replaced. To find the effective resistance, Ohm's law is applied to the circuit as a whole and to its parts. The total voltage drop across the three resistors is equal to the potential difference across the generator, 120 V. The total voltage drop across the three resistors is also equal to the sum of the voltage drops across the individual resistors. That is,

$$V = V_1 + V_2 + V_3.$$

Goal: You will gain understanding of series and parallel circuits and their applications.

Suggested demonstrations: Use large demonstration ammeters and voltmeters and known resistances to set up the circuits discussed in this chapter.

In a series circuit, the current is the same at all points along the wire.

An effective resistance is the resistance cf a single resistor that could replace all the resistors in a circuit.

In a series circuit, the sum of the voltage drops equal the voltage drop across the entire circuit.

403

FIGURE 24-1. A series circuit can be represented both pictorially and schematically. The total resistance of a series circuit is equal to the sum of the individual resistances.

According to Ohm's law, the voltage drop across R_1 is given by $V_1 = IR_1$, where I is the current through the circuit. Therefore,

$$V = IR_1 + IR_2 + IR_3$$
$$V = I(R_1 + R_2 + R_3)$$

If the three resistors were replaced by a single resistor with resistance R, the voltage drop across R could be found using Ohm's law: $V = IR$. Comparing this equation with the one above shows that in a series circuit

$$\boxed{R = R_1 + R_2 + R_3.}$$

The effective resistance in a series circuit is the sum of the individual resistances.

The effective resistance, R, of resistors in series is the sum of the resistances. Note that the resistance of R is larger than that of any one of the resistors.

The current through a series circuit is found by calculating the effective resistance R, and then using Ohm's law in the form of $I = V/R$.

EXAMPLE

Current in a Series Circuit

Four 15-Ω resistors are connected in series to a 30-V battery. What is the current in the circuit?

$$R = R_1 + R_2 + R_3 + R_4$$
$$= 15\ \Omega + 15\ \Omega + 15\ \Omega + 15\ \Omega = 60\ \Omega$$

Then apply Ohm's law to the circuit.

$$I = \frac{V}{R} = \frac{30\ \text{V}}{60\ \Omega} = 0.5\ \text{A}$$

FIGURE 24-2. Use with the Example.

1. a. 60 Ω
   b. 2 A

Problems

1. Three 20-Ω resistors are connected in series across a 120-V generator.

a. What is the effective resistance of the circuit?
b. What is the current in the circuit?

2. A 10-Ω resistor, a 15-Ω resistor, and a 5-Ω resistor are connected in series across a 90-V battery.
   a. What is the effective resistance of the circuit?
   b. What is the current in the circuit?

   2. a. 30 Ω
      b. 3 A

3. Ten Christmas tree bulbs connected in series have equal resistances. When connected to a 120-V outlet, the current through the bulbs is 0.6 A.
   a. What is the effective resistance of the circuit?
   b. What is the resistance of each bulb?

   3. a. 200 Ω
      b. 20 Ω

4. A lamp having a resistance of 10 Ω is connected across a 15-V battery.
   a. What is the current through the lamp?
   b. What resistance must be connected in series with the lamp to reduce the current to 0.5 A?

   4. a. 2 A
      b. 20 Ω

24:2 Voltage Drops in a Series Circuit

The voltage drop across a device in a series circuit can be calculated by Ohm's law: $V = IR$. First find the effective resistance of the circuit. Next use the effective resistance to find the current, I. Then multiply I by the resistance of the device to find the voltage drop.

EXAMPLE

Voltage Drops in a Series Circuit

A 5.0-Ω resistor and a 10.0-Ω resistor are connected in series and placed across a 45.0-V potential difference.
   a. What is the effective resistance of the circuit?
   b. What is the current through the circuit?
   c. What is the voltage drop across each resistor?
   d. What is the total voltage drop across the circuit?

Given: $R_1 = 5.0$ Ω   **Unknowns:** R, I, V_1, V_2
            $R_2 = 10.0$ Ω   **Basic equation:** $V = IR$
            $V = 45.0$ V

FIGURE 24-3. Use with the Example.

Solution:

a. $R = R_1 + R_2$
    $= 5.0$ Ω $+ 10.0$ Ω $= 15.0$ Ω

b. $I = \dfrac{V}{R} = \dfrac{45.0 \text{ V}}{15.0 \text{ Ω}} = 3.00$ A

c. The voltage drop across R_1 is
    $V_1 = IR_1 = (3.00 \text{ A})(5.0 \text{ Ω}) = 15$ V

FIGURE 24-4. Use with the Example.

The voltage drop across R_2 is

$$V_2 = IR_2$$
$$= (3.00 \text{ A})(10.0 \text{ } \Omega) = 30.0 \text{ V}$$

d. $V = V_1 + V_2$
$$= 15 \text{ V} + 30.0 \text{ V} = 45 \text{ V}$$

An important application of series resistors is the voltage divider. The voltage divider is designed to obtain a desired voltage from a battery that supplies a larger voltage. Consider the circuit in Figure 24-4. Two resistors, R_1 and R_2, are connected in series across a battery of voltage V. The effective resistance of the circuit is $R = R_1 + R_2$. The current, I, is given by $I = V/R = V/(R_1 + R_2)$. The desired voltage, V_2, is the voltage drop across resistor R_2. According to Ohm's law, V_2 equals IR_2. Replacing I by its equivalent calculated by the equation above gives

$$V_2 = IR_2 = \left(\frac{V}{R_1 + R_2} \right) \cdot R_2 = \frac{VR_2}{R_1 + R_2}$$

EXAMPLE

Voltage Divider

A 9.0-V battery and two resistors, $R_1 = 400 \text{ } \Omega$ and $R_2 = 500 \text{ } \Omega$, are connected as a voltage divider. What is the voltage across R_2?

Given: $V = 9.0 \text{ V}$ **Unknown:** V_2

$R_1 = 400 \text{ } \Omega$ **Basic equation:** $V_2 = \dfrac{VR_2}{R_1 + R_2}$

$R_2 = 500 \text{ } \Omega$

Solution:

$$V_2 = \frac{VR_2}{R_1 + R_2} = \frac{(9 \text{ V})(500 \text{ } \Omega)}{400 \text{ } \Omega + 500 \text{ } \Omega} = 5 \text{ V}$$

A photoresistor is a device whose resistance is changed by light striking it. Photoresistors are made of semiconductors like selenium or cadmium sulfide. A typical photoresistor can have a resistance of 400 Ω when light strikes it but 400 000 Ω when in the dark. When a photoresistor is used in a voltage divider, the output voltage across the photoresistor is determined by the amount of light striking the photoresistor. This circuit can be used as a light meter or "electric eye." Examples include automatic door openers and burglar alarms.

A voltage divider is a pair of resistors used to obtain a desired voltage from a battery that supplies a higher voltage.

Problems

5. a. 50.0 Ω
   b. 2.2 A
   c. 44 V, 66 V
   d. 110 V

5. A 20.0-Ω resistor and a 30.0-Ω resistor are connected in series and placed across a 110-V potential difference.
   a. What is the effective resistance of the circuit?
   b. What is the current in the circuit?
   c. What is the voltage drop across each resistor?
   d. What is the total voltage drop across the circuit?

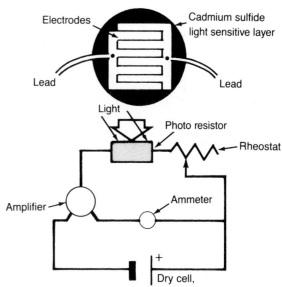

FIGURE 24-5. A lightmeter (a) and schematic diagram (b).

6. Three 30.0-Ω resistors are connected in series and placed across a difference in potential of 135 V.

   a. What is the effective resistance of the circuit?

   b. What is the current in the circuit?

   c. How much voltage is dropped across each resistance?

   d. What is the total voltage drop across all three resistors?

6. a. 90.0 Ω
  b. 1.50 A
  c. 45.0 V
  d. 135 V

7. Three resistors of 3.0 Ω, 5.0 Ω, and 4.0 Ω are connected in series across a 12-V battery.

   a. What is the effective resistance of the three resistors?

   b. What is the current in the circuit?

   c. What is the voltage drop across each resistor?

   d. What is the total voltage drop across the circuit?

7. a. 12 Ω
  b. 1.0 A
  c. 3.0 V, 5.0 V, 4.0 V
  d. 12 V

8. A 10.0-Ω resistor and a variable resistor are connected in series and placed across a 12-V source. The variable resistor is adjusted until the current in the circuit is 0.6 A.

   a. At what resistance is the variable resistor set?

   b. What are the voltage drops across the resistor and across the variable resistor?

8. a. 10 Ω
  b. 6 V, 6 V

9. In a voltage divider with $V = 9.0$ V, $R_1 = 500$ Ω and R_2 is a photoresistor.

   a. What is the output voltage, V_2, across R_2 when a bright light strikes the photocell and $R_2 = 4.0 \times 10^2$ Ω

   b. When the light is dim, $R_2 = 4.0 \times 10^3$ Ω. What is V_2?

   c. When the photoresistor is in the dark, $R_2 = 4.0 \times 10^5$ Ω. What is V_2?

9. a. 4 V
  b. 8 V
  c. 8 V

10. 5.0×10^1 Ω

10. A student is designing a voltage divider using a 12-V battery and a 100.0-Ω resistor. What must be the value of R_2 if the student wants an output voltage of 4.0 V across it?

24:3 Parallel Circuits

In a parallel circuit, each resistor provides a new path for electrons to flow.

In a parallel circuit, the current can flow through several paths. Consider rapids in a river. The water can divide into several channels. Some channels may have a large flow of water, some a small flow. However, the sum of the flows is equal to the total flow of water in the river. By analogy, in a parallel electrical circuit, the total current is the sum of the currents through each resistor.

The water drops the same height as it flows through the rapids. In a parallel circuit, the electric potential difference across each path is the same.

Figure 24-6 shows three resistors connected in parallel across a 120-V potential difference. Each line from A to B is a complete circuit across the generator and operates as if the other lines were not present. A 60-Ω resistor across a difference in potential of 120 V allows a current of 2 A to flow.

$$I = \frac{V}{R} = \frac{120 \text{ V}}{60 \text{ } \Omega} = 2 \text{ A}$$

Each 60-Ω resistor in Figure 24-6 allows 2 A of current to flow between points A and B. Thus, the total current between the two points is 6 A. The potential difference across each resistor is 120 V. Ohm's law shows the circuit as a whole has a resistance of only 20 Ω. The effective resistance of a parallel circuit is the resistance of a single resistor that could replace all the parallel resistors in the circuit.

$$R = \frac{V}{I} = \frac{120 \text{ V}}{6 \text{ A}} = 20 \text{ } \Omega$$

Placing resistors in parallel always decreases the effective resistance of

FIGURE 24-6. In a parallel circuit, the reciprocal of the total resistance is equal to the sum of the reciprocals of the individual resistances. Here you see three 60-ohm resistors connected in parallel. For each resistor, the voltage drop is 120 volts and the current is 2 amperes.

the circuit. The effective resistance decreases because each new resistor provides an additional path for the electrons to follow between points A and B. Notice that the effective resistance of the circuit is less than the resistance of any single resistor in the circuit. The effective resistance of a parallel circuit can be found by using the fact that total current in the circuit is the sum of the currents through the branches of the circuit. If I is the total current, and I_1, I_2, and I_3 are the currents through each of the branches, then

> *The total resistance of a parallel circuit decreases as each new resistor is added.*

$$I = I_1 + I_2 + I_3$$

The current through R_1 can be calculated using $I_1 = V/R_1$. The total current through the effective resistance R of the circuit is given by $I = V/R$. All voltage drops in a parallel circuit are the same. Therefore, the above equation for the current becomes

> *Total current in a parallel circuit is the sum of the currents in its branches.*

$$\frac{V}{R} = \frac{V}{R_1} + \frac{V}{R_2} + \frac{V}{R_3}$$

Dividing both sides of the equation by V gives

> *The voltage drop across each branch is equal to the voltage of the source.*

$$\boxed{\frac{1}{R} = \frac{1}{R_1} + \frac{1}{R_2} + \frac{1}{R_3}}$$

The effective resistance of the circuit shown in Figure 24-5 is thus

$$\frac{1}{R} = \frac{1}{60\ \Omega} + \frac{1}{60\ \Omega} + \frac{1}{60\ \Omega} = \frac{3}{60\ \Omega} = \frac{1}{20\ \Omega}$$

$$R = 20\ \Omega$$

EXAMPLE

Total Resistance and Current in a Parallel Circuit

Three resistors of 60.0 Ω, 30.0 Ω, and 20.0 Ω are connected in parallel across a 90.0-V difference in potential, Figure 24-7.

   a. Find the effective resistance of the circuit.
   b. Find the current in the entire circuit.
   c. Find the current through each branch of the circuit.

FIGURE 24-7. Use with the Example.

Given: $R_1 = 60.0\ \Omega$ **Unknowns:** R, I, I_1, I_2, I_3
         $R_2 = 30.0\ \Omega$ **Basic equation:** $V = IR$
         $R_3 = 20.0\ \Omega$
         $V = 90.0\ V$

Solution:

a. $\dfrac{1}{R} = \dfrac{1}{60.0\ \Omega} + \dfrac{1}{30.0\ \Omega} + \dfrac{1}{20.0\ \Omega}$

     $\dfrac{1}{R} = \dfrac{6}{60.0\ \Omega}$

     $R = 10.0\ \Omega$

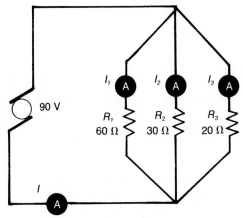

b. $I = \dfrac{V}{R} = \dfrac{90.0 \text{ V}}{10.0 \text{ }\Omega} = 9.00$ A

c. The voltage drop across each resistor is 90.0 V.

$$(\text{for } R_1) \ I_1 = \frac{V}{R_1} = \frac{90.0 \text{ V}}{60.0 \text{ }\Omega} = 1.50 \text{ A}$$

$$(\text{for } R_2) \ I_2 = \frac{V}{R_2} = \frac{90.0 \text{ V}}{30.0 \text{ }\Omega} = 3.00 \text{ A}$$

$$(\text{for } R_3) \ I_3 = \frac{V}{R_3} = \frac{90.0 \text{ V}}{20.0 \text{ }\Omega} = 4.50 \text{ A}$$

The largest current flows through the smallest resistor. The sum of the current in the lines is 9.00 A as shown in Part b. Dividing the voltage by the sum of the currents yields the effective resistance of the circuit. The solution is the same as was found in Part a.

Problems

11. a. 5.00 Ω
    b. 6.00 A
    c. 2.00 A

11. Three 15.0 Ω resistors are connected in parallel and placed across a difference in potential of 30.0 V.
   a. What is the effective resistance of the parallel circuit?
   b. What is the current through the entire circuit?
   c. What is the current through each branch of the circuit?

12. a. 5.0 Ω
    b. 3.0 A
    c. 1.5 A

12. Two 10.0-Ω resistors are connected in parallel and placed across the terminals of a 15-V battery.
   a. What is the effective resistance of the parallel circuit?
   b. What is the total current in the circuit?
   c. What is the current through each branch of the circuit?

13. a. 20.0 Ω
    b. 6.00 A
    c. 1.00 A, 2.00 A, 3.00 A

13. A 120.0-Ω resistor, a 60.0-Ω resistor, and a 40.0-Ω resistor are connected in parallel and placed across a potential difference of 120.0 V.
   a. What is the effective resistance of the parallel circuit?
   b. What is the current in the entire circuit?
   c. What is the current through each branch of the circuit?

14. a. 6.0 A, 2.0 a, 0.40 A
    b. 8.4 A
    c. 4.3 Ω

14. A 6.0-Ω resistor, an 18-Ω resistor, and a 90.0-Ω resistor are connected in parallel and placed across a 36-V potential difference.
   a. What is the current through each resistor?
   b. What is the total current in the circuit?
   c. What is the effective resistance of the circuit?

15. a. 2.0 A
    b. 1.0 A
    c. 3.0 A
    d. 5.0 × 10¹ Ω
    e. 3.0 A, yes

15. A 75-Ω heater and a 150-Ω lamp are connected in parallel across a potential difference of 150 V.
   a. What is the current through the 75-Ω heater?
   b. What is the current through the 150-Ω lamp?
   c. What is the current through the entire circuit?

d. What is the effective resistance of the entire circuit?

e. Divide the voltage by the effective resistance. Does the result agree with the solution to Part **c**?

FIGURE 24-8. A 60 Ω, a 20 Ω, and a 10 Ω resistor are connected in parallel across a 120-V source. The current through the circuit will cause the fuse to melt.

24:4   Applications of Parallel Circuits

Figure 24-8 shows resistors of 60 Ω, 20 Ω, and 10 Ω connected in parallel across a 120-V source. The circuit also contains a 15-A fuse in series with the resistors. The effective resistance of the circuit is

In a parallel circuit, each resistor can be operated independently.

$$\frac{1}{R} = \frac{1}{60 \ \Omega} + \frac{1}{20 \ \Omega} + \frac{1}{10 \ \Omega} = \frac{10}{60 \ \Omega}$$

$$R = 6 \ \Omega$$

The current flowing through the lines is

$$I = \frac{V}{R} = \frac{120 \ V}{6 \ \Omega} = 20 \ A$$

Notice that 20 A exceeds the capacity of the 15-A fuse. This will cause the fuse to melt, or "blow," cutting off current to the entire circuit.

Fuses and circuit breakers are switches in the line that act as safety devices. They prevent circuit overloads that can occur when too many appliances are turned on at the same time. When appliances are connected in parallel, each additional appliance placed in operation reduces the effective resistance in the circuit and causes more current to flow through the wires. The additional current may produce enough thermal energy (I^2R) to melt the insulation on wires, causing a short circuit.

Fuses and circuit breakers are safety devices that prevent too much current from flowing in a circuit.

FIGURE 24-9. When the current in a circuit is too great, the metal bar in this circuit breaker is pulled away from its contact points. The current stops flowing.

a

Switch-operating electromagnet

Iron bar

Spring

Electron flow

b

a

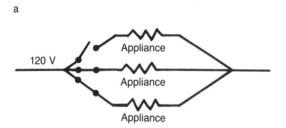

120 V

Appliance

Appliance

Appliance

b

FIGURE 24-10. The wiring arrangement in this house (a) will permit the use of one or more appliances at the same time. This wiring diagram (b) indicates the parallel nature of the circuit.

A fuse is a short piece of metal that melts when the heating effect of the current reaches a set magnitude. A circuit breaker is an automatic switch that opens when the current reaches some set value. If an overload occurred in the circuit shown in Figure 24-9, the fuse would melt. Then no current would flow anywhere in the circuit. Usually, a house is wired with several separate parallel circuits located in different parts of the house. Such an arrangement tends to prevent an overload in any single circuit.

A short circuit occurs when a new circuit containing a very low resistance is accidentally formed. The current in this circuit becomes very large. This large current could start a fire if there were no fuse or circuit breaker in the circuit. For example, if a lamp cord becomes frayed, its input and return wires could accidentally be brought together. A piece of copper wire in the lamp cord might have a resistance of only 0.010 Ω. When placed across 120 V, this resistance would cause a current of

FIGURE 24-11. The metal wire in a fuse melts when the circuit is overloaded. The fuse must then be replaced.

$$\frac{120 \text{ V}}{0.010 \ \Omega} = \text{ or } 12\ 000 \text{ A}$$

The fuse or circuit breaker reacts immediately to the increase in current and breaks the circuit. Thus, the wire is prevented from becoming hot and starting a fire.

24:5 Series-Parallel Circuits

Often a circuit consists of a combination of series and parallel circuits. The current in a complex circuit can be found by first calculating the effective resistance of the parallel circuits. Then the effective resistance of the parallel circuits and all the series resistances can be combined into one total effective resistance, and the total current determined. The voltage drop across each resistor can be found by using Ohm's law.

EXAMPLE

Series-Parallel Circuit

In Figure 24-12, a 30.0-Ω resistor is connected in parallel with a 20.0-Ω resistor. The parallel connection is placed in series with an 8.0-Ω resistor, and the entire circuit is placed across a 60.0-V difference of potential.

a. What is the effective resistance of the parallel portion of the circuit?
b. What is the effective resistance of the entire circuit?
c. What is the current in the entire circuit?
d. What is the voltage drop across the 8.0-Ω resistor?
e. What is the voltage drop across the parallel portion of the circuit?
f. What is the current in each line of the parallel portion of the circuit?

Solution:

a. R_2 and R_3 are connected in parallel. Their effective resistance is

$$\frac{1}{R_{2,3}} = \frac{1}{R_2} + \frac{1}{R_3} = \frac{1}{30.0\ \Omega} + \frac{1}{20.0\ \Omega} = \frac{5}{60.0\ \Omega}$$

$$R_{2,3} = 12.0\ \Omega$$

In analyzing series-parallel circuits, first combine parallel resistors. Then combine series resistors.

b. The circuit is equivalent to a series circuit with an 8.0-Ω resistor and a 12.0-Ω resistor in series, Figure 25-13.

$$R = R_1 + R_{2,3}$$

$$= 8.0\ \Omega + 12.0\ \Omega = 20.0\ \Omega$$

c. The current in the circuit is

$$I = \frac{V}{R}$$

$$= \frac{60.0\ V}{20.0\ \Omega} = 3.00\ A$$

Ohm's law can be used on each separate part of a series-parallel circuit.

FIGURE 24-12. Use with the Example.

d. The voltage drop across the 8-Ω resistor is
$$V_1 = IR_1$$
$$= (3.00\ A)(12.0\ \Omega) = 24.0\ V$$

e. The parallel branch (R_2 and R_3) behaves as a 12.0-Ω resistor. Therefore, the voltage drop across it is
$$V_p = IR_{2,3}$$
$$= (3.00\ A)(12.0\ \Omega) = 36.0\ V$$

f. The 36.0-V drop across the parallel portion of the circuit is the same across all parts of the parallel circuit. Therefore, the current through the 30.0-Ω resistor is

$$I_2 = \frac{V}{R_2}$$
$$= \frac{36.0\ V}{30.0\ \Omega} = 1.20\ A$$

The current through the 20.0-Ω resistor is

$$I_3 = \frac{V}{R_3}$$
$$= \frac{36.0\ V}{20.0\ \Omega} = 1.80\ A$$

The current through the parallel part of the circuit is
$$1.20\ A + 1.80\ A,\ \text{or}\ 3.00\ A$$

This value agrees with the value for current calculated in Part c.

Problems

16. a. See Teacher's Guide.
   b. 30 Ω
   c. 60 Ω
   d. 2 A
   e. 60 V
   f. 60 V
   g. 1 A

16. Two 60-Ω resistors are connected in parallel. This parallel arrangement is connected in series with a 30-Ω resistor. The entire circuit is then placed across a 120-V potential difference.
  a. Draw a diagram of the circuit.
  b. What is the effective resistance of the parallel portion of the circuit?
  c. What is the effective resistance of the entire circuit?
  d. What is the current in the circuit?
  e. What is the voltage drop across the 30-Ω resistor?
  f. What is the voltage drop across the parallel portion of the circuit?
  g. What is the current in each branch of the parallel portion of the circuit?

17. a. "diagram"

17. Three 15-Ω resistors are connected in parallel. This arrangement is connected in series with a 10-Ω resistor. The entire circuit is then placed across a 45-V difference in potential.
  a. Draw a diagram of the circuit.

b. What is the effective resistance of the parallel portion of the circuit?

c. What is the effective resistance of the entire circuit?

d. What is the current in the entire circuit?

e. What is the voltage drop across the 10-Ω resistor.

f. What is the voltage drop across the parallel portion of the circuit?

g. What is the current in each branch of the parallel portion of the circuit?

b. 5.0 Ω
c. 15 Ω
d. 3.0 A
e. 30 V
f. 15 V
g. 1.0 A

18. Three 15-Ω resistors are connected in parallel. They are connected in series to a second set of three 15-Ω resistors, also connected in parallel. The entire circuit is then placed across the terminals of a 12-V battery.

a. What is the effective resistance of the circuit?

b. What is the circuit current?

c. What is the current through each resistor?

18. a. 1.0×10^1 Ω
b. 1.2 A
c. 0.40 A

24:6 Ammeters and Voltmeters

An **ammeter** is used to measure the current in a circuit. An ammeter is placed in a circuit in series with the resistors. The resistance of an ammeter must be very low. A high resistance increases the effective resistance of the circuit; an increased resistance causes a reduced current. Thus, an ammeter with a high resistance would change the value of the current the meter was used to measure.

An ammeter measures current in a circuit.

An ammeter should have as low a resistance as possible.

FIGURE 24-13. A multi-meter can be used to measure currents and voltage drops in electric circuits.

A voltmeter measures voltage drop across a circuit.

A voltmeter should have as high a resistance as possible.

FIGURE 24-24. A battery tester (a) and a standard laboratory voltmeter (b) measure potential differences. Ammeters are always placed in series within a circuit (c) and voltmeters are placed in parallel (d).

A **voltmeter** is used to measure the voltage drop across an entire circuit or a part of a circuit. A voltmeter is placed in parallel with the part of a circuit across which the voltage drop is to be measured. A voltmeter must have a very high resistance so that the current through it is very small. Consider the circuit shown in Figure 24-14d. It is important to remember that the voltage drop across the entire circuit remains constant. The effective resistance of the branch containing R_2 and a low-resistance voltmeter would be less than R_2 alone. Therefore, the effective resistance of the entire circuit would also be decreased and the current in the circuit would increase. This increased current would cause a larger voltage drop across R_1, and the voltage drop across the R_2 branch would decrease. Thus, a low-resistance voltmeter would change the value of the voltage it is used to measure. The resistance of a voltmeter is at least 20 000 Ω. Many electronic voltmeters now in use have resistances of 10^7 Ω.

a

b

c

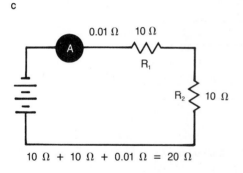

$$10\ \Omega\ +\ 10\ \Omega\ +\ 0.01\ \Omega\ =\ 20\ \Omega$$

d

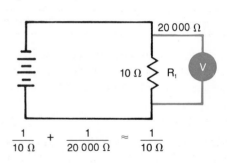

$$\frac{1}{10\ \Omega}\ +\ \frac{1}{20\ 000\ \Omega}\ \approx\ \frac{1}{10\ \Omega}$$

Summary

1. The current is the same everywhere in a series circuit.   24:1

2. The sum of the voltage drops across the resistors in a series circuit is equal   24:1
to the potential difference across the voltage source.

3. The effective resistance of a series circuit is the sum of the resistances of   24:1
its parts.

4. A voltage divider is a series circuit used to provide a potential difference   24:2
of specific value.

5. The voltage drops across all branches of a parallel circuit are the   24:3
same.

6. In a parallel circuit, the total current is equal to the sum of the currents in   24:3
the branches.

7. The reciprocal of the effective resistance of a parallel circuit is equal to the   24:3
sum of the reciprocals of the individual resistances.

8. If any branch of a parallel circuit is opened, there is no current in that   24:4
branch. The current in the other branches is unchanged.

9. A circuit is often a combination of series and parallel circuits. The   24:5
parallel circuit is first reduced to a single resistance. Then the series
circuit is replaced by a single resistance.

10. An ammeter is used to measure the current in a circuit or in a part of a   24:6
circuit. An ammeter is always connected in series.

11. A voltmeter measures the potential difference (voltage) across any part of   24:6
a circuit or across the entire circuit. A voltmeter is always connected in
parallel.

Detailed answers to all Questions and Problems are given in the Teacher's Guide at the front of this book.

Questions

1. Circuit A contains three 60-Ω resistors in series. Circuit B contains three
60-Ω resistors in parallel. How does the current in the second 60-Ω resistor
change if a switch cuts off the current to the first 60-Ω resistor in
   a. circuit A?
   b. circuit B?

2. Why is there a difference in total resistance between three 60-Ω resistors
connected in series and three 60-Ω resistors connected in parallel?

3. An engineer needs a 10-Ω control resistor or a 15-Ω control resistor. But, there are only 30-Ω resistors in stock. Must new resistors be bought? Explain.

4. For each part of this question, write the form that applies: series circuit or parallel circuit.

  a. The current is the same throughout.
  b. The total resistance is equal to the sum of the individual resistances.
  c. The voltage drop is the same across each resistor.
  d. The voltage drop is proportional to the resistance.
  e. Adding a resistor decreases the total resistance.
  f. Adding a resistor increases the total resistance.
  g. If one resistor is turned off or broken, there is no current in the entire circuit.
  h. If one resistor is turned off, the current through all other resistors remains the same.
  i. Suitable for house wiring.

5. Explain the function of a fuse in an electric circuit.

6. What is a short circuit? Why is a short circuit dangerous?

7. Why does an ammeter have a very low resistance?

8. Why does a voltmeter have a very high resistance?

Problems–A

1. a. 12 Ω
b. 1.0 A
c. 1.0 A
d. 5 V, 7 V

1. Two resistors of 5 Ω and 7 Ω are connected in series across a 12-V battery.
  a. What is the effective resistance of the circuit?
  b. What is the current through the 5-Ω resistor?
  c. What is the current through the 7-Ω resistor?
  d. What is the voltage drop across each resistor?

2. a. 15 Ω
b. 0.40 A
c. 2.4 V, 2.4 V, 1.2 V

2. Two 6.0-Ω resistors and a 3.0-Ω resistor are connected in series. A potential difference of 6.0 V is applied to the circuit.
  a. What is the effective resistance of the circuit?
  b. What is the current in the circuit?
  c. What is the voltage drop across each resistor?

3. 1.0 × 10¹ Ω

3. A light bulb has a resistance of 2.0 Ω. It is connected in series with a variable resistor. A difference in potential of 6.0 V is applied to the circuit. An ammeter indicates that the current of the circuit is 0.50 A. At what resistance is the variable resistor set?

4. 7 Ω

4. What resistance is connected in series with an 8-Ω resistor connected to a 60.0-V generator if the current through the resistors is 4.0 A?

5. Ten Christmas tree lights are connected in series. When they are plugged into a 120-V outlet, the current through the lights is 0.75 A. What is the resistance of each light?

5. 16 Ω

6. A 20-Ω lamp and a 5-Ω lamp are connected in series and placed across a difference in potential of 50 V.
a. What is the effective resistance of the circuit?
b. What is the current in the circuit?
c. What is the voltage drop across each lamp?
d. What is the power used in each lamp?

6. a. 25 Ω
   b. 2 A
   c. 40 V, 10 V
   d. 80 W, 20 W

7. A 20.0-Ω lamp and a 5.0-Ω lamp are connected in parallel and placed across a difference in potential of 50.0 V.
a. What is the effective resistance of the circuit?
b. What is the current in the circuit?
c. What is the current through each resistor?
d. What is the voltage drop across each resistor?
e. What is the power used by each lamp?
f. Compare this result to the result of the preceding problem.

7. a. 4.0 Ω
   b. 13 A
   c. 2.50 A, 1.0 × 10¹ A
   d. 5.0 × 10¹ V,
      5.0 × 10¹ V
   e. 130 W , 5.0 × 10² W
   f. Resistors in parallel
      consume more power.

8. A 16.0-Ω and a 20.0-Ω resistor are connected in parallel. A difference in potential of 40.0 V is applied to the combination.
a. Compute the effective resistance of the parallel circuit.
b. What is the current in the circuit?
c. What is the current through the 16.0-Ω resistor?

8. a. 8.89 Ω
   b. 4.50 Ω
   c. 2.50 A

9. A household circuit contains six 240-Ω lamps (60-W bulbs) and a 10.0-Ω heater. The voltage across the circuit is 120 V.
a. What is the current in the circuit when four lamps are on?
b. What is the current when all six lamps are on?
c. What is the current in the circuit if all six lamps and the heater are operating?

9. a. 2.0 A
   b. 3.0 A
   c. 15 A

10. Determine the reading of each ammeter and each voltmeter in Figure 24-15.

10. 2.25 A, 0.750 A, 22.5 V,
    22.5 V, 22.5 V

FIGURE 24-15. Use with Problem 10.

11. 0.667 A, 0.800 A, 2.00 A,
     20.0 V, 12.0 V, 48.0 V

12. 50.6 W, 16.9 W

11. Find the reading of each ammeter and each voltmeter in Figure 24-16.

12. Determine the power in watts used by each resistance shown in Figure 24-15.

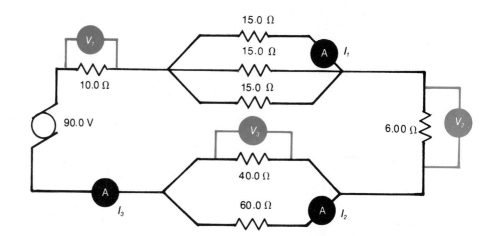

FIGURE 24-16. Use with Problem 11.

Problems–B

1. a. See Teacher's Guide.
     b. 1.0 × 10³ s

1. During a laboratory exercise, you are supplied with the following apparatus:
   - a battery of potential difference V,
   - two heating elements of low resistance that can be placed in water,
   - an ammeter of negligible resistance,
   - a voltmeter of extremely high resistance,
   - wires of negligible resistance,
   - a beaker that is well-insulated and has negligible heat capacity,
   - 100.0 g of water at 25°C.

   a. By means of a diagram using standard symbols, show how these components should be connected to heat the water as rapidly as possible.

   b. If the voltmeter reading holds steady at 50.0 V and the ammeter reading holds steady at 5.0 A, estimate the time in seconds required to completely vaporize the water in the beaker. Use 4.2 J/g · C° as the specific heat of water and 2300 J/g as the heat of vaporization of water.

2. a. 240.50 Ω
     b. 0.50 A
     c. 0.25 V

2. A typical home circuit is diagrammed in Figure 24-17. Note that the lead lines to the kitchen lamp have very low resistances. The lamp contains a typical 60-W incandescent bulb of resistance 240.00-Ω. Although the circuit is a parallel circuit, the lead lines are in series with each of the components of the circuit.

a. Compute the effective resistance of the circuit consisting of just the light and the lead lines to and from the light. We will assume that the power saw and wall outlets are not in use.
b. Show that the current to the bulb is essentially 0.5 amperes and that the bulb is a 60-W device.
c. Since the current in the bulb is 0.5 A, the current in the lead lines must also be 0.5 A. Calculate the voltage drop due to the two leads.

3. A power saw is operated by an electric motor. When electric motors are first turned on, they have very low resistances. In Chapter 26 we will study why the resistance is low. Suppose that the kitchen light discussed in Problem 2 is on and the power saw is suddenly turned on. The saw plus the lead lines between the saw and the light have an initial total resistance of 6.0 Ω.

3. a. 6.4 Ω
   b. 19 A
   c. 9.5 V
   d. 110 V remains

a. Compute the effective resistance of the light-saw parallel circuit.
b. What current flows through the two leads to the light?
c. What is the total voltage drop across the two leads to the light?
d. What voltage remains to operate the light? Will this voltage cause the light to dim temporarily? (You may have noticed this effect before.)

FIGURE 24-17. Use with Problems 2 and 3.

Readings

Hughes, Thomas, P., "The Inventive Continuum." *Science*, November, 1984.

Liao, Thomas, "Design and Performance of Electric Vehicles." *The Physics Teacher*, November, 1983.

Ong, P. P., "A Short-Circuit Method for Networks." *The Physics Teacher*, October, 1983.

Owen, Bill, "Energy Miser For Air Conditioners." *Radio Electronics*, July, 1984.

Rosenberg, Robert, "American Physics and the Origins of Electrical Engineering." *Physics Today*, October, 1983.

As a child you have probably played with small magnets. You know that opposite poles of a magnet attract while like poles repel. The Fermilab accelerator contains one thousand magnets. The magnets are used to control the paths of charged atomic particles moving through the accelerator. High energy particles are directed at a target in the hopes of unlocking the secrets of the atom. What are some other uses of magnets?

Magnetic Fields

Chapter 25 introduces the basic properties of magnets, the concept of a magnetic field, and the unit of magnetic induction. Electromagnetism is defined and the fields about variously-shaped current-bearing wires are found by using left-hand rules. The force on a moving charge in a magnetic field is treated quantitatively.

No investigation of electricity is complete without a study of magnetism. The two cannot be separated. Whenever electrons move, magnetic effects occur. Our study of magnetism begins with a review of the properties of magnets. The magnetic field produced by magnets is studied next. Then the magnetic field produced by electric currents is introduced. Finally, the forces that magnetic fields exert on electric currents are studied. As you will see, the operation of many devices such as motors, television sets, and tape recorders depends on the magnetic effects of electric currents.

Goal: You will gain understanding of permanent magnets and electromagnets and the forces that magnetic fields exert on currents and moving charges.

25:1 General Properties of Magnets

The properties of naturally occurring magnetic rocks (lodestones) have been known for over 2000 years. The first thorough investigation of magnetism was made by William Gilbert in 1600. The properties of natural and artificial magnets can be summarized as follows.

We begin with a brief review of the principles of magnetism.

1. A magnet has polarity. The end of a suspended magnet that points north is the north-seeking pole (N-pole) of the magnet. The end that points south is its south-seeking pole (S-pole). These poles are distinct. However, they cannot be separated.

2. Like magnetic poles repel one another. Unlike poles attract one another.

Unlike poles attract; like poles repel.

3. A compass is a small, suspended, needle-shaped magnet. The north-seeking pole of the compass needle points north. The magnetic north pole of the earth and the geographic north pole of the earth are not in the same place. A compass needle points toward the magnetic north pole.

4. Cobalt and nickel are important magnetic substances. Permanent magnets are made from alloys of these metals. Most commercial permanent magnets are made of ALNICO, an alloy of ALuminum, NIckel, CObalt. Permanent magnets retain their magnetism for a long time.

5. Iron, cobalt, and nickel may be magnetized by induction. When a piece of iron, for example, touches a permanent magnet, the iron becomes a magnet itself. The iron is a temporary magnet; as soon as it is removed from the permanent magnet, the iron ceases to be a magnet.

25:2 Magnetic Fields Around Permanent Magnets

All magnets, permanent and temporary, exert forces on other magnets at a distance. These forces can be explained in terms of **magnetic fields** that exist around the magnets.

The presence of a magnetic field around a magnet can be shown by covering the magnet with a piece of paper and sprinkling iron filings onto the paper. The filings are long, thin pieces of iron, each of which becomes a small magnet by induction. The filings arrange themselves in lines running from pole to pole, as shown in Figure 25-2. These lines help you to visualize magnetic field lines.

Note that the magnetic field lines are imaginary. However, you can use these lines to picture how magnets placed close together affect one another. The number of magnetic field lines in any given region is called the **magnetic flux.** The flux per unit area is an indication of the strength of the magnetic field as shown in Figure 25-2b. The iron filings are most concentrated where the flux per unit area, that is, the magnetic field, is the greatest — at the poles.

See Teacher's Guide for suggested demonstrations.

Magnetic field lines are imaginary lines that indicate the direction and magnitude of the field about a magnet.

Magnetic flux density is magnetic flux per unit area.

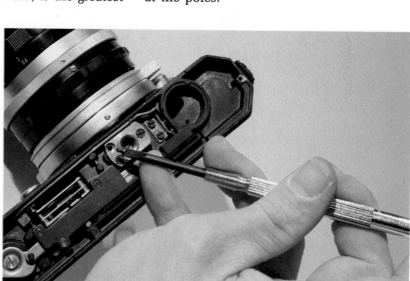

FIGURE 25-1. Magnetic tools are useful in working with small intricate parts.

a

b

FIGURE 25-2. Magnetic flux lines extend from the N-pole to the S-pole outside the magnet and from the S-pole to the N-pole inside the magnet.

The direction of the magnetic field lines is the direction to which the N-pole of a compass points when it is placed in the magnetic field. Outside the magnet, the field lines run from the N-pole of the magnet to its S-pole. Inside the magnet, the field lines run from the S-pole to the N-pole of the magnet. Field lines always form closed loops.

Magnetic fields outside a magnet run from north pole to south pole.

Electric field lines start and end on electric charges. If magnetic poles could be separated and isolated, the magnetic field lines would start and end on the isolated poles. However, magnetic poles always occur in pairs. No isolated magnetic pole (called a magnetic monopole) has ever been discovered.

Magnetic poles always occur in pairs.

The behavior of fields from pairs of magnetic poles may be observed by placing a sheet of paper over the like poles (N and N, or S and S) of two magnets held close together. If the paper is sprinkled with iron filings, the pattern of the magnetic field may be observed. Figure 25-3a shows the field lines between the like poles. By contrast, two unlike poles (N and S) placed close together show another pattern. The filings show that the field lines between the magnets run directly from one magnet to the other.

a

b

FIGURE 25-3. The field lines for like poles (a) and unlike poles (b).

The force exerted by a magnetic field on an N-pole is in the direction of the field lines. Thus, an N-pole will have a force exerted on it directing it away from the N-pole of the magnet producing the field and toward the S-pole of this magnet. The force exerted on an S-pole in a magnetic field is in the direction opposite the field lines. An S-pole will have a force exerted on it directing it away from the S-pole and toward the N-pole of the magnet producing the field. In summary, unlike poles of magnets attract one another; like poles repel.

a

b

FIGURE 25-4. This experimental train is magnetically levitated (a). Moving along a magnetic cushion allows the train to reach extremely high speeds. The lead sphere (b) floats between two lead rings that carry electric currents when the temperature is near absolute zero. The repulsion between magnetic fields of the sphere and rings balances the sphere's weight so that it floats.

1. The end pointing in the direction of the field lines has the induced N-pole.

2. a. repulsive
   b. attractive

FIGURE 25-5. The magnetic field produced by current in a straight wire conductor is shown.

Problems

1. An iron filing is placed in the magnetic field shown in Figure 25-2. Which end of the filing has the induced N-pole?

2. A student holds a bar magnet in each hand. If she brings her hands close together, will the force be attractive or repulsive if the magnets are held so that

   a. the two N-poles are brought close together?

   b. an N-pole and an S-pole are brought together?

25:3 Electromagnetism

In 1820, the Danish physicist Hans Christian Oersted (1777-1851) made a very important discovery about magnetism. While experimenting with electric currents in wires, Oersted laid one of his wires across the top of a small compass. He observed that each time he sent a current through the wire, the compass needle moved. Oersted knew a magnetic field could exert a force on a magnet. Thus, the presence of an

a

b

electric current in the wire was somehow causing a magnetic field to appear around the wire. Further studies by Oersted showed that any wire carrying an electric current has a magnetic field around it. Electric currents produce magnetic fields.

The magnetic field around a current-bearing wire can easily be studied by placing a wire vertically through a piece of cardboard on which iron filings are sprinkled. When the cardboard is tapped, the filings form a pattern around the current-carrying wire. The pattern consists of concentric circles (circles with a common center) around the wire.

The circular lines indicate that magnetic field lines form closed loops. The strength of the magnetic field around the wire varies directly with the magnitude of the current flowing in the wire. The strength of the magnetic field varies inversely with the distance from the wire.

The **left-hand rule** can be used to find the direction of the magnetic field around a current-bearing straight wire. Grasp the wire with the left hand. Keep the thumb of that hand pointed in the direction of electron flow. The fingers of the hand circle the wire pointing in the direction of the magnetic field.

Problems

3. A wire runs from north to south.

  a. A compass needle placed above the wire points with its N-pole toward the east. In what direction is the current flowing?

  b. If a compass is put underneath the wire, in which direction will it point?

4. Two wires carry equal currents and run parallel to each other.

  a. If the two currents are in the opposite directions, where will the field from the two wires be larger than the field from either wire alone?

  b. Where will the field be exactly twice as large?

  c. If the currents are in the same direction, where will the magnetic field be exactly zero?

Current

Left hand

Direction of magnetic field

FIGURE 25-6. The left-hand rule for a current-bearing straight wire shows the direction of the magnetic field.

The first left-hand rule gives the direction of the magnetic field around a current-carrying wire.

3. a. north to south
   b. west

4. a. points between the two wires
   b. half way between the wires
   c. half way between the wires

25:4 Magnetic Field Around a Coil

When an electric current flows through a single circular loop of wire, a magnetic field appears all around the loop. By applying the left-hand rule, as in Figure 25-7b, to any part of the wire loop, it can be shown that the direction of the field inside the loop is always the same. In the case shown in the diagram, it is always up out of the page. Outside the loop, it is always down into the page.

a

b

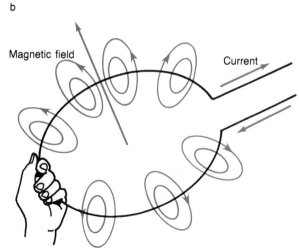

FIGURE 25-7. The magnetic field about a circular loop of current-bearing wire is shown.

Suppose wire is looped several times to form a coil. When a current flows through the coil, the field around all loops will be in the same direction. Inside the coil, there is a continuous magnetic field that acts in a single direction. The field outside the coil will act in the opposite direction.

When an electric current flows through a coil of wire, the coil behaves like a permanent magnet. When this current-carrying coil is brought close to a suspended bar magnet, one end of the coil repels the north pole of the magnet. The other end of the coil attracts the north pole of the magnet. Thus, the current-carrying coil has a north and south pole and is itself a magnet. This type of magnet is called an **electromagnet**.

A second left-hand rule can be used to find the north and south poles of an electromagnet.

The direction of the field produced by an electromagnet may be found by using a **second left-hand rule**. Grasp the coil with the left hand. Curl the fingers around the loops in the direction of electron flow. The thumb points toward the N pole of the electromagnet.

FIGURE 25-8. The second left-hand rule can be used to determine the polarity of an electromagnet.

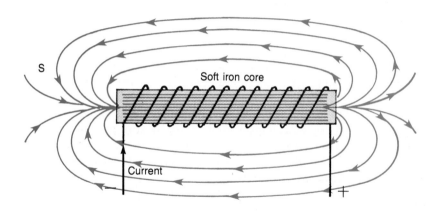

The strength of an electromagnet can be increased by placing an iron rod or core inside the coil. The field inside the coil magnetizes the core by induction. The magnetic strength of the core adds to that of the coil to produce a much stronger magnet.

The strength of the magnetic field around a current-carrying wire is proportional to the current in the wire. The strength of field of an electromagnet is proportional to the current flowing through the coil. The magnetic field produced by each loop of a coil is the same as that produced by any other loop. These fields are in the same direction, and thus all contribute to the total field. Therefore, increasing the number of loops in an electromagnet increases the strength of the magnetic field. The strength of the field of an electromagnet is proportional to the current and to the number of loops, and depends on the nature of the core.

The strength of the field about an electromagnet can be increased by placing an iron core inside the coil.

The strength of the field about an electromagnet varies directly with the current.

Problem

5. The loop in Figure 25-7 has current running in a clockwise direction (from left to right above the cardboard). If a compass is placed on the cardboard beneath the loop, in which direction will the N-pole point?

5. The N-pole will point toward the bottom of the page.

25:5 Magnetic Materials

The behavior of an electromagnet is similar to that of a permanent bar magnet. In the early 19th century, a theory of magnetism was proposed by Andre Ampere (1775-1836) to explain this behavior. Ampere knew that the magnetic effects of an electromagnetic coil result when an electric current flows through its loops. He reasoned that the effects of a bar magnet must result from tiny "loops" of current within the bar. In essence, Ampere's reasoning was correct.

Each electron in an atom acts like a tiny electromagnet. The magnetic fields of electrons in a group of neighboring atoms can add together. Such a group is called a **domain**. Although domains are much larger than individual atoms, they are still very small. Thus, even a small sample of iron contains a huge number of domains.

When a piece of iron is not in a magnetic field, the domains do not all point in the same direction. Their magnetic fields cancel one another. However, if the iron is placed in a magnetic field, the domains tend to align with the external field, as shown in Figure 25-9. In a temporary magnet, after the external field is removed, the domains return to their random arrangement. In permanent magnets, the iron has been alloyed with other substances that keep the domains aligned after the external magnetic field is removed.

Sound or video tape recorders use electronic devices to create electric signals representing the sounds or pictures being recorded. The electric signals produce currents in an electromagnet called a recording head. Magnetic recording tape passes directly over the recording head. The tape has many very tiny pieces of magnetic

FIGURE 25-9. A model of the domain theory shows magnetic properties appearing only when domains align.

The field about an electromagnet also varies directly with the number of loops in the coil.

All the domains can be lined up in the same direction.

a

b

FIGURE 25-10. A representation of forces on currents in magnetic fields.

material bonded to thin plastic tape. When these pieces pass the recording head, their domains are aligned by the magnetic fields of the head. The direction of the alignment depends on the direction of the current in the recording head. The directions of the magnetic fields of the tiny pieces become a magnetic record of the sounds or pictures being recorded. In Chapter 26, the method of playing back the sound or picture will be described. "Floppy disks" used in computers are magnetically-coated disks that record computer data in the same way.

Tiny pieces of magnetic material have been found in bacteria and in the brains of certain birds. Scientists believe this magnetic material may help these organisms navigate by using the earth's magnetic field.

25:6 Forces on Currents in Magnetic Fields

Electric currents produce magnetic fields similar to the fields of permanent magnets. So, Ampere reasoned, a magnetic field should cause a force on a current-carrying wire in the same way the field exerts a force on a permanent magnet.

The force on a wire in a magnetic field can be demonstrated using the arrangement shown in Figure 25-10. The cross on the wire in Figure 25-10a indicates that the current is flowing down into the page. The dot on the wire in Figure 25-10b shows the current is flowing out of the page. Think of the current as an arrow. The cross suggests tail feathers going away from the reader. The dot represents the point of the arrow.

The strength of a magnetic field is called **magnetic induction**. The symbol for magnetic induction is **B**. Magnetic induction is a vector quantity, which can be indicated by an arrow. Several vectors are shown in Figure 25-11. Vectors pointing into or out of the page follow the same convention as that used for current flow.

FIGURE 25-11. Directions of magnetic fields are indicated by directional arrows (a) when the field is in the same plane as the page, by crosses (b) when the field is into the page, and by dots (c) when the field is out of the page toward you.

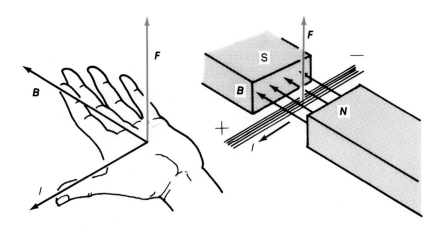

FIGURE 25-12. The third left-hand rule is used to determine the direction of force when the current and magnetic fields are known.

Michael Faraday (1791–1867) found that the force on the wire is at right angles to the direction of the magnetic field. The force is also at right angles to the direction of the current. The direction of the force on a current-carrying wire in a magnetic field can be found by using a **third left-hand rule**, shown in Figure 25-12. Point the fingers of the left hand in the direction of the magnetic field. Point the thumb in the direction of the electron flow in the wire. The palm of the hand then faces in the direction of the force acting on the wire.

The force on a wire is at right angles to the wire and to the magnetic field.

A third left-hand rule is used to determine the direction of force on a current-carrying wire placed in a magnetic field.

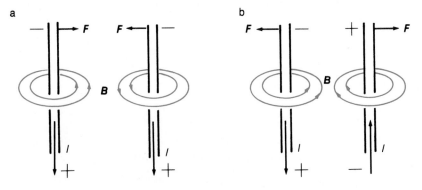

FIGURE 25-13. Two current-bearing conductors (a) are attracted when the currents are in the same direction, and (b) are repelled when the currents are in opposite directions.

Figure 25-13 shows that the direction of the magnetic field around each of the current-bearing wires follows the left-hand rule. In Figure 25-13a, we see that the fields between the wires are in opposition. Since magnetic fields add vectorially, the field between the wires is weak. The field outside the wires remains normal strength. Thus, the wires are forced together, or attract each other. In Figure 25-13b, we see the opposite situation. Here, the fields between the wires act in the same direction. Thus, the field between the wires is strengthened. Outside the wires, the fields are at normal strength. Thus, the wires are forced apart by the stronger field between them.

Suggested demonstration: Place a wire between the poles of a large electromagnet. Alternate the direction of the current to demonstrate the use of the left-hand rule.

FIGURE 25-14. Earth's magnetic field lines run from the south magnetic pole to the north magnetic pole.

Magnetic induction is measured in teslas (T). One tesla is one newton per ampere-meter (N/A·m).

25:7   Measuring the Force on a Wire

Imagine a current-carrying wire passing through a magnetic field at right angles to the wire. The magnitude of the force on the wire is proportional to three factors:

1. the magnetic induction or strength, **B**, of the field,

2. the current, I, in the wire, and

3. the length, L, of the wire that lies in the magnetic field.
   The magnitude of the force is given by the expression

$$F = BIL$$

Therefore, the strength of the field, **B**, is then given by

$$B = \frac{F}{IL}$$

The SI unit that measures the strength, or induction, of a magnetic field is the tesla, T. One tesla is equivalent to one newton per ampere-meter, N/A · m. The strength of a magnetic field is measured in terms of the force on a wire one meter long carrying one ampere of current.

A magnetic field of 1 T (1 N/A · m) field strength is a very strong field, found only in powerful electromagnets. The magnetic fields of most magnets found in the laboratory are much smaller than 1 T. The earth's magnetic field has a strength of approximately 5×10^{-5} T. The direction of the earth's field is toward the north magnetic pole, which is in arctic Canada. The field does not point along the surface of the earth, but mostly down into the earth, as shown in Figure 25-14.

EXAMPLE

Magnetic Induction

A wire 1.0 m long carries a current of 5.0 A. The wire is at right angles to a uniform magnetic field. The force on the wire is 0.2 N. What is the magnitude of the magnetic induction **B** of the field?

Given: $F = 0.2$ N   **Unknown:** Magnetic induction (B)

$I = 5.0$ A   **Basic equation:** $B = F/IL$

$L = 1.0$ m

Solution: $B = \dfrac{F}{IL} = \dfrac{0.2 \text{ N}}{(5.0 \text{ A})(1.0 \text{ m})} = 0.04 \text{ N/A} \cdot \text{m} = 0.04 \text{ T}$

EXAMPLE

Force on a Current-Carrying Wire in a Magnetic Field

A wire 1.0×10^1 cm long is at right angles to a uniform magnetic field. The field has magnetic induction 0.060 T. The current through the wire is 4.0 A. Find the magnitude of the force.

Given: $L = 1.0 \times 10^{-1}$ m   **Unknown:** F

$B = 6.0 \times 10^{-2}$ T   **Basic equation:** $B = F/IL$

$I = 4.0$ A

Solution: $F = BIL$

$= (6.0 \times 10^{-2} \text{ T})(4.0 \text{ A})(1.0 \times 10^{-1} \text{ m})$

$= \left(6.0 \times 10^{-2}\frac{\text{N}}{\text{A} \cdot \text{m}}\right)(4.0 \text{ A})(1.0 \times 10^{-1} \text{ m})$

$= 2.4 \times 10^{-2}$ N

A loudspeaker uses the force on a current-carrying wire in a magnetic field to change electrical energy to sound energy. A loudspeaker consists of a coil of fine wire mounted on a paper cone and placed in a magnetic field, as shown in Figure 25-15. The amplifier driving the loudspeaker sends a current through the coil. A force is exerted on the coil because it is in a magnetic field. The force pushes the coil either into or out of the magnetic field, depending on the direction of the current. The motion of the coil causes the cone to vibrate, creating sound waves in the air. An electric signal that represents a musical tone consists of a current that changes direction between 20 and 20 000 times each second, depending on the pitch of the tone.

Problems

6. A wire 0.10 m long carrying a current of 2.0 A is at right angles to a magnetic field. The force on the wire is 0.04 N. What is the magnitude of magnetic induction of the field?

6. 0.20 T

7. A wire 0.5 m long carrying a current of 8.0 A is at right angles to a field of magnetic induction 0.40 T. What is the magnitude of the force acting on the wire?

7. 1.6 N

a

b

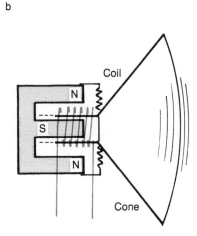

FIGURE 25-15. A loudspeaker (a) can be represented as a schematic diagram (b).

8. A wire 75 cm long carrying a current of 6.0 A is at right angles to a uniform magnetic field. The magnitude of the force acting on the wire is 0.6 N. What is the magnitude of magnetic induction of the field?

9. A copper wire 40 cm long carries a current of 6.0 A and weighs 0.35 N. Placed in a certain magnetic field, the wire remains suspended in the field. What is the magnitude of the magnetic induction of the field?

10. A wire 6.0×10^2 cm long is in a field of magnetic induction 0.40 T. The magnitude of force acting on the wire is 1.8 N. What current is in the wire?

11. A power line carries 2.0×10^2 A of current from east to west parallel to the surface of the earth.
   a. What is the magnitude of the force acting on each meter of the wire due to the earth's magnetic field?
   b. What is the direction of the force?
   c. In your judgment, would this force be important in designing towers to hold these power lines?

25:8 Galvanometers

The **galvanometer** is a device used to measure very small currents and is used in almost every voltmeter and ammeter.

A galvanometer consists of a small coil of wire placed in the strong magnetic field of a permanent magnet. The current passing through a wire loop in a magnetic field goes in one side of the loop and out the other side. Applying the third left-hand rule to each side of the loop, we find that one side of the loop is forced down while the other side of the loop is forced up. As a result, the loop rotates.

A galvanometer, a sensitive current meter, consists of a coil of wire in a magnetic field.

FIGURE 25-16. If a wire loop is placed in a magnetic field, the loop will rotate when current flows.

The magnitude of the force acting on the loop depends on the amount of current in the loop. Figure 25-16 shows how the force exerted on a loop of wire in a magnetic field can be used to measure current.

The force acting on the coil is proportional to the magnitude of the current. The coil turns against the restraining action of a small spring. The meter is calibrated by finding out how much the coil turns when known currents are sent through it. The meter is then used to measure unknown currents.

Many galvanometers produce a full-scale deflection with as little as 50 μA (50 × 10⁻⁶ A) current flow. The resistance of the coil of wire in a sensitive galvanometer is about 1000 Ω. Such a galvanometer can be converted into an ammeter by placing a resistor with resistance smaller than that of the galvanometer in parallel with the meter. Most of the current flows through the resistor, called the shunt, because the current is inversely proportional to resistance. A galvanometer can also be connected as a voltmeter. For this instrument a resistor, called the multiplier, is placed in series with the meter. The galvanometer measures the current through the multiplier. According to Ohm's law, $I = V/R$, V is the voltage across the voltmeter and R the effective resistance of the galvanometer and the multiplier resistor. The resistor is chosen so that at the desired full-scale voltage, the current through the meter and resistor causes the meter to be deflected full scale.

FIGURE 25-17. The components of an electric meter are shown.

25:9   Electric Motors

The simple loop of wire used in a galvanometer cannot rotate more than 180°. In Figure 25-16, the force acting upward on the right side of the loop pushes the loop up. At the same time, the force acting downward on the left side of the loop pushes that side down. The loop turns until it reaches the vertical position. The loop will not continue to turn because the force acting on the right side of the loop is still directed up. It cannot move down through the field. Similarly, the left side of the loop will not move up through the field because the force acting on it is still directed down.

For the loop to rotate 360° in the field, the current running through the loop must reverse direction just as the loop reaches its vertical position. This reversal allows the loop to continue rotating (Figure 25-18). To reverse current direction, a split-ring commutator is used. Brushes rub against the split-ring commutator, conducting current into the loop. A brush is a piece of graphite that makes a rubbing contact with the commutator and allows current to flow. The split ring is arranged so that each half of the commutator changes brushes just as the loop reaches the vertical position. Changing brushes reverses the current in the loop. As a result, the direction of the force on each side of the loop is reversed and the loop continues to rotate. This process is repeated each half-turn. Thus, the loop spins in the magnetic field.

An electric motor consists of a loop of wire in a magnetic field. When current flows in the loop, the loop rotates.

A split-ring commutator enables the loop in a motor to rotate 360°.

FIGURE 25-18. In an electric motor, split-ring commutators allow the wire loops in the motor to rotate 360°.

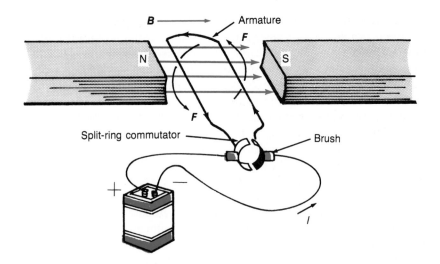

In practice, electric motors have several rotating loops. Together they make up the armature of the motor. The total force acting on the armature is proportional to $nBIL$, where n is the total number of loops on the armature and L is the length of wire in each loop that moves through the magnetic field. The magnetic field can be produced either by permanent magnets or by an electromagnet called a field coil. The force on the armature, and as a result the speed of the motor, is controlled by varying the current flowing through the motor.

25:10 The Force on a Single Charged Particle

The force exerted by a magnetic field on a current-carrying wire is a result of the forces on the individual electrons that make up the current flow. The electrons do not have to be confined to a wire, but can move across a region as long as the air has been removed to prevent collisions between the electrons and air molecules.

FIGURE 25-19. A television uses a cathode-ray tube to form pictures for viewing.

The picture tube, or cathode-ray tube, in a television set uses electrons deflected by magnetic fields to form the pictures to be viewed. In the tube, electrons are pulled off atoms by electric fields at the negative electrode, or cathode. Additional electric fields gather, accelerate, and focus the electrons into a narrow beam. Magnetic fields are used to deflect the beam back and forth and up and down across the screen of the tube. The screen is coated with a phosphor that glows when struck by the electrons, producing the picture.

In a television picture tube, magnetic fields are used to exert forces on a beam of electrons.

The force produced by a magnetic field on a single electron can be found by starting with the force on a current-carrying wire in a magnetic field, $F = BIL$. Consider a single electron flowing in a wire of length, L. The current, I, is equal to the charge per unit time entering the wire, $I = q/t$. In this case, q is the charge of the electron and t is the time it takes to move the length of the wire, L. The time required for a particle with velocity v to travel a distance L is found by using the equation of motion, $d = vt$, or here, $t = L/v$. As a result, the current $I = q/t$ may be replaced by qv/L. Therefore, the force on a single electron moving through a magnetic field of strength B is

The force acting on a single charged particle as it moves through a magnetic field is Bqv.

$$F = BIL = B\left(\frac{qv}{L}\right)L = Bqv$$

The particle charge is measured in coulombs, the velocity in m/s, and the magnetic induction in T (N/A · m).

The direction of the force is given by the third left-hand rule with the thumb pointed along the velocity of the particle.

The path of a charged particle in a magnetic field is circular because the force is always perpendicular to its velocity. The circular motion allows charged particles to be trapped and held in magnetic fields. Electrons trapped in the magnetic field of the earth, shown in Figure 25-20, form the Van Allen radiation belts. A disturbance on the sun can disturb the earth's magnetic field. The disturbance can cause particles to leave the belts and enter the earth's atmosphere at the magnetic poles of the earth, producing the aurora borealis, the northern lights. A proposed magnetic confinement fusion reaction would use strong magnetic fields to confine protons and other nuclei. The nuclei would collide at high speed, resulting in large amounts of energy. The details are discussed in Chapter 31.

A charged particle moves in a circular path in a magnetic field.

EXAMPLE

Force on a Charged Particle in a Magnetic Field

A beam of electrons travels at 3.0×10^6 m/s through a uniform magnetic field. The magnetic induction is 4.0×10^{-2} T.

  a. The beam is at right angles to the magnetic field. What is the magnitude of the force acting on each electron?

  b. Compare the force acting on a proton moving at the same speed and in the same direction to the force acting on the electron in Part *a*.

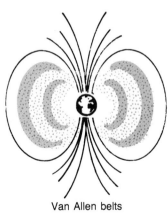

Van Allen belts

FIGURE 25-20. A representation of the Van Allen radiation belts around Earth.

Given: $v = 3.0 \times 10^6$ m/s   **Unknown:** F

$B = 4.0 \times 10^{-2}$ T   **Basic equation:** $F = Bqv$

$q = 1.6 \times 10^{-19}$ C

Solution:

a. $F = Bqv$

$= (4.0 \times 10^{-2} \text{ T})(1.6 \times 10^{-19} \text{ C})(3.0 \times 10^6 \text{ m/s})$

$= \left(4.0 \times 10^{-2}\dfrac{\text{N}}{\text{A} \cdot \text{m}}\right) (1.6 \times 10^{-19} \text{ C})(3.0 \times 10^6 \text{ m/s})$

$= 1.9 \times 10^{-14}$ N

b. The magnitude of the force is exactly the same on a proton as it is on an electron. The proton and the electron have exactly the same charge. However, because the proton has the opposite charge, it is deflected in the opposite direction.

Problems

12. 2.4×10^{-13} N

12. A beam of electrons moves at right angles to a magnetic field of magnetic induction 6.0×10^{-2} T. The electrons have a velocity of 2.5×10^7 m/s. What is the magnitude of the force acting on each electron?

13. 3.2×10^{-13} N

13. An electron passes through a magnetic field at right angles to the field at a velocity of 4.0×10^6 m/s. The strength of the magnetic field is 0.50 T. What is the magnitude of the force acting on the electron?

14. 8.6×10^{-16} N

14. A stream of doubly-ionized particles (missing two electrons and thus carrying a net charge of two elementary charges) moves at a velocity of 3.0×10^4 m/s perpendicularly to a magnetic field of 9.0×10^{-2} T. What is the magnitude of the force acting on each ion?

15. 1.7×10^{-13} N

15. Triply-ionized particles in a beam carry a net positive charge of three elementary charge units. The beam enters a field of magnetic induction 4.0×10^{-2} T at right angles to the field. The particles have a velocity of 9.0×10^6 m/s. What is the magnitude of the force acting on each particle?

16. 6.4×10^{-16} N

16. Doubly-ionized helium atoms (alpha particles) are traveling at right angles to a magnetic field at a speed of 4.0×10^4 m/s. The induction of the field is 5.0×10^{-2} T. What force acts on each particle?

17. 2.4×10^{-12} N

17. A beta particle (high-speed electron) is traveling at right angles to a magnetic field of induction 0.6 N/A·m. It has a speed of 2.5×10^7 m/s. What force acts on the particle?

18. 2.7×10^{18} m/s²

18. The mass of an electron is about 9.0×10^{-31} kg. What acceleration does the beta particle in Problem 17 undergo in the direction of the force acting on it?

Summary

1. Like magnetic poles repel, unlike magnetic poles attract.   25:1

2. Magnetic fields run from the north pole of a magnet to its south   25:2
pole.

3. Magnetic field lines always form closed loops.   25:2

4. Whenever an electric current flows in a wire, a magnetic field appears   25:3
about the wire.

5. A coil of wire (solenoid) through which a current flows also has a magnetic   25:4
field. The field about the coil will be similar to the field about a permanent
magnet.

6. When a current-bearing wire is placed in a magnetic field, current interacts   25:6, 25:7, 25:8
with the external magnetic field to produce a force. Galvanometers are
based on this principle.

7. The intensity of a magnetic field is called magnetic induction. The unit of   25:7
magnetic induction is the tesla (newton per amper-meter).

8. An electric motor consists of a coil of wire placed in a magnetic field. When   25:9
a current is introduced into the coil, the coil rotates due to the interaction
between the field about the coil and the external field.

Detailed answers to all Questions and Problems are given in the Teacher's Guide at the front of this book.

Questions

1. State the principle of magnetic attraction and repulsion.

2. Name the three most important magnetic elements.

3. How does a temporary magnet differ from a permanent magnet?

4. Draw a small bar magnet and show the magnetic field lines as they appear around a magnet. Use arrows to show the direction of the field lines.

5. Draw the field between two like magnetic poles and two unlike magnetic poles. Show the directions of the fields.

6. Draw the field around a straight current carrying wire. Show its direction.

7. Explain the left-hand rule to determine the direction of a magnetic field around a straight current carrying wire.

8. Explain the left-hand rule to determine the polarity of an electromagnet.

9. Explain the left-hand rule to determine the direction of force on a current-carrying wire placed in a magnetic field.

10. What three factors control the force that acts on a wire carrying a current in a magnetic field?

Problems—A

1. 0.10 T

1. A wire 0.50 m long carrying a current of 8.0 A is at right angles to a uniform magnetic field. The force on the wire is 0.40 N. What is the strength of the magnetic field?

2. 0.45 N

2. A wire 25 cm long is at right angles to a uniform magnetic field of magnetic induction 0.30 T. The current through the wire is 6.0 A. What force acts on the wire?

3. 4.0×10^{-2} T

3. A wire 1.50 m long carrying a current of 10.0 A is at right angles to a uniform magnetic field. The force acting on the wire is 0.60 N. What is the induction of the magnetic field?

4. 2.4 N

4. The current through a wire 0.80 m long is 5.0 A. The wire is perpendicular to a magnetic field of induction 0.60 T. What force acts on the wire?

5. 3×10^3 A

5. The force on a wire 0.80 m long that is perpendicular to the magnetic field of the earth is 0.12 N. What current flows through the wire?

6. 0.60 m

6. The force acting on a wire at right angles to a magnetic field is 3.6 N. The current flowing through the wire is 7.5 A. The magnetic field has an induction of 0.80 T. How long is the wire?

7. 4.2×10^6 m/s

7. A singly-ionized particle experiences a force of 4.1×10^{-13} N when it travels at right angles through a magnetic field of induction 0.61 T. What is the velocity of the particle?

8. 2 chg

8. A force of 5.78×10^{-16} N acts on an unknown particle traveling at a 90° angle through a magnetic field. If the velocity of the particle is 5.65×10^4 m/s and the induction of the field is 3.20×10^{-2} T, how many elementary charges does the particle carry?

9. 7.4×10^{-1} T

9. A muon (a particle with the same charge as an electron) is traveling at 4.21×10^7 m/s at right angles to a magnetic field. The muon experiences a force of 5.00×10^{-12} N. What is the induction of the field?

10. 2.7×10^{16} m/s²

10. The mass of a muon is 1.88×10^{-28} kg. What acceleration does the muon in Problem 9 experience?

Problems—B

1. a. 4.8×10^{-13} N
   b. 3.1 m

1. In a nuclear research laboratory a proton moves in a particle accelerator through a magnetic field of intensity 0.10 T at a speed of 3.0×10^7 m/s.

   a. If the proton is moving perpendicular to the field, what force acts on it?
   b. If the proton continues to move in a direction that is constantly perpendicular to the field, what is the radius of curvature of its path? (mass of protron = 1.67×10^{-27} kg)

2. An electron is accelerated from rest through a potential difference of 20 000 V, which exists between the plates P_1 and P_2, Figure 25–21. The electron then passes through a small opening into a magnetic field of uniform field strength **B**. As indicated, the magnetic field is directed into the page.

   a. State the direction of the electric field between the plates as either P_1 to P_2 or P_2 to P_1.

   b. In terms of the information given, calculate the electron's speed at plate P_2.

   c. Describe the motion of the electron through the magnetic field.

3. A current is sent through a vertical spring as shown in Figure 25-22. The end of the spring is in a cup filled with mercury. What will happen? Why?

2. a. P_2 to P_1
   b. 8.4×10^7 m/s
   c. clockwise circle

3. The spring will oscillate up and down. (The demonstration is called Roget's spiral.)

FIGURE 25-21. Use with Problem 2.

FIGURE 25-22. Use with Problem 3.

Readings

Kryder, Mark, "Magnetic Information Technology." *Physics Today*, December, 1984.

Monforte, John, "The Digital Reproduction of Sound." *Scientific American*, December, 1984.

Rubin, Laurence, "High Magnetic Fields for Physics." *Physics Today*, August, 1984.

Ruby, Daniel, "G. E. Superconducting Magnet." *Popular Science*, January, 1984.

Tierney, John, "The Little Engine That Might Not." *Science 84*, July, 1984.

An electric current can be used to produce a magnetic field. Conversely, a magnetic field can induce an electric current in a wire under certain conditions. This effect is called electromagnetic induction. The principle of electromagnetic induction is used in the design and operation of generators. These generators in the Hoover Dam hydroelectric facility are used to convert mechanical energy to electricity. Not all generators are the size shown here. What devices do you use every day that contain generators?

Electromagnetic Induction

Chapter 26 introduces electromagnetic induction and discusses the factors affecting the generation of electric currents by the relative motion of a wire and a magnetic field. Electric generators, both DC and AC, are described and the equations for effective current and voltage in an AC circuit are given. Lenz's law, self-induction and transformers are also discussed.

Oersted discovered that an electric current produces a magnetic field. Michael Faraday was convinced that a magnetic field should in turn be able to produce an electric current. For ten years, he tried unsuccessfully to produce a current using steady magnetic fields. However, in 1831 he found that a changing magnetic field could generate current flow. An American high school teacher, Joseph Henry, discovered the same fact at almost the same time. Applications of this discovery have included electric generators and transformers, which make possible the wide use of electricity in our society.

Goals: You will gain understanding of the origin and applications of induced electromotive forces.

26:1 Faraday's Discovery

Faraday experimented with a moving wire in a magnetic field. He found that when a wire is moved across a magnetic field, an electric current is induced in the wire. Figure 26-1 shows Faraday's experiments. A wire that is part of a closed (complete) circuit is held in a magnetic field. When the wire is moved through the field, the meter indicates that there is an electric current in the wire. If the wire moves up through the field, the current moves in one direction. When the wire moves down through the field, the current moves in the opposite direction. If the wire is held stationary or is moved parallel to the field, there is no current in the circuit. An electric current is generated in a wire only when the wire cuts the magnetic field lines.

For a current to be produced, either the conductor can move through a field or the field can move past a conductor. In both cases, it is the

When a wire is moved through a magnetic field, a current is generated in the wire.

Suggested demonstration: Connect a length of wire to a galvanometer. Gather the wire into several loops. Quickly move the loops between the poles of a strong magnet. The deflections of the galvanometer should be easily visible.

443

FIGURE 26-1. When a wire is moved in a magnetic field, an electric current flows in the wire, but only while the wire is moving. The direction of electron current flow depends on the direction the wire is moving through the field.

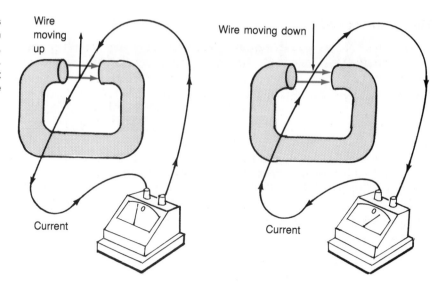

Electromagnetic induction is the process of generating a current by the relative motion between a wire and a magnetic field.

relative motion between the wire and the magnetic field that produces the current. The process of generating a current in this way is called **electromagnetic induction.**

If a wire moves through a magnetic field at an angle to the field, only the component of the wire's velocity that is perpendicular to the direction of the field generates a current.

The force acting on the free electrons in a wire as the wire moves through a magnetic field is perpendicular to both the direction in which the wire is moving and the direction of the magnetic field. To find the direction of the electron current that flows in a conductor moving through a magnetic field, use the left-hand rule described in Chapter 25. Hold the left hand so that the thumb points in the direction in which the wire is moving and the fingers point in the direction of the magnetic field. The palm of the hand points in the direction of the force acting on the electrons (Figure 26-2).

FIGURE 26-2. The left-hand rule can be used to find the direction of a current flowing through a conductor that is moving in a magnetic field.

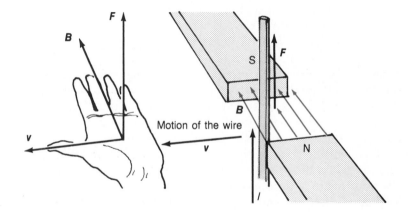

26:2 Induced EMF

When we studied electric circuits, we learned that an electron pump is needed to produce a current flow. The potential difference, or voltage, given to the electrons by the pump is sometimes called the **electromotive force,** or **EMF**. Note that the term *EMF* is misleading. Electromotive force is not a force; it is a potential difference and is measured in volts. Unfortunately, this term originated before electricity was well understood and is still in use.

EMF is the energy per charge, or potential.

When a wire is moved through a magnetic field, the energy of the electrons in the wire is increased. Their electric potential is raised. The difference in potential is called the induced *EMF*. The *EMF*, measured in volts, depends on the magnetic induction, **B,** the length of the wire in the magnetic field, L, and the velocity of the wire in the field, **v.** If **B**, L, and **v** are mutually perpendicular

Induced EMF is the energy given to electrons when a wire moves through a magnetic field.

$$EMF = BLv$$

EMF is the product of magnetic induction, wire length, and velocity of the wire.

If the moving wire is part of a closed circuit, a current will flow in the circuit.

A microphone is a simple application of induced *EMF*. Some microphones are similar to loudspeakers. The microphone in Figure 26-3 has a diaphragm attached to a coil of wire that is free to move in a magnetic field. Sound waves vibrate the diaphragm, which moves the coil in the magnetic field. The motion of the coil in turn induces an *EMF* across the ends of the coil. The voltage generated is small, typically 10^{-3} V, but it can be increased, or amplified, by electronic devices.

EXAMPLE

Induced EMF

A wire 0.20 m long moves perpendicularly through a magnetic field of magnetic induction 8.0×10^{-2} T at a speed of 7.0 m/s.   **a.**   What EMF is induced in the wire?   **b.**   The wire is part of a circuit that

a

b

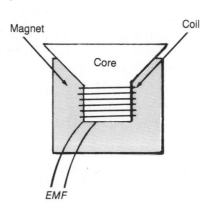

FIGURE 26-3. A microphone (a) and schematic diagram (b).

has a resistance of 0.50 Ω. What current flows in the circuit? (Remember that 1 T = 1 N/A $\cdot$ m.)

Given: $L = 0.20$ m   **Unknowns: a.** *EMF*   **b.** *I*

$B = 8.0 \times 10^{-2}$ T   **Basic equation:** $EMF = BLv$

$V = 7.0$ m/s

$R = 0.50$ Ω

Solution: a. $EMF = BLv = (8.0 \times 10^{-2}$ T$)(0.20$ m$)(7.0$ m/s$)$

$= (8.0 \times 10^{-2}$ N/A $\cdot$ m$)(0.20$ m$)(7.0$ m/s$)$

$= 0.11 \dfrac{\text{(N) (m) (m)}}{\frac{\text{C} \cdot \text{m}}{\text{s}} \text{(s)}}$

$= 0.11 \dfrac{\text{N} \cdot \text{m}}{\text{C}} = 0.11$ J/C $= 0.11$ V

b. $I = \dfrac{V}{R}$

$= \dfrac{0.11 \text{ V}}{0.50 \text{ } \Omega} = 0.22$ A

Problems

1. A wire 0.5 m long cuts straight up through a field of magnetic induction 0.4 N/A $\cdot$ m at a speed of 20 m/s.
   a. What *EMF* is induced in the wire?
   b. The wire is part of a circuit of total resistance 6.0 Ω. What is the current in the circuit?

2. A wire 2.0×10^1 m long is mounted on an airplane flying at 1.20×10^2 m/s. The wire moves perpendicularly through the earth's magnetic field (B $= 5.0 \times 10^{-5}$ N/A $\cdot$ m).
   a. What EMF is induced in the wire?
   b. If the wire is part of a circuit with a total resistance of 3.0×10^2 Ω, what current will flow?

3. A permanent magnet is mounted with the field lines vertical. If a student passes a wire between the poles and pulls it toward himself, the current through the wire is from right to left. Which is the N-pole of the magnet?

4. An instructor connects both ends of a copper wire of total resistance 0.10 Ω to the terminals of a galvanometer. The galvanometer has a resistance of 0.80 Ω. The instructor then holds part of the wire in a field of magnetic induction 2.0×10^{-2} T. The length of the wire between the magnetic poles is 10.0 cm. If the instructor moves the wire up through the field at 5.0 m/s, what current will the galvanometer indicate?

5. A wire 30.0 m long moves at 2.0 m/s perpendicularly through a field of magnetic induction 1.0 T.

   a. What *EMF* is induced in the wire?

   b. The total resistance of the circuit of which the wire is a part is 15.0 Ω. What is the current?

5. a. 6.0×10^1 V
   b. 4.0 A

26:3   Electric Generators

The **electric generator** was invented by Michael Faraday. It converts mechanical energy to electric energy. In essence, an electric generator consists of a number of wire loops placed in a strong magnetic field. All of the loops together form an armature, similar to that of an electric motor.

The wire loops are mounted so that they rotate freely in the field. As the loops turn, they cut through magnetic field lines. An EMF is induced. For clarity, Figure 26-4 shows only one loop of a generator. Increasing the number of loops in the armature increases the length of the wire in the field. In accordance with the expression $EMF = BLv$, the induced *EMF* also increases. If the generator is connected in a closed circuit, current will move through the circuit.

Using Figure 26-3 and the left-hand rule, notice that the current induced in the loop moves in opposite directions in the two sides of the loop. Therefore, there is a current through the entire loop. Only while the loop is in a horizontal position do the two segments move through the field at a right angle. In this position, the current is at maximum. The maximum occurs in this position because the loop cuts through the maximum number of magnetic field lines per unit time. As the loop moves from the horizontal to the vertical position, it moves through the magnetic field lines at an ever-increasing angle. Thus, it cuts through fewer magnetic field lines per unit time, and the current decreases. When the loop is in the vertical position, the segments move parallel to the field and the current is zero. As the loop continues to turn, the segment that was moving up begins to move down. The segment that was moving down begins to move up. Thus, the direction of the current

A generator consists of loops of wire placed in a magnetic field. As the loops are turned, current is induced in the wire. All of the wire loops together form the armature of the generator.

If you don't have a demonstration generator, a galvanometer can be connected to the terminals of any permanent magnet motor to show the generating action. If the motor has a commutator it will be a DC generator.

Maximum current and voltage are produced when the loops move at right angles to the field.

Zero current and voltage are produced when the loops move parallel to the field.

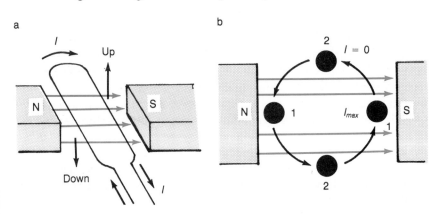

FIGURE 26-4. An electric current is generated in a wire loop as the loop rotates (a). This cross-sectional view (b) shows the position of the loop when maximum current is generated (1) and when no current is generated (2).

FIGURE 26-5. This graph shows the variation of current with time as a loop rotates.

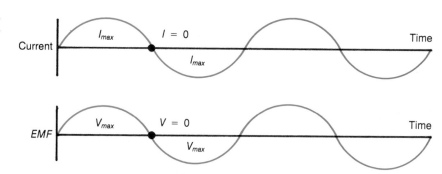

FIGURE 26-6. This graph shows the variation of voltage with time as a loop rotates.

The current induced in a wire loop changes direction each time the loop rotates 180°.

in the loop changes. This change in direction takes place each time the loop turns through 180°. The current changes smoothly from zero to some maximum value and back to zero during each half-turn of the loop. Then it reverses direction. The graph of current versus time yields the curve shown in Figure 26-5, which is called a sine curve.

In the previous section, we found that the EMF, or voltage, developed in a wire moving through a magnetic field is equal to the product BLv. A generator consists of a coil of wire rotating in a strong magnetic field. Thus, the EMF (voltage) developed by the generator depends upon the magnetic induction, *B,* the length of wire rotating in the field, *L,* and the rate at which the coil (armature) turns in the field, **v.**

As the armature turns in the magnetic field, its loops move through the field at different angles. Thus, the voltage changes in the same way that the current changes. The voltage is at maximum value when the loops are moving at right angles to the field. The voltage is zero when the loops are moving parallel to the field, Figure 26-6.

26:4   Alternating Current Generator

An energy source turns the armature of a generator at a set number of revolutions per second in a magnetic field. Commercially, in the United States, this frequency is usually 60 Hz. The current changes direction, or alternates, 120 times a second.

In Figure 26-7, an alternating current in an armature is transmitted to the rest of the circuit. The brush-slip-ring arrangement permits the armature to turn freely while still allowing the current to pass into the external circuit. As the armature turns, the alternating current varies between some maximum value and zero. The light in the circuit does not appear to dim or brighten because the changes are too fast for the eye to detect.

The power produced by a generator is the product of the current and voltage. Power is always positive because I and V are both either positive or negative at the same time. However, because I and V are sometimes zero, the power delivered by alternating current is less than the power supplied by direct current with the same I_{max} and V_{max}. In fact, $P_{AC} = \frac{1}{2}P_{DC}$.

Permanent magnet

Armature

Slip rings

Brush

FIGURE 26-7. Alternating current generators transmit current to an external circuit by way of a brush-slip-ring arrangement.

Since alternating currents and voltages are constantly changing with time, it is common to describe these quantities in terms of effective currents and voltages. Recall that $P = I^2R$. Thus, power can be written in terms of the effective current, $P_{AC} = I^2_{eff}R$.

$$P_{AC} = \frac{1}{2}P_{DC}$$
$$I^2_{eff}R = \frac{1}{2}(I^2_{max}R)$$
$$I_{eff} = \sqrt{\frac{1}{2}(I^2_{max})} = 0.707\ I_{max}$$
$$V_{eff} = 0.707\ V_{max}$$

Similarly,

The effective current is 0.707 maximum current.

The 120-V AC voltage, generally available at wall outlets, is the value of the effective voltage, not the maximum voltage.

The effective voltage is 0.707 maximum voltage.

EXAMPLE

Effective Voltage and Effective Current

An AC generator develops a maximum voltage of 1.00×10^2 V and delivers a maximum current of 20.0 A to a circuit.   **a.** What is the effective voltage of the generator?   **b.** What effective current is delivered to the circuit?   **c.** What is the resistance of the circuit?

Given: $V_{max} = 1.00 \times 10^2$ V   **Unknowns: a.** V_{eff} **b.** I_{eff} **c.** R

$I_{max} = 20.0$ A   **Basic equations:**

a. $V_{eff} = 0.707\ V_{max}$

b. $I_{eff} = 0.707\ I_{max}$

You may wish to plot $V_{max}\sin(2\pi ft)$ • $I_{max}\sin(2\pi ft)$ and show that this curve goes between 0 and $V_{max}I_{max}$. It is easy to see that the average height is $(V_{max}I_{max})/2$.

Solution: **a.** $V_{eff} = 0.707\ (V_{max}) = 0.707\ (100.0\ V) = 70.7\ V$
   b. $I_{eff} = 0.707\ (I_{max}) = 0.707\ (20.0\ A) = 14.1\ A$
   c. $R = \dfrac{V_{eff}}{I_{eff}} = \dfrac{70.7\ V}{14.1\ A} = 5.00\ \Omega$

Problems

6. a. 120 V
   b. 0.49 A

6. A generator in a power plant develops a maximum voltage of 170 V.
   a.   What is the effective voltage?
   b.   A 60-W light bulb is placed across the generator. A maximum current of 0.70 A flows through the bulb. What effective current flows through the bulb?

7. a. 165 V
   b. 7.8 A

7. The effective voltage of an AC household outlet is 117 V.
   a.   What is the maximum voltage across a lamp connected to the outlet?
   b.   The effective current through the lamp is 5.5 A. What is the maximum current in the lamp?

8. a. 3.00 × 10² V
   b. 0.600 A

8. An AC generator delivers a peak voltage of 425 V.
   a.   What is the effective voltage in a circuit placed across the generator?
   b.   The resistance of the circuit is $5.00 \times 10^2\ \Omega$. What is the effective current?

26:5   Generators and Motors

Generators and motors are identical in construction, but perform opposite energy transformations. A generator converts mechanical energy to electric energy. A motor converts electric energy to mechanical energy.

A generator converts mechanical energy to electric energy; a motor converts electric energy to mechanical energy.

FIGURE 26-8. This experimental electric car runs on electric energy from its batteries rather than from fossil fuels.

In a generator, an armature is mechanically turned in a magnetic field to induce a voltage. This voltage causes current to flow. In a motor, a voltage is placed across an armature coil in a magnetic field. The voltage causes current to flow in the coil and the armature turns.

Electric cars and trucks have been developed recently to reduce our reliance on gasoline. These vehicles use electric energy stored in batteries. When the accelerator is pressed, electric energy drives the motor, which gives the car kinetic energy. Present batteries have limited energy storage capacity, which limits the operating range of the vehicle.

26:6 Lenz's Law

In a generator, motion of the armature wire through the magnetic field causes current to flow. However, current flowing through a wire in a magnetic field gives rise to a force on that wire. Thus, the wires in the armature of a generator have a force exerted on them as a result of the current flow through the wires in the magnetic field. The direction of the force on the wires is to oppose the motion of the wires. That is, the force acts to slow down the rotation of the armature. The direction of the force was first determined in 1834 by H. F. E. Lenz and is called **Lenz's law.** *The current is induced in a direction such that the magnetic effects produced by the current oppose the change in flux that induced the current.* Note that it is the *change* in flux and not the flux itself that is opposed by the induced magnetic effects.

If the generator supplies little current, then the opposing force will be small and the armature will be easy to turn. If the generator supplies a larger current, the force will be larger and the armature will be correspondingly more difficult to turn. A generator supplying a large current is producing a large amount of electrical power. The opposing force on the armature means that a large amount of mechanical power must be supplied to the generator to produce the electrical power.

Lenz's law also applies to motors. When a current-carrying wire moves in a magnetic field, an *EMF* is generated. The *EMF*, called the back-*EMF*, is in a direction that opposes the current flow. When a motor is first turned on, a large current flows because of the low resistance of the motor. As the motor begins to turn, the motion of the wires across the magnetic field induces back-*EMF* that opposes the current flow. Therefore, the net current flowing through the motor is reduced. If a mechanical load is placed on the motor, slowing it down, the back-*EMF* is reduced and more current flows. If the load causes the motor to stop, current flow can be so high that wires overheat.

The heavy current flow when a motor is started can cause voltage drops across the resistance of the wires that carry current to the motor. The voltage drop across the wires causes a reduction in voltage across the motor. If a second device, such as a light bulb, is in a parallel circuit

Suggested demonstration: Connect an ammeter in series with a motor. Have students observe current when the motor is turned on, running at high speed, and running with a heavy load.

A motor produces a back-EMF as it rotates. The generated current opposes the current operating the motor, reducing the current flow.

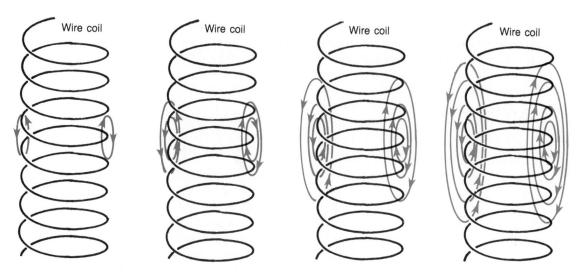

FIGURE 26-9. EMF is generated as a current increases in a coil.

with the motor, the voltage at the device will drop when the motor is started. The bulb will dim. As the motor picks up speed, the voltage will rise again and the bulb will brighten.

When the current to the motor is interrupted by turning off a switch in the circuit or pulling the motor's plug from a wall outlet, the sudden decrease in the magnetic field generates a back-*EMF* that can be large enough to cause a spark across the switch or between the plug and the wall outlet.

26:7   Self-Inductance

As Faraday showed, *EMF* is induced whenever a wire cuts lines of magnetic flux. Consider the coil of wire shown in Figure 26-9. When no current flows through the wire, there are no magnetic flux lines in the coil. When a steady current flows, a constant number of lines pass through the coil. Flux lines are always closed loops. As the magnetic field increases, new flux lines are created. The flux lines cut through the coil wires as they increase. An *EMF* is thus generated as the current increases in a coil. This effect is called **self-inductance.** The magnitude of the *EMF* is proportional to the rate at which flux lines cut through the wires. The direction of the *EMF* is to oppose the increase in current. The result of the opposing *EMF* is that the current through the coil reaches its maximum value, not instantaneously, but over a short period of time. When the current is steady, the magnetic flux is constant and the *EMF* is zero. When the current decreases, an *EMF* is generated that tends to prevent the reduction in magnetic flux and current.

When the coil is connected to an AC source, the field produced by the coil is always changing. Therefore, the induced *EMF* never ceases. The opposition (which is not a true resistance) to alternating current

As current in a coil changes, an induced EMF appears in that same coil. This effect is called self-inductance.

flow by a coil is called **inductive reactance.** Inductive reactance depends on the magnitude of the magnetic field. Therefore, a coil with an iron core has a larger inductive reactance than one without a core.

Inductive reactance impedes the flow of current in an AC current.

26:8 Transformers

A **transformer** is a device that is used to increase or to decrease AC voltages. Transformers are widely used because they change the voltage essentially with no loss of energy. A transformer is an application of electromagnetic induction.

A transformer can be used to increase voltage or to decrease voltage.

A transformer has two coils, electrically insulated from each other, wound around the same iron core. One coil is called the **primary coil.** The other coil is called the **secondary coil.** When the primary coil is connected to a source of AC voltage, the changing current flow creates a varying magnetic field. The varying magnetic flux is carried by the core to the secondary coil. In the secondary coil, the varying flux induces a varying *EMF*. This effect is called mutual inductance.

In a transformer, two coils of different numbers of turns are wound around the same core.

The *EMF* induced in the secondary, called the secondary voltage, is proportional to the primary voltage. The secondary voltage also depends on the ratio of turns in the secondary to the primary.

$$\frac{\text{Secondary voltage}}{\text{Primary voltage}} = \frac{\text{Number of turns on secondary}}{\text{Number of turns on primary}}$$

The number of turns in a coil is a count and is therefore considered to be an exact number.

$$\boxed{\frac{V_s}{V_p} = \frac{N_s}{N_p}}$$

$$V_s = \frac{N_s}{N_p}V_p$$

If the secondary voltage is larger than the primary voltage, the transformer is called a **step-up transformer.** If the voltage out of the transformer is smaller than the voltage put in, then it is called a **step-down transformer.**

In an ideal transformer, the power delivered to the secondary circuit is equal to the power consumed in the primary.

In an ideal transformer, the electric power delivered to the secondary circuit equals the power used by the primary. An ideal transformer uses no power itself. Since $P = VI$,

$$V_pI_p = V_sI_s$$

FIGURE 26-10. For a transformer, the ratio of input voltage to output voltage depends upon the ratio of the number of turns of the primary to the number of turns of the secondary.

Step-up transformer

Step-down transformer

a

b

FIGURE 26-11. Transformers are used to increase the voltage of current leaving the power station.

The current that flows in the primary depends on how much current is required in the secondary circuit. A step-up transformer increases voltage; the current in the primary circuit is greater than in the secondary. In a step-down transformer, the current is greater in the secondary circuit than in the primary.

As was discussed in Chapter 23, long distance transmission of electric energy is economical only if low currents and very high voltages are used. Step-up transformers are used at power sources to develop voltages as high as 240 000 V. The high voltage reduces the current flow required in the transmission lines, keeping I^2R losses low. When the energy reaches the consumer, step-down transformers provide appropriately low voltages for consumer use.

There are many other important uses of transformers. Television picture tubes require up to 2.0×10^4V, which is developed by a transformer within the set. The spark or ignition coil in an automobile is a transformer designed to step up the 12 V from the battery to thousands of volts. The "points" interrupt the DC current from the battery to produce the changing magnetic field needed to induce *EMF* in the secondary coil. Arc welders require currents of 10^4 A. Large step-down transformers are used to provide these currents, which can heat metals to 3000°C or more.

EXAMPLE

Step-Up Transformer

A step-up transformer has 2.00×10^2 turns on its primary coil and 3.00×10^3 turns on its secondary coil.   **a.** The primary coil is supplied with an alternating current at 90.0 V. What is the voltage in the secondary circuit?   **b.** The current flowing in the secondary circuit is 2.00 A. What current flows in the primary circuit? **c.** What is the power in the primary? In the secondary?

Given: $N_p = 2.00 \times 10^2$ **Unknowns:** **a.** V_s **b.** I_p **c.** P

$N_s = 3.00 \times 10^3$ **Basic equation:** **a.** $\dfrac{V_p}{V_s} = \dfrac{N_p}{N_s}$

$V_p = 90.0$ V

$I_s = 2.00$ A   **b.** $V_p I_p = V_s I_s$

Solution: **a.** $\dfrac{V_p}{V_s} = \dfrac{N_p}{N_s}$ or $V_s = \dfrac{V_p N_s}{N_p}$

$$= \frac{(90.0 \text{ V})(3.00 \times 10^3)}{2.00 \times 10^2} = 1350 \text{ V}$$

b. $V_p I_p = V_s I_s$ or $I_p = \dfrac{V_s I_s}{V_p}$

$$I_p = \frac{(1350 \text{ } \cancel{V})(2.00 \text{ A})}{90.0 \text{ } \cancel{V}} = 30.0 \text{ A}$$

c. $V_p I_p = (90.0 \text{ V})(30.0 \text{ A}) = 2.70 \times 10^3 \text{ W}$
$V_s I_s = (1350 \text{ V})(2.00 \text{ A}) = 2.70 \times 10^3 \text{ W}$

Problems

9. An ideal step-up transformer's primary has 50 turns. Its secondary has 1500 turns. The primary is connected to an AC generator having an *EMF* of 120 V.
   a. Calculate the *EMF* of the secondary.
   b. Find the current in the primary circuit if the current in the secondary is 3.0 A.
   c. What power develops in the primary? In the secondary?

9. a. 3600 V
b. 9.0 × 10¹ A
c. 11 000 W,
11 000 W

10. The secondary of a step-down transformer has 50 turns. The primary has 1500 turns.
    a. The *EMF* of the primary is 3600 V. What is the *EMF* of the secondary?
    b. The current in the primary is 3.0 A. What current flows in the secondary?

10. a. 120 V
b. 9.0 × 10¹ A

11. A step-up transformer has 300 turns on its primary and 90 000 (9.000 × 10⁴) turns on its secondary. The *EMF* of the generator to which the primary is attached is 60.0 V.
    a. What is the *EMF* in the secondary?
    b. The current flowing in the secondary coil is 0.50 A. What current flows in the primary?

11. a. 1.80 × 10⁴ V
b. 1.5 × 10² A

12. A step-down transformer has 7500 turns on its primary and 125 turns on its secondary. The voltage across the primary is 7200 V.
    a. What voltage is across the secondary?

12. a. 120 V

12. b. 0.60 A

13. a. 1.20×10^5 V
    b. 0.100 A

14. a. 1/200
    b. 0.20 A

15. a. 750
    b. 38
    c. 7.5

b. The current in the secondary is 36 A. What current flows in the primary?

13. A step-up transformer is connected to a generator that is delivering 1.20×10^2 V and 1.00×10^2 A. The ratio of the turns on the secondary to the turns on the primary is 1000 to 1.

a. What voltage is across the secondary?

b. What current flows in the secondary?

14. In a hydroelectric plant, electric energy is generated at 1200 V. It is transmitted at 240 000 V.

a. What is the ratio of the turns on the primary to the turns on the secondary of a transformer connected to one of the generators?

b. One of the plant generators can deliver 40.0 A to the primary of its transformer. What current is flowing in the secondary?

15. The primary of a transformer has 150 turns. It is connected to a 120-V source. Calculate the number of turns on the secondary needed to supply the following.

a. 6.0×10^2 V   **b.** 3.0×10^1 V   **c.** 6.0 V

Physics Focus

Trains That Levitate and Move Magnetically

Most trains run on wheels in contact with a steel rail. The resulting vibration and noises annoy passengers and people living and working near the railway.

A new generation of levitating trains eliminates both vibration and noise by floating on magnetic fields. A Japanese design uses superconducting agents cooled to $-260°C$ with liquid helium, eliminating most of the resistance of electron flow and producing very strong electromagnets. As the magnets, located in the bottoms of the cars, pass over metal coils in the guideway, a magnetic field of the same polarity as that in the coils is induced, resulting in a repulsion that lifts the cars 10 to 12 cm. Experimental trains have attained speeds of over 500 km/h. A German design uses electromagnets attached to the cars and wrapped around steel rails under the cars. Attraction to the rail lifts the cars about 8 mm.

Both trains are propelled by linear induction motors. Magnets in the guideway ahead of the train have the opposite polarity of magnets on the train and thus pull the train by attraction. As the train passes a given point, the guideway magnet's polarity is reversed suddenly by computer, and the train is "pulsed" forward by repulsion.

| | **Summary** | |

1. Michael Faraday discovered that if work is done to move a wire through a   26:1
   magnetic field an electric current will be induced in the wire.

2. The direction taken by the current in a wire moving through a magnetic   26:2
   field depends upon the direction in which the wire is moving.

3. The current produced depends upon the angle between the velocity of the   26:2
   wire and the magnetic field. Maximum current occurs when the wire is
   moving at right angles to the field.

4. Electromotive force, EMF, is the energy imparted to each unit of charge by   26:2
   the energy source. EMF is measured in volts.

5. EMF is the product of the magnetic induction, **B**, the length of the wire in   26:2
   the field, L, and the speed of the moving wire, **v**.

6. An electric generator consists of a number of wire loops placed in a   26:3, 26:4
   magnetic field. Because each side of the coil moves alternately up and
   down through the field, the current alternates direction in the loops. The
   generator develops alternating voltage and current.

7. A generator and a motor are the same device. A generator converts   26:5
   mechanical energy to electric energy, while a motor converts electric
   energy to mechanical energy.

8. Lenz's law states that an induced current always acts in opposition to the   26:6
   change in flux that is causing the current.

9. A transformer has two coils wound about the same core. The introduction   26:8
   of an AC voltage across the primary coil induces an EMF in the secondary
   coil. The voltages in alternating current circuits may be stepped up or
   down by the use of transformers.

Detailed answers to all Questions and Problems are given in the Teacher's Guide at the front of this book.

| | **Questions** | |

1. How can a wire and a magnet be used to generate an electric current?

2. What is the difference between the current generated in a wire when the
   wire is moved up through a magnetic field and when the wire is moved
   down through the same field?

3. What causes an electron to move in a wire when the wire is moved
   through a magnetic field?

4. What is EMF?

5. Substitute units to show that the unit of BLv is volts.

6. Sketch and describe an AC generator.

7. What is the armature of an electric generator?

8. What is the difference between a generator and a motor?

9. What is the effective value of an AC current?

10. What factors determine the *EMF* of a generator?

11. State Lenz's law.

12. What causes the back-*EMF* of an electric motor?

13. Why is the self-inductance of a coil an important factor when the coil is in an AC circuit and a minor factor when the coil is in a DC circuit?

14. Upon what does the ratio of the *EMF* in the primary of a transformer to the *EMF* in the secondary of the transformer depend?

15. A transformer is connected to a battery through a switch. The secondary circuit contains a light bulb. Which of these statements best describes when the lamp will be lighted? As long as the switch is closed. Only the moment it is closed. Only the moment the switch is opened. Explain.

Problems–A

1. 0.18 V

1. A wire segment 3.0×10^1 cm long moves straight up through a field of magnetic induction 4.0×10^{-2} T at a speed of 15.0 m/s. What *EMF* is induced in the wire?

2. a. 3.6 V
   b. 0.80 A

2. A wire 0.75 m long cuts straight up through a field of magnetic induction 0.30 T at a speed of 16 m/s.
   a. What *EMF* is induced in the wire?
   b. The wire is part of a circuit of total resistance of 4.5 Ω. What current flows in the circuit?

3. 4.0×10^1 V

3. A wire 20.0 m long moves at 4.0 m/s perpendicularly through a field of magnetic induction 0.50 T. What *EMF* is induced in the wire?

4. a. 110 V
   b. 21.2 A

4. An AC generator develops a maximum voltage of 150 V. It delivers a maximum current of 30.0 A to an external circuit.
   a. What is the effective voltage of the generator?
   b. What effective current does it deliver to the external circuit?

5. a. 310 V
   b. 2.0×10^1 A

5. An electric stove is connected to a 220-V AC source.
   a. What is the maximum voltage across one of the stove's elements when it is operating?
   b. The resistance of the operating element is 11 Ω. What effective current flows through it?

6. 399 V

6. An AC generator develops a maximum *EMF* of 565 V. What effective *EMF* does the generator deliver to an external circuit?

7. A step-up transformer has 80 turns on its primary coil. It has 1200 turns on its secondary coil. The primary coil is supplied with an alternating current at 120 V.

   a. What voltage is across the secondary coil?

   b. The current in the secondary coil is 2.0 A. What current flows in the primary circuit?

   c. What is the transformer power input and output?

7. a. 1800 V
  b. 3.0 × 10¹ A
  c. 3600 W, 3600 W

Problems–B

1. An instructor is moving a loop of copper wire down through a magnetic field B as shown in Figure 26–12 .

   a. Will the induced current move to the right or left in the wire segment shown in the diagram?

   b. As soon as the wire is moved in the field, a current appears in it. Thus, the wire segment is a current-carrying wire located in a magnetic field. A force must act on the wire. What will be the direction of the force acting on the wire due to the induced current?

1. a. right
  b. up

2. An inventor proposes that a considerable amount of gasoline could be conserved each year by mounting antennalike wire segments on the roofs of automobiles. When the autos move perpendicular to or at some angle with the earth's magnetic field, a current would be generated in the wires that could be used to charge storage batteries. The batteries could, in turn, power the auto.

   a. The earth's magnetic field in the United States has an average induction of about 5.0×10^{-5} T. If an auto were moving 72.0 km/h perpendicular to that field (east-west), what would have to be the total length of the wire segments on its roof to develop an *EMF* of 12 V?

   b. If due to its low weight, aluminum wire of resistance 2.6×10^{-4} Ω per meter is used for the wire segments, what maximum current could be developed?

2. a. 1.2×10^4 m
  b. 3.8 A

FIGURE 26-12. Use with Problem 1.

Readings

Parker, E. N., "Magnetic Fields in the COSMOS." *Scientific American,* August, 1983.

Patterson, Walt, "A New Way to Burn." *Science 83,* April, 1983.

Reich, Leonard, "From Edison's Wastebasket." *Science 84,* November, 1984.

Reid, T. R., "The Chip." *Science 85,* January, 1985.

Stifter, Francis, "Protecting Your Computer from Power Line Disturbances." *Computers and Electronics,* October, 1983.

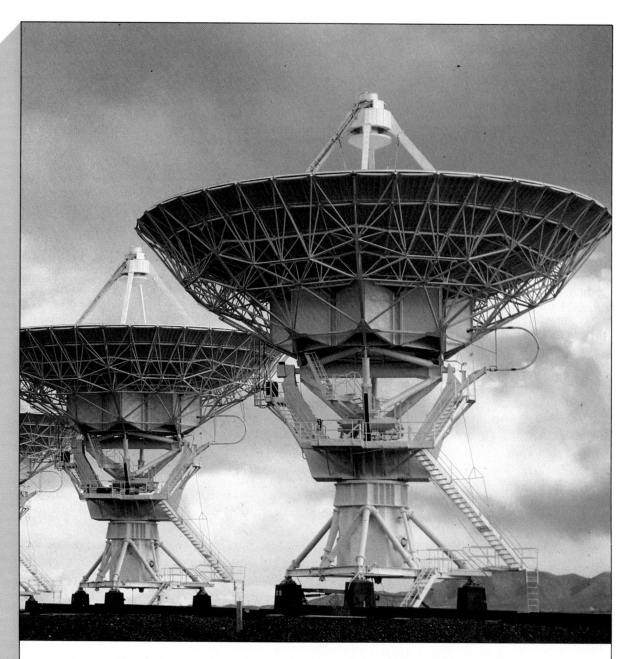

The electromagnetic spectrum includes radiation with wavelengths as short as 10^{-14} meters and as long as 10^7 meters. Radio waves originating in outer space are detected using large radio antennas. Scientists are gathering data about events which occurred in space over 300 years ago using radio telescopes. The technology associated with using electromagnetic waves has enabled us to learn more about our universe. What devices do you use every day that operate by using electromagnetic waves? You may be surprised.

Electric and Magnetic Fields

Chapter 27 describes the behavior of charged particles in electric and magnetic fields leading to a discussion of the cathode-ray tube and the mass spectrograph. The generation and transmission of electromagnetic waves is discussed.

Electric and magnetic fields exert forces on charged particles. Many valuable instruments have been developed using the two kinds of fields acting together. Some of these instruments will be explored in this chapter.

Oersted showed that current-carrying wires produced magnetic fields. Faraday and Henry demonstrated that changing magnetic fields produced electric currents. In 1864, James Clark Maxwell (1831–1879) showed that even without wires, changing electric fields caused magnetic fields, and that the changing magnetic fields produced electric fields. The result is energy transmitted across empty space in the form of electromagnetic waves. Maxwell's theory, soon tested experimentally by Heinrich Hertz, led to a complete description of electricity and magnetism. It also gave us radio, television, and many other devices important to our lives.

Goal: You will gain understanding of the use of separated electric and magnetic fields to study the properties of charged particles, and the way coupled electric and magnetic fields produce electromagnetic waves, including light.

27:1 Mass of the Electron

Electrons are not only part of every atom, they also are the source of electric fields and currents. Therefore, it is important to know the properties of electrons. The magnitude of charge is known from the Millikan oil drop experiment. The mass is too small to measure on an ordinary balance. However, it is possible to find the ratio of the mass to the charge by balancing the forces of electric and magnetic fields acting on the electron.

The ratio of the mass to charge of the electron was first measured in 1897 by the British physicist J. J. Thomson (1856–1940). He used a cathode-ray tube similar to the one shown in Figure 27-1. All air is removed from the glass tube. Electrons are emitted by the cathode, a hot tungsten wire. An electric field accelerates the electrons, some of which go through a hole in the anode. Electric fields act like optical lenses. They focus the electrons into a tiny beam that hits a fluorescent screen. The screen glows at the point where the electrons strike.

FIGURE 27-1. The Thomson m/q tube.

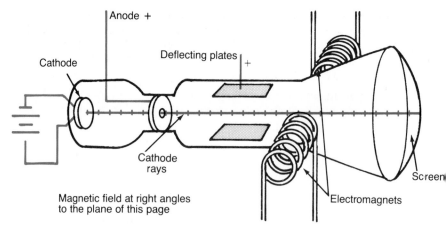

Anode +

Cathode

Deflecting plates

+

Cathode rays

Screen

Magnetic field at right angles to the plane of this page

Electromagnets

Thomson observed the deflection of electrons in both electric and magnetic fields. The electric field, the magnetic field, and the electron beam are all perpendicular to one another.

In the middle of the tube, a pair of parallel plates produces a uniform electric field perpendicular to the beam. The field intensity, **E,** produces a force, $q\mathbf{E}$, that acts on the electrons to deflect the beam upward. A magnetic field is placed in the same region as the electric field. Two coils produce the magnetic field at right angles to both the beam and the electric field. The force exerted by the magnetic field is equal to Bqv. Here, B is the magnetic induction, and v is the electron velocity. The magnetic force acts downward.

When both the electric and magnetic fields are present, they can be adjusted until the beam of electrons follows a straight or undeflected path. Then the magnitude of the force on the electrons due to the electric field is equal to the magnitude of the force due to the magnetic field.

To find the velocity of the electrons, the fields are adjusted until electrons follow an undeflected path.

$$Bqv = Eq$$

Solving this equation for v, we obtain the expression

$$v = \frac{Eq}{Bq}$$

$$= \frac{E}{B}$$

If the potential difference is removed from the plates, the only force acting on the electrons is due to the magnetic field. This force acts at a 90° angle with the direction of motion of the electrons. Thus, the magnetic force causes a centripetal acceleration. The electrons follow a circular path with radius, r. Newton's second law gives

When electrons move through a magnetic field, they follow a circular path.

$$Bqv = m\frac{v^2}{r}$$

Solving for m/q gives

$$\boxed{\frac{m}{q} = \frac{Br}{v}}$$

Thomson calculated the velocity, v, using the measured values of E and B. He measured the distance between the undeflected spot and the position of the spot when only the magnetic field acted on the electrons. Using this distance and the size of the field region, he calculated the radius of the circular path of the electron, r. Therefore, Thomson could calculate m/q. The average of many experimental trials gave the value $m/q = 5.686 \times 10^{-12}$ kg/C. Using Millikan's value of $q = 1.602 \times 10^{-19}$ C gives the mass of the electron, m.

The mass of a proton can be measured by the same method.

$$\frac{m}{q} = 5.686 \times 10^{-12} \text{ kg/C}$$

$$m = (5.686 \times 10^{-12} \text{ kg/C})(q)$$
$$= (5.686 \times 10^{-12} \text{ kg/}\cancel{C})(1.602 \times 10^{-19} \cancel{C})$$
$$= 9.109 \times 10^{-31} \text{ kg} = 9.11 \times 10^{-31} \text{ kg}$$

The Thomson method can be used to find m/q for any charged particle. Protons can be obtained by removing the electrons from hydrogen atoms. A hydrogen atom consists of a single proton and a single electron. A small amount of hydrogen gas is put into a vacuum tube similar to the one shown in Figure 27-2. A beam of accelerated electrons bombards the hydrogen gas and separates it into protons and electrons. The protons are accelerated through a small hole in one electrode by a second electric field. The proton beam then passes through electric and magnetic deflecting fields and to the fluorescent screen of the Thomson m/q tube. The mass of the proton is determined in the same manner as was the mass of the electron. The mass of the proton is 1.67×10^{-27} kg.

Thomson actually used the value of the charge on the electron found from electrochemistry experiments. We can use Millikan's value.

EXAMPLE

Straight-Line Motion of an Electron in an m/q Tube

A beam of electrons travels an undeflected path in a tube. E is 7.0×10^3 N/C. B is 3.5×10^{-2} T. What is the speed of the electrons as they travel through the tube?

Accelerating field

Electron beam

Gas entry

Positive ion beam

To vacuum pump

FIGURE 27-2. Production of positive ions by an electron beam.

Given: $E = 7.0 \times 10^3$ N/C   **Unknown:** v

$B = 3.5 \times 10^{-2}$ T   **Basic equation:** $v = E/B$

Solution: $v = \dfrac{E}{B}$

$$= \frac{7.0 \times 10^3 \text{ N/C}}{3.5 \times 10^{-2} \text{ N/A} \cdot \text{m}} = 2.0 \times 10^5 \text{ m/s}$$

EXAMPLE

Path of an Electron in a Magnetic Field

An electron of mass 9.11×10^{-31} kg moves with a speed of 2.0×10^5 m/s across a magnetic field. The magnetic induction is 8.0×10^{-4} T. What is the radius of the circular path followed by the electrons while in the field?

Given: $m = 9.11 \times 10^{-31}$ kg   **Unknown:** r

$v = 2.0 \times 10^5$ m/s   **Basic equation:** $Bqv = mv^2/r$

$B = 8.0 \times 10^{-4}$ T

$(q = 1.6 \times 10^{-19}$ C)

Solution:

$$Bqv = \frac{mv^2}{r}$$

$$r = \frac{mv}{Bq} = \frac{(9.11 \times 10^{-31} \text{ kg})(2.0 \times 10^5 \text{ m/s})}{(8.0 \times 10^{-4} \text{ N/A} \cdot \text{m})(1.6 \times 10^{-19} \text{ C})}$$

$$r = 1.4 \times 10^{-3} \text{ m}$$

Problems

Assume the direction of all moving charged particles is perpendicular to the magnetic fields.

1. 8×10^3 m/s

1. Protons passing through a field of magnetic induction of 0.6 T are deflected. An electric field of intensity 4.5×10^3 N/C is introduced. The protons are brought back to their undeflected path. What is the speed of the moving protons?

2. 1×10^{-4} m

2. A proton moves at a speed of 7.5×10^3 m/s as it passes through a field of magnetic induction 0.6 T. Find the radius of the circular path. The mass of a proton is 1.7×10^{-27} kg. The charge carried by the proton is equal to that of the electron, but it is positive.

3. 5.0×10^4 m/s

3. Electrons move through a field of magnetic induction 6.0×10^{-2} T. An electric field of 3.0×10^3 N/C prevents the electrons from being deflected. What is the speed of the electrons?

4. 4.7×10^{-6} m

4. Calculate the radius of the circular path the electrons in Problem 3 follow in the absence of the electric field. The mass of an electron is 9.11×10^{-31} kg.

5. A proton enters a magnetic field that has a magnetic induction of 6.0 × 10⁻² T with a speed of 5.4 × 10⁴ m/s. What is the radius of the circular path it follows?

6. A proton moves across a field of magnetic induction 0.36 T. It follows a circular path of radius 0.2 m. What is the speed of the proton?

7. Electrons move across a field of magnetic induction 4.0 × 10⁻³ T. They follow a circular path of radius 2.0 × 10⁻² m.
   a. What is their speed?
   b. An electric field is applied perpendicularly to the magnetic field. The electrons then follow a straight-line path. Find the magnitude of the electric field.

5. 9.6 × 10⁻³ m

6. 7 × 10⁶ m/s

7. a. 1.4 × 10⁷ m/s
   b. 5.6 × 10⁴ N/C

27:2 Mass Spectrograph

A mass spectrograph, an adaptation of the Thomson tube, is used to measure masses of positive ions. The positive ions are formed in an apparatus similar to the one described in the last section, Figure 27–2. They are accelerated to a specific kinetic energy by an electric field and emerge through a hole in one electrode.

The ions pass into a region with a strong, uniform magnetic field and are deflected into a circular path, Figure 27-3. The radius of the path is found using the equation $Bqv = mv^2/r$. Solving for r yields

$$r = \frac{mv}{qB}$$

FIGURE 27-3. Schematic diagram of a mass spectrograph.

Point out that the equation $KE = \frac{1}{2}mv^2$ is used here in connection with electric effects. This is another example of the universality of physical laws.

The velocity can be found from the equation for the kinetic energy of ions accelerated through a known potential difference V

$$KE = \tfrac{1}{2}mv^2 = qV$$

$$v = \sqrt{\frac{2Vq}{m}}$$

Substituting this expression for v in the previous equation, the radius of the circular path is given by

$$r = \frac{1}{B}\sqrt{\frac{2Vm}{q}}$$

From this equation, the mass to charge ratio of the ion can be found to be

$$\frac{m}{q} = \frac{B^2 r^2}{2V}$$

The ions hit a photographic film where they leave a mark. The radius, r, is found by measuring the distance between the mark and the hole in the electrode. This distance is twice the radius of the circular path.

In a mass spectrograph, the beam of ions is first accelerated in an electric field so that only ions of the same energy continue through the magnetic field.

A **mass spectrograph** determines the ratio of mass to charge of the ion. The mass depends on the type of atom used. The charge on the ion, however, can be varied. The charge depends on how many electrons were removed in the ion source. It takes more energy to remove a second electron. For low values of the acceleration voltage, V, only one electron is removed from an atom. However, when V is increased, both singly- and doubly-charged ions are produced. The operator of the mass spectrograph can choose the charge on the ion.

The first spectrograph was designed by F. W. Aston in England in 1913. When it was put into use, Aston was surprised by the appearance of more than one spot on the film. This occurred each time he attempted to measure the mass of an ionized atom. It could only mean some elements have atoms with the same chemical properties but with differing masses. Aston had verified the existence of isotopes.

The mass spectrograph is used to measure the masses of atoms.

Mass spectrographs are used to separate isotopes of atoms such as uranium. Instead of film, cups are used to collect the separated isotopes. A mass spectrograph (often called an MS) often is used by chemists as a very sensitive tool to find small amounts of atoms in substances. Many dangerous contaminants in the environment have been detected with this device.

EXAMPLE

The Mass of a Neon Atom

The operator of a mass spectrograph produces a beam of doubly-ionized neon atoms. The accelerating voltage is $V = 34$ V. Using a magnetic induction of $B = 0.50$ T, the ions move in a radius, $r = 0.053$

m. Note the charge of the ions is $q = 2(1.60 \times 10^{-19}$ C).   **a.** Calculate the mass of a neon atom.   **b.** How many proton masses are in the neon atom mass? (The mass of a proton is 1.67×19^{-27} kg.)

Given: $V = 34$ V

  $B = 0.050$ N/A $\cdot$ m

  $r = 0.053$ m

  $q = 3.2 \times 10^{-19}$ C

Unknown: m

Basic equation: $\dfrac{m}{q} = \dfrac{B^2 r^2}{2V}$

Solution: **a.** $m = qB^2 r^2 / 2V$

$$= \frac{(3.2 \times 10^{-19} \text{ C})}{2(34 \text{ V})} (0.050 \text{ T})^2 (0.053 \text{ m})^2$$

$$= 3.3 \times 10^{-26} \text{ kg}$$

  b.   proton masses $= \dfrac{3.3 \times 10^{-26} \text{ kg}}{1.67 \times 10^{-27} \text{ kg/proton}}$

$$= 20 \text{ proton masses}$$

Problems

8. A stream of singly-ionized lithium atoms is not deflected as it passes through a field of magnetic induction 1.5×10^{-3} T perpendicular to an electric field of 6.0×10^2 N/C.
  a. What is the speed of the lithium atoms as they pass through the crossed fields?
  b. The lithium atoms move into a field of magnetic induction 0.18 T. They follow a circular path of radius 0.165 m. What is the mass of a lithium atom?

8. a. 4.0×10^5 m/s
   b. 1.2×10^{-26} kg

9. A mass spectrograph gives data for a beam of doubly-ionized argon atoms. The values are $B = 5.0 \times 10^{-2}$ T, $q = 2(1.60 \times 10^{-19}$ C), $r = 0.106$ m, and $V = 66.0$ V. Find the mass of an argon atom.

9. 6.8×10^{-26} kg

10. A mass spectrograph gives data for a beam of singly-ionized oxygen atoms. The values are $B = 7.2 \times 10^{-2}$ T, $q = 1.60 \times 10^{-19}$ C, $r = 0.085$ m, and $V = 110$ V. Calculate the mass of an oxygen atom.

10. 2.7×10^{-26} kg

27:3 Electric and Magnetic Fields in Space

Faraday's investigations showed that a changing magnetic field induced an electric current in a wire. He had demonstrated earlier that a current was caused by an electric field exerting a force on electrons in a conductor. These observations led Faraday to conclude that even in the absence of a conductor a changing magnetic field would induce an electric field (Figure 27-4a). The field lines of the induced electric field must be loops because without a conductor there are no charges on which the lines can begin or end.

A changing magnetic field generates a changing electric field.

See Teacher's Guide for suggested demonstrations.

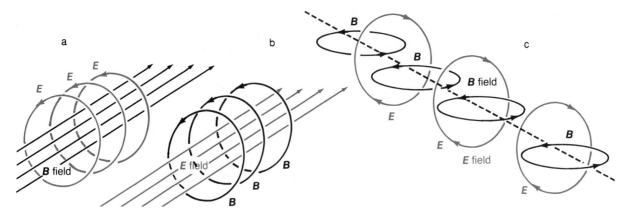

FIGURE 27-4. Representation of an induced electric field (a), magnetic field (b), and both electric and magnetic fields (c).

Maxwell made a great contribution by showing that the opposite is also true. A changing electric field produces a magnetic field in space (Figure 27-4b). For example, an electron in a wire produces an electric field around the wire. If the electron moves, the electric field changes. The changing electric field produces a magnetic field in space.

A changing electric field generates a changing magnetic field.

Together, these two discoveries mean that a changing electric field generates a changing magnetic field, which in turn generates a changing electric field, and so on, as suggested in Figure 27-4c. The fields move away from the original source, which in the diagram is an electric field. The fields continue to spread through space whether or not the original electric field still exists.

A view of part of the fields at an instant in time (Figure 27-5) shows that the fields form a transverse wave in space. The electric and magnetic fields are at right angles to each other and to the direction of motion of the wave. Maxwell showed that the combined wave, called an **electromagnetic wave,** moved at the speed of light in a vacuum, 3.00×10^8 m/s. This finding suggested that light was not a special phenomenon but simply a kind of electromagnetic wave, generated by electric and magnetic fields.

FIGURE 27-5. A look at portions of the fields at an instant in time.

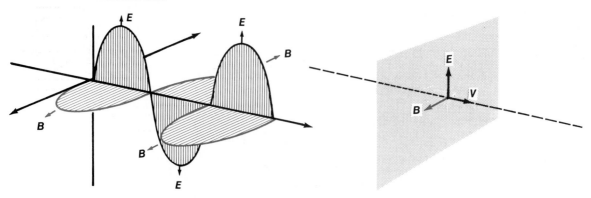

27:4   Production of Electromagnetic Waves

Electromagnetic waves can be produced by accelerating electrons back and forth in a wire. The oscillation of the electrons causes the changing electric fields, which in turn generate the changing magnetic fields. One method of creating the oscillation has already been described, the AC generator. In fact, all alternating current transmission lines create electromagnetic waves. The frequency of the waves is the same as the frequency of the current. Frequency can be changed by varying the speed at which the generator is rotated. The highest frequency that can be generated this way is about 1000 Hz.

The most common method of generating higher frequencies is to use a coil and capacitor connected in a circuit. If the capacitor is charged by a battery, the potential difference across the capacitor creates an electric field. When the battery is removed, the capacitor discharges, and the stored electrons flow through the coil creating a magnetic field. As the magnetic field of the coil changes, a back *EMF* develops that recharges the capacitor, this time in the opposite direction. The capacitor again discharges, and so on. One complete oscillation cycle is shown in Figure 27-6. The number of oscillations each second is called the frequency, which depends on the size of the coil and capacitor.

An **antenna** made of a conductor, such as wire, is connected across the capacitor. The electrons in the antenna oscillate at the same frequency as the electrons in the circuit and radiate electromagnetic waves, as shown in Figure 27-7.

Accelerated charges generate electromagnetic waves.

When electrons oscillate in an antenna, electromagnetic waves are generated.

FIGURE 27-6. Production of electromagnetic waves.

E field strongest

B field strongest

B field strongest

a

b

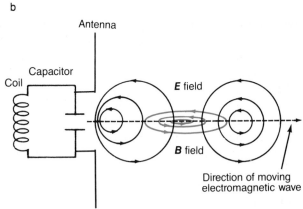

Antenna

Capacitor

Coil

E field

B field

Direction of moving
electromagnetic wave

**FIGURE 27-7. Electromagnetic
waves are generated as electrons in an antenna oscillate at
the same frequency as electrons
in a circuit.**

To understand the action of electrons in a coil and capacitor
combination, consider a pendulum. The mass represents the electrons
in the coil and capacitor circuit (Figure 27-8). The mass moves fastest at
the lowest point of the swing. This is similar to the largest current
flowing in the coil. When the mass is at its greatest angle, its
displacement from the vertical is largest; it has a velocity of zero. This
position compares to the time when the capacitor holds the largest
charge. The kinetic energy of the pendulum is zero and the potential
energy is greatest when the velocity of the mass is zero, at the top of the
swing. When the mass is moving fastest, at the low point in the swing,
kinetic energy is at a maximum, and potential energy is zero. The sum
of the potential and kinetic energy, which is the total energy, is
constant.

The coil produces a magnetic field that contains energy. The
capacitor has an electric field that also contains energy. When the
maximum current is flowing, all the energy is in the magnetic field and

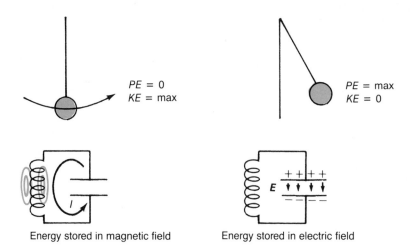

$PE = 0$
$KE = max$

$PE = max$
$KE = 0$

E

**FIGURE 27-8. A pendulum is
analogous to the action of electrons in a coil and capacitor
combination.**

Energy stored in magnetic field

Energy stored in electric field

the electric field energy is zero. When there is no current flowing but the electric field of the capacitor is greatest, all the energy is in the electric field. The total energy, the sum of magnetic field and electric field energy, is constant.

There is energy in both electric fields and magnetic fields.

Just as a pendulum will stop swinging if left alone, the electron oscillations in a coil and capacitor will die out if not replenished. Gentle pushes, applied at the correct times, will keep a pendulum moving. To obtain the largest swing, the frequency of the pushing must be the same as the frequency of the swinging (Figure 27-9). To keep a coil and capacitor oscillating, a small fraction of the current is taken from the coil, amplified by an electronic device, and returned to the coil in phase with the circuit oscillation. The current supplies the "push" needed to continue the oscillation. The coil and capacitor are called a resonant circuit. The circuit is said to resonate when driven by a current of the correct frequency. This kind of circuit will produce frequencies up to about 10^9 Hz.

A system readily absorbs energy that is offered at the natural frequency of the system.

To increase the oscillation frequency of the coil and capacitor, the size of the devices must be made smaller. Above 10^9 Hz, separate coils and capacitors will not work. For these electromagnetic waves, called microwaves, a rectangular box, called a resonant cavity, acts as both a coil and a capacitor. The size of the box determines the frequency of oscillation. Such a cavity is in every microwave oven.

Coils and capacitors are not the only method of generating oscillating currents. Quartz crystals have a property called **piezoelectricity**. These crystals generate an *EMF* when they are bent. They also bend when a voltage is applied across them. Just as a piece of metal will vibrate at a specific frequency when it is bent and released, so will a quartz crystal. A crystal can be cut so that it will vibrate at a desired frequency. An applied voltage starts it vibrating, and the piezoelectric EMF that is produced is amplified and returned to the crystal to keep it vibrating. Quartz crystals are used in wristwatches because the frequency of the vibrations is so constant. Frequencies in the range from 10^3 to 10^6 Hz can be generated this way.

Crystals are used to generate high-frequency waves.

The natural frequency of a crystal depends on its size and shape.

FIGURE 27-9. Resonance in the pendulum analogy.

TABLE 27-1

Electromagnetic Spectrum				
Frequency	Wavelength	Name	Source	Use
1000 Hz	300 km	Radio and television	Electric circuits	Communication
10^9 Hz	30 cm	Microwaves	Resonant cavities	Communication, cooking
10^{12} Hz	0.3 mm	Infrared	Molecules	Heat
4.3×10^{14} Hz – 7.5×10^{14} Hz	700 nm – 400 nm	Visible light	Atoms	Vision
10^{17} Hz	3 nm	Ultraviolet X rays, Gamma rays	Atoms Atoms' nuclei	Germicidal lamps Medical diagnosis

Light waves are electromagnetic waves generated by the acceleration of electrons within an atom.

At frequencies of infrared waves, the size of coils and capacitors or even resonant cavities would have to be reduced to the size of molecules. The oscillating electrons that produce infrared waves are in fact within the molecules. Visible and ultraviolet waves are generated by electrons in atoms.

X rays can be generated by electrons in heavy atoms. **Gamma rays** are the result of accelerating charges in the nucleus of an atom. All electromagnetic waves arise from accelerated charges and travel at the speed of light.

Electromagnetic waves can be generated over a wide range of frequencies. Table 27-1 lists the electromagnetic spectrum.

27:5 Reception of Electromagnetic Waves

Electromagnetic waves are caused by some disturbance that accelerates electrons in the source of the waves. A disturbance can, in turn, be caused when the electromagnetic waves strike matter. However, matter is not affected by all frequencies of waves. A **receiver** is a device designed to detect radio or television waves. In a receiver, electrons are accelerated in direct response to electromagnetic waves. This fact was first demonstrated by Heinrich Hertz in 1887. An antenna is a conductor that is used to detect the electric fields of the electromagnetic waves. The electrons in the antenna are accelerated by incoming electromagnetic waves and produce an oscillating current. The current is largest if the length of the antenna is half the wavelength of the electromagnetic wave. For that reason, an antenna designed to receive radio waves is much longer than one designed to receive microwaves.

An antenna operates most efficiently at one particular frequency.

Radio and television waves are used to transmit information across a distance. However, there are many different radio and television stations producing electromagnetic waves at the same time. The waves of a particular station must be selected if the information is to be understood. To select waves of a particular frequency and reject the others, a coil and capacitor circuit is connected to the antenna. The capacitance is adjusted until the oscillation frequency of the circuit equals the frequency of the desired electromagnetic waves. Only this frequency can cause the oscillation of the electrons in the circuit. The oscillations are then made larger by an amplifier (Figure 27-10) and ultimately drive a loudspeaker.

At microwave and infrared frequencies, the electromagnetic waves accelerate electrons in molecules. The energy of the electromagnetic waves is converted to thermal energy in the molecules. Microwaves cook foods in this way. Infrared waves from the sun warm us.

Visible light waves can transfer energy to electrons in atoms. In photographic film, this energy causes a chemical reaction that results in a permanent record of the light reflected from the subject. In the eye, the energy produces a chemical reaction that stimulates a nerve, resulting in a response in our brain that we call vision.

FIGURE 27-10. Schematic diagram of an amplifier.

27:6 X rays

In 1895 in Germany, Wilhelm Roentgen (1845–1923) sent electrons through an evacuated discharge tube. Roentgen used a very high voltage across the tube to give the electrons a large kinetic energy. When the electrons struck the glass wall of the tube, Roentgen noted a glow on a phosphorescent screen a short distance away. The glow continued even if a piece of wood was placed between the tube and the screen. He concluded that some kind of highly-penetrating rays were coming from the discharge tube.

Because Roentgen did not know what these strange rays were, he called them X rays. A few weeks later, Roentgen found that photographic plates were affected by X rays. He also discovered that while soft body tissue was transparent to the rays, bone blocked the rays. He produced an X-ray picture of his wife's hand. Within months, doctors recognized the medical uses of this phenomenon.

X rays are high-frequency electromagnetic waves generated when electrons strike an anode.

FIGURE 27-11. This apparatus is used in producing X rays.

a

b

	Summary

27:1   **1.** J. J. Thomson measured the ratio of mass to charge of the electron.

27:1   **2.** Thomson's result can be combined with Millikan's measurement of the electron charge to find the mass of the electron.

27:2   **3.** The mass spectrograph uses both electric and magnetic fields to measure the masses of atoms and molecules.

27:3   **4.** A changing electric field in space generates a changing magnetic field.

27:3   **5.** A changing magnetic field generates a changing electric field in space.

27:3   **6.** Changing electric and magnetic fields can couple to produce electromagnetic waves that move through space.

27:4   **7.** Oscillating electrons in an antenna generate electromagnetic waves.

27:4   **8.** A resonating coil and capacitor circuit can produce oscillating currents at any desired frequency.

27:5   **9.** Electromagnetic waves can be detected by the electric currents they produce in an antenna. The most efficient antenna is one half wavelength long.

27:5   **10.** Microwave and infrared waves can accelerate electrons in molecules, producing thermal energy.

27:6   **11.** When high energy electrons strike an anode in an evacuated tube their kinetic energies are converted to electromagnetic waves of very high energy called X rays.

Detailed answers to all Questions and Problems are given in the Teacher's Guide at the front of this book.

	Questions

1. The electrons in a Thomson tube travel from left to right. Which deflection plate should be charged positively in order to bend the electron beam up?

2. The electron beam of Question 1 has a magnetic field to make the beam path straight. What would be the direction of the magnetic field needed to bend the beam down?

3. A mass spectrograph operates on neon ions. What is the direction of the magnetic field needed to bend the beam in a clockwise semicircle?

4. A vertical antenna wire transmits radio waves. Sketch the antenna and the electric and magnetic fields it produces.

5. Auto radio antennas are vertical. What is the direction of the electric fields they detect?

6. The frequency of television waves broadcast on channel 2 are about 58 MHz, while those of channel 7 are about 180 MHz. Which channel requires a longer antenna?

7. Which television channel, 2 or 7, requires a larger capacitor in the resonant circuit in the television set?

Problems–A

1. A mass spectrograph yields data for a beam of doubly-ionized sodium atoms. These values are $B = 8.0 \times 10^{-2}$ T, $q = 2(1.60 \times 10^{-19}$ C), $r = 0.077$ m, and $V = 156$ V. Calculate the mass of a sodium atom.

1. 3.9×10^{-26} kg

2. Television channel 6 broadcasts on a frequency of 85 MHz.
   a. What is the wavelength of the electromagnetic wave broadcast on channel 6?
   b. What is the length of an antenna that will detect channel 6 most easily?

2. a. 3.5 m
   b. 1.8 m

3. What energy is given to an electron to transfer it across a difference in potential of 4.0×10^5 V?

3. 6.4×10^{-14} J

Problems–B

1. An alpha particle has a mass of approximately 6.6×10^{-27} kg and bears a double elementary positive charge. Such a particle is observed to move through a magnetic field of induction 2.0 T along a path of radius 0.15 m.
   a. What speed does it have?
   b. What is its kinetic energy?
   c. What potential difference would be required to give it this kinetic energy?

1. a. 1.5×10^7 m/s
   b. 7.4×10^{-13} J
   c. 2.3×10^6 V

2. The difference in potential between the cathode and anode of a spark plug is 1.00×10^4 V.
   a. What energy does an electron give up as it passes between the electrodes?
   b. One-fourth of the energy given up by the electron is converted to electromagnetic radiation. What is the frequency of the waves?

2. a. 1.6×10^{-15} J
   b. 6.1×10^{17} Hz

Readings

Bertsch, George, "Vibrations of the Atomic Nucleus." *Scientific American*, May, 1983.

Ganon, Robert, "Electromagnetic Pollution—Are They Zapping You?" *Popular Science*, December, 1983.

Langone, John, "X-Raying Egyptian Mummies." *Discover*, November, 1984.

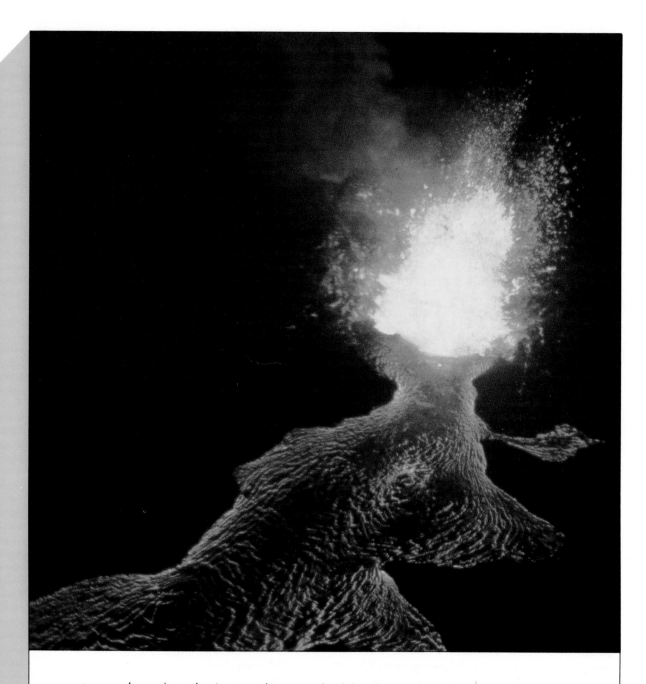

In previous chapters, you have examined the characteristics and behavior of light and other electromagnetic radiation. How is light produced? This question gives us a clue to determining the nature of atoms. How does the molten rock produce light? How does the nature of the radiation that is produced depend upon the structure of the atom?

Quantum Theory

Chapter 28 introduces the quantum aspect of electromagnetic radiation and the wave nature of particles. The photoelectric effect is discussed in detail.

In 1887 the experiments of Heinrich Hertz confirmed the predictions of Maxwell's theory. It seemed as though all of optics could be explained by electromagnetic theory. Only two small problems remained. The spectrum of light emitted by a hot body defied description by the wave theory. Also, as discovered by Hertz himself, ultraviolet light discharged electrically charged metal plates. This effect, called the photoelectric effect, could not be explained by Maxwell's wave theory.

Solution of these two problems required a total change in our knowledge of the properties of matter as well as electromagnetic energy. It was shown that the energy of particles was quantized; that is, the energy did not vary continuously, but could have only a few specific values. Electromagnetic energy was also shown to be quantized. It must consist of discrete bundles of energy called light quanta or photons. The theory that explains the discrete properties of matter and electromagnetic energy is called the quantum theory. The development of this theory and its experimental confirmation is one of the highlights of the history of the twentieth century.

28:1 Radiation from Incandescent Bodies

The electromagnetic radiation emitted by a hot body, such as an ordinary light bulb, covers a wide range of frequencies. The radiation is produced by the vibration of the charged particles within the atoms of

Goal: You will gain understanding of the particle nature of light and the wave nature of particles.

Light is made up of discrete bundles of energy called photons.

A body heated until it emits light is called incandescent.

An incandescent body emits a broad spectrum of light.

477

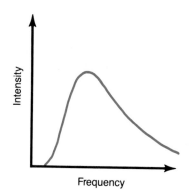

FIGURE 28-1. This graph shows the spectrum of an incandescent body.

The energy emitted by an incandescent body increases very rapidly with temperature.

the hot, or **incandescent**, body. Figure 28-1 shows a **spectrum** of an incandescent body. A spectrum is a graph of the light intensity emitted at various frequencies. If the light from an incandescent body is sent through a prism, all the colors are seen.

The color of an incandescent body changes from deep red through orange to yellow and finally to white as the temperature of the body is increased. The color observed by the eye depends on the amount of emission at various frequencies. Figure 28-2 shows spectra of incandescent bodies at various temperatures. The higher the temperature, the "whiter" the body appears. The spectrum of an incandescent body does not depend on the material out of which the body is made. The sun, with a surface temperature of 5800 K, has a yellow color. The frequency at which the maximum amount of light is emitted is proportional to the temperature measured in kelvins. The amount of energy emitted in electromagnetic waves is proportional to the absolute temperature raised to the fourth power (T^4). Thus, as shown in the figure, hotter sources radiate considerably more energy than cooler bodies. The sun, for example, is a dense ball of gases heated to incandescence by the energy produced within it. The sun radiates 4×10^{26} W, a truly enormous amount of power. Each square meter on the earth receives about one thousand joules of energy each second.

Between 1887 and 1900, many physicists tried to predict the spectrum of a hot body using existing physical theory, but all failed. In 1900, the German physicist Max Planck (1858-1947) found that he could calculate the spectrum if he introduced a revolutionary hypothesis. Planck assumed that the energy of vibration of the atoms in a solid could have only those frequencies given by the equation

$$E = nhf$$

Here f is the frequency of vibration of the atom, h is a constant, and

Intensity of Blackbody Radiation versus Frequency

FIGURE 28-2. This graph shows spectra of incandescent bodies at various temperatures.

n is an integer like 0, 1, 2, 3. The energy E could have the values hf, $2\,hf$, $3\,hf$, etc., but never, for example, $\frac{2}{3}\,hf$. Further, Planck proposed that atoms did not continuously radiate electromagnetic waves as predicted by Maxwell. Instead, they could emit radiation only when their vibration energy changed. For example, when the energy changed from $3\,hf$ to $2\,hf$, the atom emitted radiation with energy hf. Planck's theory is usually called the theory of blackbody radiation. A blackbody is an object that absorbs and emits radiation at all frequencies.

Planck found that the constant h had an extremely small value, about 6×10^{-34} J/Hz. This meant that a quantum change in energy value was tiny, not noticeable in macroscopic bodies. Still, the introduction of a quantized energy was extremely troubling to physicists, especially Planck himself. It was the first hint that the physics of Newton and Maxwell might be valid only under certain conditions.

The spectrum of an incandescent body can be explained only if energy is quantized.

A property is quantized if it occurs only in certain distinct values.

28:2 Photoelectric Effect

The second troubling experimental result was that a negatively-charged zinc plate was discharged when ultraviolet, but not visible light, fell on it. A positively-charged plate did not discharge when either ultraviolet or visible light fell on it. Further study showed that zinc, as well as some other metals, emitted electrons when ultraviolet light illuminated it. This phenomenon is called the photoelectric effect.

Figure 28-3 shows a photocell that contains two metal electrodes sealed in an evacuated tube. The tube is made of quartz to permit ultraviolet light to pass through. The tube is evacuated to keep the metal surface clean and to prevent electrons from being stopped by air molecules. A potential difference is placed across the plates.

Suggested displays: photocells and devices operated by them.

FIGURE 28-3. A diagram of a photocell circuit (a) shows the ejection of electrons from the a metal. Photocells are used in the automatic control of street lights (b).

a

b

When light is absent, current does not flow in the circuit. However, when light of the proper frequency falls on the zinc electrode, a current, indicated by the meter, flows in the circuit. This is because the light ejects electrons, called photoelectrons, from the zinc plate. The electrons travel to the positive plate.

Photoelectrons are electrons ejected from metal as a result of light hitting it.

The frequency of the light must be a certain minimum value, which varies with the metal, to eject electrons from the electrode. The minimum frequency is called the threshold frequency, f_o, of that metal. Light of a frequency below f_o does not eject any electrons from the metal, no matter how great the intensity of light. On the other hand, light at or above the threshold frequency causes electrons to leave the metal immediately, even if the light is very faint. The greater the intensity of light, the larger the flow of photoelectrons. The electromagnetic wave theory of light cannot explain these facts. In the wave theory, a more intense light has stronger electric and magnetic fields. According to wave theory, the electric field accelerates the electrons, ejecting them from the metal. With very faint light shining on the metal, electrons would require a very long time before they acquired enough energy to be ejected.

The threshold frequency is the minimum frequency of light needed to eject a photoelectron.

In 1905, Albert Einstein published a revolutionary theory of the photoelectric effect. According to Einstein, light consists of discrete bundles of energy, later called photons. The energy of each photon depends on the frequency of the light. The energy of a photon is given by the equation $E = hf$, where h is Planck's constant, 6.6×10^{-34} J/Hz.

Einstein explained the photoelectric effect by proposing that light consists of photons.

It is important to note that Einstein's theory of the photon extends Planck's theory of hot bodies. While Planck proposed that the vibrating atoms emitted radiation with energy hf, he did not suggest that radiation, including light, had a particle nature. Einstein's theory of the photon reinterpreted and extended Planck's theory of hot bodies.

Einstein's photoelectric effect theory explains the existence of a threshold frequency. To be ejected from the metal, an electron requires a minimum energy, hf_o. Only one photon interacts with one electron. An electron cannot accumulate photons until it has enough energy. Photons with frequencies below f_o do not have the energy needed to allow an electron to escape.

Light with frequency above the threshold frequency gives kinetic energy to the electron.

When light with a frequency greater than f_o strikes a zinc plate in a photocell, the energy above hf_o becomes the kinetic energy of the electron. The kinetic energy of the ejected electrons can be measured by a device similar to the one pictured in Figure 28-4. A variable potential difference is placed across the tube, and electrode B is made slightly negative. When light of the chosen frequency illuminates the zinc plate, electrode A, the potential difference opposes the movement of ejected electrons to electrode B. The experimenter increases the opposing potential difference, making the electrode A more positive. Electrons need higher and higher kinetic energies to reach electrode B. An ammeter measures the current flowing through the circuit. At some

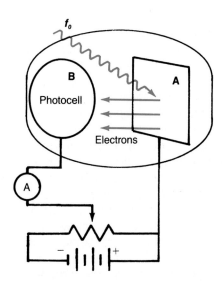

FIGURE 28-4. The kinetic energy of the ejected electrons can be measured with this device. An ammeter is used to measure the current flowing through the circuit.

voltage, called the stopping potential, no electrons have enough energy to reach electrode B, and the current is zero. The work done by the stopping potential equals the maximum kinetic energy of the electrons,

The kinetic energy of ejected electrons can be found by determining the work needed to bring them to rest.

$$KE_{max} = qV_o$$

Here, V_o is the stopping potential in volts (J/C) and q is the charge of the electron (1.60×10^{-19} C).

The joule is not a convenient unit of energy to use with atomic systems. A more convenient energy unit is the electron volt (eV). One electron volt is the energy of an electron accelerated across a potential difference of one volt. That is,

An electron volt is the energy of an electron accelerated through a potential difference of one volt.

$$1 \text{ eV} = 1.60 \times 10^{-19} \text{ J}$$

EXAMPLE

Maximum Kinetic Energy of a Photoelectron

   The stopping potential that prevents electrons from flowing across a photocell is 4.0 V. What is the maximum kinetic energy given to the electrons by the incident light? Give the answer in both J and eV.

Given: stopping potential   **Unknown:** KE_{max}
          $(V_o) = 4.0$ V   **Basic equation:** $KE_{max} = qV_o$

Solution: $KE_{max} = qV_o$

$= (1.60 \times 10^{-19} \text{ C})(4.0 \text{ J/C})$

$= (6.4 \times 10^{-19} \text{ J})(1 \text{ eV}/1.6 \times 10^{-19} \text{ J})$

$= 4.0 \text{ eV}$

   A graph of the maximum kinetic energies of the electrons ejected from a metal versus the frequencies of the incident photons is a straight line (Figure 28-5). All metals have similar graphs with the same slope.

FIGURE 28-5. This graph shows the kinetic energy of ejected electrons versus frequency of incident radiation.

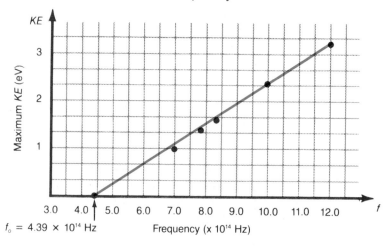

KE_{max} of Photoelectrons versus Frequency

$f_o = 4.39 \times 10^{14}$ Hz

The graphs differ only in the threshold frequency needed to free electrons. The slope of the line is Planck's constant, h.

$$h = \frac{\Delta KE}{\Delta f} = \frac{\text{Maximum kinetic energy of ejected electrons}}{\text{Frequency of incident photons}}$$

The energy needed to free the most weakly-bound electron from a metal is called the work function of the metal. The work function is the product of the threshold frequency and Planck's constant, hf_o. The maximum kinetic energy of the emitted electron is then the total energy given the electron by the photon, hf, less the work function hf_o. That is,

> The work function of a metal is the energy needed to free an electron from the metal.

$$\boxed{KE_{max} = hf - hf_o}$$

This equation is called the photoelectric equation.

Robert A. Millikan performed the experiments that proved Einstein's photoelectric theory to be correct. Einstein won the Nobel prize in 1921 for his work on the photoelectric effect.

EXAMPLE

Photoelectric Equation

The threshold frequency of sodium is 5.6×10^{14} Hz. **a.** What is the work function of sodium in J and eV? **b.** Sodium is illuminated by light of frequency 8.6×10^{14} Hz. What is the maximum kinetic energy of the ejected electrons in eV?

Given: threshold frequency
$(f_o) = 5.6 \times 10^{14}$ Hz

illumination frequency
$(f) = 8.6 \times 10^{14}$ Hz

Unknown: KE_{max}

Basic equation:

$$KE_{max} = hf - hf_o$$

Solution:

a. Work function $= hf_o$

$$= (6.6 \times 10^{-34} \text{ J/Hz})(5.6 \times 10^{14} \text{ Hz})$$
$$= 3.7 \times 10^{-19} \text{ J}$$
$$= (3.7 \times 10^{-19} \text{ J})/(1.6 \times 10^{-19} \text{ J/eV})$$
$$= 2.3 \text{ eV}$$

b. $hf = [(6.6 \times 10^{-34} \text{ J/Hz})(8.6 \times 10^{14} \text{ Hz}) \times (1 \text{ eV}/1.6 \times 10^{-19} \text{ J})]$
$$= 3.5 \text{ eV}$$

$$KE_{max} = hf - hf_o = 3.5 \text{ eV} - 2.3 \text{ eV} = 1.2 \text{ eV}$$

The wavelength of light is more easily measured than its frequency. If the wavelength is given in a problem, the frequency may be found using the equation $\lambda = c/f$. The energy (in eV) of a photon with wavelength λ (in nm) is given by the formula

$$E = hf = hc/\lambda$$

$$E = \frac{(6.62 \times 10^{-34} \text{ J})(3.00 \times 10^8 \text{ m/s}) \times (1 \text{ eV}/1.6 \times 10^{-19} \text{ J})}{(\lambda)(10^{-9} \text{ m/nm})}$$

$$= \frac{1240}{\lambda} \text{eV} \cdot \text{nm}$$

(In this equation, the value of λ must be in nanometers.)

Problems

1. The stopping potential to prevent current through a photocell is 3.2 V. Calculate the maximum kinetic energy in J of the photoelectrons within the cell.

1. 5.1×10^{-19} J

2. The stopping potential for a photoelectric cell is 5.7 V. Calculate the maximum kinetic energy in J of the photoelectrons within the cell.

2. 9.1×10^{-19} J

3. The threshold wavelength of zinc is 310 nm (310×10^{-9} m).

    a. Find the threshold frequency of zinc.
    b. What is the work function of zinc?
    c. Zinc in a photocell is irradiated by ultraviolet light of 240 nm wavelength. What is the maximum kinetic energy of the photoelectrons in eV?

3. a. 9.7×10^{14} Hz
   b. 4.0 eV
   c. 1.2 eV

28:3   Compton Effect

The photon has kinetic energy just as a particle does. In 1916, Einstein predicted that the photon should have another property of a particle, momentum. He showed that the momentum of a photon is hf/c. Since $f/c = 1/\lambda$, the photon's momentum is $p = h/\lambda$. Einstein's theory was tested by the American Arthur Holly Compton in 1922.

Einstein predicted that a photon has momentum.

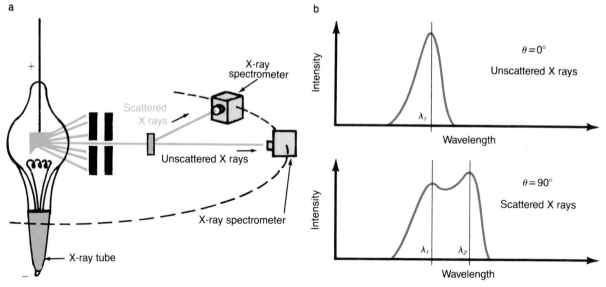

a

b

FIGURE 28-6. Diagram of apparatus used by Compton to study the nature of photons. An increased wavelength denotes that the X ray photons have lost energy.

Compton directed X rays of known wavelength at a graphite target and measured the wavelengths of the X rays scattered by the target. He found that some of the X rays were scattered without change in wavelength. However, other X rays were scattered with a longer wavelength, as shown in Figure 28-6. The energy of a photon is hf, which equals hc/λ. Thus, an increased wavelength meant that the X-ray photons had lost energy. Compton also predicted that electrons were ejected from the graphite block during the experiment. He concluded that the X-ray photons collided with electrons in the graphite target and transferred energy and momentum. These collisions were similar to the elastic collisions experienced by two billiard balls. In later experiments, Compton measured the energy of the ejected electrons, and he found that the energy and momentum gained by the electrons just equalled the energy and momentum lost by the photons. Photons acted in accordance with the laws of conservation of momentum and energy.

The Compton effect shows that photons have the particlelike properties of energy and momentum.

Compton's experiments further verified Einstein's theory. A photon is a particle that has energy and momentum. However, unlike matter, a photon has no mass and travels at the speed of light.

28:4 Matter Waves

Electromagnetic waves had been shown to have particle properties. The French physicist Louis-Victor de Broglie (di broy-lee) (1892-) suggested in 1923 that material particles have wave properties. By analogy with the momentum of the photon h/λ, the momentum of a particle is given by the equation

de Broglie proposed that particles have wave properties.

$$mv = h/\lambda$$

Thus, the wavelength of the particle is given by

$$\lambda = h/mv$$

According to de Broglie, particles, such as electrons or protons, should exhibit the wave properties of diffraction and interference. These effects had never been observed, so de Broglie's work was greeted with considerable doubt. However, Einstein read de Broglie's papers and stated his support of de Broglie's ideas. In 1927, the results of two different experiments showed the diffraction of electrons. One experiment was conducted by the Englishman G. P. Thomson, the son of J. J. Thomson, and the other by two Americans, C. J. Davisson and L. H. Germer. The experiments used a beam of electrons and a small crystal as a target. The atoms in the crystal formed a meshlike pattern that acted like a diffraction grating. Electrons diffracted from the crystal formed the same patterns that X rays of a similar wavelength formed (Figure 28-7). The two experiments proved that material particles have wave properties.

The wave nature of ordinary matter is not obvious because the wavelengths are so extremely short that wavelike behavior such as diffraction and interference is not observed. Consider the de Broglie wavelength of a baseball with a mass of 0.25 kg when it leaves a bat with a speed of 20 m/s.

$$\lambda = \frac{h}{mv} = \frac{6.6 \times 10^{-34} \text{ J} \cdot \text{s}}{(0.25 \text{ kg})(20 \text{ m/s})} = 1.3 \times 10^{-34} \text{ m}$$

The wavelength is far too small to be measured. On the other hand, consider an electron moving with a velocity of 7.3×10^6 m/s which it would obtain from an acceleration through a potential difference of 150 V. The de Broglie wavelength of the electron is

$$\lambda = \frac{h}{mv} = \frac{6.6 \times 10^{-34} \text{ J} \cdot \text{s}}{(9.11 \times 10^{-31} \text{ kg})(7.3 \times 10^6 \text{ m/s})} = 9.9 \times 10^{-11} \text{ m}$$

This wavelength is approximately the distance between the atoms in a crystal. For this reason, a crystal used as a grating produces diffraction and interference effects, making the wave properties of very small particles of matter observable.

FIGURE 28-7. Electron diffraction patterns demonstrate the wave characteristic of particles.

4. a. 9.4×10^6 m/s
   b. 7.7×10^{-11} m

Problem

4. a. Find the speed of an electron accelerated by a potential difference of 250 V.

   b. What is the de Broglie wavelength of this electron?

28:5   Particles and Waves

A particle has definite characteristics. A particle has mass, volume, kinetic energy, and momentum. Particles do not show diffraction and interference effects.

A wave, on the other hand, has a definite frequency, wavelength, and amplitude. A wave must be at least one wavelength long, and thus is spread out in space. A wave travels with a certain velocity. It produces effects like diffraction and interference.

Light and other electromagnetic waves have been shown to have properties of both a wave and a particle. Even matter, which is normally considered to be made of particles, can behave like a wave.

In the years since the work of Einstein, de Broglie, and others, many physicists and philosophers have tried to work out a satisfactory answer to this question. Some have suggested that the nature of light depends on the experiment. In the Compton effect, for example, the X ray is a particle when it is scattered from the graphite target. It is considered a wave when its wavelength is measured by diffraction from a crystal. The viewpoint currently accepted by most physicists is that the wave and particle aspects show complementary views of the true nature of light. Either picture, particle or wave, is incomplete.

Particles have wavelike properties and waves have particlelike properties.

The German physicist Werner Heisenberg suggested that the properties of an object can only be defined by thinking of an experiment that can measure them. One cannot simply say that a particle is at a certain location moving with a specific speed. Rather, an experiment must be described that will locate the particle and measure its speed.

The uncertainty principle applies to photons as well. The narrower the slit used to determine the location of a photon, the wider the diffraction pattern becomes. This is due to a spread in photon momenta.

In order to know the location of a particle, light must be reflected from it. The reflected light then must be collected by an instrument or the human eye. Our study of diffraction showed that the resolution of an optical instrument depends on the size of the instrument and the wavelength of light. In order to have good resolution and thereby accurately find the position of a particle, very short wavelengths must be used. However, the Compton effect demonstrates that when light of short wavelengths strikes a particle, the velocity, and hence the momentum, of the particle is changed. Therefore, the act of making a measurement of the location of an object disturbs its momentum. In the same way, if the momentum of the particle is measured, the position of the particle will be changed. The position and momentum of a particle cannot both be precisely known at the same time. This fact is called the **Heisenberg uncertainty principle** and is a result of the dual wave and particle description of light and matter.

The Heisenberg uncertainty principle is the inability to measure precisely both the position and momentum of a particle at the same time.

Summary

1. Hot, or incandescent, bodies emit light because of the vibrations of the particles within their atoms.   28:1

2. The spectrum of incandescent bodies covers a wide range of wavelengths. The spectrum depends on their temperature.   28:1

3. The photoelectric effect is the emission of electrons by certain metals when exposed to light.   28:2

4. Einstein explained the photoelectric effect by postulating that light came in bundles of energy, called photons.   28:2

5. The photoelectric effect allows the measurement of Planck's constant, h.   28:2

6. The work function of metals, the energy with which electrons are held inside metals, is measured by the threshold frequency in the photoelectric effect.   28:2

7. Einstein claimed that light also has momentum. The Compton effect demonstrates the momentum of photons.   28:3

8. Photons, or light quanta, are massless and always travel at the speed of light. Yet they have energy, hf, and momentum, h/λ.   28:3

9. The wave nature of material particles was suggested by de Broglie and verified experimentally by diffracting electrons off crystals.   28:4

10. The particle and wave aspects of matter and light show complementary parts of the complete nature of matter and light.   28:5

11. The Heisenberg uncertainty principle states that the position and momentum of a particle (light or matter) cannot both be known precisely at the same time.   28:5

Detailed answers to all Questions and Problems are given in the Teacher's Guide at the front of this book.

Questions

1. Two iron rods are held in a fire. One glows dark red while the other is glowing a bright orange.
   a. Which rod is hotter?
   b. Which rod is radiating more energy?

2. Potassium in a photocell emits photoelectrons when struck by blue light. Tungsten emits them only when ultraviolet light is used.
   a. Which metal has a higher threshold frequency?
   b. Which metal has a larger work function?

3. Light above the threshold frequency shines on a metal in a photocell. How does Einstein's theory explain that as the light intensity is increased the current of photoelectrons increases?

4. Explain how Einstein's theory explains why light below the threshold frequency produces no photoelectrons, no matter how intense it is.

5. How does the Compton effect demonstrate that photons have momentum as well as energy?

6. The momentum of a material particle is mv. Can mv be used to express the momentum of a photon? Explain.

7. Compare the de Broglie wavelength of a baseball moving 20 m/s with the size of the baseball.

8. What type of experiments could be done to demonstrate the wave nature of particles?

Problems–A

1. 6.1×10^{-19} J

1. To block the current in a photocell a stopping potential of 3.8 V is used. What is the maximum kinetic energy of the photoelectrons in the cell in J?

2. a. 2.5×10^{-7} m
   b. 5.0 eV
   c. 2.4 eV

2. The threshold frequency of tin is 1.2×10^{15} Hz.
   a.   What is the threshold wavelength?
   b.   What is the work function of tin in eV?
   c.   Light of 167 nm wavelength falls on tin. What is the maximum kinetic energy of the ejected electrons in eV?

3. a. 2.6×10^{-7} m
   b. 0 eV

3. The work function of iron is 4.7 eV.
   a.   What is the threshold wavelength of iron?
   b.   Iron is exposed to radiation of wavelength 150 nm. What is the kinetic energy of the ejected electrons in eV?

4. 8.0×10^{-12} m

4. Find the de Broglie wavelength of a deuteron of mass 3.3×10^{-27} kg that moves with a speed of 2.5×10^4 m/s.

5. a. 4.4×10^6 m/s
   b. 1.6×10^{-10} m

5. An electron is accelerated across a potential difference of 54 V.
   a.   Find the velocity of the electron.
   b.   Calculate the de Broglie wavelength of the electron.

6. a. 2.2×10^3 m/s
   b. 1.8×10^{-10} m

6. A neutron is held in a trap with a kinetic energy of only 0.025 eV.
   a.   What is the velocity of the neutron?
   b.   Find the de Broglie wavelength of the trapped neutron.

7. 4.0×10^{-13} m

7. What is the de Broglie wavelength of a proton moving with a speed of 1.00×10^6 m/s? The mass of a proton is 1.67×10^{-27} kg.

Problems–B

1. A home uses about 4×10^{11} J of energy each year. In many parts of the United States, there are about 3000 h of sunlight each year.
   a. How much energy from the sun falls on one square meter each year?
   b. If the solar energy can be converted to useful energy with an efficiency of 20%, how large an area of converters would produce the energy needed by the house?

2. The electron in a hydrogen atom has an energy of 13.65 eV.
   a. Find the velocity of the electron.
   b. Calculate the de Broglie wavelength of this electron.
   c. Compare your answer with the radius of the hydrogen atom, 5.19 nm.

3. The shortest wavelength of visible light is 400 nm.
   a. Find the velocity of an electron with a de Broglie wavelength of 400 nm.
   b. Calculate the energy of this electron in eV.
   c. An electron microscope is useful because the de Broglie wavelength of electrons can be made smaller than the wavelength of visible light. What energy (in eV) has to be given to an electron to have a de Broglie wavelength of 20 nm?

1. a. 1×10^7 J/m^2
   b. 2×10^5 m

2. a. 2.19×10^6 m/s
   b. 3.3×10^{-10} m
   c. $\frac{1}{16}$ the radius of the atom

3. a. 2×10^3 m/s
   b. 1×10^{-5} eV
   c. 4×10^{-3} eV

Readings

Ferris, Timothy, "The Other Einstein." *Science 83*, October, 1983.

Jones, Edwin, "Observational Evidence for Atoms." *The Physics Teacher*, September, 1984.

Kindel, Steve, "World's Fastest LASER Stops Action at the Quantum Limit." *Popular Science*, February, 1983.

Yaffe, Laurence, "Large-N Quantum Mechanics and Classical Units. *Physics Today*, August, 1983.

The atom has long been a puzzle. However, using a field ion emission micro-scope, scientists can study some crystal patterns like that of tungsten shown in this photograph and infer the structure of atoms. Theorizing that all substances are made of the same kinds of fundamental particles, how can you explain the great differences in properties such as chemical activity, solubility, crystal structure, color, and conductivity?

The Atom

Chapter 29 discusses the methods used by Rutherford and Bohr to find the organization of the atom. Various models of the atom are discussed.

By the end of the nineteenth century most scientists agreed that atoms existed. The successful kinetic theory of gases required the existence of atoms. Chemical reactions could be understood only if atoms existed.

However, the discovery of the electron by J. J. Thomson (1856–1940) showed that the atom was not a single, indivisible particle. All the atoms Thomson tested contained electrons. Yet atoms were known to be electrically neutral and much more massive than electrons. Therefore, atoms must contain a massive, positively charged part as well as electrons.

Discovering the nature of the unknown part of the atom, and the arrangement of this part and of the electrons, was a major challenge to scientists. Physicists and chemists from many countries cooperated and competed in searching for the solution to this puzzle. The result provided not only knowledge of the structure of the atom, but a totally new approach to both physics and chemistry. The story of this work is one of the most exciting stories of the twentieth century.

Goal: You will gain understanding of the structure of the atom and the applications of this knowledge.

29:1 The Nuclear Model

J. J. Thomson believed that the atom was filled with massive, positively charged substance. The electrons were arranged within this substance like raisins in a muffin. However, Ernest Rutherford, then working in England, performed a series of brilliant experiments that showed that the atom was very different.

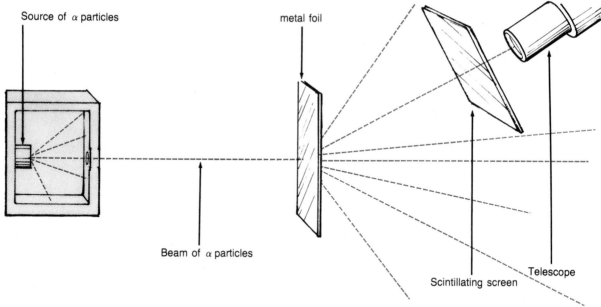

Source of α particles

metal foil

Beam of α particles

Scintillating screen

Telescope

FIGURE 29-1. After bombarding metal foil with alpha particles, Rutherford's team concluded that most of the mass of the atom was concentrated in the nucleus.

Becquerel discovered that radiation was being emitted from uranium compounds.

Radiation causes some materials to scintillate, or emit brief flashes of light.

Rutherford's group studied atomic structure by bombarding metal foils with alpha particles.

Rutherford's experiments used the findings of the French physicist Henri Becquerel (1852–1908) as a tool. In 1896 Becquerel was studying compounds containing the element uranium. To his surprise, he found that covered photographic plates became fogged or partially exposed when uranium compounds were anywhere near the plates. This fogging suggested that some kind of ray had passed through the plate coverings. Several materials other than uranium or its compounds were also found to emit these penetrating rays. Materials that emit this kind of radiation are called **radioactive materials.**

Further studies of radioactive materials showed that one type of radiation emitted was composed of positively charged, relatively massive particles moving at high speed. These were called alpha (α) particles. The α particles could be detected by means of a small fluorescent screen that emitted a small flash of light, or **scintillation** (sint uhl AY shuhn) each time an α-particle hit it.

Rutherford directed a beam of α particles at a thin sheet of metal, only a few hundred atoms thick. He noticed that while most of the α particles passed through the sheet, the beam was spread slightly by the metal. In 1910 two members of Rutherford's team, Hans Geiger and Ernest Marsden, studied the α particles deflected by metal sheets. They found that while most of the particles passed through the sheet without deflection, some were deflected at large angles, even larger than 90° (Figure 29-1). Rutherford was amazed. He said that it was as surprising as if you had fired a 15-inch cannon shell at tissue paper and the shell had come back and hit you.

Rutherford analyzed the experimental results using Coulomb's force law and Newton's laws of motion. He found that the large angle deflections could be explained only if all of the positive charge of the atom were concentrated in a tiny, massive central core, now called the nucleus. Rutherford's model is, therefore, called the nuclear model of the atom. All of the positive charge is in the nucleus, which also contains essentially all the mass of the atom. Electrons are outside the nucleus and do not contribute a significant amount of mass. The atom is 10 000 times larger than the nucleus, and so is mostly empty space.

The nature of the deflection of alpha particles by atoms in the metal foil indicates that most of the mass of an atom is located in a central nucleus.

Rutherford's analysis predicted that for any atom, the number of α particles deflected through a given angle should be proportional to the square of the charge of the nucleus. At that time only the mass of an atom was known. The number of electrons, and thus the charge of the nucleus, was not known. For many of the lighter elements the mass of the atom was almost exactly the mass of the hydrogen atom multiplied by some whole number. That whole number is called the atomic mass number.

Point out that this once again illustrates the universality of physical laws (even though Rutherford was lucky in that for this particular case quantum mechanics, which was not yet invented, gives the same answer as ordinary mechanics).

Rutherford and his co-workers experimented with sheets of carbon, aluminum, and gold. In each case the charge of the nucleus was determined to be roughly half the atomic mass number times the elementary unit of charge. This finding meant that the number of electrons in an atom was also roughly half of the atomic mass number. The carbon atom was found to contain 6 electrons, aluminum contained 13 electrons, and gold contained 79 electrons.

In an atom, the number of electrons is equal to the number of protons.

29:2 The Proton and the Neutron

The proton is the name given to the nucleus of the hydrogen atom. The proton is positively charged with one unit of elementary charge. Its mass is one **atomic mass unit** (1 atomic mass unit or 1 amu = 1.66×10^{-27} kg). Assuming that protons are the charged particles in all nuclei, carbon must have six protons and aluminum 13. However, the mass of the carbon atom is that of 12 protons, not six. To account for the excess mass in the nucleus, Rutherford postulated the existence of a neutral particle with the mass of the proton. In 1932 James Chadwick, a student of Rutherford's, demonstrated the existence of this particle, called the neutron. A neutron is a particle with no charge and with a mass almost equal to that of the proton.

The proton, the nucleus of the hydrogen atom, has a positive charge and a mass of about one amu.

The nucleus of every atom except hydrogen contains both neutrons and protons. The mass of the nucleus is the sum of the masses of the protons and neutrons. The sum of the number of neutrons and protons is the atomic mass number, approximately equal to the mass of the nucleus in amu. The mass number of carbon is 12 while that of aluminum is 27.

The neutron has no charge and a mass of approximately one amu.

Atomic mass of an atom in amu is approximately numerically equal to the number of protons and neutrons in the nucleus of the atom.

The charge of the nucleus is equal to the sum of the charges of the protons. The number of protons in the nucleus is called the atomic number. The atomic number of carbon is 6 and that of aluminum is 13.

29:3   Atomic Spectra

The puzzle of the arrangement of the electrons about the nucleus of the atom was clarified by studying the light emitted by atoms. The set of wavelengths of light emitted by an atom is called the **emission spectrum** of that atom.

When a body is heated, it becomes incandescent. The light given off comes from the atoms. However, all incandescent solids emit the same spectrum. The properties of individual atoms become apparent only when they are not tightly packed into a solid. Many substances can be vaporized by heating them in a flame. Then they can emit light that is characteristic of the elements making up the substance. For example, if sodium chloride is put on a wire and held in a flame, the sodium ions will emit a bright yellow light. Similarly, lithium salts emit red light, and barium salts, green light.

Gas atoms can be made to emit their characteristic colors by a method shown in Figure 29-2. A glass tube containing neon gas has metal electrodes at each end. When a high voltage is applied across the tube, electrons pass through the gas. The electrons collide with the neon atoms, transferring energy to them. When they give up this extra energy, it is emitted in the form of light. The light has a red color. Nitrogen and argon emit a bluish color, and mercury, greenish blue.

The emission spectrum of an atom can be studied in greater detail using the instrument shown in Figure 29-3b. In this **spectroscope** the light passes through a slit and is then dispersed by passing through a prism. A lens system focuses the dispersed light for viewing through a telescope or on a photographic plate. Each wavelength of light forms an image of the slit. The spectrum of an incandescent body is a continuous

Atoms in a gaseous state emit light at a few wavelengths that are unique to the element.

FIGURE 29-2. A gas discharge tube apparatus (a). Neon (b), helium (c), and hydrogen (d) gases glow when high voltage is applied.

a

b

c

d

a

b

Prism

Slit

Gas discharge tube

c

d

FIGURE 29-3. A prism spectroscope (a) can be used to observe emission spectra (b). The emission spectra of neon (c) and molecular hydrogen (d) show characteristic lines.

band of colors from red through violet. However, the spectrum of a gas is a series of lines of different colors. Each line corresponds to a particular wavelength of light emitted by the atoms. Suppose an unidentified gas such as mercury, argon, or nitrogen is contained in a tube. The gas will emit light at wavelengths characteristic of the atoms of that gas. Thus, the gas can be identified by noting the lines present in the spectrum. Some emission spectra are shown in Figure 29-3c,d.

When the emission spectrum of a combination of elements is photographed, analysis of the lines on the photograph can indicate both the elements present and their relative amounts. If the substance being examined contains a large amount of any particular element, the lines for that element on the photograph are more intense. By comparing the intensities of the lines, the percentage composition of the substance can be determined. An emission spectrum is a useful analytical tool.

A gas that is cool and does not emit light will absorb light at characteristic wavelengths. This set of wavelengths is called an **absorption spectrum**. To obtain an absorption spectrum, white light is sent through a gas and into a prism. As a result, the normally continuous spectrum of the white light now has dark lines in it. These lines show that some wavelengths are missing. It has been found that the bright lines of the emission spectrum of a gas and the dark lines of the absorption spectrum occur at the same wavelengths. Cool gaseous

Gaseous atoms can also absorb light. The wavelength absorbed is the same emitted by excited, hot atoms.

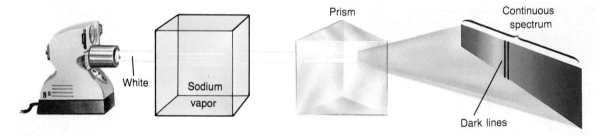

FIGURE 29-4. This apparatus is used to produce the absorption spectrum of sodium.

elements absorb the same wavelengths that they emit when excited. An atom that emits blue light absorbs blue light. An unknown gas through which white light shines produces a nearly continuous spectrum with a few missing lines. Analysis of the wavelengths of the missing lines can indicate the composition of the gas.

While examining the absorption spectrum of sunlight in 1814, Josef von Fraunhofer (1787–1826) noticed some dark lines. The dark lines he found in the sun's spectrum are now called Fraunhofer lines. To account for these lines, he assumed that the sun has a relatively cool atmosphere of gaseous elements. As light leaves the sun, it passes through these gases. The gases absorb light at their characteristic wavelengths. As a result, these wavelengths are missing from the sun's absorption spectrum. By comparing the missing lines with the known lines of the various elements, the composition of the sun was determined. In this manner the element helium was discovered in the sun before it was found on earth. Spectrographic analysis has made it possible to determine the composition of stars.

Both emission and absorption spectra are valuable scientific tools. As a result of the characteristic spectrum emitted by each element, chemists are able to analyze unknown materials by observing the spectra they emit. Not only is this an important research tool, it is important in industry as well. For example, steel mills reprocess large quantities of scrap iron of varying compositions. The exact composition of a sample of scrap can be determined in a matter of minutes by

Helium was found on the sun, by means of spectroscopy, before it was found on the earth.

Analysis of spectra allows the identification of the elements that make up a compound or mixture.

FIGURE 29-5. The emission spectrum (a) and the absorption spectrum (b) of sodium.

FIGURE 29-6. Fraunhofer lines appear in the absorption spectrum of the sun.

a

b

a

b

spectrographic analysis. The composition of the steel can then be adjusted to suit commercial specifications. Aluminum, zinc, and other metal processing plants employ the same method.

The study of spectra is a branch of science known as spectroscopy. Spectroscopists are scientists who specialize in this field and are employed throughout the research and industrial sectors.

FIGURE 29-7. A spectrograph is used in research to measure the electromagnetic emissions from a subatomic reaction (a) as well as in industry to measure the spectra of alloys (b).

29:4   The Bohr Model of the Atom

In the nineteenth century many physicists tried to use the spectra of atoms to determine the structure of the atom. Hydrogen, being the lightest element, would seem also to have the simplest structure. At that time the visible spectrum of hydrogen consisted of four lines, red, green, blue, and violet. The Swedish scientist A. J. Angstrom (1814-1874) made very careful measurements of the wavelengths of these lines. Any theory that explained the structure of the atom would have to account for those wavelengths.

Any valid theory of the structure of the atom would also have to be based on Rutherford's results. Rutherford's nuclear model of the atom proposed a tiny, massive nucleus at the center of the atom, surrounded by a cloud of negatively charged electrons. However, in this model, the force of attraction between the protons and electrons should cause the electrons to be pulled into the nucleus, collapsing the atom. The solar system provided a model of a system of bodies that attracted each other, but did not collapse. By analogy, the electrons could orbit the nucleus much as the planets orbit the sun. There was a problem with this planetary model. An electron in an orbit undergoes centripetal acceleration. As discussed in Chapter 27, accelerated electrons radiate

FIGURE 29-8. Bohr's planetary model of the atom postulated that electrons moved in fixed orbits around the nucleus.

Rutherford's model did not account for (1) the lack of emission of radiation as electrons move about the nucleus and (2) the unique spectrum of each element.

energy by emitting electromagnetic waves. As the electron radiated energy, it would spiral into the nucleus in only 10^{-9} s. However, atoms are known to be stable and to last for long times. Thus, the planetary model was not consistent with the laws of electromagnetism. In addition, the radiation of the accelerated electron should be at all wavelengths. However, as we have seen, the light emitted by different atoms is radiated only at certain wavelengths.

The Danish physicist Niels Bohr (1885–1962) went to England in 1911 and soon joined Rutherford's group. Bohr worked on the problem of the atom. He tried to unite the nuclear model with Einstein's quantum theory of light. It should be remembered that in 1911 Einstein's revolutionary theory of the photoelectric effect had not yet been confirmed by experiment and was not widely believed.

Bohr suggested that negative electrons could move about the positive nucleus without the emission of radiation.

Bohr accepted the planetary arrangement of electrons, but made the bold hypothesis that the laws of electromagnetism do not operate inside atoms. He postulated that an electron in a stable orbit does not radiate energy. Therefore, the electron does not spiral into the nucleus, destroying the atom.

Bohr assumed that the light emitted by the hydrogen atoms accompanied changes in the energy of the electrons. He noted that the specific wavelengths in an atomic spectrum mean an atomic electron cannot absorb or emit just any wavelength of light. According to Einstein, the energy of a photon of light is given by the equation $E = hf$. Thus, an electron can emit or absorb only specific amounts of energy. Bohr theorized that this means that the atomic electrons are only allowed certain amounts of energy. That is, the energy of an electron in an atom is **quantized.**

The quantization of energy in atoms is unlike everyday experience. For example, if the energy of a pendulum were quantized, it could oscillate only with certain amplitudes, such as 10 cm or 20 cm.

Bohr assumed that atomic electrons can have only certain amounts of energy. They exist in specific states or energy levels.

The different amounts of energy that an atomic electron is allowed are called **energy levels.** When an electron has the smallest allowed amount of energy, it is in the lowest energy level. This level is also called the **ground state.** If an electron absorbs energy it can make a transition to a higher energy level, called an **excited state.** Atomic electrons usually remain in excited states only a very small fraction of a second before returning to the ground state and emitting light.

According to Bohr, the energy of an orbiting electron in an atom is the sum of the kinetic energy of the electron and the potential energy resulting from the attractive force between the electron and nucleus. Work has to be done to move an electron from an orbit near the nucleus to one farther away. Therefore, the energy of an electron in an orbit near the nucleus is less than that of an electron in an orbit farther away. The electrons in excited states have larger orbits and thus higher energies.

According to Bohr, the energy of the photon emitted or absorbed by an atom is equal to the change in energy of the atom.

Einstein's theory says the light photon has an energy hf. Bohr postulated that the difference in the energy of the atomic electron before and after a photon is absorbed is equal to the energy of the photon. That is

$$hf = E_{excited} - E_{ground}$$

When the electron makes the return transition to the ground state, a photon is emitted. The energy of the photon is equal to the energy difference between the excited and ground states. Molecules also have discrete energy levels. Furthermore, molecules have many ways to absorb energy. For example, they can rotate and vibrate, which atoms cannot do. As a result molecules can emit a much wider variety of light frequencies than can atoms (Figure 29-3d).

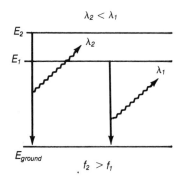

FIGURE 29-9. The energy of the emitted photon is equal to the difference between the excited and the ground state energies.

29:5 Fluorescence and Phosphorescence

So far we have discussed two ways in which atoms can be excited, thermal excitation and electron collision.

Consider a fluorescent lamp filled with mercury vapor. When a high voltage is applied across the tube, electrons collide with the Hg atoms, causing them to emit ultraviolet photons. These photons strike a material called a phosphor, coated on the surface of the glass tube. The ultraviolet photons are absorbed by the atoms in the phosphor. The atoms are excited, emitting photons of visible rather than ultraviolet light. Collision with photons, then, is another method of exciting atoms.

Both fluorescent and phosphorescent materials contain atoms that are easily excited. The two types of substances differ in the time it takes their excited atoms to return to their normal energy levels. When an atom of a **fluorescent** material is in the excited state the atoms return to their normal energy levels at once. The atoms have no stability in the higher energy levels. A **phosphorescent** material contains atoms that, once excited, can remain in higher than normal energy levels for some time. Thus, a fluorescent reflector on an automobile will glow only

FIGURE 29-10. Photons can be emitted by excited atoms in three ways: thermal excitation (a), electron excitation (b), and photon excitation (c).

while it is being irradiated by the photons from the headlights of another automobile. Thus the coating on a fluorescent lamp emits light only when current flows through the tube.

The screen of a television picture tube is coated with a phosphor that emits light when electrons strike it. In a color television the screen is coated with dots of phosphors that glow red, blue, or green. The correct colors are produced by aiming electrons at the correct dot (or dots).

A doctor's fluoroscope works in the same way as the TV picture tube, with one exception. In the fluoroscope, X rays are used instead of electrons to bombard the screen and excite atoms. If a picture of an organ is required, a heavy atom is introduced into the body to block the X rays. For example, if a patient swallows a barium solution, his stomach and intestines block the X rays and thus produce a shadow on the screen of the fluoroscope.

Phosphorescence is a matter of degree. Some phosphors are nearly fluorescent. Atoms remain in higher energy levels only a bit longer than in fluorescent substances. There is no sharp dividing line between fluorescence and phosphorescence. Generally, if an atom remains in a higher energy level for 10^{-3} seconds or longer, the substance is a "phosphor."

Different substances produce different colors of light as they fluoresce. These colors are due to the different allowed transitions as atoms move from higher to lower energy levels as explained in the next section. Many posters show attractive colors when flooded with light. Often such posters appear quite drab in white light but become very colorful when exposed to violet light. This is because the violet light is more energetic and produces many more excited atoms in the materials than do the lower energy red and green light.

FIGURE 29-11. In a luminescent organism, enzymatic chemical reactions cause the excitation of molecules to a high energy state. The return to the ground state results in the emission of visible light. The color of light produced is determined by the enzyme protein.

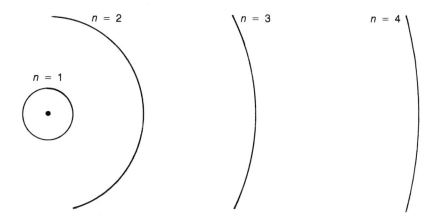

FIGURE 29-12. Radii of electron orbits for the first four energy levels of hydrogen according to the Bohr model.

29:6 Predictions of the Bohr Model

A scientific theory must do more than present postulates; it must allow predictions to be made that can be checked against experimental data. A good theory can also be applied to many different problems and ultimately provide a simple, unified explanation of some part of the physical world.

Bohr was able to show that his two postulates could be used together with the known laws of physics to calculate the wavelengths of light emitted by hydrogen. The calculations were in excellent agreement with the values measured by Angstrom. As a result, Bohr's model was widely accepted. However, the model could not predict the spectrum of the next simplest element, helium. In addition, the postulates could not be explained, and not even Bohr believed that his model was a complete theory of the structure of the atom.

Despite its shortcomings, the Bohr model describes hydrogen and hydrogenlike atoms remarkably well. We will outline the method used by Bohr to calculate the wavelengths of light emitted by an atom. Bohr's calculations start with Newton's law, $F = ma$, applied to an electron of mass m and charge $-q$, in a circular orbit of radius r about a massive proton of charge q.

Frequency and wavelength of emitted photons can be calculated with the Bohr theory.

$$\frac{Kq^2}{r^2} = \frac{mv^2}{r}$$

K is the constant 9.0×10^9 N $\cdot$ m²/C² from Coulomb's law.

Bohr proposed a third postulate. The product of the momentum of the electron and the radius of its orbit, mvr, can have only certain values. These values are given by the equation $mvr = nh/2\pi$, where h is Planck's constant and n is an integer. Because the quantity mvr can have only certain values, it is quantized.

Bohr's theory requires that the quantity mvr is quantized.

The result of Coulomb's law and the quantization of mvr can be combined using simple algebra to give the radius of the orbit.

The Bohr theory predicts the radius of the electron orbit.

$$r = \frac{h^2}{4\pi^2 Kmq^2} n^2$$

Substituting SI values for the quantities into the equation, we can calculate the radius of the innermost orbit of the hydrogen atom.

$$r = \frac{(6.64 \times 10^{-34} \text{ J} \cdot \text{s})^2 \times (1)^2}{(4)(3.14)^2(9.00 \times 10^9 \text{ N} \cdot \text{m}^2/\text{C}^2)(9.11 \times 10^{-31} \text{ kg})(1.60 \times 10^{-19} \text{ C})^2}$$

$$r = 5.3 \times 10^{-11} \frac{\text{J}^2 \cdot \text{s}^2}{\text{N} \cdot \text{m}^2 \cdot \text{kg}}$$

$$r = 5.3 \times 10^{-11} \text{ m, or } 0.053 \text{ nm}$$

A little more algebra shows that the total energy of the electron in its orbit, the sum of the potential and kinetic energy of the electron, is given by

$$E = \frac{-2\pi^2 K^2 m q^4}{h^2} \times \frac{1}{n^2}$$

A numerical value of the energy can be found by using the values of the constants above

$$E = -2.17 \times 10^{-18} \text{ J}(1/n^2)$$

or, in electron volts

$$E = -13.6 \text{ eV}(1/n^2)$$

Both the radius of an orbit and the energy of the electron can have only certain values. That is, they are both quantized. The integer n is called the principle **quantum number.** The number n determines the values of r and E. The radius increases as the square of n, as shown in Figure 29-12. The energy depends on $1/n^2$. The energy is negative because energy has to be added to the electron to free it from the attractive force of the nucleus. The energy levels of hydrogen are shown in Figure 29-13.

EXAMPLE

Orbital Energy of Electrons in the Hydrogen Atom

a. Determine the energy associated with the innermost energy level of the hydrogen atom ($n = 1$).   **b.** Determine the energy associated with the second energy level of the hydrogen atom.   **c.** What is the energy difference between the first and second energy levels of the hydrogen atom?

Given: $n = 1, n = 2$ **Unknowns:** E_1, E_2, ΔE

Basic equation: $E = -13.6 \text{ eV } (1/n^2)$

Solution: **a.** $E_1 = \dfrac{-13.6 \text{ eV}}{(1)^2} = -13.6 \text{ eV}$

b. $E_2 = \dfrac{-13.6 \text{ eV}}{(2)^2} = -3.4 \text{ eV}$

c. $\Delta E = E_f - E_i = E_2 - E_1$
$= -3.4 \text{ eV} - (-13.6 \text{ eV}) = 10.4 \text{ eV}$

EXAMPLE

Frequency and Wavelength of Emitted Photons

An electron drops from the second energy level to the first energy level within an excited hydrogen atom.   **a.** Determine the energy of the photon emitted.   **b.** Calculate the frequency of the photon emitted.   **c.** Calculate the wavelength of the photon emitted.

Given: $n = 2, n = 1$ **Unknowns:** hf, f, λ

Basic equation: $hf = E_i - E_f$

Solution:

a. $hf = E_i - E_f = E_2 - E_1 = -3.4 \text{ eV} - (-13.6 \text{ eV}) = 10.2 \text{ eV}$

b. $f = \dfrac{(10.2 \text{ eV})(1.60 \times 10^{-19} \text{ J/eV})}{6.64 \times 10^{-34} \text{ J/Hz}} = 2.46 \times 10^{15} \text{ Hz}$

c. $\lambda = \dfrac{c}{f} = \dfrac{3.00 \times 10^8 \text{ m/s}}{2.46 \times 10^{15} \text{ Hz}} = 1.22 \times 10^{-7} \text{ m}$

Problems

1. The discussion on page 502 shows how to calculate the radius of the innermost orbit of the hydrogen atom. Note that all factors in the equation are constants with the exception of n^2. Use the solution to the Example to find the radius of the orbit associated with the second, third, and fourth allowable energy levels in the hydrogen atom.

2. Calculate the energies associated with the second, third, and fourth energy levels in the hydrogen atom.

3. Calculate the energy difference between E_3 and E_2 in the hydrogen atom. Do the same between E_4 and E_3.

1. 5.3×10^{-11} m, 2.1×10^{-10} m, 4.8×10^{-10} m, 8.5×10^{-10} m

2. -3.4 eV, -1.5 eV, -0.85 eV

3. 1.9 eV, 0.65 eV

4. a. 4.6×10^{14} Hz, 6.5×10^{-7} m
   b. 1.6×10^{14} Hz, 1.9×10^{-6} m

4. Determine the frequency and wavelength of the photon emitted when an electron drops from

a. E_3 to E_2 in an excited hydrogen atom.
b. E_4 to E_3 in an excited hydrogen atom.

5. 12.8 eV

5. What is the difference between the energy associated with the energy level E_4 and E_1 of the hydrogen atom?

6. 3.1×10^{15} Hz, 9.7×10^{-8} m

6. Determine the frequency and wavelength of the photon emitted when an electron drops from E_4 to E_1 in an excited hydrogen atom.

29:7 Present Theory of the Atom

The Bohr model of the atom was a major contribution to the understanding of the structure of the atom. Using the spectra of the elements, Bohr and his students were able to determine the energy levels of many elements. They were also able to calculate the ionization energy of a hydrogen atom. The ionization energy of an atom is the energy needed to free an electron completely from an atom. The calculated value was in good agreement with experimental data. The Bohr model also provided an explanation of some of the chemical properties of the elements. The idea that atoms have electron arrangements unique to each element is the foundation of much of our knowledge of chemical reactions and bonding.

However, the postulates Bohr made could not be explained on the basis of known physics. Electromagnetism required that accelerated particles radiate energy. This radiation would cause the rapid collapse of all atoms, and thus the universe. In addition, the reason for the quantized values of the quantity mvr was not known.

The first hint to the solution of these problems was provided by de Broglie. As you recall from Section 28:4, he proposed that particles have wave properties just as light waves have particle properties. The wavelength of a particle with momentum mv is given by $\lambda = h/mv$. Therefore, the quantity $mvr = hr/\lambda$. The Bohr quantization condition, $mvr = nh/2\pi$ can be written as

$$\frac{hr}{\lambda} = mvr = \frac{nh}{2\pi}$$

Thus

$$\frac{hr}{\lambda} = \frac{nh}{2\pi}$$

or

$$n\lambda = 2\pi r$$

Note that the circumference of the Bohr orbit ($2\pi r$) is equal to a whole number multiple (n) of the wavelength of the electron (λ).

In 1926 the German physicist Erwin Schroedinger (1887–1961) used de Broglie's wave picture to create a theory of the atom based on waves. Further work by Werner Heisenberg, Wolfgang Pauli, Max Born, and others, developed this theory into a fairly complete description of the

The Bohr model of the atom was a major contribution to understanding the atom.

Bohr's model of the atom explained many of the chemical properties of elements.

The assumptions of Bohr's model could not be explained on the basis of known (classical) physics.

de Broglie suggested that particles have wave characteristics.

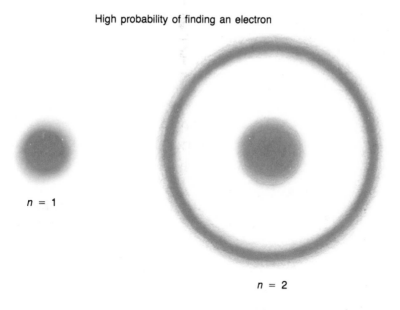

High probability of finding an electron

$n = 1$

$n = 2$

FIGURE 29-14. The electron cloud model of the atom shows regions of high and low probability.

atom. The theory is mathematical, and does not provide a simple planetary picture of an atom as in the Bohr model. In particular, the radius of the electron orbit is not like the radius of the orbit of a planet about the sun. The wave-particle nature of matter means that it is impossible to know both the position and momentum of an electron at the same time. Thus, the modern theory of the atom predicts only the probability that an electron is at a specific location. The Bohr orbit is the most probable distance of the electron from the nucleus. The probability that the electron is at any radius can be calculated, and a three-dimensional shape can be constructed that shows regions of equal probability. The region in which there is a high probability of finding the electron is called the **electron cloud** (Figure 29-14).

The present theory of the atom is difficult to visualize. However, **quantum mechanics,** which uses this model, has been extremely successful in predicting mathematically many details of the structure of the atom. These details are very difficult to calculate exactly for all but the simplest atoms. Even the largest computers can only make highly accurate approximations for the heavier atoms. In addition, the structure of many molecules has been calculated, allowing chemists to determine the arrangement of atoms in the molecules. Guided by quantum mechanics, chemists have been able to create new and useful molecules not otherwise available.

Quantum mechanics also allows calculation of the details of the emission and absorption of light by atoms. As a result of this theory, a new source of light has been developed.

The present model of the atom is a mathematical model. It gives the probability of finding an electron at any given location.

FIGURE 29-15. Waves of in-coherent light (a) and coherent light (b).

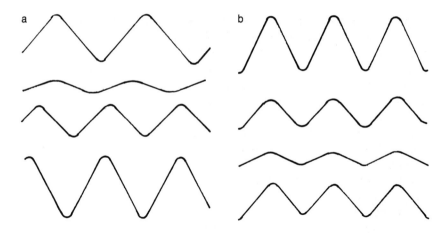

FIGURE 29-15. Waves of in-coherent light (a) and coherent light (b).

Photons emitted by ordinary light sources are not in phase. They are incoherent.

Einstein predicted that an atom in an excited state struck by a photon with the correct energy could be stimulated to emit another photon and return to the ground state.

FIGURE 29-16. An atom in an excited state is struck by a photon (a) and returns to ground state by emitting a photon in phase with the stimulating photon (b).

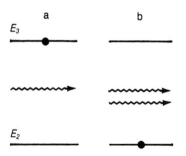

29:8 Lasers

Light is emitted by an incandescent source at many wavelengths and in all directions. Light produced by an atomic gas consists of only a few different wavelengths, but is also emitted in all directions. The light waves emitted by gas at one end of a discharge tube are not necessarily in phase with the waves from the other end. That is, the waves are not necessarily all at the same point in their cycle (Figure 29-15). Such light is called incoherent.

Consider an atom in an excited state. After a short time, it normally returns to the ground state, giving off a photon of the same energy that it had absorbed. This is called spontaneous emission. In 1917, Einstein considered what would happen to an atom already in an excited state if it were struck by another photon of the same energy that the atom would spontaneously emit. He showed the atom will return to the ground state, emitting a second photon. This is called **stimulated emission.** The two photons leaving the atom will not only have the same wavelength, they will also be in phase (Figure 29-16b).

The two photons can now strike other excited atoms, producing additional photons that are in phase with the original photons. This process can continue, producing an avalanche of photons, all in phase. However, if this is to happen, certain conditions must be met. First, of course, there must be other atoms in the excited state. Second, the photons must be collected so that they strike the excited atoms. A device that can do this was invented in 1959 and is called a **laser.** The word laser is an acronym. It stands for **L**ight **A**mplification by **S**timulated **E**mission of **R**adiation.

The atoms in a laser can be put into the excited state, or *pumped*, in different ways. An intense flash of light with wavelength shorter than that of the laser can pump it. The photons produced by the flash collide with and excite the lasing atoms. A brief flash or pulse of laser light is emitted. Alternatively, an electric discharge can also be used to put atoms in the excited state. The resulting laser light is continuous rather than pulsed. The lasers often seen in classrooms are continuous lasers that use a mixture of helium and neon gas atoms.

The photons are collected by placing the glass tube containing the atoms between two parallel mirrors. One mirror reflects all the light hitting it while the other allows about 1% to pass through. When a photon strikes an atom in the excited state it stimulates the atom to make a transition to the lower state. Thus, two photons leave the atom. These photons can strike other atoms and produce more photons. Photons that are directed toward the sides of the container will escape, while most of those directed toward the ends will be reflected back into the gas by the mirrors. However, some of the photons pass through the partially reflecting mirror, producing the laser beam.

A laser contains atoms in excited states. It has mirrors that confine the emitted photons to the location of the atoms.

Laser light is highly directional because of the parallel mirrors. The light beam is very small in diameter, so the light is very intense. The light is all of one wavelength, or monochromatic, because only one pair of energy levels in an atom is involved. Finally, laser light is coherent because the stimulated photon is emitted in phase with the photon that struck the atom.

Laser light is directional, monochromatic, intense, and coherent.

Many substances, including solids, liquids, and gases, can be made to "lase." Most produce laser light at only one wavelength. For example, red is produced by a helium-neon laser, blue by argon, and green by helium-cadmium. However, the light from liquid lasers can be tuned, or adjusted, over a range of wavelengths.

All lasers are very inefficient. No more than 1% of the electrical energy delivered to the laser is converted to light energy. Despite this

FIGURE 29-17. A laser produces a beam of coherent light.

inefficiency, the unique properties of laser light have led to many applications. The laser beam is narrow and highly directional. It does not spread out over long distances. Surveyors use laser beams for this reason. Laser light shows are dramatic examples of this property.

Laser light can be directed into a tiny glass fiber. The fiber is designed to transmit light over many kilometers with little loss. The laser is modulated, or switched on and off, rapidly. By this means, it transmits information over the fiber. In many cities, glass fibers are replacing copper wires for the transmission of telephone calls, computer data, and even television pictures.

The single wavelength of light emitted by lasers makes lasers valuable in spectoscopy. The laser light is used to excite other atoms. The atoms then return to the ground state, emitting characteristic spectra. Samples with extremely small numbers of atoms can be analyzed this way. In fact, the presence of single atoms has been detected using laser excitation.

Holograms are made possible by the coherent nature of laser light. A hologram is a photographic recording of the phase as well as the intensity of the light. Holograms form realistic three-dimensional images and can be used in industry to study the vibration of sensitive parts.

The concentrated power of laser light is used in a variety of ways. In medicine, lasers can be used to repair the retina in an eye. Lasers can also be used in surgery in place of a knife to cut flesh with little loss of blood. In industry, lasers are used to cut steel as well as to weld materials together. Lasers may be able to produce nuclear fusion for an inexhaustible energy source.

FIGURE 29-18. An example of laser surgery (a) and a hologram produced by lasers (b).

a

b

Summary

1. In 1896 Becquerel discovered that uranium compounds are radioactive.   29:1
   They emit highly penetrating radiation.

2. One kind of radiation is α particles, which are massive, positively-   29:1
   charged, high speed particles.

3. Ernest Rutherford directed α particles at thin metal sheets. He found that   29:1
   atoms are mostly empty space with a tiny, massive, positively charged
   nucleus at the center.

4. The nucleus has been found to contain positively charged protons and   29:2
   uncharged neutrons.

5. Atoms of an element produce characteristic spectra which can be used to   29:3
   identify that element.

6. If white light passes through a gas, the gas can absorb the same   29:3
   wavelengths it would emit if excited. When the emergent white light is
   sent through a prism, an absorption spectrum is produced.

7. In a model of the atom developed by Niels Bohr, the electrons are allowed   29:4
   to have only certain energy levels.

8. In the Bohr model electrons can make transitions between energy levels.   29:4
   As they do, they emit or absorb electromagnetic radiation.

9. The frequency and wavelength of the absorbed and emitted radiation can   29:6
   be calculated using the Bohr model. The calculations agree with the
   experiment.

10. The present model of the atom cannot be visualized easily. Only the   29:7
    probability that an electron is at a specific location can be calculated.

11. Quantum mechanics, which uses the present model of the atom, is   29:7
    extremely successful in calculating the properties of atoms.

12. Lasers produce light that is directional with high power, monochromatic,   29:8
    and coherent. Each property has given rise to applications.

Detailed answers to all Questions and Problems are given in the Teacher's Guide at the front of this book.

Questions

1. How did Rutherford determine that the positive charge in an atom is
   concentrated in a tiny region rather than being spread out throughout the
   atom?

2. Compare and contrast the properties of the neutron and the proton.

3. What are the problems with a planetary model of the atom?

E_4

E_3

E_2

E_1

FIGURE 29-19. Use with Question 6.

4. What three assumptions did Bohr make in developing his model of the atom?

5. How does the Bohr model account for the spectra emitted by atoms?

6. A certain atom has energy levels as shown in Figure 29-19. If an electron can make transitions between any two levels, how many spectral lines can the atom emit? Which transition gives the photon with the highest energy?

7. Compare the present theory of the atom with the Bohr model.

8. **a.** What properties of the laser lead to its use in laser light shows?
   b. Does a laser that emits red light, green light, or blue light produce photons with the highest energy?

Problems–A

1. 1.3 × 10⁻⁹ m, 1.9 × 10⁻⁹ m

2. −3.4 eV, −1.5 eV, −0.85 eV, −0.54 eV, −0.38 eV

3. a. 0.16 eV
   b. 1.12 eV
   c. 2.6 eV
   d. 2.86 eV
   e. 0.96 eV

1. Calculate the radius of the orbital associated with the energy levels E_5 and E_6 of the hydrogen atom.

2. What energy is associated with the hydrogen atom energy levels E_2, E_3, E_4, E_5, and E_6?

3. Calculate these values for the hydrogen atom.
   a. $E_6 - E_5$ **c.** $E_4 - E_2$ **e.** $E_5 - E_3$
   b. $E_6 - E_3$ **d.** $E_5 - E_2$

FIGURE 29-20. Use with Problems A-6 and A-7.

4. Use Problem 3 solutions to determine the frequencies of the photons emitted when the hydrogen atom passes through the energy differences.

5. Use Problem 4 solutions to determine the wavelengths of the photons having the frequencies listed.

Use Figure 29-20 to answer Problems 6 and 7.

6. A mercury atom is in the excited state when its energy level is 6.67 eV above the ground state. A photon of energy 2.15 eV strikes the mercury atom and is absorbed by it. The mercury atom is raised to which energy level?

7. A mercury atom drops from 8.81 eV above its ground state to 6.67 eV above its ground state. What is the energy of the photon emitted by the mercury atom?

4. a. 3.9×10^{13} Hz
   b. 2.7×10^{14} Hz
   c. 6.1×10^{14} Hz
   d. 6.9×10^{14} Hz
   e. 2.3×10^{14} Hz

5. a. 7.7×10^{-6} m
   b. 1.1×10^{-6} m
   c. 4.9×10^{-7} m
   d. 4.3×10^{-7} m
   e. 1.3×10^{-6} m

6. E_9

7. 2.14 eV

Problems–B

1. For a hydrogen atom in the $n = 3$ Bohr orbital, find
   a. the radius of the orbital.
   b. the electric force acting on the electron.
   c. the centripetal acceleration of the electron.
   d. the orbital speed of the electron. Compare this speed with the speed of light.

2. A hydrogen atom has the electron in the $n = 2$ level.
   a. If a photon with a wavelength of 332 nm strikes the atom, will the atom be ionized?
   b. If the atom is ionized, assume the electron receives the excess energy from the ionization. What will be the kinetic energy in J of the electron?

1. a. 5.3×10^{-11} m,
      4.8×10^{-10} m
   b. 1.01×10^{-9} N
   c. 1.11×10^{21} m/s^2
   d. 7.3×10^5 m/s,
      0.24% of c

2. a. Yes, the atom is ionized.
   b. 4.8×10^{-20} J

Readings

Boraiko, Allen, "A Splendid Light." *National Geographic*, March, 1984.

Feynman, Richard, "Los Alamos From Below." *Science 84*, December, 1984.

Rohrlich, F., "Facing Quantum Mechanical Reality." *Science*, September 23, 1983.

Wheaton, Bruce, "Louis de Broglie and the Origins of Wave Mechanics." *The Physics Teacher*, May, 1984.

Wynne, James, "Current Trends in Atomic Spectroscopy." *Physics Today*, November, 1983.

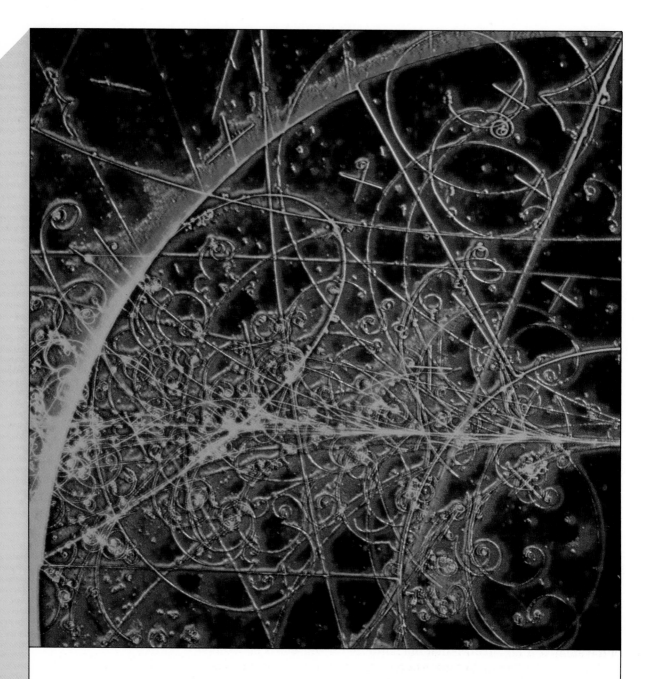

It was once thought that the electron, proton, and neutron were the smallest pieces of matter in the universe. However, evidence such as this computer-enhanced photograph showing the trails of subatomic particles in a bubble chamber indicate there are still smaller pieces of matter. What are these basic pieces of matter? How are they related?

The Nucleus

Chapter 30 discusses the organization of the nucleus and the methods used to study it. The quark model of nucleons is described.

After the discovery of radioactivity by Becquerel in 1896, many scientists studied this new phenomenon. In Canada, Ernest Rutherford and Frederick Soddy discovered that uranium atoms were changed, or transmuted, to other atoms. The French scientists Marie and Pierre Curie discovered the new elements polonium and radium in radioactive uranium. Further study of radioactivity has led to an understanding of the structure of the nucleus and many useful applications. Artificially produced radioactive isotopes have been widely used in medicine and other fields. Electricity produced from the energy of the nucleus may lessen our reliance on fossil fuels.

Studies of nuclei have also led to an understanding of the structure of the particles found in the nucleus, the proton and the neutron, and the nature of the forces binding the nucleus together.

Goals: You will gain understanding of the structure of the nucleus, nuclear decay, the present theory of nuclear forces, and the machines used to test these theories.

30:1 Description of the Nucleus

Rutherford found that the nucleus is a very small body in the center of the atom. It is now known that the radius of the nucleus is between 1.3 fm (1.3×10^{-15} m) in hydrogen and 8.1 fm in uranium. The nucleus is composed of protons and neutrons. The number of protons, which is equal to the number of electrons surrounding the nucleus of a neutral atom, is given by the **atomic number, Z.** All atoms of a given element contain the same number of protons. The sum of the number of protons and neutrons is equal to the **mass number, A.**

The mass of the nucleus is approximately equal to the mass number, A, multiplied by the atomic mass unit (amu), 1.66×10^{-27} kg.

The nucleus, composed of protons and neutrons, is an extremely tiny, massive body at the center of the atom.

The nucleus is described by the atomic number Z, equal to the number of protons, and the atomic mass number A, equal to the sum of neutrons and protons in the nucleus.

513

FIGURE 30-1. The isotopes of neon and hydrogen.

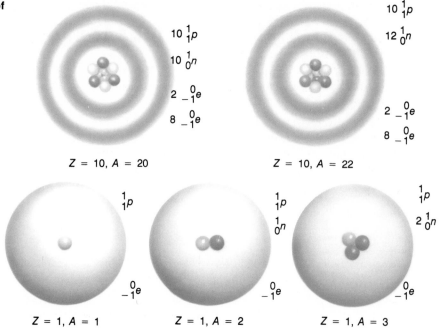

$10 \, {}_{1}^{1}p$
$10 \, {}_{0}^{1}n$
$2 \, {}_{-1}^{0}e$
$8 \, {}_{-1}^{0}e$

$Z = 10, A = 20$

$10 \, {}_{1}^{1}p$
$12 \, {}_{0}^{1}n$
$2 \, {}_{-1}^{0}e$
$8 \, {}_{-1}^{0}e$

$Z = 10, A = 22$

${}_{1}^{1}p$
${}_{-1}^{0}e$

$Z = 1, A = 1$

${}_{1}^{1}p$
${}_{0}^{1}n$
${}_{-1}^{0}e$

$Z = 1, A = 2$

${}_{1}^{1}p$
$2 \, {}_{0}^{1}n$
${}_{-1}^{0}e$

$Z = 1, A = 3$

30:2 Isotopes

For some time, scientists all over the world were puzzled by the fact that the masses of the atoms of most elements, measured in atomic mass units, were not exactly whole numbers. For example, careful measurements of the mass of the boron atom consistently yield 10.8 amu. If, as was thought, the nucleus is made up of protons and neutrons each with a mass of approximately 1 amu, then the total mass of any atom should be near a whole number.

The problem of atomic masses that were not integral numbers of amu was solved with the mass spectrometer (Chapter 27). The mass spectrometer demonstrated that an element could have atoms with different masses, but that behaved exactly the same chemically. For example, neon had atoms of two different masses. When analyzing a pure sample of neon, not one, but two spots appeared on the film of the spectrometer. The two spots were produced by neon atoms of different masses. One variety of neon atom was found to have a mass of 20 amu; the second type had a mass of 22 amu. All neon atoms have ten protons in their nuclei and ten electrons about their nuclei. However, one kind of neon atom has ten neutrons in its nucleus, while the other has twelve neutrons. The two kinds of atoms are called **isotopes** of neon. The nucleus of an isotope is called a **nuclide**. All nuclides of an element have the same number of protons, but different numbers of neutrons. All isotopes of an element have the same number of electrons around the nuclei and behave the same chemically.

Isotopes are atoms that contain the same number of protons but different numbers of neutrons.

Most elements have many isotopic forms that occur naturally. The measured mass of neon gas is 20.183 amu. This figure is now understood to be the average mass of the isotopes of neon. Thus while the mass of an individual atom of neon is close to a whole number of amu, the atomic mass of a sample of neon atoms is not. The mass of the isotope of carbon, $^{12}_6C$, is used to define the amu. One amu is $^1/_{12}$ the mass of the $^{12}_6C$ isotope.

The atomic mass unit is defined as $^1/_{12}$ of the mass of a $^{12}_6C$ atom.

A special method of notation is used to describe an isotope. A subscript for the atomic number, Z, is written to the lower left of the symbol for the element. A superscript written to the upper left of the symbol is the mass number, A. This notation takes the form ^A_ZE. For example, the two isotopes of neon, with atomic number 10, are written as $^{20}_{10}Ne$ and $^{22}_{10}Ne$.

The general form for the symbol of an isotope is ^A_ZE, where E represents the symbol for the element.

Problems

1. An isotope of oxygen has a mass number of 15. The atomic number of oxygen is 8. How many neutrons are in the nuclei of this isotope?

2. Three isotopes of uranium have mass numbers of 234, 235, and 238 respectively. The atomic number of uranium is 92. How many neutrons are in the nuclei of each of these isotopes?

3. How many neutrons are in an atom of the mercury isotope $^{200}_{80}Hg$?

4. Write the symbolic expression for the three isotopes of hydrogen in Figure 30-1 with 0, 1, and 2 neutrons in the nucleus.

1. 7

2. 142, 143, 146

3. 120

4. ^1_1H , ^2_1H , ^3_1H

30:3 Radioactive Decay

In 1896 Henri Becquerel was working with compounds containing the element uranium. To his surprise, he found that covered photographic plates became fogged or partially exposed when these uranium compounds were anywhere near the plates. This fogging suggested some kind of ray had passed through the plate coverings. Several materials other than uranium or its compounds were also found to emit these penetrating rays. Materials that emit this kind of radiation are said to be **radioactive** and to undergo **radioactive decay.**

In 1899 Rutherford discovered uranium compounds produce three different kinds of radiation. He separated them according to their penetrating ability and named them **α** (alpha), **β** (beta), and **γ** (gamma) radiation.

The α radiation can be stopped by a thick sheet of paper (Figure 30-2). Rutherford later showed that an α particle is the nucleus of a helium atom, ^4_2He. Beta particles were later identified as high speed electrons. Six millimeters of aluminum are needed to stop most β particles. Several centimeters of lead are required to stop γ rays, which proved to be high energy photons. Alpha particles and γ rays are

Rutherford found that naturally radioactive materials emit three types of radiation. Alpha particles are doubly-ionized helium nuclei. Beta particles are high-speed electrons. Gamma rays are high-frequency photons.

emitted with an energy characteristic of the particular radioactive isotope. However, β particles are emitted with a wide range of energies.

Since α particles contain protons and neutrons, they must come from the nucleus of an atom. Therefore, the nucleus produced by the emission of an α particle, a process called α **decay**, will have a mass and charge different from that of the original nucleus. A change in nuclear charge means that a radioactive element has been transmuted into a different element. The mass number, A, of an α particle, ^4_2He, is four, so the mass number, A, of the decaying nucleus is reduced by four. The atomic number, Z, of ^4_2He is two, and therefore the atomic number of the nucleus, the number of protons, is reduced by two. For example, when $^{238}_{92}\text{U}$ emits an α particle, the atomic number, Z, changes from 92 to 90. From Table C-5 of the Appendix, we find that $Z = 90$ is thorium. The mass number of the nucleus is $A = 238 - 4 = 234$. Thus a thorium isotope, $^{234}_{90}\text{Th}$, is formed. The uranium isotope is transmuted into thorium.

Beta particles are negative electrons emitted by the nucleus. Since the mass of an electron is a tiny fraction of an amu, the atomic mass of a nucleus that undergoes β decay is changed only a tiny amount. The mass number is unchanged. Within the nucleus, a neutron is changed to a proton when the electron is emitted. The number of protons, and thus the atomic number, is increased by one. For example, the isotope $^{234}_{90}\text{Th}$, produced by the decay of $^{238}_{92}\text{U}$, is unstable and emits a β particle. $^{234}_{90}\text{Th}$ becomes a protactinium isotope, $^{234}_{91}\text{Pa}$.

Gamma radiation results from the redistribution of the charge within the nucleus. The γ ray is a high energy photon. Neither the mass number nor the atomic number is changed in γ decay.

The atomic mass of an element is represented by the letter A.

The atomic number of an element is represented by the letter Z.

The nucleus resulting from an α decay has an atomic number reduced by 2 and a mass number reduced by 4.

The nucleus resulting from β decay has an atomic number increased by 1. There is no change in mass number.

Neither A nor Z change in γ decay.

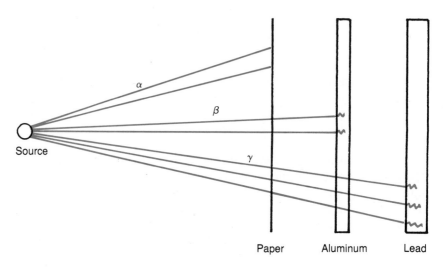

FIGURE 30-2. Alpha, beta, and gamma radiation have different penetrating properties.

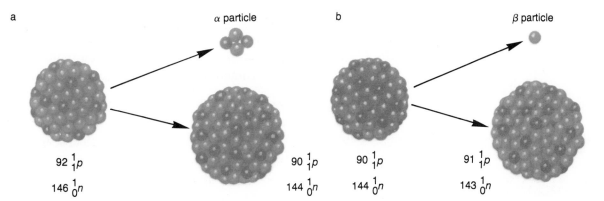

FIGURE 30-3. The emission of an alpha particle (a) by uranium-238 results in the formation of thorium-234. The emission of a beta particle (b) by thorium-234 results in the formation of proactinium-234.

Radioactive elements often go through a series of successive decays, or **transmutations,** until they form a stable nucleus. For example, $^{238}_{92}\text{U}$, an unstable isotope of uranium, undergoes fourteen separate transmutations before becoming the stable lead isotope $^{206}_{82}\text{Pb}$.

30:4 Nuclear Equations

A **nuclear reaction** occurs whenever the number of neutrons or protons in a nucleus changes. Some nuclear reactions occur with a release of energy, while others occur only when energy is added to a nucleus.

While most nuclei are stable, some spontaneously emit particles. The emission of particles by radioactive nuclei is one form of nuclear reaction. In this reaction, a radioactive nucleus releases its excess energy in the form of the kinetic energy of the emitted particles.

Nuclear reactions can be expressed in equation form. Nuclear equations are symbolic forms that make the calculation of atomic number and mass number in transmutations simpler. For example, the word equation for the transmutation of uranium to thorium due to α decay is

$$\text{Uranium 238} \rightarrow \text{Thorium 234} + \alpha \text{ particle}$$

The nuclear equation for this reaction is

$$^{238}_{92}\text{U} \rightarrow {}^{234}_{90}\text{Th} + {}^{4}_{2}\text{He}$$

No nuclear particles are destroyed during the transmutation process. Thus, the sum of the superscripts on the right side of the equation must equal the sum of the superscripts on the left side of the equation. The sum of the superscripts on both sides of the equation is 238. Electric charge is also conserved. Thus, the sum of the subscripts on the right is equal to the sum of the subscripts on the left.

Transmutation is the change of one element into another through a change in atomic number.

A nuclear equation is a short-hand way of describing a nuclear reaction.

The symbol for an alpha particle is $^{4}_{2}\text{He}$.

In a nuclear equation, the sum of the superscripts on the right side must be equal to the sum of the superscripts on the left side.

Students should be able to write
nuclear equations involving alpha
and beta decay.

EXAMPLE

Nuclear Equation—Alpha Decay

Write the nuclear equation for the transmutation of a radioactive
radium isotope, $^{226}_{88}Ra$, in a radon isotope, $^{222}_{86}Rn$, by the emission of an
α particle.

Solution: $^{226}_{88}Ra \rightarrow {}^{222}_{86}Rn + {}^4_2He$

The symbol for a beta particle is
$_{-1}^{0}e$.

A β particle is represented by the symbol $_{-1}^{0}e$. This indicates that the
electron has one negative charge and an atomic mass number of zero.
The equation for the transmutation of a thorium atom by the emission
of a β particle is

$$^{234}_{90}Th \rightarrow {}^{234}_{91}Pa + {}_{-1}^{0}e$$

In a nuclear equation, the sum of
the subscripts on the right side
must be equal to the sum of the
subscripts on the left side.

The sum of the superscripts on the right side of the equation equals the
sum of the superscripts on the left side of the equation. Also, the sum of
the subscripts on the right side of the equation equals the sum of the
subscripts on the left side of the equation.

EXAMPLE

Nuclear Equation—Beta Decay

Write the nuclear equation for the transmutation of a radioactive lead
isotope, $^{209}_{82}Pb$, into a bismuth isotope, $^{209}_{83}Bi$, by the emission of a β
particle.

Solution: $^{209}_{82}Pb \rightarrow {}^{209}_{83}Bi + {}_{-1}^{0}e$

Problems

5. $^{234}_{92}U \rightarrow {}^{230}_{90}Th + {}^4_2He$

5. Write the nuclear equation for the transmutation of a radioactive
uranium isotope, $^{234}_{92}U$, into a thorium isotope, $^{230}_{90}Th$, by the
emission of an α particle.

6. $^{230}_{90}TH \rightarrow {}^{226}_{88}Ra + {}^4_2He$

6. Write the nuclear equation for the transmutation of a radioactive
thorium isotope, $^{230}_{90}Th$, into a radioactive radium isotope, $^{226}_{88}Ra$,
by the emission of an α particle.

7. $^{226}_{88}Ra \rightarrow {}^{222}_{86}Rn + {}^4_2He$

7. Write the nuclear equation for the transmutation of a radioactive
radium isotope, $^{226}_{88}Ra$, into a radon isotope, $^{222}_{86}Rn$, by the
emission of an α particle.

8. $^{214}_{82}Pb \rightarrow {}^{214}_{83}Bi + {}_{-1}^{0}e$

8. A radioactive lead isotope, $^{214}_{82}Pb$, can change to a radioactive
bismuth isotope, $^{214}_{83}Bi$, by the emission of a β particle. Write the
nuclear equation.

9. $^{214}_{83}Bi \rightarrow {}^{214}_{84}Po + {}_{-1}^{0}e$

9. A radioactive bismuth isotope, $^{214}_{83}Bi$, emits a β particle. Use Table
C-5 of the Appendix to determine the element formed. Write the
nuclear equation.

10. A radioactive polonium isotope, $^{210}_{84}Po$, emits an α particle. Use Table C-5 of the Appendix to determine the element formed. Write the nuclear equation.

10. $^{210}_{84}Po \rightarrow \,^{206}_{82}Pb + \,^{4}_{2}He$

11. An unstable chromium isotope, $^{56}_{24}Cr$, emits a β particle. Write a complete equation and show the element formed.

11. $^{56}_{24}Cr \rightarrow \,^{56}_{25}Mn + \,^{0}_{-1}e$

30:5 Half-Life

The time required for half of the atoms in any given quantity of a radioactive element to disintegrate is the **half-life** of that element. The half-life of a pure radioactive isotope is unique to that particular isotope. For example, the half-life of radium isotope $^{226}_{88}Ra$ is 1600 years. In other words, in 1600 years, half of a given quantity of $^{226}_{88}Ra$ will disintegrate and form another element. In another 1600 years, half of the remaining sample will have disintegrated. Only one-fourth of the original amount will remain at that time.

The rate, or number of decays per second, of a radioactive substance is called its **activity**. Activity is proportional to the number of radioactive atoms present. Therefore, the activity of a particular sample is reduced by one-half in one half-life. For example, consider $^{131}_{53}I$ with a half-life of 8.07 days. If the activity of a certain sample is 8 $\times 10^5$ decays per second when the $^{131}_{53}I$ is produced, 8.07 days later, its activity will be 4×10^5 decays per second. After another 8.07 days, its activity will be 2.0×10^5 decays per second.

The half-life of an element is the time required for half of the radioactive nuclei to decay.

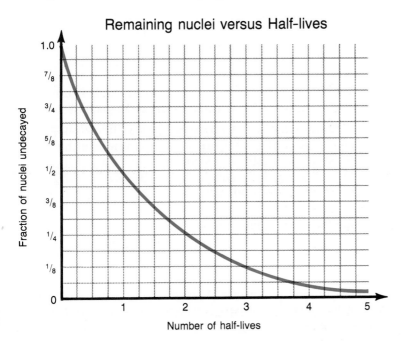

Remaining nuclei versus Half-lives

Fraction of nuclei undecayed

Number of half-lives

FIGURE 30-4. Use this half-life graph with Problems 12 through 15 on page 520.

The half-lives of radioactive
isotopes differ widely.

TABLE 30-1

Half-Life of Selected Isotopes			
Element	Isotope	Half-Life	Radiation Produced
hydrogen	$^3_1$H	12.3 years	β
carbon	$^{14}_6$C	5730 years	β
iodine	$^{131}_{53}$I	8.07 days	β, γ
lead	$^{212}_{82}$Pb	10.6 hours	β, γ
polonium	$^{194}_{84}$Po	0.5 seconds	α
polonium	$^{210}_{84}$Po	138 days	α
uranium	$^{227}_{92}$U	1.3 minutes	α
uranium	$^{235}_{92}$U	7.1×10^8 years	α, γ
uranium	$^{238}_{92}$U	4.51×10^9 years	α, γ
plutonium	$^{236}_{94}$Pu	2.85 years	α, γ
plutonium	$^{242}_{94}$Pu	3.79×10^5 years	α

Problems

These problems require the use of Figure 30-4 and Table 30-1.

12. 0.25 g

12. A sample of 1.0 g of tritium, $^3_1$H , is produced. What will be the mass of tritium remaining after 24.6 years?

13. 0.38 g

13. The isotope $^{238}_{93}$Np has a half-life of 2.0 days. If 4.0 g are produced on Monday, what will be the approximate mass remaining the following Monday?

14. 5 × 10⁵ decays/s

14. A sample of $^{210}_{84}$Po is purchased for a physics class on September 1. Its activity is 2×10^6 decays per second. The sample is used in an experiment on June 1. What activity can be expected?

15. ¾ original brightness

15. Tritium is used in some watches to produce a fluorescent glow so the watch can be read in the dark. If the brightness of the glow is proportional to the activity of the tritium, what will be the brightness of the watch, in comparison to the original brightness, when the watch is six years old?

30:6   Nuclear Bombardment

Rutherford bombarded many elements with α particles. He used the α particles to cause a nuclear reaction. When nitrogen gas was bombarded, Rutherford noted that high energy hydrogen nuclei, or protons, were emitted from the gas. A proton has a charge of one, while an α particle has a charge of two. Rutherford hypothesized that the nitrogen had been artificially transmuted by the α particles. The

If a particle (α, proton, electron, neutron, or γ) strikes a nucleus with enough energy, it can cause a nuclear reaction.

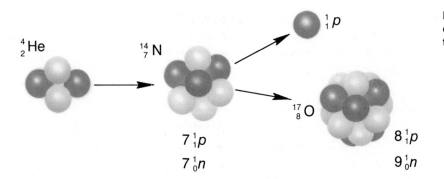

FIGURE 30-5. Production of oxygen-17 from the artificial transmutation of nitrogen.

unknown results of the transmutation can be written $_Z^A X$, and the nuclear reaction could be written

$$_2^4 He + {_7^{14}}N \rightarrow {_1^1}H + {_Z^A}X$$

Simple arithmetic shows the atomic number of the unknown isotope $Z = 2 + 7 - 1 = 8$ and $A = 4 + 14 - 1 = 17$. From Table C-5, the isotope must be $_8^{17}O$. The identity of the $_8^{17}O$ isotope was confirmed by a mass spectrograph several years later.

Bombarding $_4^9 Be$ with α particles produced a radiation more penetrating than any previously discovered. In 1932 Irene Curie (daughter of Marie and Pierre Curie) and her husband Frederic Joliot discovered that high speed protons were expelled from paraffin wax that was exposed to this new radiation from beryllium. In 1932 James Chadwick showed that the particles emitted from beryllium were uncharged, but approximately the same mass as protons. That is, the beryllium emitted the particle Rutherford had theorized must be in the nucleus: the neutron. The reaction can be written using the symbol for the neutron, $_0^1 n$

$$_2^4 He + {_4^9}Be \rightarrow {_6^{12}}C + {_0^1}n$$

Neutrons, being uncharged, are not repelled by the nucleus. As a result, neutrons are often used to bombard nuclei.

Alpha particles from radioactive materials have fixed energies. It is also difficult to obtain sources that emit a large number of particles per second. Means of artificially accelerating particles to high energies are needed. Energies of several million electron volts are required to produce nuclear reactions. Several types of particle accelerators have been developed. The linear accelerator and synchrotron are two accelerators in greatest use today.

Particle accelerators have been developed to give particles very high energy in order to study the structure of the nucleus.

30:7 Linear Accelerators

A **linear accelerator** consists of a series of hollow tubes within a long evacuated chamber. Each tube is connected to a source of high

Ion Source   Alternating Voltage   Vacuum chamber   Target

frequency alternating voltage, Figure 30-6. Protons are produced in a ion source similar to that described in Chapter 27. Protons are accelerated into the first tube when that tube has a negative potential. There are no electric fields within any of the tubes; therefore, the protons are not accelerated within the tubes. The length of the tube and the frequency of the voltage is adjusted so that when the protons have reached the far end of the first tube the potential of the second tube is negative with respect to that of the first. The resulting electric field in the gap between the tubes accelerates the protons into the second tube. This process continues, with the protons receiving an acceleration between each pair of tubes. The energy of the protons is increased by 10^5 eV by each acceleration. The proton rides along the crest of an electric field wave much like a surf board on the ocean. At the end of the accelerator, the protons can have energies of many million electron volts.

Linear accelerators can be used with both electrons and protons. The largest linear accelerator is at Stanford University in California. It is 3.3 km long and accelerates electrons to energies of 20 GeV (2.0×10^{10} eV).

30:8 The Synchrotron

An accelerator may be made smaller by using a magnetic field to bend the path of the particles into a circle. In a device known as a **synchrotron,** the bending magnets are separated by accelerating regions. In these regions, high frequency alternating voltage accelerates the particles. The strength of the magnetic field and the length of the path are chosen so that the particles reach the location of the alternating electric field when the field's polarity will accelerate them. The largest synchrotron in operation is at the Fermi National Accelerator Laboratory near Chicago.

30:9 Particle Detectors

Photographic films become "fogged" or exposed when α particles, β particles, or γ rays strike them. Thus, photographic film is used to detect these particles and rays. Many other devices are used to detect charged particles and γ rays. Most of these devices use the principle

FIGURE 30-7. Fermi Laboratory's synchrotron has a diameter of 2 km.

that a high-speed particle removes electrons from atoms. The high-speed particles energize the matter that they bombard. For example, some substances fluoresce when exposed to certain types of radiation. Thus, fluorescent substances can be used in detecting radiation, Section 29:5.

> Some flourescent substances can be used to detect radiation.

The **Geiger-Müller tube** employs an avalanche effect, Figure 30-8. The tube contains a gas at low pressure (10 kPa). At one end of the tube is a very thin "window" through which charged particles or gamma rays are allowed to pass. Inside the tube is a copper cylinder with a negative charge. A rigid wire with a positive charge runs down the center of this cylinder. The voltage across the wire and cylinder is kept just below the point at which a spontaneous discharge occurs. When a charged particle or gamma ray enters the tube, it ionizes a gas atom located between the copper cylinder and the wire. The positive ion produced is accelerated toward the copper cylinder by the potential difference. The electron is accelerated toward the positive wire. As these new particles move toward the electrode, they strike other atoms and form even more ions in their path.

> A Geiger-Müller tube is a sensitive detector of radioactive emissions.

FIGURE 30-8. A Geiger counter can be used to detect gamma rays.

FIGURE 30-9. In a bubble chamber, charged particles produce trails of tiny vapor bubbles in liquid hydrogen as they pass through the chamber.

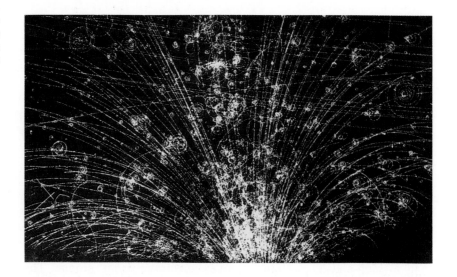

Thus an avalanche of charged particles is created and a pulse of current flows through the tube. The current causes a potential difference across a resistor in the circuit. The voltage is amplified and registers the arrival of a particle by advancing a counter or producing an audible signal such as a click. The potential difference across the resistor lowers the voltage across the tube so that the current flow stops. Thus the tube is ready for the beginning of a new avalanche when another particle or gamma ray enters it.

Another device used to detect particles is the **Wilson cloud chamber.** The chamber contains an area supersaturated with water vapor or ethanol vapor. When charged particles travel through the chamber, leaving a trail of ions in their paths, the vapor tends to condense into small droplets on the ions. In this way, visible trails of droplets, or fog, are formed.

Cloud and bubble chambers produce records of the paths of charged particles.

The **bubble chamber** operates on a similar principle. The pressure on a large volume of liquid hydrogen is adjusted so that the liquid is very close to the boiling point. The ions produced by the charged particles provide centers about which tiny bubbles of hydrogen vapor form. Cameras record the string of bubbles. An analysis of the film allows measurement of the energy and momentum of charged particles. The presence of neutral particles in reactions can be determined by using the laws of conservation of energy and momentum in collisions, as described in Chapter 11.

30:10 The Fundamental Particles

The atom was once thought to be the smallest particle into which matter could be divided. Then Rutherford found that the atom had a nucleus surrounded by electrons. After the proton was discovered it was also thought to be indivisible. However, experiments in which protons are bombarded by other protons accelerated by synchrotrons to very high energies suggest that the proton is composed of yet smaller bodies. The neutron also appears to be composed of several smaller bodies. The structure of the proton and neutron is closely related to the strong nuclear forces that act between neutrons and protons.

In the present view of physicists, the particles out of which all matter is made are grouped into two families, quarks and leptons. **Quarks** make up protons and neutrons. **Leptons** are particles with little or no mass, the electron and neutrino. There are also particles that carry, or transmit, forces between particles. The photon is the carrier of the electromagnetic force. Eight particles, called **gluons,** carry the strong force that binds quarks into protons and the protons and neutrons into nuclei. Three particles, the **weak bosons,** are involved in the weak interaction which operates in beta decay. The **graviton** is the name given to the yet-undetected carrier of the gravitational force. These particles are summarized in Tables 30-2 and 30-3. Charges are given in units of the electron charge and masses are stated as energy equivalents.

All matter is believed to be made up of two families of particles, quarks and leptons.

TABLE 30-2

Quarks				Leptons			
Name	Symbol	Mass	Charge	Name	Symbol	Mass	Charge
down	d	330 Mev	$-1/_3$	electron	e	0.511 Mev	$-3/_3$
up	u	330 Mev	$2/_3$	neutrino	$\bar{\nu}_e$	0	0

TABLE 30-3

Force Carriers				
Force	Name	Symbol	Mass	Charge
Electromagnetic	photon	γ	0	0
Weak	weak bosons	W^+	82 Gev	$3/_3$
		W^-	82 Gev	$-3/_3$
		Z^0	93 Gev	0
Strong	gluons (8)	g	0	0
Gravitational	graviton	G	0	0

Each quark and each lepton also has its antiparticle. The antiparticles are identical with the particles except they have the opposite charge. When a particle and antiparticle collide, they annihilate each other and are transformed into energy. The total number of quarks and the total number of leptons in the universe is constant. That is, quarks and leptons are created or destroyed only in particle-antiparticle pairs. The number of charge carriers is not

There is an antiparticle for every particle.

Annihilation occurs when a particle meets an antiparticle.

conserved; however, the total charge is conserved. Gravitons, photons, gluons, and weak bosons can be created or destroyed if there is enough energy. After exploring the production and annihilation of antiparticles, we will return to the quark and lepton theory of matter.

30:11 Particles and Antiparticles

The α particles and γ rays emitted by radioactive nuclei have single energies characteristic of the particular nucleus. For example, the energy of the α particle emitted by $^{234}_{90}\text{Th}$ is always 4.2 MeV. However, β particles are emitted with a wide range of energies. It would be thought that the energy of the β particle should be equal to the difference between the energy of the nucleus before decay and the energy of the nucleus produced by the decay. The range of energies of electrons emitted during β decay suggested to Niels Bohr that energy is not conserved in nuclear reactions. Wolfgang Pauli in 1931 and Enrico Fermi in 1934, however, suggested that an unseen neutral particle was emitted with the β particle. Named the **neutrino,** or "little neutral one" in Italian by Fermi, the particle (actually an antineutrino) was not directly observed until 1956.

In a stable nucleus the neutron does not decay. However, in unstable nuclei the neutron can decay by emitting a β particle. Sharing the energy with the β particle is an antineutrino ($^{0}_{0}\bar{\nu}$).

The antineutrino has zero mass and is uncharged, but like the photon it carries momentum and energy. The neutron decay equation is written

$$^{1}_{0}n \rightarrow {}^{1}_{1}p + {}^{\ 0}_{-1}e + {}^{0}_{0}\bar{\nu}$$

When an isotope decays by emission of a **positron** (antielectron), the inverse of a β decay occurs. A proton within the nucleus changes into a neutron with the emission of a positron and a neutrino ($^{0}_{0}\nu$). The decay reaction is written

$$^{1}_{1}p \rightarrow {}^{1}_{0}n + {}^{0}_{1}e + {}^{0}_{0}\nu$$

The decay of neutrons into protons and vice-versa cannot be explained by the strong force. The existence of β decay indicates there must be another force or interaction, called the **weak interaction,** acting in the nucleus.

The positron is an example of an antiparticle, or a particle of antimatter. When a positron and an electron collide the two annihilate each other, resulting in energy in the form of γ rays. Matter is directly converted into energy.

The amount of energy can be calculated using Einstein's equation for the energy equivalent of mass

$$E = mc^2$$

Experiments showing that beta particles are emitted with a wide range of energies suggested the existence of the neutrino.

A neutrino has no mass and no charge.

A positron has one positive charge. Like an electron, it has little mass.

Neutron → Electron + Proton + Antineutrino
Proton → Positron + Neutrino + Neutron

FIGURE 30-10. The collision of a positron and an electron result in gamma ray production.

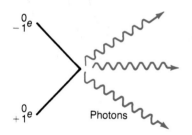

The mass of the electron is 9.11×10^{-31} kg. The mass of the positron is the same. Therefore, the energy equivalent of the positron and the electron together is

$$E = 2(9.11 \times 10^{-31} \text{ kg})(3.00 \times 10^8 \text{ m/s})^2$$
$$= (1.64 \times 10^{-13} \text{ J})(1 \text{ eV}/1.60 \times 10^{-19} \text{ J})$$
$$= 1.02 \times 10^6 \text{ eV or } 1.02 \text{ MeV}$$

When a positron and an electron annihilate each other, the sum of the energies of the γ rays emitted is 1.02 MeV.

The inverse of annihilation can also occur. That is, energy can be converted directly to matter. If a γ ray with at least 1.02 MeV energy passes close by a nucleus, a positron and electron pair can be produced. Individual positrons or electrons, however, cannot be produced, because such an event would violate the law of conservation of charge. Matter and antimatter particles must always be produced in pairs.

FIGURE 30-11. The production of a positron-electron pair as photographed in a bubble chamber.

a

b

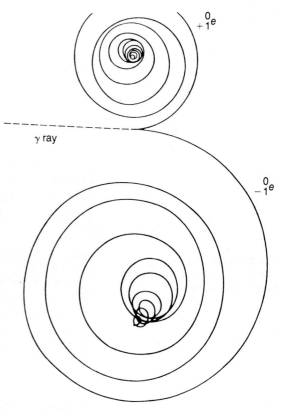

Photons with energies in excess of 1.02 MeV are capable of causing pair production.

The production of a positron-electron pair is shown in the bubble chamber photograph of Figure 30-11. A magnetic field around the bubble chamber causes the oppositely charged particles to curve in opposite directions. The γ ray that produced the pair disappears. If the energy of the γ ray is larger than 1.02 MeV, the excess energy goes into kinetic energy of the positron and electron. The positron soon collides with another electron and they are annihilated, resulting in the production of two or three γ rays with a total energy of 1.02 MeV.

Antiprotons also exist. An antiproton has a mass equal to that of the proton, but is negatively charged. Protons have 1836 times as much mass as electrons. The energy needed to create proton-antiproton pairs is comparably larger. The first proton-antiproton pair was produced and observed at Berkeley, California in 1955.

Problem

16. a. 1.5×10^{-10} J
    b. 938 MeV
    c. 1.88 GeV

16. The mass of a proton is 1.67×10^{-27} kg.
   a. Find the energy equivalent of the proton's mass in joules.
   b. Convert this value to eV.
   c. Find the lowest energy of a γ ray that could produce a proton-antiproton pair.

30:12 The Quark Model of Nucleons

The quark model describes the proton and the neutron as an assembly of quarks. According to this model, forces are the result of the emission and absorption or decay of force carrier particles. Gluons carry the strong force, W and Z bosons carry the weak force, and photons carry the electromagnetic force.

FIGURE 30-12. A battery of devices are waiting to detect the decay of a proton in a water molecule in this subterranean lake.

In the quark model, nucleons are each made up of three quarks. The proton has two up quarks and one down quark. A proton is described as p = (uud). The charge on the proton is the sum of the charges of the three quarks, $2/3 + 2/3 + -1/3 = 1$. The neutron is made up of one up quark and two down quarks, n = (udd). The charge of the neutron is $2/3 + -1/3 + -1/3 = 0$.

In the quark model, nucleons are made up of three quarks.

Individual quarks cannot be observed because the strong force that holds them together becomes larger as the quarks are pulled farther apart. The strong force acts like the force of a spring, unlike the electric force, which becomes weaker as charged particles are moved farther apart. In the quark model, the strong force is the result of the emission and absorption of gluons that carry the force.

According to the present theory, the weak interaction involves three charge carriers, the W^+, W^-, and Z^0 bosons. Beta decay, the decay of a neutron into a proton, electron, and antineutrino, occurs in two steps. As was shown before, the neutron and the proton differ by one quark. In β decay, one d quark in a neutron changes to a u quark with the emission of a W^- boson.

In the quark model, beta decay involves the change of a d quark into a u quark. This changes the neutron into a proton.

$$d \rightarrow u + W^-$$

The W^- boson then decays into an electron and an antineutrino.

$$W^- \rightarrow e^- + \bar{\nu}^-$$

Similarly, the inverse β decay of an antineutron involves the emission of a W^+ boson. This decays into a positron and neutrino.

The emission of a Z^0 boson is not accompanied by a change from one quark to another. The Z^0 boson produces an interaction between the nucleons and the electrons in atoms. This interaction is much weaker than the electromagnetic force holding the atom together. The interaction was first detected in 1979. The W^+, W^-, and Z^0 bosons were first observed directly in 1983.

The quark change is accompanied by emission of a W particle. The W produces the electron and antineutrino.

The force between charged particles, the electromagnetic interaction, is carried by photons in much the same way as weak bosons carry the weak force. The electric force acts over a long range because the photon has zero mass, while the weak force acts over short distances because the W and Z bosons are so relatively massive. However, the mathematical structures of the theories of the weak interaction and electromagnetic interaction are similar. In high energy collisions produced by accelerators, the electromagnetic and weak interactions have the same strength and range.

Astrophysical theories of supernovae indicate that during these massive stellar explosions, the two interactions are identical. Present theories of the origin of the universe suggest that the two forces were identical during the early moments in the life of the cosmos as well. For this reason, the electromagnetic and weak forces are said to be unified by this theory into a single force, called the **electroweak** force.

The electromagnetic and weak interactions are unified into the electroweak interaction.

Bombardment of particles at high energies creates many particles of medium and large mass that have very short lifetimes. Some can be explained as combinations of two or three u or d quarks. Particles made of two quarks are called **mesons,** while those composed of three quarks are called **baryons.** However, combinations of the u and d quarks cannot account for all the particles produced. Combinations of four other quarks are necessary to form all known baryons and mesons. Two additional pairs of leptons are also produced at high energy collisons. The additional quarks and leptons are listed in Tables 30-4 and 30-5. No one knows the functions of the additional particles or if there are still other undiscovered particles.

Baryons are made up of a combination of three quarks. Mesons are made up of a quark and an antiquark.

In addition to the quarks and leptons found in ordinary matter, at high energies four more quarks and four more leptons are needed.

TABLE 30-4

Additional Quarks			
Name	Symbol	Mass	Charge
strange	s	510 MeV	$-1/3$
charm	c	1.6 GeV	$2/3$
bottom	b	5.2 GeV	$-1/3$
top	t	40 GeV	$2/3$

TABLE 30-5

Additional Leptons			
Name	Symbol	Mass	Charge
muon	μ	105 Mev	$-3/3$
muon neutrino	ν_μ	0	0
tau	τ	1.8 GeV	$-3/3$
tau neutrino	ν_τ	0	0

In the same way that the electromagnetic and weak forces were unified into the electroweak force during the 1970's, physicists are presently trying to create a Grand Unified Theory that includes the strong force as well. Work is still incomplete. One prediction of current theories is that the proton should not exist forever, but decay into leptons and photons. The proton half-life should be 10^{31} years. Experiments to test this prediction on a large number of protons have been underway for over a year. Although several decays should have occurred, not one has been observed. The experiment continues and theories are being revised. A fully unified theory which includes gravitation as well requires even more work.

In Grand Unified Theories, the strong and electroweak forces are unified.

The field of physics that studies these particles is called high energy or elementary particle physics. The field is very exciting because new discoveries occur almost every week. Each new discovery seems to raise as many questions as it answers. The question of what makes up the universe does not yet have a complete answer.

Summary

1. The number of protons in a nucleus is given by the atomic number.   30:1

2. The sum of the number of protons and neutrons in a nucleus is indicated by the mass number.   30:1

3. Atoms having nuclei with the same number of protons but different number of neutrons are called isotopes.   30:2

4. An unstable nucleus undergoes radioactive decay, changing, or transmuting, into another element.   30:3

5. Radioactive decay produces three kinds of particles. Alpha (α) particles are helium nuclei; beta (β) particles are high speed electrons; and gamma (γ) rays are high energy photons.   30:3

6. Nuclear reactions do not change the sum of the mass numbers (A) or atomic numbers (Z) of the nuclei involved.   30:4

7. The half-life of a radioactive isotope is the time required for half of the nuclei to decay.   30:5

8. The rate of radioactive decay, the activity, is also reduced by a factor of two in a time equal to the half-life.   30:5

9. Bombardment of nuclei by protons, neutrons, alpha particles, electrons, or gamma rays can produce a nuclear reaction.   30:6

10. Linear accelerators are used to produce very high energy protons and electrons.   30:7

11. Synchrotrons are circular accelerators which produce the highest energy protons.   30:8

12. The Geiger counter and other particle detectors use the ionization of charged particles passing through matter.   30:9

13. In beta decay the uncharged, massless antineutrino is emitted with the electron.   30:11

14. A positron (antimatter electron) and a neutrino are emitted by radioactive nuclei in a process called inverse beta decay.   30:11

15. When antimatter and matter combine all mass is converted into energy.   30:11

16. By pair production energy is transformed into a matter-antimatter particle pair.   30:11

17. The weak interaction, or weak force, operates in beta decay. The strong force binds the nucleus together.   30:12

18. Protons and neutrons, together called nucleons, are composed of still smaller particles, quarks.   30:12

19. All matter appears to be made up of two families of particles, quarks and leptons.   30:12

Detailed answers to all Questions and Problems are given in the Teacher's Guide at the front of this book.

Questions

1. Define the term transmutation in nuclear physics and give an example.

2. What happens to the atomic number and mass number of a nuclei that emits an alpha particle?

3. What happens to the atomic number and mass number of a nuclei that emits a beta particle?

4. What happens to the atomic number and mass number of a nuclei that emits a positron?

5. Give the symbol, mass, and charge of the following particles.
   a. proton   **c.** positron   **e.** α particle
   b. neutron   **d.** electron

6. If the half-life of an isotope is 2 years, what fraction of the isotope remains after 6 years?

7. What would happen if a meteorite made of antiprotons, antineutrons, and positrons landed on the earth?

8. What would be the charge of a particle composed of three u quarks?

9. The charge of an anti-quark is opposite that of a quark. A pion is composed of a u quark and an anti-d quark. What would be the charge of this pion?

10. Find the charges of the following pions made of
    a. u and anti-u quark pair.
    b. d and anti-u quarks.
    c. d and anti-d quarks.

Problems–A

1. 12

2. 8

3. a. 64
   b. 126
   c. 125
   d. 45
   e. 0
   f. 22
   g. 78

4. $^{25}_{13}\text{Al} + ^4_2\text{He} \rightarrow ^1_0 n + ^{28}_{15}\text{P}$

1. An atom of an isotope of magnesium has an atomic mass of about 24 amu. The atomic number of magnesium is 12. How many neutrons are in the nucleus of this atom?

2. An atom of an isotope of nitrogen has an atomic mass of about 15 amu. The atomic number of nitrogen is 7. How many neutrons are in the nucleus of this isotope?

3. List the number of neutrons in an atom of each of these isotopes.
   a. $^{112}_{48}\text{Cd}$ **c.** $^{208}_{83}\text{Bi}$ **e.** ^1_1H **g.** $^{132}_{54}\text{Xe}$
   b. $^{209}_{83}\text{Bi}$ **d.** $^{80}_{35}\text{Br}$ **f.** $^{40}_{18}\text{Ar}$

4. An aluminum isotope, $^{25}_{13}\text{Al}$, when bombarded by α particles absorbs an alpha particle and then emits a neutron. Write a nuclear equation for this transmutation.

5. During a reaction, two deuterons combine to form a helium isotope, $^3_2$He. (The symbol for a deuteron is $^2_1$H.) What other particle is produced?

6. On the sun, the nuclei of four ordinary hydrogen atoms combine to form a helium isotope, $^4_2$He. What type of particles are missing from the following equation for this reaction?

$$4^1_1\text{H} \rightarrow {}^4_2\text{He} + ?$$

5. $^1_0 n$

6. $4\,^1_1\text{H} \rightarrow {}^4_2\text{He} + 2\,^0_{+1}e$

Problems–B

1. The half-life of strontium-90 is 28 years. After 280 years, how would the intensity of a sample of strontium-90 compare to the original intensity of the sample?

2. A 1.00 μg-sample of a radioactive material contains 6.00×10^{14} nuclei. After 48 hours, 0.25 μg of the material remains.
   a. What is the half-life of the material?
   b. How could one determine the activity of the sample at 24 hours using this information?

1. 9.8×10^{-2}%

2. a.   24 h
    b.   See Teacher's Guide

Readings

Brown, Gerald, "The Structure of the Nucleon." *Physics Today*, February, 1983.

Finkbeiner, Ann, "What's Going On Inside The Sun?" *Science 85*, January, 1985.

Guillen, Michael, "The Paradox of Antimatter." *Science Digest*, February, 1985.

Schechter, Bruce, "The Moment of Creation." *Discover*, April, 1983.

Taubes, Gary, "Waiting for the Protons to Die." *Discover*, April, 1984.

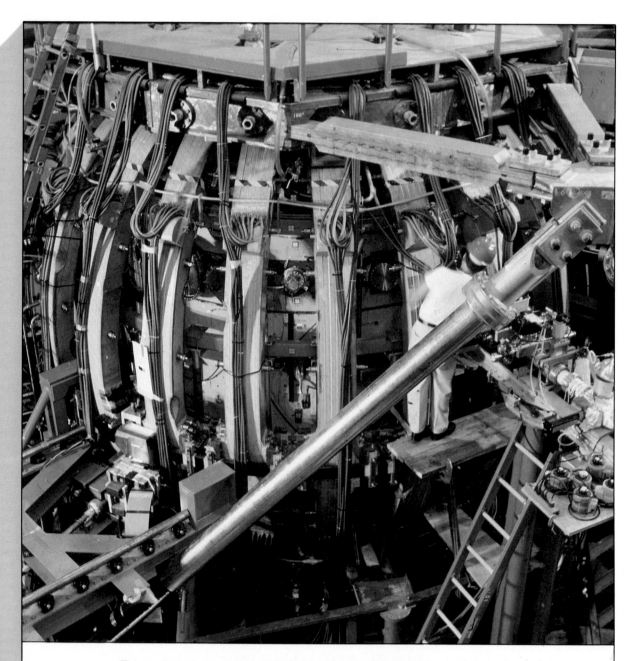

The nucleus of an atom is the target of much research today. The atom is a tremendous powerhouse of energy. Scientists feel that nuclear reactions involving hydrogen isotopes may prove to be our greatest energy resource. This fusion reactor is still in experimental stages. Maintaining the conditions necessary for a fusion reaction to occur is the most significant problem to be resolved. Why is fusion research so important? What are the advantages of using fusion as a source of energy?

Nuclear Applications

Chapter 31 introduces nuclear reactions and equation writing. Mass-energy relationships involved in nuclear processes are discussed.

In no other area of physics has basic knowledge led to applications as quickly as in the field of nuclear physics. The medical use of radioactive radium began within 20 years of its discovery. Proton accelerators were tested for medical applications less than one year after being invented. In the case of nuclear fission, the military application was under development before the basic physics was even known. Peaceful applications followed in less than 10 years. The question of the uses of nuclear reactors in our society is an important one for all citizens today. In this chapter we will explore some applications of nuclear physics.

Goal: You will gain understanding of the applications of nuclear physics.

31:1 Forces within the Nucleus

The electrons that surround the positively charged nucleus of an atom are held in place by the electric force of attraction. The nucleus consists of positively charged protons and neutral neutrons. The protons are very close together. There exists a strong electric repulsive force that might be expected to cause them to fly apart. This does not happen because an even stronger attractive force exists within the nucleus. This force is called the **strong nuclear** force. The strong force acts between protons and neutrons that are very close together, as they are in a nucleus. The strong force is always attractive, and is of the same magnitude between protons and protons, protons and neutrons, and neutrons and neutrons. As a result of this equivalence, both neutrons and protons are called **nucleons.**

The strong force holds the nucleons in the nucleus. If a nucleon were to be pulled out of a nucleus, work would have to be done to overcome the attractive force. Doing work is the same as adding energy to the nucleus. If every proton and neutron in a nucleus were pulled apart, the amount of energy that would be added is called the **binding energy** of the nucleus.

The strong force acts the same between neutrons and protons as it does between protons and protons or neutrons and neutrons.

Neutrons and protons are forms of nucleons.

The binding energy of a nucleus is the energy that would have to be added to separate it into separate nucleons.

31:2   Binding Energy of the Nucleus

The binding energy of a nucleus is expressed in a reduced mass of the nucleus. $E = mc^2$ shows the equivalence.

The binding energy exists in the form of an equivalent amount of mass, given by the equation $E = mc^2$. Energy has to be added to take a nucleus apart. As a result, the mass of the assembled nucleus is less than the sum of the masses of the nucleons that compose the nucleus. For example, the helium nucleus, $^4_2$He, consists of 2 protons and 2 neutrons. The mass of a proton is 1.007825 amu. The mass of a neutron is 1.008665 amu. Thus the mass of the nucleons that make up the helium nucleus is equal to the sum of the masses of the two protons and the neutrons, or 4.032980 amu. However, careful measurement shows the mass of a helium nucleus to be only 4.00260 amu. The mass of the helium nucleus is less than the mass of its constituent parts. This difference is called the **mass defect** of the nucleus. An amount of energy equivalent to the mass defect multiplied by the speed of light squared, would be required to separate the He nucleus into two protons and two neutrons. The binding energy can be calculated from the experimentally determined mass defect by using $E = mc^2$ to compute the energy equivalent.

Masses are normally measured in atomic mass units. It will be useful, then, to determine the energy equivalent of 1 amu = 1.66×10^{-27} kg. The most convenient unit of energy to use is the electron volt.

$$E = mc^2$$
$$= (1.66 \times 10^{-27} \text{ kg})(3.00 \times 10^8 \text{ m/s})^2$$
$$= (14.9 \times 10^{-11} \text{ J})(1 \text{ ev}/1.60 \times 10^{-19} \text{ J})$$
$$= 9.31 \times 10^8 \text{eV}$$
$$E = 931 \text{ MeV}$$

EXAMPLE

Mass Defect and Nuclear Binding Energy

The mass of a proton is 1.007825 amu. The mass of a neutron is 1.008665 amu. The mass of the nucleus of the radioactive hydrogen isotope tritium, $^3_1$H, is 3.016049 amu.   **a.** What is the nuclear mass defect of this isotope?   **b.** What is the binding energy of tritium?

Solution: **a.** As indicated by the superscript and subscript in the symbol for tritium, its nucleus contains 1 proton and 2 neutrons. Its mass defect can be found as follows.

$$\text{Mass of 1 proton} = 1.007825 \text{ amu}$$
$$\text{Mass of 2 neutrons} = (2)(1.008665 \text{ amu}) = \underline{2.017330 \text{ amu}}$$
$$\text{Total} = 3.025155 \text{ amu}$$
$$\text{Mass of tritium nucleus} = \underline{3.016049 \text{ amu}}$$
$$\text{Mass defect} = 0.009106 \text{ amu}$$

b. Since 1 amu is equivalent to 931 MeV, the binding energy of the tritium nucleus can be calculated.

The energy equivalence of one amu is 931.5 MeV.

Binding energy of $^{3}_{1}$H nucleus $= (0.009106$ amu$)(931$ MeV/amu$)$

$$= 8.48 \text{ MeV}$$

Problems

Use these values in the following problems: mass of a proton = 1.007825 amu, mass of a neutron = 1.008665 amu, and 1 amu = 931 MeV.

1. A carbon isotope, $^{12}_{6}$C, has a nuclear mass of 12.0000 amu.

   a. Calculate its mass defect.

   b. Calculate its binding energy in MeV.

1. a. 0.098940 amu
   b. 92.1 MeV

2. The isotope of hydrogen that contains 1 proton and 1 neutron is called deuterium. The mass of its nucleus is 2.0140 amu.

   a. What is its mass defect?

   b. What is the binding energy of deuterium in MeV?

2. a. 0.00249 amu
   b. 2.32 MeV

3. A nitrogen isotope, $^{15}_{7}$N, has 7 protons and 8 neutrons. Its nucleus has a mass of 15.00011 amu.

   a. Calculate the mass defect of this nucleus.

   b. Calculate the binding energy of the nucleus.

3. a. 0.12399 amu
   b. 115 MeV

4. An oxygen isotope, $^{16}_{8}$O, has a nuclear mass of about 15.99491 amu.

   a. What is the mass defect of this isotope?

   b. What is the binding energy of its nucleus?

4. a. 0.13701 amu
   b. 128 MeV

The answers to the problems above show that heavier nuclei are bound more strongly than lighter nuclei. A useful relationship is shown by a graph of the binding energy per nucleon, which is shown in Figure 31-1.

FIGURE 31-1. A graph of the binding energy per nucleon.

The binding energy per nucleon is largest for iron-56.

Except for a few nuclei, the binding energy per nucleon increases as A increases to a value of 56 (iron). $^{56}_{26}Fe$ is the most tightly bound nucleus. Nuclei larger than iron are less strongly bound.

A nuclear reaction will occur naturally if energy is released by the reaction. Energy will be released if the nucleus that results from the reaction is more tightly bound than the original nucleus. When a heavy nucleus, such as $^{238}_{92}U$, decays by releasing an alpha particle, the binding energy per nucleon of the resulting $^{234}_{90}Th$ is larger than that of the uranium. The excess energy of the $^{238}_{92}U$ nucleus is transferred into kinetic energy of the alpha particle. At low atomic numbers, reactions that add nucleons to a nucleus increase the binding energy of the nucleus and are energetically favored. In the sun and stars the production of heavier nuclei like helium and carbon from hydrogen releases energy that eventually becomes the electromagnetic radiation by which we see the stars.

31:3 Artificial Radioactivity

Marie and Pierre Curie had noted as early as 1899 that substances placed close to radioactive uranium became radioactive themselves. In 1934 Irene Curie and Frederic Joliot-Curie bombarded aluminum with alpha particles, producing neutrons by the reaction

$$^4_2He + ^{27}_{13}Al \rightarrow ^{30}_{15}P + ^1_0n$$

In addition to neutrons, the Curies found another particle coming from the aluminum, a positively charged electron, or positron. The positron, a particle with the same mass as the electron, but with a positive charge, had been discovered two years earlier by the American Carl Anderson. The most interesting result of the Curies' experiment was that the positrons continued to be emitted after the alpha bombardment stopped. The positrons were found to come from the phosphorus isotope $^{30}_{15}P$. The Curies had produced a radioactive isotope never previously found.

Bombardment of nuclei can produce radioactive isotopes not otherwise found in nature.

Radioactive isotopes can be formed from stable isotopes by bombardment with alpha particles, protons, neutrons, electrons, or gamma rays. The resulting unstable nuclei emit radiation until they are transmuted into stable isotopes. The radioactive nuclei may emit alpha, beta, and gamma radiation as well as positrons.

Artificially produced radioactive isotopes have many uses, especially in medicine. In many medical applications the patients are administered specific radioactive isotopes. The detection of the decay products of these isotopes allows doctors to trace the movement of the isotopes, and of the molecules to which they are attached, through the body. For that reason, these isotopes are called tracer isotopes. Certain elements are concentrated in particular organs of the body. Iodine, for example, is primarily used in the thyroid gland. A patient can be given

Tracer isotopes allows doctors to follow the path of molecules through the body.

an iodine compound containing radioactive $^{131}_{53}\text{I}$. The iodine will concentrate in the thyroid gland. A doctor can use a Geiger-Müller counter to monitor the activity of $^{131}_{53}\text{I}$ in the region of the thyroid and thus measure the amount of iodine that goes to this gland. In this way the functioning of the thyroid can be checked.

A recently invented instrument, the Positron Emission Tomography Scanner, or PET scanner, uses isotopes which emit positrons. The positron annihilates with an electron, emitting two gamma rays. The PET scanner detects the gammas and pinpoints the location of the positron emitting isotope. A computer is then used to make a three dimensional map of the isotope distribution. By this means details such as the use of nutrients in particular regions of the brain can be traced. For example, if a person in a PET scanner were solving a physics problem, more nutrients would flow to the part of the brain used to solve the problem. The decay of the positrons in this part of the brain would increase, and the PET scanner could map this area.

The PET scanner makes a three-dimensional map of the distribution of decaying nuclei in the body.

Another use of radioactivity in medicine is to destroy cells with radiation. Often gamma rays from the isotope $^{60}_{27}\text{Co}$ are used to treat cancer patients. Or, the ionizing radiation produced by radioactive iodine can be used to destroy cells in a diseased thyroid gland, with minimal harm to the rest of the body. Another method of reducing damage to healthy cells is to use unstable particles produced by particle accelerators like the synchrotron. These particles pass through body tissue without doing damage. When they decay, the emitted particles can destroy cells. The doctor adjusts the accelerator so that the particles decay only in the cancerous tissue.

Ionizing radiation can destroy cancerous cells.

FIGURE 31-2. PET scanner preparation and results.

a

b

5. a. $^{14}_{6}\text{C} \rightarrow \, ^{14}_{7}\text{N} + \, ^{0}_{-1}e$

   b. $^{55}_{24}\text{Cr} \rightarrow \, ^{55}_{25}\text{Mn} + \, ^{0}_{-1}e$

6. $^{238}_{92}\text{U} \rightarrow \, ^{234}_{90}\text{Th} + \, ^{4}_{2}\text{He}$

7. $^{214}_{84}\text{Po} \rightarrow \, ^{210}_{82}\text{Pb} + \, ^{4}_{2}\text{He}$

9. $^{7}_{3}\text{Li} + \, ^{1}_{1}\text{H} \rightarrow 2 \, ^{4}_{2}\text{He}$

10. a. $^{30}_{15}\text{P} \rightarrow \, ^{30}_{14}\text{Si} + \, ^{0}_{+1}e$

    b. $^{205}_{82}\text{Pb} \rightarrow \, ^{205}_{81}\text{Tl} + \, ^{0}_{+1}e$

11. a. $^{21}_{11}\text{Na} \rightarrow \, ^{21}_{10}\text{Ne} + \, ^{0}_{+1}e$

    b. $^{49}_{24}\text{Cr} \rightarrow \, ^{49}_{23}\text{V} + \, ^{0}_{+1}e$

12. a. $^{14}_{7}\text{N} + \, ^{4}_{2}\text{He} \rightarrow \, ^{18}_{9}\text{F}$

    b. $^{27}_{13}\text{Al} + \, ^{4}_{2}\text{He} \rightarrow \, ^{31}_{15}\text{P}$

13. a. $^{65}_{29}\text{Cu} + \, ^{1}_{0}n \rightarrow \, ^{65}_{28}\text{Ni} + \, ^{1}_{1}\text{H}$

    b. $^{14}_{7}\text{N} + \, ^{1}_{0}n \rightarrow \, ^{14}_{6}\text{C} + \, ^{1}_{1}\text{H}$

14. a. Lithium

    b. $^{10}_{5}\text{B} + \, ^{1}_{0}n \rightarrow \, ^{7}_{3}\text{Li} + \, ^{4}_{2}\text{He}$

8. a. $^{210}_{82}\text{Pb} \rightarrow \, ^{210}_{83}\text{Bi} + \, ^{0}_{-1}e$

   b. $^{210}_{83}\text{Bi} \rightarrow \, ^{210}_{84}\text{Po} + \, ^{0}_{-1}e$

   c. $^{234}_{90}\text{Th} \rightarrow \, ^{234}_{91}\text{Pa} + \, ^{0}_{-1}e$

   d. $^{239}_{93}\text{Np} \rightarrow \, ^{239}_{94}\text{Pu} + \, ^{0}_{-1}e$

Problems

5. Use Table C-5 of the Appendix to complete the following nuclear equations.

  a. $^{14}_{6}\text{C} \rightarrow \, ? + \, ^{0}_{-1}e$ **b.** $^{55}_{24}\text{Cr} \rightarrow \, ? + \, ^{0}_{-1}e$

6. Write the nuclear equation for the transmutation of a uranium isotope, $^{238}_{92}\text{U}$, into a thorium isotope, $^{234}_{90}\text{Th}$, by emission of an alpha particle.

7. A radioactive polonium isotope, $^{214}_{84}\text{Po}$, undergoes alpha decay and becomes lead. Write the nuclear equation.

8. Write the nuclear equations for the beta decay of these isotopes.

  a. $^{210}_{82}\text{Pb}$ **b.** $^{210}_{83}\text{Bi}$ **c.** $^{234}_{90}\text{Th}$ **d.** $^{239}_{93}\text{Np}$

9. When bombarded by protons, a lithium isotope, $^{7}_{3}\text{Li}$, absorbs a proton and then ejects two alpha particles. Write the nuclear equation for this reaction.

10. Complete the nuclear equations for these transmutations.

  a. $^{30}_{15}\text{P} \rightarrow \, ? + \, ^{0}_{+1}e$ **b.** $^{205}_{82}\text{Pb} \rightarrow \, ? + \, ^{0}_{+1}e$

11. The radioactive nuclei indicated in each equation disintegrate by emitting a positron. Complete each nuclear equation.

  a. $^{21}_{11}\text{Na} \rightarrow \, ? + \, ^{0}_{+1}e$ **b.** $^{49}_{24}\text{Cr} \rightarrow \, ? + \, ^{0}_{+1}e$

12. Each of the nuclei given below can absorb an alpha particle. Complete the equations. Assume that no secondary particles are emitted by the nucleus that absorbs the alpha particle.

  a. $^{14}_{7}\text{N} + \, ^{4}_{2}\text{He} \rightarrow \, ?$ **b.** $^{27}_{13}\text{Al} + \, ^{4}_{2}\text{He} \rightarrow \, ?$

13. In each of these reactions, a neutron is absorbed by a nucleus. The nucleus then emits a proton. Complete the equations.

  a. $^{65}_{29}\text{Cu} + \, ^{1}_{0}n \rightarrow \, ? + \, ^{1}_{1}\text{H}$ **b.** $^{14}_{7}\text{N} + \, ^{1}_{0}n \rightarrow \, ? + \, ^{1}_{1}\text{H}$

14. When a boron isotope, $^{10}_{5}\text{B}$, is bombarded with neutrons, it absorbs a neutron and then emits an alpha particle.

  a. What element is also formed?

  b. Write the nuclear equation for this reaction.

31:4 Nuclear Fission

The possibility of obtaining useful forms of energy from nuclear reactions was discussed in the 1930's. The most promising results came from bombarding substances with neutrons. In Italy in 1934 Enrico Fermi and Emilio Segré produced many new radioactive isotopes by bombarding uranium with neutrons. They believed they had formed new elements with atomic numbers larger than 92, that of uranium.

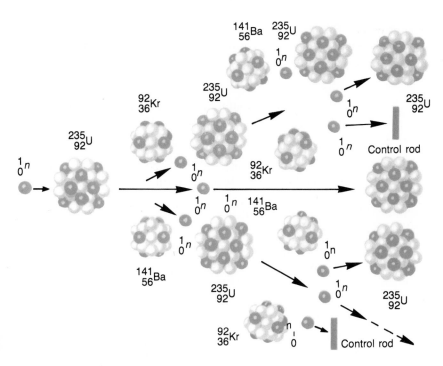

FIGURE 31-3. The nuclear fission chain of uranium-235 takes place in the core of a nuclear reactor.

Careful chemical studies of the results of bombardment of uranium by neutrons by the German chemists Otto Hahn and Fritz Strassmann in 1939 showed that the resulting atoms acted chemically like barium. The two chemists could not understand how barium, with an atomic number 56, could be produced from uranium. One week later Lise Meitner and Otto Frisch proposed that the neutrons had caused an "explosion" of the uranium into two smaller nuclei, with a large release of energy. A division of a nucleus into two or more fragments is called **fission**. The possibility that fission could be not only a source of energy, but an explosive weapon, was immediately realized by many scientists.

Fission is the splitting of a nucleus into two or more fragments of almost equal size. Fission is accompanied by the release of large amounts of energy.

The uranium isotope $^{235}_{92}U$ undergoes fission when bombarded with neutrons. The elements barium and krypton are common results of fission as shown in Figure 31-3. The reaction is

$$^{1}_{0}n + {}^{235}_{92}U \rightarrow {}^{92}_{36}Kr + {}^{141}_{56}Ba + 3\ {}^{1}_{0}n + 200\ \text{MeV}$$

The energy released by each fission can be found by calculating the masses of the atoms on each side of the equation. The total mass on the right hand side of the equation is 0.215 amu smaller than that on the left. The energy equivalent of this mass is 3.21×10^{-11} J or 200 MeV.

The neutron needed to cause the fission of $^{235}_{92}U$ can be one of the three neutrons produced by the fission process. If one or more of the neutrons causes a fission, that fission releases three more neutrons, each of which can cause more fission. This process is a chain reaction.

In a chain reaction, the neutrons released by one fissioning nucleus induce other fissions.

31:5 Nuclear Reactors

Most of the neutrons released by the fission of $^{235}_{92}$U atoms are moving at high speed and are unable to cause the fission of another $^{235}_{92}$U atom. In addition, naturally occurring uranium consists of less than 1% the isotope $^{235}_{92}$U and more than 99% $^{238}_{92}$U. When a $^{238}_{92}$U nucleus absorbs a fast neutron it does not undergo fission, but becomes a new isotope, $^{239}_{92}$U. The absorption of neutrons by $^{238}_{92}$U keeps most of the neutrons from reaching the fissionable $^{235}_{92}$U atoms.

Fermi suggested that a chain reaction would occur if the uranium were broken up into small pieces and placed in a material that can slow down, or moderate, the fast neutrons. When a neutron collides with a light atom it transfers momentum and energy to the atom. In this way the neutron loses energy. The **moderator** creates many slow neutrons that are more likely to be absorbed by $^{235}_{92}$U than by $^{238}_{92}$U. The larger number of slow neutrons greatly increases the probability that a neutron released by a fissioning $^{235}_{92}$U nucleus will cause another $^{235}_{92}$U nucleus to fission. If there is enough uranium in the sample, a chain reaction can occur.

The lightest atom, hydrogen, would be an ideal moderator. However, fast neutrons cause a nuclear reaction with the most common hydrogen nuclei. For this reason when Fermi produced the first controlled chain reaction on December 2, 1942, he used graphite (carbon) as a moderator. Heavy water, in which the hydrogen, $^{1}_{1}$H, is replaced by the isotope deuterium, $^{2}_{1}$H, does not absorb fast neutrons. Since heavy water does not absorb fast neutrons it is used as a moderator with natural uranium in the Canadian CANDU reactors.

Ordinary water can be used as a moderator if the number of $^{235}_{92}$U nuclei in the uranium sample is increased. The process that increases the number of fissionable nuclei is called **enrichment.** Enrichment of uranium is difficult and requires large, expensive equipment. The United States government operates the plants that produce the enriched uranium used in most of the nuclear reactors in the western world.

A nuclear reactor consists of about 200 metric tons of uranium sealed in hundreds of metal rods. The rods are immersed in water. The water is both the moderator and the means of transferring the thermal energy from the fissioning uranium. Between the uranium rods are rods of the metal cadmium. Cadmium absorbs neutrons easily. The cadmium rods are moved in and out of the reactor to control the rate of the chain reaction. These rods are called **control rods.** When the control rods are inserted completely into the reactor they absorb enough neutrons to prevent the chain reaction. As they are removed from the reactor the rate of energy release increases.

A slow neutron is a more effective bombarding particle than a fast neutron.

FIGURE 31-4. Diagram of a nuclear pile reactor indicating graphite block moderators, the cadmium control rods, and the uranium-235 fuel cylinders (a). The blue glow surrounding the reactor core is called the Cerenkov effect (b).

a

Uranium fuel rods

Cadmium
control rods

Carbon
(graphite)
blocks

b

FIGURE 31-5. In a nuclear power plant the thermal energy released in nuclear reactions is converted to electric energy.

The energy released by the fission heats the water surrounding the uranium rods. This water is pumped to a heat exchanger (Figure 31-5) where it causes other water to boil. The steam produced turns turbines. The turbines are connected to generators that produce electrical energy. At present about 10% of the electricity used in the United States is produced by nuclear energy.

Fission of $^{235}_{92}$U nuclei produces Kr, Ba, and other atoms. Most of these atoms are radioactive. Approximately once each year some of the uranium fuel rods must be replaced. Although no longer suitable for a reactor, the old rods are still extremely radioactive and must be stored in safe locations. Research is now being done on methods of safe, permanent storage of these radioactive waste products. Among the waste products is an isotope of plutonium, $^{239}_{94}$Pu. This isotope is extremely toxic and can also be used in nuclear weapons. However, there is hope that in the future this fissionable isotope might be removed from radioactive waste and recycled to fuel other reactors.

The supply of uranium is limited. If nuclear reactors are used to supply a large fraction of the world's energy, uranium will become scarce. In order to extend the supply of uranium, **breeder reactors** are being developed. If plutonium and $^{238}_{92}$U are both present in a reactor, the plutonium will undergo fission in the manner of $^{235}_{92}$U. During the process many of the free neutrons from the fission of plutonium are absorbed by the $^{238}_{92}$U. This reaction produces additional $^{239}_{94}$Pu. For every two plutonium atoms that undergo fission, three new ones are

A breeder reactor produces more atoms of fissionable material than it originally contained.

formed. More fissionable fuel can be recovered from this reactor than was originally present. Research on breeder reactors is underway in France, the United States, and the Soviet Union.

31:6 Nuclear Fusion

Fusion is the union of small nuclei to form larger nuclei.

Fusion is the combination of nuclei with small masses to form a nucleus with a larger mass. In the process energy is released. The larger nucleus is more tightly bound (Figure 31-1) so its mass is less than the sum of the masses of the smaller nuclei. A typical example of fusion is the process that occurs in the sun. Four hydrogen nuclei (protons) fuse in several steps to form one helium nucleus. The mass of the four protons is greater than the mass of the helium nucleus that is produced. The energy equivalence of this mass difference, given by $E = mc^2$, is transferred to the kinetic energy of the resultant particles. The energy released by the fusion of one helium nucleus is 25 MeV. In comparison, the energy released when one dynamite molecule reacts chemically is almost 20 eV, about one million times less energetic.

Fusion reactions release even larger quantities of energy per mass of matter than fission reactions.

Fusion in the sun occurs in steps. The most important process is called the proton-proton chain.

The proton-proton reaction chain produces most of the energy in stars.

$$^1_1H + {}^1_1H \rightarrow {}^2_1H + {}^0_1e + {}^0_0\nu$$

$$^1_1H + {}^2_1H \rightarrow {}^3_2He$$

$$^3_2He + {}^3_2He \rightarrow {}^4_2He + 2\,{}^1_1H$$

The first two reactions must occur twice in order to produce the two ^3_2He particles needed for the final reaction. The net result is that four protons produce one ^4_2He, two positrons, and two neutrinos.

Fusion reactions take place only when the nuclei have large amounts of thermal energy—large enough to overcome the electrical repulsion between them. For that reason fusion reactions are often called

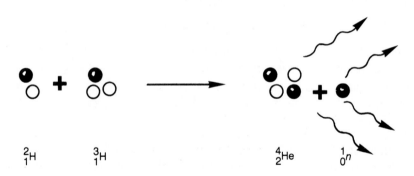

FIGURE 31-6. The fusion of deuterium and tritium produces helium.

^2_1H ^3_1H ^4_2He ^1_0n

FIGURE 31-7. In laser confinement, pellets of hydrogen are forced to implode producing helium and large amounts of thermal energy.

thermonuclear reactions. The proton-proton chain requires temperatures of about 2×10^7 K, which are found in the center of the sun. Fusion reactions also occur in a "hydrogen," or thermonuclear, bomb. In this device the high temperature necessary to produce the fusion reaction is achieved by means of a uranium, or "atomic," bomb.

Fusion reactions are also called thermonuclear reactions because they take place at extremely high temperatures, such as those of the sun's interior.

31:7 Controlled Fusion

Safe energy from fusion requires control of the fusion reaction. One reaction favored in controlled fusion is

$$^2_1\text{H} + ^3_1\text{H} \rightarrow ^4_2\text{He} + ^1_0\text{n} + 17.6 \text{ MeV}$$

Deuterium, ^2_1H, is available in large quantities in sea water, and tritium, ^3_1H, is easily produced from deuterium. Therefore controlled fusion would give the world an almost limitless source of energy. However, in order to control fusion, some very difficult problems must be solved.

Fusion reactions require that the atoms be raised to temperatures of millions of degrees. No material can withstand temperatures even as high as 5000 K. Likewise, confinement by a material would cause the atoms to cool. However, magnetic fields can confine charged particles.

Magnetic fields are used to confine the plasmas in a fusion reactor.

Energy is added to the atoms, stripping away electrons and forming separated plasmas of electrons and ions. A sudden increase in the magnetic field will compress the plasma, raising its temperature. Fusion has been achieved this way.

A useful reactor must produce more energy than it consumes. So far the energy produced by fusion has been only a tiny fraction of the energy required to create and confine the plasma. The confinement of plasma is a very difficult problem because instabilities in the magnetic field allow the plasma to escape. One of the most promising fusion reactors under development is the Tokamak reactor. The Tokamak provides a doughnut-shaped magnetic field in which the plasma is confined. Research has led to the confinement of larger amounts of plasma for longer periods of time. The next large Tokamak built should produce as much energy as it consumes.

The Tokamak reactor is a device for studying controlled fusion reactions.

Laser beams are used to implode tiny glass spheres containing liquefied deuterium and tritium. The compression creates high enough temperatures to produce fusion.

A second approach to controlled fusion is called **inertial confinement.** Deuterium and tritium are liquefied under high pressure and confined in tiny glass spheres. Multiple laser beams are directed at a sphere. The energy deposited by the lasers causes the pellet to implode, or burst inward. The resulting tremendous compression of the hydrogen raises the temperature to levels needed for fusion.

Physics Focus

Preserving Food With Radiation

Conventional methods of preserving food include canning, refrigeration, freezing, addition of chemicals, heating, or dehydration. Each has advantages and disadvantages. In another process, food is irradiated with gamma rays or with high-energy electrons. Radiation can be done before or after packaging. This process has not been used extensively by the American food industry because of the stigma of radiation. However, fear of developing cancer from irradiated food is unfounded.

The radiation source is a rack of cobalt or cesium alloy rods. Food passed around this source is exposed equally on all sides. The amount of radiation received is determined by density of the food and time of exposure.

Low doses of radiation will sterilize insects, destroy insect eggs and fungi, prevent sprouting of tuberous produce, and slow or stop ripening of other produce. Medium to high doses will destroy all pathogens. There is no harm to produce or consumer.

Irradiation is the only known safe replacement for the fumigant ethylene dibromide (EDB), a known carcinogen and mutagen. Radiation could also eliminate salmonella bacterial contamination.

Summary

1. The strong force binds the nucleus together.   31:1

2. The energy released in a nuclear reaction can be calculated by finding the   31:2
difference in mass of the particles before and after the reaction. $E = mc^2$ is
then used to find the energy equivalent of the mass. The energy equivalent
of 1 amu is 931 MeV.

3. Bombardment can produce radioactive isotopes not found in nature. These   31:3
are called artificial radioactive nuclei and are often used in medicine.

4. In nuclear fission the uranium nucleus is split into two smaller nuclei with   31:4
a release of neutrons and energy.

5. Nuclear reactors use the energy released in fission to generate electrical   31:5
energy.

6. The fusion of hydrogen nuclei into helium releases the energy which   31:6
allows stars to shine.

7. Controlling fusion for use on Earth might safely provide large amounts of   31:7
energy.

Detailed answers to all Questions and Problems are given in the Teacher's Guide at the front of this book.

Questions

1. What is the mass defect of a nucleus? To what is it related?

2. Use the graph of binding energy per nucleon to determine if the reaction
$^2_1H + {}^1_1H = {}^3_2He$ is energetically possible.

3. A newspaper claims that scientists have been able to cause iron nuclei to
undergo fission. Why or why not could this report be true?

4. Give an example of naturally and artificially radioactive isotopes. Explain
the difference.

5. Explain how it might be possible for a fission reactor to produce more
fissionable fuel than it consumes? What are such reactors called?

6. What two processes are being studied to control the fusion process?

7. Fission and fusion are opposite processes. How can each release energy?

8. **a.** Does the fission of a uranium nucleus or the fusion of four hydrogen
nuclei produce more energy?
   b. Does the fission of a kilogram of uranium nuclei or the fusion of a
gram of deuterium produce more energy?
   c. Why are your answers to Parts *a* and *b* different?

9. In a nuclear reactor, the water that passes through the core of the reactor flows through one loop, while the water that produces steam for the turbines flows through a second loop. Why are there two loops?

10. Breeder reactors generate more fuel than they consume. Is this a violation of the law of conservation of energy?

| Problems–A |

1. a. gold

b. $^{200}_{80}Hg + ^{2}_{1}H \rightarrow$
$\qquad ^{198}_{79}Au + ^{4}_{2}He$

2. a. 0.11236 amu
b. 105 MeV

3. 7.5 MeV/nucleon

4. a. 0.10426 amu
b. 97.1 MeV

5. 58 N

1. A mercury isotope, $^{200}_{80}Hg$, is bombarded with deuterons ($^{2}_{1}H$). The mercury nucleus absorbs the deuteron and then emits an α particle.
   a. What element is formed by this reaction?
   b. Write the nuclear equation for the reaction.

2. A nitrogen isotope, $^{14}_{7}N$, has a nuclear mass of approximately 14.00307 amu.
   a. Calculate the mass defect of the nucleus.
   b. What is the binding energy of this nucleus?

3. Assume that each nucleon shares equally in the binding energy of the nucleus. Calculate the energy needed to eject a neutron from the nucleus of a nitrogen isotope, $^{14}_{7}N$.

4. A carbon isotope, $^{13}_{6}C$, has a nuclear mass of 13.00335 amu.
   a. What is the mass defect of this isotope?
   b. What is the binding energy of its nucleus?

5. The two positively charged protons in a helium nucleus are separated by about 2.0×10^{-15} m. Find the electric force of repulsion between the two protons. The result will give you an indication of the strength of the strong nuclear force.

| Problems–B |

1. a. 23.8 MeV
b. 2.29×10^{12} J/mole
c. 7.9×10^{5} mole

1. One fusion reaction is $^{2}_{1}H + ^{2}_{1}H \rightarrow ^{4}_{2}He$.
   a. What energy is released in this reaction?
   b. Deuterium exists as a diatomic (two atom) molecule. One mole of deuterium contains 6.02×10^{23} molecules. Find the amount of energy released, in joules, in the fusion of one mole of deuterium molecules.
   c. When 6.02×10^{23} molecules of deuterium burn, they release 2.9×10^{6} J. How many moles of deuterium molecules would have to burn to release just the energy released by the fusion of one mole of deuterium molecules?

2. The energy released in the fission of one atom of $^{235}_{92}U$ is 2.0×10^2 MeV. One mole of uranium atoms (6.02×10^{23}) has a mass of 0.235 kg.

   a. How many atoms are in 1.00 kg of $^{235}_{92}U$?

   b. How much energy would be released if all the atoms in 1.00 kg of $^{235}_{92}U$ would undergo fission?

   c. A typical large nuclear reactor produces fission energy at a rate of 3600 MW (3.0×10^9 J/s). How many kilograms of $^{235}_{92}U$ are used each second?

   d. How much $^{235}_{92}U$ would be used in one year?

2. a. 2.56×10^{24} atoms/kg
  b. 8.2×10^{13} J/kg
  c. 3.7×10^{-5} kg/s
  d. 1.2×10^3 kg/y

Readings

Edelson, Edward, "Scanning the Body Magnetic." *Science 83*, July, 1983.

Greiner, Walter, "Hot Nuclear Matter." *Scientific American*, January, 1985.

Lightman, Alan, "To Cleave an Atom." *Science 84*, November, 1984.

Rosenthal, Elisabeth, "The Hazards of Everyday Radiation." *Science Digest*, March, 1984.

Surko, C. M., "Waves and Turbulence in a Tokamak Fusion Plasma." *Science*, August 26, 1983.

Appendix A

Relativity

Of all physicists, living or dead, Albert Einstein is best known. Relativity is the theory most closely associated with Einstein's name. Why, then, is relativity left for an appendix at the end of the text? Relativity uses the results of mechanics, optics, and electricity and magnetism. Thus, in order to present relativity as a single unit, it must be placed near the end of the text.

Relativity encompasses two theories, called special relativity and general relativity. Special relativity treats motion at constant velocity, while general relativity includes accelerated motion and motion in a gravitational field. Special relativity can be understood with mathematics no more complicated than algebra, while general relativity requires considerably more complex mathematics. For this reason, we will consider only special relativity.

Working as a clerk in the patent office in Bern, Switzerland, Albert Einstein published three papers in the year 1905. One, on the photoelectric effect, won him the 1921 Nobel prize. The second, on the random motion of particles called Brownian motion, explained this important demonstration of kinetic theory. The third, "On the Electrodynamics of Moving Bodies," presented the special theory of relativity, and won him a central place in physics and recognition not only by scientists but the general public as well. At the time the paper was published, relativity was ignored by some physicists and opposed by others. However, the results of every experimental test have confirmed its predictions. Thus, it has become accepted as one of the foundations of modern physics. It has solved major problems in physics.

A:1 Galilean Relativity

In Chapter 7 it was shown that the shape of a trajectory depends on the observer. Consider a ball tossed straight up in an airplane flying at a constant horizontal velocity of 200 m/s. A passenger in the airplane finds the horizontal velocity of the ball zero. However, a person on the ground viewing the ball through a telescope would see the ball thrown with a 200 m/s horizontal velocity. Each person could define a coordinate system, an x-axis and a y-axis, and use Newton's laws to analyze the motion. Each coordinate system in called a frame of reference. Newton's laws work in these two frames of reference. The only difference in the two frames is the horizontal velocity of the ball. To the passenger, the velocity is zero; to the person on the ground, it is 200 m/s. The frame of reference of the passenger is moving at a velocity of 200 m/s with respect to the frame of reference of the ground. The two frames are said to be equivalent because Newton's laws can be used to analyze motion in either frame. Although the ball is initially at rest in one frame—that is, its horizontal velocity is zero—there is nothing special about that frame.

Suppose an airplane, initially at rest, accelerates forward. A passenger on the plane will notice that a ball lying on the floor begins to move backward. The passenger will find the ball accelerating even though there is no force on it in the direction of the acceleration. Newton's laws will be violated. However, the person on the ground will see the ball remaining stationary. Newton's laws will still work as far as he is concerned. The two frames of reference are not equivalent because one is accelerated.

The fact that Newton's laws, the laws of mechanics, are true in any nonaccelerated frame of reference is called Galilean relativity. Galilean relativity also applies if the ball has a horizontal velocity in both frames. Suppose the airplane is moving again at a constant 220 m/s, but this time the ball is thrown forward. If the passenger measures the velocity of the ball as 10 m/s relative to the plane, the observer on the ground would measure the velocity as 220 m/s + 10 m/s = 230 m/s. That is, the velocity of the ball is the sum of the relative velocity of the frames of reference plus the velocity of the ball in the moving frame.

A:2 Electromagnetism

Einstein was only 16 when he posed a question for himself. What, he thought, would a light wave look like if you were moving alongside it at the speed of light? The electric fields would now be stationary. But stationary electric fields do not induce magnetic fields. Thus, Einstein reasoned, the laws of electromagnetism are not true in this frame of reference. That is, Galilean relativity does not hold for one frame of reference moving with the velocity of light with respect to another.

There was another problem with electromagnetism. Nineteenth-century physicists, believing that mechanics was the most important part of physics, tried to build mechanical models of everything, including electromagnetic waves. Sound is a pressure wave traveling through a medium. What is the medium for a light wave traveling through space? A substance was invented, the *ether*, in which the electric and magnetic fields oscillated. The ether was at rest, making it the preferred frame of reference, and all bodies moved through it. This gave the ether some

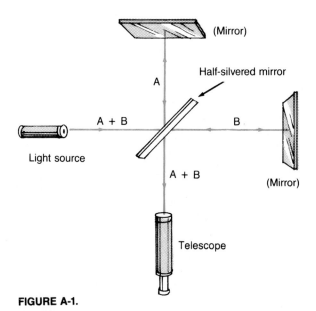

(Mirror)

Half-silvered mirror

A

A + B

Light source

B

A + B

(Mirror)

Telescope

FIGURE A-1.

remarkable properties. For instance, it was very rigid, but the earth passed through it without resistance.

The American physicist Albert Michelson thought of a method of measuring the earth's motion through the ether. In 1887, he split a light beam in two by using a partially silvered mirror, sending one path parallel to the motion of the earth and the other path perpendicular to it. The two beams were each reflected back to the mirror and recombined to be viewed in a telescope. If the light took the same length of time on the two paths, the two light beams would constructively interfere, producing lightness. If one took half an oscillation period less time, the interference would be destructive, and there would be darkness.

Michelson assumed that the motion of light through the ether was like that of a swimmer in a stream. The time needed to swim a certain distance depends on whether the swimmer is moving with or against the stream, or perpendicular to its motion. In a similar manner, the time required for light to travel from the half-silvered mirror to the reflecting mirror and back should depend on whether the light is moving parallel to the motion of the ether or perpendicular to it. As a result, the interference observed in the telescope should be constructive or destructive, depending on which arm of the instrument is moving parallel to the motion of the ether.

The earth was supposed to be moving through the ether, dragging the instrument with it. The instrument could be rotated to bring first one arm and then the other arm parallel to the motion of the earth through the ether. Thus, the interference should

change from dark to light as the instrument is rotated. However, as the apparatus was rotated, no change was seen. Michelson later joined the American E. W. Morley and repeated the experiment, using a much more sensitive instrument. Again, there was no effect. The motion of the earth through the ether could not be detected. Many explanations were offered for this puzzling result. However, all were *ad hoc*. That is, they were invented to cure this single problem. None was convincing.

A:3 Einstein's Postulates

In his 1905 paper, Einstein presented two postulates. One postulate he called the **principle of relativity.** *All frames of reference are equivalent for electromagnetism as well as mechanics.* That is, there is no reference frame that is more important than any other. There is no *true* frame, no frame absolutely at rest. There is no ether. The second postulate stated that light always moves in space at the same velocity. *The speed of light is independent of the motion of the source and the motion of the observer.* Light emitted by the headlight of an airplane moves at 3×10^8 m/s with respect to the plane and 3×10^8 m/s with respect to the ground. If a particle moving at half the velocity of light emits a γ ray, that γ ray moves away from the particle at the velocity of light. The γ ray also moves at the same velocity when measured by an observer on the earth. Velocities no longer add in the normal way.

A:4 The Meaning of Time

Einstein noted that these postulates seemed to contradict each other. Taken together, they did not seem to make sense. The problem, wrote Einstein, was that the measurement of position and time had to be considered very carefully.

Time, said Einstein, is something measured by a clock. Consider a special clock installed on a satellite. At one end of a stick of length L_s is a flash lamp and a detector. At the other end is a mirror. The light flashes and the mirror reflects the flash to the detector. The detector triggers the lamp, producing another flash. Each flash is like the tick of a clock. Now, this is not a practical clock, but it is one that illustrates the principle. An astronaut at rest with respect to the clock would find that the time between ticks, t_s, would be equal to the distance traveled, $2L_s$, divided by the speed of light, c. That is, $t_s = 2L_s/c$. In other words, $ct_s = 2L_s$.

If the satellite is moving with velocity v in a direction perpendicular to the stick, consider what an observer on the earth would see. The lamp would flash, but in the time it takes the flash to reach the mirror, t_m, the mirror would have moved a distance

Clock at rest

L_s $ct_s/2$

ct_m ct_m

L_s

vt_m vt_m

Moving clock

FIGURE A-2. Experimental apparatus to measure time using light.

vt_m. As shown in Figure A-3, the path taken by the light is the hypotenuse of a right triangle. The altitude is L_s, or $ct_s/2$ and the base is vt_m. Because light moves at the same velocity c for all observers, the distance traveled by the light is ct_m. The Pythagorean theorem states

$$\left(\frac{ct_s}{2}\right)^2 + (vt_m)^2 = (ct_m)^2, \text{ or}$$

$$t_m = \frac{ct_s}{2\sqrt{c^2 - v^2}}$$

The return trip to the detector takes the same amount of time. Let t_e be the time between "ticks" measured by the observer on the earth. Then $t_e = 2t_m$, which is

$$t_e = \frac{t_s}{\sqrt{1 - \dfrac{v^2}{c^2}}}$$

The velocity is always smaller than c, so the denominator is always smaller than one. Thus t_e is always larger than t_s. That is, the moving clock on the satellite runs slowly as measured by an observer on the ground. This is called time dilation.

If the clock were on the earth and the measurement were made from the satellite, the astronaut would find the earth's clock to be slow. There is complete symmetry. This rather surprising result is in agreement with the principle of relativity. That is, there is no preferred frame of reference in which clocks give the *correct* time.

A test of time dilation will be described later. However, you may have heard of one application called the *Twin Effect* or *Twin Paradox*. One twin boards a very fast rocket ship while the other stays at home. Moving clocks, including biological clocks

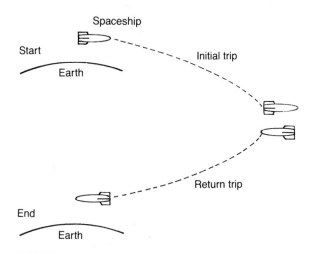

Spaceship

Start

Earth

Initial trip

Return trip

End

Earth

FIGURE A-3. The twin in the spaceship underwent a deceleration in returning to Earth.

that control aging, run slow. Therefore, the twin in the rocket ages much more slowly than the twin staying at home. When they meet again after the trip, the traveling twin is young, the one who remained at home is old. But, you may say, all reference frames are the same. Why does the twin on the rocket not see the earth twin speeding away, and thus the earth twin aging less slowly? The key to the paradox is the requirement that the twins be reunited. This means the traveling twin must make a round trip, reversing the direction of motion in the middle of the trip. It is this reversal that breaks the symmetry and allows you to tell which twin moved, and thus which twin aged less.

If a rocket is to be started and stopped, acceleration must also be present, and special relativity does not work with acceleration. However, when the acceleration is treated with general relativity, the result is unchanged. The twin effect was tested in 1971 when a very precise atomic clock was carried in commercial airplanes around the globe. When the clock returned home, it was found to have run slower by an amount equal to that predicted by Einstein's theory.

A:5   Length Contraction

Einstein next considered the measurement of length. Suppose our clock is used as a measure of the length of the stick. Once again the clock is in a satellite, but this time the clock is arranged so that the meter stick is parallel to the velocity, v, of the satellite. To an astronaut on the satellite, everything is normal. The length of the meter stick as measured by the astronaut is L_s. As before, $2L_s = ct_s$. Suppose an observer on earth wished to measure the length of the moving stick. We will call this length L_e. The observer

FIGURE A-4. Experimental apparatus to measure length by using light.

could measure the time between clock flashes from the satellite. Then the measured time could be corrected for time dilation to find t_e. The time required for the light to move from the lamp to the mirror is t_m. In this time, the stick moves a distance vt_m. The distance the light travels from the lamp to the mirror is thus $L_e + vt_m$. Therefore, $ct_m = L_e + vt_m$. On the return trip, which takes a time t_r, the distance the light travels is $L_e - vt_r$. Thus, $ct_r = L_e - vt_r$. The total time between flashes is $t_e = t_m + t_r$. That is,

$$t_m = \frac{L_e}{c - v} \qquad t_r = \frac{L_e}{c + v}$$

$$t_e = t_m + t_r = \frac{L_e}{c - v} + \frac{L_e}{c + v}$$

$$t_e = \frac{2L_e c}{c^2 - v^2} = \frac{2L_e}{c\left(1 - \frac{v^2}{c^2}\right)}$$

But we know that

$$t_e = \frac{t_s}{\sqrt{1 - \frac{v^2}{c^2}}}$$

And we know that $t_s = \frac{2L_s}{c}$. Thus,

$$\frac{\frac{2L_s}{c}}{\sqrt{1 - \frac{v^2}{c^2}}} = \frac{\frac{2L_e}{c}}{\sqrt{1 - \frac{v^2}{c^2}}}$$

Or,

$$\frac{2L_s}{c} = \frac{\frac{2L_e}{c}}{\sqrt{1 - \frac{v^2}{c^2}}}$$

Finally, $L_e = L_s \sqrt{1 - \frac{v^2}{c^2}}$

The term in the square root is always less than one, and so $L_e < L_s$. That is, the length of the moving stick, measured from earth, is shorter than that of the same stick on earth, measured on earth. Note that the astronaut would find the measure of the stick to be exactly the same as the earth observer would find for the earth-bound stick. Moving lengths shrink. However, only those dimensions parallel to the motion shrink. For example, if a one meter long body moves at 60% the speed of light, its length is measured by an observer at rest as $(1.00 \text{ m}) (\sqrt{1 - (0.6)^2} = 0.80 \text{ m}$.

A:6   An Experimental Test

An experimental test of both time dilation and length contraction involves muons, medium mass elementary particles that are short-lived, heavy electrons. (See Chapter 30.) The lifetime of a muon at rest is 2.20×10^{-6} s. It decays into an electron plus a neutrino and an antineutrino. Muons are produced by cosmic rays, which are energetic protons from the sun or interstellar space. The protons hit the nuclei of molecules in the earth's atmosphere about 7 km above the surface of the earth. Among the particles produced by these collisions are muons, some of which have been found to be moving at 99.80% of the speed of light, or 2.992×10^8 m/s. At this velocity, during one average lifetime, a muon could travel a distance

$$d = vt$$
$$= (2.992 \times 10^8 \text{ m/s})(2.20 \times 10^{-6} \text{ s})$$
$$d = 6.58 \times 10^2 \text{ m}.$$

Thus, a muon produced 7.00 km above the surface of the earth could never reach the surface. Yet muons do reach the surface.

The lifetime of a muon is like a clock, and moving clocks run slowly. To the muon, one lifetime is $t_o = 2.20 \times 10^{-6}$ s, but to an observer on earth, the muon lifetime, t, is

$$t = \frac{t_o}{\sqrt{1 - \dfrac{v^2}{c^2}}}$$
$$= \frac{2.20 \times 10^{-6} \text{ s}}{\sqrt{1 - \dfrac{(2.992 \times 10^8)^2}{(2.998 \times 10^8)^2}}}$$
$$t = 3.48 \times 10^{-5} \text{ s}$$

In this amount of time, the muon can travel

$$d = vt$$
$$= (2.992 \times 10^8 \text{ m/s})(3.489 \times 10^{-5} \text{ s})$$
$$d = 10.4 \text{ km}$$

Thus, the muon can easily travel the 7.00 km to the earth's surface.

The flight of the muon can also be seen from the viewpoint of the muon. To the muon, it is stationary and the earth is moving. Moving lengths contract, so the 7.00 km distance L_e to the earth appears shorter to the muon. As seen by the muon, the distance traveled to the earth is

$$L = L_e \sqrt{1 - \frac{v^2}{c^2}}$$
$$= 7.00 \text{ km} \sqrt{1 - \frac{(2.992 \times 10^8)^2}{(2.998 \times 10^8)^2}}$$
$$L = 443 \text{ m}$$

As we have seen, the muon can travel over 600 m in its lifetime, so to its clock, the distance to the earth requires less than one average lifetime. The muon can reach the surface.

The number of muons at the top of Mt. Washington in New Hampshire and the number at sea level have been carefully measured and the result is in excellent agreement with the predictions of the relativity theory.

A:7   Addition of Velocities

The results of time dilation and length contraction make it necessary to write a new rule for addition of velocities. Suppose an object moves with velocity v as seen by an astronaut in a satellite. The satellite is moving at velocity u with respect to an observer on the ground. Then the velocity of the object seen from the ground, v', is given by

$$v' = \frac{v + u}{1 + \dfrac{uv}{c^2}}$$

For example, if the satellite moves with $u = 0.60\,c$ and the object at $v = 0.50\,c$, then to the observer on the ground,

$$v' = \frac{(0.60\,c) + (0.50\,c)}{1 + \left(\dfrac{0.60\,c}{c}\right)\left(\dfrac{0.50\,c}{c}\right)} = \frac{1.10\,c}{1.30} = 0.85\,c$$

This is to be compared with the velocity $1.1\,c$, greater than the speed of light, obtained by the normal method of adding velocities.

This rule for addition of velocities solves Einstein's problem of moving along a light wave. In the above equation, if $v = c$ then $v' = c$. As measured by the observer, the wave will still appear to be moving with a velocity c. Light always moves with velocity c with respect to any observer. If both u and v are small in comparison to c, the new relativistic rule becomes the old rule of Galilean relativity, $v' = v + u$.

A:8   Mass and Energy

Einstein showed that the mass of a moving object increases. He determined that if the mass of an object is m_o when measured at rest, then when it moves at velocity v,

$$m = \frac{m_o}{\sqrt{1 - \dfrac{v^2}{c^2}}}$$

Mass is the inertia of the body, that is, the ratio of the force applied, **F**, to the resulting acceleration, **a**. m = F/a. An increase in mass means that for the same force, the resulting acceleration will be smaller. Note that in the above equation, as the velocity approaches the velocity of light, the denominator approaches zero and the mass approaches infinity! Therefore, the acceleration possible from a finite force also approaches zero. In other words, the force required to accelerate a body to the velocity of light is infinite. For this reason, no massive body can travel at the speed of light.

Particles accelerated to high velocities by linear accelerators or synchrotrons (Chapter 30) show the effects of increased mass. As more and more energy is added to the particles, their accelerations become smaller and smaller and their velocities approach the velocity of light very slowly. Experience with accelerators has verified the correctness of Einstein's equation.

A:9   Mass-Energy Equivalence

A few months after writing his relativity paper, Einstein wrote a three-page paper that further explored the relativistic increase of mass.

For velocities small in comparison with the speed of light, one can write

$$m = m_o + \frac{\frac{1}{2}m_o v^2}{c^2}.$$

This approximation causes an error of only 3% when v is as large as $c/5$. However, $\frac{1}{2}m_o v^2 = KE$, the kinetic energy of the moving body. Thus, Einstein showed that the relativistic increase in mass, $m - m_o$, is equal to the kinetic energy divided by the speed of light squared. Because c is very large, the increase in mass is small.

The equation can be rewritten $mc^2 = m_o c^2 + KE$. Both sides of the equation are energies. The left-hand side, mc^2, is the total energy of the body. On the right-hand side is the kinetic energy plus $m_o c^2$, the energy content of the body at rest. When $KE = 0$, $E = m_o c^2$, Einstein's famous equation for the energy equivalence of the mass m_o.

The speed of light is large, and so even a tiny increase in mass requires a large amount of energy. In nuclear reactions, the mass decreases a small but significant amount. As a result, the energy released can be very large. Not only nuclear weapons and reactors, but the sun and other stars release energy in this way.

A:10   The Realm of Relativity

Einstein's special relativity does not contradict the physics of Newton. Both give the same results for objects moving slowly. Relativistic effects are important only for objects moving with velocity near the speed of light. We have no direct experience with such high velocities, and thus effects such as time dilation, length contraction, and mass increase are far from our daily experiences.

Relativity is important to us because it forces us to examine common ideas closely. For example, we have looked at the measurement of time and distance more closely and found surprising new results. Similar examination of ideas that we have previously taken for granted always leads to a new appreciation of our world and sometimes to equally surprising results.

Questions   See Teacher's Guide.

1. A flight attendant on a jet passenger plane traveling at 200 m/s pours a cup of coffee for a passenger.
   a. What is the horizontal velocity of the coffee as observed by the flight attendant?
   b. What is the horizontal velocity of the coffee as observed by a stationary observer on the earth?

2. Two children are throwing a ball up and down the aisle of a passenger car that is part of a train moving at 32 m/s. If they throw the ball at 4.0 m/s,
   a. What is the velocity of the ball as observed by a seated passenger in the same car?
   b. What are the velocities of the ball as measured by a stationary observer standing on a platform next to the track?

3. A pion, a subnuclear particle, has a lifetime when at rest of 2.6×10^{-8} s. What is the lifetime, measured by an observer at rest, of a pion traveling at $v = 0.80\ c$?

4. The rest mass of a pion is 2.49×10^{-28} kg. What is its mass when it moves at $v = 0.80\ c$?

5. When a pion decays, it emits a muon. If the pion decays at rest, the muon is emitted at a velocity of $0.80\ c$. If the pion is moving at a velocity of $0.50\ c$, and the muon is emitted in the same direction as the pion, what is the velocity of the muon as seen by an observer at rest?

6. Suppose a rocket could be built that reaches a velocity of half the speed of light. An astronaut takes a quartz watch and a meter stick aboard. What changes would the astronaut observe in these items?

7. The rocket is 20.0 m long. It now moves with $v = 0.50\ c$. What would be its length as measured by an observer at rest?

8. What would be the length of a 100.0 m long soccer field on earth as measured from the rocket?

9. The rocket is to make a round-trip to a star 30.0 light-years away. One light-year is the distance light travels in one year. How long would it take the rocket traveling at half the speed of light to make the one-way trip? Assume that the time needed for acceleration and deceleration can be ignored.

10. From the point of view of the astronauts on the trip, how long would the round-trip require?

Appendix B

B:1 Law of Cosines

To use the trigonometry of the right triangle, two of the sides of a triangle must be perpendicular. That is, you must have a right triangle. But sometimes you will need to work with a triangle that is not a right triangle. The law of cosines applies to all triangles. Consider the two triangles shown in Figure B-1. They are not right triangles. When angle C is known, the lengths of the sides obey the following relationship.

$$c^2 = a^2 + b^2 - 2ab \cos C$$

If a, b, and angle C are known, the length of side c is

$$c = \sqrt{a^2 + b^2 - 2ab \cos C}$$

In triangle 1 of Figure B-1, the length of side a is 4.00 cm, side b is 5.00 cm, and angle C is 60.0°. Substituting the values in the equation, side c is obtained. Substituting the appropriate values yields

$$a^2 = (4.0 \text{ cm})^2 = 16.0 \text{ cm}^2$$
$$b^2 = (5.0 \text{ cm})^2 = 25.0 \text{ cm}^2$$
$$2ab \cos \theta = 2(4.00 \text{ cm})(5.00 \text{ cm})(\cos 60.0°)$$
$$= 2(4.00 \text{ cm})(5.00 \text{ cm})(0.500)$$
$$2ab \cos \theta = 20.0 \text{ cm}^2$$

Therefore,

$$c = \sqrt{a^2 + b^2 - 2ab \cos \theta}$$
$$= \sqrt{16.0 \text{ cm}^2 + 25.0 \text{ cm}^2 - 20.0 \text{ cm}^2}$$
$$= \sqrt{21.0 \text{ cm}^2}$$
$$c = 4.58 \text{ cm}$$

If angle C is larger than 90°, its cosine is negative and is numerically equal to the cosine of its supplement. In triangle 2, Figure B-1, angle C is 120.0°. Therefore, its cosine is the negative of the cosine of (180.0° − 120.0°) or 60.0°. The cosine of 60.0° is 0.500. Thus, the cosine of 120.0° is −0.500.

B:2 Law of Sines

Just as the law of cosines applies to all triangles, the law of sines also applies to all triangles. The relationship is

$$\frac{a}{\sin A} = \frac{b}{\sin B} = \frac{c}{\sin C}$$

Using the values for triangle 1 shown in Figure B-1, angle A can be calculated by the law of sines.

$$\frac{a}{\sin A} = \frac{c}{\sin C}$$

$$\sin A = \frac{a}{c} \sin C$$

$$\sin A = \frac{4.00 \text{ cm}}{4.50 \text{ cm}} \sin (60.0°)$$

$$= \frac{(4.00 \text{ cm})(0.867)}{(4.58 \text{ cm})}$$

$$= 0.757$$

$$A = 49.2°$$

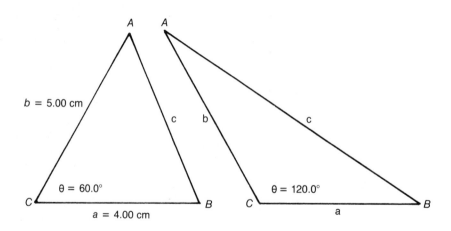

FIGURE B-1.

Appendix C

TABLE C-1
SI Base Units

Measurement	Unit	Symbol
length	meter	m
mass	kilogram	kg
time	second	s
electric current	ampere	A
temperature	kelvin	K
amount of substance	mole	mol
intensity of light	candela	cd

TABLE C-2
SI Prefixes

Prefix		Multiplication Factor	Prefix		Multiplication Factor
exa	E	$1\ 000\ 000\ 000\ 000\ 000\ 000 = 10^{18}$	deci	d	$0.1 = 10^{-1}$
peta	P	$1\ 000\ 000\ 000\ 000\ 000 = 10^{15}$	centi	c	$0.01 = 10^{-2}$
tera	T	$1\ 000\ 000\ 000\ 000 = 10^{12}$	milli	m	$0.001 = 10^{-3}$
giga	G	$1\ 000\ 000\ 000 = 10^{9}$	micro	μ	$0.000\ 001 = 10^{-6}$
mega	M	$1\ 000\ 000 = 10^{6}$	nano	n	$0.000\ 000\ 001 = 10^{-9}$
kilo	k	$1\ 000 = 10^{3}$	pico	p	$0.000\ 000\ 000\ 001 = 10^{-12}$
hecto	h	$100 = 10^{2}$	femto	f	$0.000\ 000\ 000\ 000\ 001 = 10^{-15}$
deka	da	$10 = 10^{1}$	atto	a	$0.000\ 000\ 000\ 000\ 000\ 001 = 10^{-18}$

TABLE C-3
Units with Special Names Derived from SI Base Units

Measurement	Unit	Symbol	Expressed in Base Units
energy, work	joule	J	$kg \cdot m^2/s^2$
force	newton	N	$kg \cdot m/s^2$
frequency	hertz	Hz	$1/s$
illuminance	lux	lx	$cd \cdot sr/m^2\ (lm/m^2)$
luminous flux	lumen	lm	$cd \cdot sr$
potential difference	volt	V	$kg \cdot m^2/A \cdot s^3\ (W/A)$
power	watt	W	$kg \cdot m^2/s^3\ (J/s)$
pressure	pascal	Pa	$kg/m \cdot s^2\ (N/m^2)$
quantity of electric charge	coulomb	C	$A \cdot s$
resistance	ohm	Ω	$m^2 \cdot kg/s^3 \cdot A^2\ (V/A)$
magnetic induction	tesla	T	$kg/C \cdot s\ (1\ N/A \cdot m)$

TABLE C-4
Reference Data: Physical Constants, Conversion Factors, Useful Equations

Physical Constants

Absolute zero temperature: $0 \text{ K} = -273°C$

Acceleration due to gravity at sea level, lat. 45°: $g = 9.806 \text{ m/s}^2$

Avogadro's number: $N_o = 6.02 \times 10^{23}$

Charge of an electron: $e = -1.602 \times 10^{-19} \text{ C}$

Constant in Coulomb's law: $K = 8.988 \times 10^9 \text{ N} \cdot \text{m/C}^2$

Gravitational constant: $G = 6.670 \times 10^{-11} \text{ N} \cdot \text{m}^2/\text{kg}^2$

Mass of an electron: $m_e = 9.109 \times 10^{-31} \text{ kg}$

Mass of a proton: $m_p = 1.672 \times 10^{-27} \text{ kg}$

Mean wavelength of sodium light: $5.893 \times 10^{-7} \text{ m}$

Planck's constant: $h = 6.626 \times 10^{-34} \text{ J/Hz} = 4.136 \times 10^{-15} \text{ eV} \cdot \text{s}$

Speed of light in a vacuum: $c = 2.997\ 93 \times 10^8 \text{ m/s}$

Conversion Factors

1 atomic mass unit $= 1.66 \times 10^{-27} \text{ kg}$

1 electronvolt $= 1.602 \times 10^{-19} \text{ J}$

1 joule $= 1 \text{ N} \cdot \text{m}$

1 joule $= 1 \text{ V} \cdot \text{C}$

1 coulomb $= 6.242 \times 10^{18}$ elementary charge units

Useful Equations

Quadratic equation: A quadratic equation may be reduced to the form

$$ax^2 + bx + c = 0$$

$$x = \frac{-b \pm \sqrt{b^2 - 4ac}}{2a}$$

then

Remember that the sign immediately preceding the coefficient is carried with the coefficient in solving for the two values of x.

Circumference of a circle: $C = 2\pi r$ or $C = \pi d$

Area of a circle: $A = \pi r^2$

Volume of a cylinder: $V = \pi r^2 h$

Surface area of a sphere: $A = 4\pi r^2$

Volume of a sphere: $V = \frac{4\pi r^3}{3}$

TABLE C-5
International Atomic Masses

Element	Symbol	Atomic number	Atomic mass	Element	Symbol	Atomic number	Atomic mass
Actinium	Ac	89	227.02777*	Neodymium	Nd	60	144.24
Aluminum	Al	13	26.98154	Neon	Ne	10	20.179
Americium	Am	95	243.06139*	Neptunium	Np	93	237.04819
Antimony	Sb	51	121.75	Nickel	Ni	28	58.70
Argon	Ar	18	39.948	Niobium	Nb	41	92.9064
Arsenic	As	33	74.9216	Nitrogen	N	7	14.0067
Astatine	At	85	209.98704*	Nobelium	No	102	255.093*
Barium	Ba	56	137.33	Osmium	Os	76	190.2
Berkelium	Bk	97	247.07032*	Oxygen	O	8	15.9994
Beryllium	Be	4	9.01218	Palladium	Pd	46	106.4
Bismuth	Bi	83	208.9804	Phosphorus	P	15	30.97376
Boron	B	5	10.81	Platinum	Pt	78	195.09
Bromine	Br	35	79.904	Plutonium	Pu	94	244.06424*
Cadmium	Cd	48	112.41	Polonium	Po	84	208.98244*
Calcium	Ca	20	40.08	Potassium	K	19	39.0983
Californium	Cf	98	251.07961*	Praseodymium	Pr	59	140.9077
Carbon	C	6	12.011	Promethium	Pm	61	144.91279*
Cerium	Ce	58	140.12	Protactinium	Pa	91	231.03590*
Cesium	Cs	55	132.9054	Radium	Ra	88	226.0254
Chlorine	Cl	17	35.453	Radon	Rn	86	222*
Chromium	Cr	24	51.996	Rhenium	Re	75	186.207
Cobalt	Co	27	58.9332	Rhodium	Rh	45	102.9055
Copper	Cu	29	63.546	Rubidium	Rb	37	85.4678
Curium	Cm	96	247.07038*	Ruthenium	Ru	44	101.07
Dysprosium	Dy	66	162.50	Samarium	Sm	62	150.4
Einsteinium	Es	99	254.08805*	Scandium	Sc	21	44.9559
Erbium	Er	68	167.26	Selenium	Se	34	78.96
Europium	Eu	63	151.96	Silicon	Si	14	28.0855
Fermium	Fm	100	257.09515*	Silver	Ag	47	107.868
Fluorine	F	9	18.998403	Sodium	Na	11	22.98977
Francium	Fr	87	223.01976*	Strontium	Sr	38	87.62
Gadolinium	Gd	64	157.25	Sulfur	S	16	32.06
Gallium	Ga	31	69.72	Tantalum	Ta	73	180.9479
Germanium	Ge	32	72.59	Technetium	Tc	43	96.90639*
Gold	Au	79	196.9665	Tellurium	Te	52	127.60
Hafnium	Hf	72	178.49	Terbium	Tb	65	158.9254
Helium	He	2	4.00260	Thallium	Tl	81	204.37
Holmium	Ho	67	164.9304	Thorium	Th	90	232.0381
Hydrogen	H	1	1.0079	Thulium	Tm	69	168.9342
Indium	In	49	114.82	Tin	Sn	50	118.69
Iodine	I	53	126.9045	Titanium	Ti	22	47.90
Iridium	Ir	77	192.22	Tungsten	W	74	183.85
Iron	Fe	26	55.847	Uranium	U	92	238.029
Krypton	Kr	36	83.80	Vanadium	V	23	50.9414
Lanthanum	La	57	138.9055	Xenon	Xe	54	131.30
Lawrencium	Lr	103	256.099*	Ytterbium	Yb	70	173.04
Lead	Pb	82	207.2	Yttrium	Y	39	88.9059
Lithium	Li	3	6.941	Zinc	Zn	30	65.38
Lutetium	Lu	71	174.97	Zirconium	Zr	40	91.22
Magnesium	Mg	12	24.305	Element 104†		104	257*
Manganese	Mn	25	54.9380	Element 105†		105	260*
Mendelevium	Md	101	258*	Element 106†		106	263*
Mercury	Hg	80	200.59	Element 107†		107	258*
Molybdenum	Mo	42	95.94	Element 108†		108	265*
				Element 109†		109	266*

*The mass of the isotope with the longest known half-life.
†Names for elements 104 and 105 have not yet been approved by the IUPAC. The USSR has proposed Kurchatovium (Ku) for element 104 and Bohrium (Bh) for element 105. The United States has proposed Rutherfordium (Rf) for element 104 and Hahnium (Ha) for element 105.

TABLE C-6 Trigonometric Functions

Angle	sin	cos	tan	Angle	sin	cos	tan
0°	.0000	1.0000	.0000	45°	.7071	.7071	1.0000
1°	.0175	.9998	.0175	46°	.7193	.6947	1.0355
2°	.0349	.9994	.0349	47°	.7314	.6820	1.0724
3°	.0523	.9986	.0524	48°	.7431	.6691	1.1106
4°	.0698	.9976	.0699	49°	.7547	.6561	1.1504
5°	.0872	.9962	.0875	50°	.7660	.6428	1.1918
6°	.1045	.9945	.1051	51°	.7771	.6293	1.2349
7°	.1219	.9925	.1228	52°	.7880	.6157	1.2799
8°	.1392	.9903	.1405	53°	.7986	.6018	1.3270
9°	.1564	.9877	.1584	54°	.8090	.5878	1.3764
10°	.1736	.9848	.1763	55°	.8192	.5736	1.4281
11°	.1908	.9816	.1944	56°	.8290	.5592	1.4826
12°	.2079	.9781	.2126	57°	.8387	.5446	1.5399
13°	.2250	.9744	.2309	58°	.8480	.5299	1.6003
14°	.2419	.9703	.2493	59°	.8572	.5150	1.6643
15°	.2588	.9659	.2679	60°	.8660	.5000	1.7321
16°	.2756	.9613	.2867	61°	.8746	.4848	1.8040
17°	.2924	.9563	.3057	62°	.8829	.4695	1.8807
18°	.3090	.9511	.3249	63°	.8910	.4540	1.9626
19°	.3256	.9455	.3443	64°	.8988	.4384	2.0503
20°	.3420	.9397	.3640	65°	.9063	.4226	2.1445
21°	.3584	.9336	.3839	66°	.9135	.4067	2.2460
22°	.3746	.9272	.4040	67°	.9205	.3907	2.3559
23°	.3907	.9205	.4245	68°	.9272	.3746	2.4751
24°	.4067	.9135	.4452	69°	.9336	.3584	2.6051
25°	.4226	.9063	.4663	70°	.9397	.3420	2.7475
26°	.4384	.8988	.4877	71°	.9455	.3256	2.9042
27°	.4540	.8910	.5095	72°	.9511	.3090	3.0777
28°	.4695	.8829	.5317	73°	.9563	.2924	3.2709
29°	.4848	.8746	.5543	74°	.9613	.2756	3.4874
30°	.5000	.8660	.5774	75°	.9659	.2588	3.7321
31°	.5150	.8572	.6009	76°	.9703	.2419	4.0108
32°	.5299	.8480	.6249	77°	.9744	.2250	4.3315
33°	.5446	.8387	.6494	78°	.9781	.2079	4.7046
34°	.5592	.8290	.6745	79°	.9816	.1908	5.1446
35°	.5736	.8192	.7002	80°	.9848	.1736	5.6713
36°	.5878	.8090	.7265	81°	.9877	.1564	6.3138
37°	.6018	.7986	.7536	82°	.9903	.1392	7.1154
38°	.6157	.7880	.7813	83°	.9925	.1219	8.1443
39°	.6293	.7771	.8098	84°	.9945	.1045	9.5144
40°	.6428	.7660	.8391	85°	.9962	.0872	11.4301
41°	.6561	.7547	.8693	86°	.9976	.0698	14.3007
42°	.6691	.7431	.9004	87°	.9986	.0523	19.0811
43°	.6820	.7314	.9325	88°	.9994	.0349	28.6363
44°	.6947	.7193	.9657	89°	.9998	.0175	57.2900
45°	.7071	.7071	1.0000	90°	1.0000	.0000	∞

Physics-Related Careers

Careers in physics-related fields are many and varied. Requirements for some jobs in these fields may consist only of on-the-job training. Others may consist of seven or eight years of formal college training plus experience through on-the-job programs.

Below is a list of just a few of the jobs open in physics-related fields. This list includes brief job descriptions and minimum training requirements. These may vary somewhat from place to place or job to job. You will want to check with local companies, schools, and professional groups for details.

Training and Education Key

Job	= On-the-job training	BS	= Bachelor of Science degree
VoTech	= Vocational or technical school	MS	= Master of Science degree
JC	= Junior college (2 yr)	PhD	= Doctor of Philosophy degree (science)

PHYSICIST

Physicists attempt to discover the basic interactions between matter and energy. Some physicists perform research to learn facts. Others (theoretical physicists) analyze data and invent theoretical models. Many theoretical and research physicists are also involved in teaching.

Career	Training	Job Description
Acoustical scientist	BS, MS	does research in the control of sound; develops acoustical systems
Astrophysicist	BS, MS, PhD	studies the structure and motion of the universe and all its bodies
Biophysicist	BS, MS, PhD	applies physics to biology, medical fields, and related areas
Elementary-particle physicist	BS, MS, PhD	studies properties of the electron, the proton, and the many other particles produced in high-energy collisions
Geophysicist	BS, MS, PhD	studies the composition and physical features of the earth
Low-temperature physicist	BS, MS	studies the behavior of materials at extremely low temperatures
Nuclear physicist	BS, MS, PhD	studies the structure of atomic nuclei and their interactions with each other
Optical scientist	BS, MS	develops optical systems; does laser research
Plasma physicist	BS, MS, PhD	studies matter in the plasma state; does research directed toward the control of fusion
Radiological physicist	BS	detects radiation and plans health and safety programs at nuclear power plants
Teacher (High school)	BS	instructs students about general areas of physics
Teacher (College)	BS, MS, PhD	instructs students about general and specific areas of physics

ENGINEER

It is often difficult to distinguish between the duties of a physicist and an engineer. It is not unusual to find an engineer engaged in pure research or a physicist designing a specialized piece of equipment. Generally, engineers apply scientific principles to practical problems. They design equipment, develop new materials, and find methods for making raw materials and power sources into useful products. Engineers are also frequently involved in sales.

Career	Training	Job Description
Aerospace engineer	BS	designs and develops flight systems, aircraft, and spacecraft
Biomedical engineer	BS	develops instruments and systems to improve medical procedures; studies the engineering aspects of the biological systems of humans and animals
Ceramic engineer	BS	develops methods for processing clay and other nonmetallic minerals into a variety of products, such as glass and heat-resistant materials

Chemical engineer	BS	plans, designs, and constructs chemical plants; develops processes
Civil engineer	BS	designs bridges, buildings, dams, and many other types of structures
Electrical engineer	BS	designs electric equipment and systems for the generation and distribution of power
Electronics engineer	BS	designs TV, radio, stereo systems; often works in the computer field
Mechanical engineer	BS	designs and develops machines that produce power, such as engines and nuclear reactors
Metallurgical engineer	BS	develops methods to process metals and convert them into useful products

COMPUTER-RELATED

Careers in the field of computers exist at all levels. People using computers for scientific or engineering applications will need training in the physical sciences as well as computer science.

Career	Training	Job Description
Computer programmer	BS	develops the detailed instructions followed by a computer in processing information.
Systems analyst	BS, MS	analyzes data flows in an organization and designs more useful and efficient data processing systems to handle these flows
Computer technician	VoTech, JC	operates and services sophisticated computers

TECHNICIAN

Technicians work directly with physicists and engineers. They are specially trained in certain aspects of science, math, and technology. They help in developing and testing laboratory and industrial equipment and processes, and are frequently involved in sales. Many opportunities exist for technicians in a variety of fields of specialization.

Career	Training	Job Description
Aeronautical technician	VoTech, JC	works with engineers and scientists to develop aircraft; works in field service
Chemical technician	JC	helps to develop, sell, distribute chemical products and equipment; conducts routine tests
Civil engineering technician	JC, Job	assists civil engineers in planning, designing and constructing bridges, dams, and other structures
Electronics technician	VoTech, Job	develops, constructs, and services a wide range of electronic equipment
Mechanical technician	VoTech, Job	helps to develop and construct automotive tools and machines
Nuclear technician	Job, JC	operates monitoring systems; supports and assists nuclear engineers

Additional Information

Following is a list of addresses for a few sources of additional information. Further information about physics-related careers and a more complete listing of additional sources can be found in the *Occupational Outlook Handbook* and *Keys to Careers in Science and Technology*. Check also with your school guidance counselors for any information they may be able to supply.

American Institute of Physics
335 East 45th Street
New York, New York 10017

Encyclopedia of Careers and Vocational Guidance
Doubleday and Co., Inc.
501 Franklin Avenue
Garden City, New York 11530

Keys to Careers in Science and Technology
National Science Teachers Association
1742 Connecticut Avenue, N.W.
Washington, D.C. 20009

Occupations
Armed Forces Vocational Testing Group
Universal City, Texas 78148

Occupational Outlook Handbook
U.S. Department of Labor
Bureau of Labor Statistics
Washington, D.C. 20212

U.S. Civil Service Commission
Washington, D.C. 20415

Glossary

absolute zero: Temperature at which gas would have zero volume.

absorption spectrum: Spectrum of energy absorbed by the gaseous atoms of an element when white light is passed through the gas.

acceleration: Rate of change of velocity.

acceleration of gravity: Rate of change of velocity due to gravitational attraction of the earth.

accuracy: Closeness of a measurement to the standard value of a quantity.

adhesion: Attraction between unlike particles.

alpha particles: Helium nuclei consisting of two protons and two neutrons.

ammeter: Electric device used to measure current.

ampere: Unit for the rate of flow of charged particles. One ampere equals a flow of one coulomb of charge per second.

amplitude: Maximum displacement from zero of any periodic phenomenon.

aneroid barometer: Device using a partially evacuated box to measure atmospheric pressure.

angle of incidence: Angle between a light ray and a line perpendicular to the surface that the ray is striking.

angle of refraction: Angle between a refracted ray and a line perpendicular to the surface that the ray is leaving.

antenna: Device used to receive or radiate electromagnetic waves.

antinodal line: Line connecting points at which two waves interfere constructively at their maximum amplitudes.

antiparticle: Particle having the same mass and spin as its counterpart but opposite charge and magnetic moment. When a particle and its antiparticle collide, both are annihilated and energy is released.

Archimedes' principle: An object immersed in a fluid is buoyed up by a force equal to the weight of the fluid displaced by the object.

armature: Coil of wire that produces current in a generator and rotation in an electric motor.

atomic number: Number of protons in the nucleus of an atom.

back-EMF: Potential difference created by the motion of the armature in an operating motor.

barometer: Device for measuring the pressure of the atmosphere.

battery or galvanic cell: Two dissimilar conductors and an electrolyte that produces a potential difference.

beat: Oscillation in amplitude of complex wave.

Bernoulli's principle: The pressure exerted by a fluid decreases as its velocity increases.

beta particles: High-speed electrons emitted by a radioactive nucleus.

bimetallic strip: Two dissimilar metals welded together so that thermal expansion causes the strip to bend.

binding energy: Energy equivalent of the mass defect representing the amount of energy required to separate the nucleus into individual nucleons.

black hole: Collapsed astronomical object of sufficient mass to prevent the escape of light.

Boyle's law: Volume of a fixed mass of gas at a constant temperature varies inversely with the pressure.

breeder reactor: A nuclear reactor that converts nonfissionable material to fissionable material with the production of energy.

components of a vector: Two or more vectors (usually perpendicular) that when added together, produce the original vector.

Compton effect: Interaction of X rays and electrons as the X rays traverse matter resulting in a lengthening of the X-ray wavelength.

concurrent forces: Forces acting on the same point.

condensation: Change of a gas to a liquid.

conductor: Material through which charged particles move readily.

control rods: Devices in a nuclear reactor used to regulate the rate of the nuclear reaction.

convection current: Current caused by motion of a body of fluid due to differences in density resulting from thermal expansion.

converging lens: Lens, thick in the middle and thin at the edge, that causes parallel rays to converge.

converging mirror: Concave mirror capable of causing parallel rays to converge.

coulomb: Unit of quantity of electric charge equal to the charge found on 6.25×10^{18} electrons.

candela: Unit of luminous intensity.

capillary action: Rise of a liquid in a narrow tube due to surface tension.

Celsius temperature scale: Scale with 0° equal to the freezing point of air-saturated water and 100° equal to the boiling point of water at standard atmospheric pressure.

center of curvature: Center of the sphere from which a spherical mirror is taken.

centripetal acceleration: Acceleration always at right angles to the velocity of a particle.

centripetal force: Force directed toward the center of a circle, keeps particles moving in uniform circular motion.

Charles' law: The volume of a fixed mass of gas at constant pressure varies directly with the absolute temperature.

chromatic aberration: Failure of a lens to bring all wavelengths of light to focus at the same point.

coherent light: Light in which all waves leaving the source are in phase.

cohesive force: Attraction between like particles.

complimentary colors: Primary and secondary color that when added produce white light.

condensation: Change from gas to liquid.

consonance: Complex sound wave perceived as chord.

Coulomb's law: $F = Kq_1q_2/d^2$, where K is a constant, q_1 and q_2 are the charges on the two objects, and d is the distance between the charges.

critical angle: Minimum angle of incidence that produces total internal reflection.

de Broglie principle: Material particles have wavelike characteristics; wavelength varies inversely with momentum.

deceleration: Negative acceleration.

derived unit: Unit of measurement defined in terms of other units.

deuteron: Nucleus of the hydrogen isotope deuterium, consisting of one proton and one neutron.

diffraction: Bending of light waves around an object in its path.

diffuse reflection: Reflected light scattered in many directions.

dimensional quantities: Physical measurements expressed in defined units.

dipole: Type of antenna used for the detection and broadcast of radio and television waves.

direct variation: Increase (or decrease) in one variable causes a proportional increase (or decrease) in another variable.

dispersion: Refraction of light into a spectrum of the wavelengths composing the light.

displacement: Vector quantity representing the change in position of an object.

dissonance: Complex sound wave perceived as unpleasant.

distance: Scalar quantity equal to the sum of the magnitude of the displacements.

diverging lens: Lens thin in the middle and thick at the edge, that causes parallel rays to diverge.

diverging mirror: Convex mirror capable of causing parallel light rays to diverge.

domain: Region of a metal in which magnetic fields in atoms are aligned in a common direction.

Doppler shift: Decrease (or increase) in wavelength as the source and detector of waves move toward (or away from) each other.

dynamics: Study of the motion of particles acted upon by forces.

echo: Rebound of a pulse from an impenetrable surface.

effective resistance: Resistance of a single resistor that could replace a combination of resistors.

efficiency: Ratio of output work to input work.

elastic collision: Collision in which the total kinetic energy of two objects is the same after the collision as before.

elasticity: Ability of object to return to its original form after removal of deforming forces.

electric circuit: Continuous path that can be followed by charged particles.

electric current: Flow of charged particles.

electric field: The property of space around a charged object that causes forces on other charged objects.

electric field intensity: Ratio of the force exerted by a field on a charged particle and the charge on the particle.

electric field lines: Lines representing the direction of the electric field.

electric force: Force between two objects due to their charges.

electromagnet: Device in which a magnetic field is generated by an electric current.

electromagnetic force: One of the fundamental forces. The force that exists between electric charges.

electromagnetic induction: Generation of an electric current by having a wire cut (or cut by) magnetic flux lines.

electromagnetic wave: Wave consisting of electric and magnetic fields that move at the speed of light in space.

electromagnetism: Interrelationship of magnetic fields and electric currents.

electromotive force (EMF): Potential difference generated by electromagnetic induction.

electron: Subatomic particle of small mass and negative charge.

electron cloud: Region of high probability of finding an electron.

electron collision excitation: Collision between an electron and an atom resulting in an excited atom.

electron gas: Free electrons present in a metallic conductor.

electroscope: Device used to detect the presence of electric charges.

emission spectrum: Spectrum produced by the excited atoms of an element.

enrichment: Process in which the number of fissionable nuclei is increased.

energy: Capacity to do work.

entropy: Measure of disorder of a system.

equilibrant: Force equal in magnitude to a resultant, but opposite in direction.

equilibrium: Condition in which the net force on an object is zero.

equivalence principle: Gravitational and inertial masses are equal.

evaporation: Change from liquid to gas.

excited atom: Atom with one or more electrons in a higher than normal energy level.

extrapolation: Extending graph beyond measured points.

eyepiece: Magnifying lens of a telescope or microscope.

fast neutron: Neutron with a kinetic energy greater than thermal energy.

fiber optics: Light-transmitting glass or plastic fibers that make use of the principle of total internal reflection to transmit light along irregular paths.

first law of thermodynamics: See *law of conservation of energy*.

fluid: a material that flows, e.g., liquids and gases.

fluorescence: Phenomenon in which atoms emit light when excited by an outside source. The light emission ceases as soon as the exciting source is removed.

focal length: Distance from the focal point to the vertex of a mirror or lens.

focal point: Point of convergence, real or apparent (virtual), of rays reflected by a mirror or refracted by a lens.

force: Action that results in accelerating or deforming an object.

frame of reference: Coordinate system used to describe motion.

Fraunhofer lines: Absorption lines in the sun's spectrum due to gases in the solar atmosphere.

frequency: Number of occurrences in a unit of time.

friction: Force opposing motion between two objects that are in contact.

fundamental: Lowest frequency sound produced by an instrument.

fundamental units: Units of measurement defined in terms of a physical standard, not in terms of other units.

gamma rays: Electromagnetic waves of extremely high frequency emitted by nuclei.

gas: State of matter in which particles follow random paths and in which the space between particles is large compared to the size of the particles themselves. Gases fill any container.

Geiger-Müller tube: Device used to detect radiation by using the ionizing property of radiation.

generator: Device using mechanical energy to produce electric energy.

graph: Plot of ordered pairs on rectangular coordinates.

gravitational field: Distortion of space due to the presence of a mass. See *field*.

gravitational force: Attraction between objects due to their masses.

grounding: Connecting a charged object to the earth to remove the object's charge.

half-life: Length of time for half of a sample of a radioactive material to decay.

heat: Quantity of thermal energy transferred from one object to another object because of a difference in temperature.

heat of fusion: Energy required to change 1 kg of a substance from solid to liquid at the melting point.

heat of vaporization: Energy required to change 1 kg of a substance from liquid to vapor (gas) at the boiling point.

hertz: Unit of frequency equal to one event (cycle) per second.

hydrodynamics: Study of fluids in motion.

hydrostatics: Study of fluids at rest.

ideal mechanical advantage (IMA): Ratio of effort distance to resistance distance in a machine.

illuminance: Rate at which light energy falls on a surface.

illuminated body: Object on which light is falling.

implode: Opposite of the explosion process in which forces are directed inward.

impulse: Product of a force and the time during which it acts.

incandescent: Emitting light due to thermal excitation.

inclined plane: Flat surface at an angle to the horizontal and vertical directions.

index of refraction: $n = (\sin i/\sin r)$, where n = index of refraction, i = angle of incidence, and r = angle of refraction.

inductive reactance: Opposition to electric current flow due to self-induction.

inelastic collision: Collision in which some of the kinetic energy of colliding objects is changed to another form of energy.

inertia: Tendency of an object not to change its motion.

inertial confinement: Method of producing fusion by the implosion of deuterium or tritium pellets by lasers.

instantaneous quantity: Value at a given instant of a quantity that is changing.

insulator: Material through which the flow of charged particles is greatly restricted.

interference: Combining of two waves (disturbances) arriving at the same point at the same time.

International System of Units (SI): A system of measurement based on the following fundamental units: mass (kilogram), length (meter), time (second), temperature (kelvin), amount of substance (mole), electric current (ampere), luminous intensity (candela).

inverse variation: Increase in one variable causes a proportional decrease in another variable.

isolated system: System not being acted upon by outside forces.

isotopes: Two or more atoms of the same element differing in masses due to different numbers of neutrons.

joule: Unit of work or energy equal to a newton-meter.

Kelvin temperature: Temperature of an object based on the Kelvin, or absolute, temperature scale.

Kelvin temperature scale: Scale with 0 = absolute zero and 273.15 = freezing point of water.

Kepler's laws: 1. Orbits of planets are ellipses with the sun at one focus. **2.** Line connecting planets and sun sweeps out equal areas in equal times. **3.** The ratio of the squares of the periods of revolution of two planets is the same as the ratio of the cubes of their average distances from the sun.

kilowatt hour: Amount of energy equal to 3.6×10^6 J

kinematics: Study of the motion of particles.

kinetic energy: Energy of an object due to its motion.

kinetic theory: Concept that all matter is made of small particles that are in constant motion.

laser: Device for producing coherent light.

law of conservation of charge: Electric charge can be neither created nor destroyed.

law of conservation of energy: In nonnuclear changes, energy can be neither created nor destroyed.

law of conservation of mass-energy: The sum of matter and energy in the universe is a constant.

law of conservation of momentum: In a system free of external forces, the total momentum is always the same.

law of cosines: $c^2 = a^2 + b^2 - 2ab \cos C$.

law of reflection: The angle of incidence is equal to the angle of reflection when a light ray strikes a surface.

law of sines: $a/\sin A = b/\sin B = c/\sin C$.

law of universal gravitation: $F = Gm_1m_2/d^2$, where G is a constant, m_1 and m_2 are the masses of two objects, and d is the distance between them.

left-hand rules: 1. If a wire is grasped in the left hand with the extended thumb pointing in the direction of electron flow, the fingers circle the wire in the direction of the magnetic field. **2.** If a coil of wire is grasped in the left hand with the fingers curved in the direction of the electron flow, the extended thumb points to the north-seeking pole. **3.** If a current-carrying wire is moving relative to a magnetic field, extend the thumb, index finger, and middle finger in mutually perpendicular directions with the thumb pointing in the direction of current flow and the index finger in the direction of the magnetic field, then the middle finger gives the direction of the force on the wire.

length: Distance between two points.

Lenz's law: The magnetic field generated by an induced current always opposes the field generating the current.

leptons: Subatomic particles with small masses.

light: Electromagnetic radiation of 4×10^{-7} meter to 7×10^{-7} meter wavelength.

linear accelerator: Device for accelerating charged particles in a straight line path.

liquid: State of matter in which particles are in close proximity but may readily change their relative positions.

longitudinal wave: Wave in which the disturbance is in the same direction as the direction of travel of the wave.

lumen: Unit of luminous flux.

luminous body: An object emitting light.

luminous flux: Flow of light from a source.

luminous intensity: Measure of light emitted by a source.

magnetic field: Space around a magnet in which magnetic forces can be detected.

magnetic flux: All the magnetic flux lines associated with a magnet.

magnetic flux density: Number of magnetic flux lines per unit area.

magnetic flux lines: Imaginary lines indicating the magnitude and direction of a magnetic field.

magnetic force: Force between two objects due to the magnetic flux of one or both objects.

magnetic induction: Strength of a magnetic field.

mass: Quantity of matter in an object measured by its resistance to a change in its motion (inertia).

mass defect: Difference in mass between the actual atomic nucleus and the sum of the particles from which the nucleus was made.

mass number: Number of protons and neutrons (nucleons) in an atom.

mass spectrograph: Device used to measure the mass of atoms and molecules.

mechanical advantage (MA): Ratio of resistance force to effort force in a machine.

mechanical wave: Disturbance traveling through a medium.

mesons: Medium mass subatomic particles.

moderator: Material used to decrease speed of fast neutrons in a nuclear reactor.

momentum: Product of an object's mass and velocity.

monochromatic light: Light of a single wavelength.

neutrino: A chargeless, massless particle emitted along with beta particles. A type of lepton.

neutron: Subatomic particle of approximate mass 1 amu and no charge.

neutron star: A collapsed star in which gravitational force has caused the combination of electrons and protons to form neutrons.

newton: SI unit of force.

Newton's laws of motion: 1. Unless acted upon by an outside force, an object at rest will remain at rest and an object in motion will remain in motion at the same speed and in the same direction. **2.** A change in motion of an object acted upon by an outside force will vary directly with the force and inversely with the mass of the object. **3.** For every action force there is a reaction force equal in magnitude and opposite in direction.

nodal line: Line connecting nodes.

node: Point in a medium or field that remains unchanged when acted upon by more than one disturbance simultaneously.

normal force: Force perpendicular to a surface.

nuclear fission: Splitting a large atomic nucleus into two approximately equal parts.

nuclear fusion: Combining of small nuclei into a larger nucleus.

nuclear moderator: Substance used to slow neutrons in a nuclear reactor.

nuclear reactor: Device for obtaining energy from a controlled fission reaction.

nuclear (strong) force: Very short range force holding protons and neutrons together in the atomic nucleus.

nuclear (strong force) equation: Equation representing a nuclear reaction.

nucleon: Proton or neutron.

nucleus: Core of an atom containing the protons and neutrons.

objective lens: Light-gathering and image-forming lens of a microscope or telescope.

ohm: Unit of electric resistance.

Ohm's law: Current flowing in a conductor varies directly with the potential difference and inversely with the resistance.

oil-drop experiment: Experiment, first performed by Robert Millikan, designed to measure the charge on the electron.

opaque material: Material that does not transmit light.

optical density: Property determining the speed of light, and thus index of refraction, in a medium.

overtones: Sound waves of higher frequency than the fundamental.

pair production: Creation of an electron-positron pair (matter) from energy.

parabolic relationship: One quantity varies as the square of another quantity.

parallax: Change in relative position of objects with change in viewing angle.

parallel circuit: Circuit in which there are two or more paths for the charged particles to follow as they complete the circuit.

pascal: Unit of pressure equal to a newton per square meter.

Pascal's principle: Applied pressure is transmitted undiminished throughout a fluid.

period: Time duration of a phenomenon or event.

phosphorescence: Emission of light by atoms excited by an outside source. The emission persists for a time after the outside source is removed.

photoelectric effect: Ejection of electrons from the surface of a metal exposed to light.

photoelectron: Electrons ejected by the photoelectric effect.

photon: Quantum of electromagnetic waves.

photon collision excitation: Collision between a photon and an atom resulting in an excited atom.

photovoltaic or solar cell: Device for converting light into electric energy.

piezoelectricity: Production of electric current by deforming certain crystals.

pitch: Perceived sound characteristic that is equivalent to frequency.

planetary model: Model of an atom in which the electron(s) orbit(s) the nucleus much as planets orbit the sun.

plasma: High temperature state of matter in which atoms are separated into electrons and positive ions or nuclei.

polarized light: Light in which the electric fields are in the same plane.

positron: Positively charged electron.

potential difference: Difference in electric potential energy at two points.

potential energy: Energy of an object due to its position.

potentiometer: Variable resistor.

power: Rate of doing work.

precision: The degree of exactness in a measurement.

pressure: Force per unit area.

primary color: Red, green, or blue light.

primary pigment: Yellow, cyan, or magenta pigment.

principal axis: Radius connecting the center of curvature of a spherical mirror with its geometric vertex.

projectile motion: Motion of objects moving in two dimensions under the influence of gravity.

proton: Subatomic particle of mass approximately 1 amu and a positive charge.

pulsar: A rotating neutron star that emits a beam of radiation.

pulse: A single disturbance in a medium or field.

pumping: Exciting a very large number of atoms in a laser.

Pythagorean theorem: $a^2 + b^2 = c^2$, where c is the hypotenuse of a right triangle with perpendicular sides a and b.

quantum: a discrete quantity of energy.

quantum mechanics: Study of matter using a wave-particle model.

quantum theory of light: Light is emitted and absorbed in small packets called quanta and the energy in each quantum can be expressed as $E = hf$, where E = energy, h = Planck's constant, and f = frequency.

quark: Basic building block of subatomic particles.

radioactive materials: Materials that exhibit the phenomenon of radioactivity.

radioactivity: Spontaneous decay of unstable nuclei.

ray: Line drawn to represent the path traveled by a wave front.

real image: Image formed by rays that actually recombine to form the image.

receiver: Device used to detect electromagnetic waves.

refraction: Change in direction of a wave front as it passes from one medium to another.

resistance: Opposition to flow of electric current.

resolution: To find the component of a vector in a given direction.

resolving power: Ability of an optical device to produce separate images of two closely spaced objects.

resonance: Large motion of a system due to excitation.

resultant: Single force that has the same effect as two or more concurrent vectors.

satellite: Object in orbit around a planet.

scalar quantity: Quantity having magnitude (size) only.

schematic diagram: Diagram of an electric circuit using symbols.

scientific notation: Expressing numbers in the form: $M \times 10^n$ where $1 \leq M \leq 10$ and n is an integer.

scintillation: Flash of light emitted when a substance is struck by radiation.

secondary color: Yellow, cyan, or magenta light.

secondary pigment: Red, green, or blue pigment.

second law of thermodynamics: Heat flows from an area of high temperature to an area of lower temperature.

self-induction: The induced EMF in a coil creates a magnetic field that opposes the field originally inducing the EMF.

series circuit: Circuit in which the charged particles must flow through each component of the circuit, one after the other.

SI: An internationally agreed-upon consistent method of using the metric system of measurement.

significant digits: The reliable digits reported in a measurement.

simple harmonic motion: Motion in which a particle repeats the same path periodically.

simple machine: Lever, pulley, wheel-and-axle, inclined plane, wedge, or screw.

slow neutron: Neutron with a kinetic energy less than that of thermal energy.

Snell's law: The ratio of the sine of the angle of incidence to the sine of the angle of refraction is a constant for two specific substances in contact where a light ray passes. See *index of refraction.*

solid: State of matter in which particles are close together and in fixed positions relative to each other.

sonic boom: Shock wave associated with an object moving through a fluid at a speed greater than that of sound.

sound wave: Audible longitudinal disturbance in matter.

specific heat: Energy required to change the temperature of 1 kg of a substance 1 kelvin.

spectrum: Array of the various wavelengths composing light.

speed: Ratio of distance traveled to the time interval.

speed of light: 3.00×10^8 m/s (in vacuum).

spherical aberration: Failure of a spherical mirror to bring all rays parallel to the principal axis to focus at the same point.

spherical concave mirror: A converging mirror that is formed of a spherical segment of one base.

standard pressure: 1.01325×10^5 Pa = 101.325 kPa = 1 atm = 760 mm Hg = 760 Torr.

standing wave: A wave whose nodes are stationary.

state: Physical condition of a material.

stopping potential: Potential difference needed to prevent the photoelectric effect for a specific metal and light of a specific frequency.

superconductivity: State of some materials at very low temperatures in which the material exhibits zero electric resistance.

surface tension: Strong attraction of surface particles for each other due to unbalanced forces.

surface wave: Surface disturbance with characteristics of both transverse and longitudinal waves.

symmetry: Property that is unchanged by altering operations or reference frames.

temperature: Measure of the average kinetic energy of molecules.

terminal velocity: Velocity of a falling object when the flow of air resistance is equal to the weight.

thermal energy: Sum of potential energy and kinetic energy of random motion of particles in an object.

thermal excitation: Exciting an atom by heating it.

thermal expansion: Moving apart of particles as their temperature rises.

thermometer: Device used to measure temperature.

thermonuclear reaction: Nuclear fusion reaction.

threshold frequency: Lowest frequency of light that will cause the photoelectric effect with a specific substance.

timbre: Quality of sound.

time: Interval between two events.

total internal reflection: Refraction of a light ray at such a large angle that the ray remains in the original medium.

trajectory: Path of a projectile.

transformer: Device used to transfer energy from one circuit to another circuit by mutual inductance across two coils.

translucent material: Material transmitting light but distorting it during passage.

transmutation: Nuclear change of one element into another.

transparent material: Material transmitting light undistorted.

transuranium element: Element with an atomic number greater than 92.

transverse wave: Wave in which the disturbance is perpendicular to the direction of travel of the wave.

trigonometry: Study of triangles and the relationships of their parts.

uncertainty principle: The more accurately one determines the position of a particle, the less accurately the momentum is known, and vice versa.

uniform circular motion: Particles moving in a circular path at a constant speed.

uniform quantity: Quantity of constant value, e.g., acceleration or speed.

vaporization: Change of a liquid to a gas.

vector quantity: Quantity having both magnitude (size) and direction.

velocity: Rate of change of position.

virtual image: Image whose rays appear to emanate from a point without actually doing so.

viscous fluids: Slow-flowing fluids.

volatile fluid: Fluid that is easily evaporated.

volt: Unit of potential difference.

voltmeter: Electric device used to measure potential difference.

watt: Unit of power equal to 1 J/s.

wave: Traveling disturbance in a field or medium.

wavelength: Distance between corresponding points on two successive waves.

weak force: Force involved in the decay of atomic nuclei and nuclear particles. A type of electromagnetic force.

weight: Gravitational attraction of the earth or celestial body for an object.

work: Product of force and displacement.

work function: Energy needed to remove an electron from metal as in the photoelectric effect.

X rays: Electromagnetic waves of very short wavelength.

Index

PHOTO CREDITS